DATE DUE

Display		
JUN 27 '68		
JUL 2 9 1968		
MAY 8 '69		
MAY 2 6 '69		
OCT 2 2 1970		
renew Nov 5		
OCT 3 0 1972		
MAR 2 8 1983		
OCT 2 1981		
NOV 1 8 1991		
DEC 3 0 1991		
GAYLORD		PRINTED IN U.S.A.

PRENTICE-HALL BIOLOGICAL SCIENCE SERIES

Editors

William D. McElroy and Carl P. Swanson

BIOLOGY
OF
INVERTEBRATA

JAMES H. WILMOTH
Harpur College
State University of New York

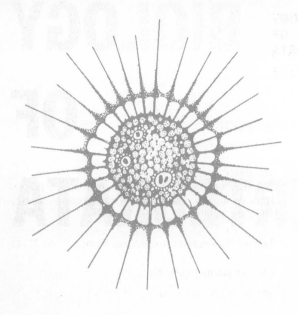

PRENTICE-HALL, *Inc., Englewood Cliffs, New Jersey*

BIOLOGY
OF
INVERTEBRATA

JAMES H. WILMOTH

© 1967 by Prentice-Hall, Inc.
Englewood Cliffs, New Jersey

Library of Congress Catalog Card Number: 67-22741

Current printing (last digit):
10 9 8 7 6 5 4 3 2 1

Printed in the United States of America

PRENTICE-HALL INTERNATIONAL, INC., London

PRENTICE-HALL OF AUSTRALIA, PTY. LTD., Sydney

PRENTICE-HALL OF CANADA, LTD., Toronto

PRENTICE-HALL OF INDIA PRIVATE LTD., New Delhi

PRENTICE-HALL OF JAPAN, LTD., Tokyo

To the teachers who inspired me,
to the students who challenge,
and especially to my wife who gave persistent
encouragement,
I inscribe this book.

PREFACE

Evolution is the great unifying force in biology. Among the invertebrates, which compose the preponderance of animals, evolution runs like a stream through subterranean channels, only occasionally taking a brief sojourn at the surface. These momentary (in terms of geologic time) glimpses serve but to stimulate man's search for understanding of the full course of the phylogenetic stream.

This book is an attempt to clarify some of the phylogenetic relationships, briefly exploring fossil evidence and more extensively examining those organ systems and processes of living animals which seem most likely to have contributed to the evolution of the group concerned. These systems and processes are concerned with locomotion, neural development, respiration, excretion, food-getting, reproduction, and embryology. It is hoped that the information and conjectures in this book will stimulate the reader to more intensive study.

The path of evolution through more than two billion years is dim, but the attempt to examine and to speculate on the evidences is in the scientific spirit and may foster a zeal for inquiry into the multitudinous riddles of evolution.

This book could not have been written without recourse to the great compilations of information in English, French, and German. Particularly the monumental contributions of Dr. Libbie H. Hyman in the series entitled *The Invertebrates* are gratefully acknowledged.

In addition, the author would like to thank the Library Staff at Harpur College, State University of New York, and especially Miss Janet Brown for obtaining literature not otherwise available locally. This was done in every instance with enthusiasm and dispatch. Thanks also are due Mr. John Riina, editor, for his advice and encouragement.

James H. Wilmoth

CONTENTS

1

INTRODUCTION

Zoology is the study of animals. Since man first began to classify, various combinations of characteristics have been used to divide the animal kingdom into major subgroups. Animals with a backbone are called vertebrates; those without, invertebrates. Many animals that lack bony vertebrae possess, at some point in their life history, features which appear in the developmental morphology of vertebrates. They have been grouped with the vertebrates into a category called the Chordata. All of this group at some stage in their life cycle exhibit such features as a notochord, a hollow, dorsal, central nervous system, paired pharyngeal gill pouches, and a postanal tail. Among more primitive chordates this combination of characteristics often is less sharply delineated, while other features are present that are shared at least partly with some of the invertebrates.

With each major category of invertebrate animals the degree of affinity with other groups depends on the number and degree of shared characteristics. The greater the number and the greater the likeness of shared characteristics, the higher is the probability that two groups of organisms are related.

The invertebrates have been divided into phyla, many of which are well established. Some groups may be considered either as separate phyla or as subgroups in established phyla, depending upon the interpretation of the evidence; such groups are subject to re-evaluation as more data are discovered.

The number of known species in the different groups (many of which have phylum status) has been estimated recently by Mayr et al. Table 1, slightly modified, gives estimates for living species of the invertebrate groups. Since it is estimated that 10,000 new species and subspecies are described each year, some of these figures may be too low.

Table I ESTIMATED SIZES OF VARIOUS INVERTEBRATE GROUPS†

Protozoa	30,000	Sipunculoidea	250
Mesozoa	50	Tardigrada	180
Cnidaria	9,000	Onychophora	65
Ctenophora	90	Linguatula	70
Porifera	4,500	Chelicerata	35,000
Platyhelminthes	6,000	Crustacea	25 000
Acanthocephala	500	Other arthropoda (excl. insecta)	13.000
Rotifera	1,500	Insecta	850,000
Gastrotricha	1,500	Mollusca	80,000
Kinorhynchia	100	Pogonophora	27
Nematomorpha	100	Bryozoa	4,000
Nematoda	10,000	Brachiopoda	260
Priapulida	5	Echinodermata	4,000
Entoprocta	60	Phoronidea	15
Nemertina	550	Chaetognatha	50
Annelida	7,000	Hemichordata	.80
Echiuroidea	60	Urochordata	1,600

†Estimated number of known species of Recent animals, adapted from Mayr (Mayr, Linsley and Usinger, 1953) Methods and principles of systematic zoology, courtesy of the McGraw-Hill Book Company.

CLASSIFICATION AND NOMENCLATURE

Taxonomy or systematics is the science of classification. Aristotle was one of the early workers in taxonomy, but this like other sciences was in a state of limbo during the Dark Ages. Late in the seventeenth century John Ray made important contributions on insect taxonomy, developed the use of keys for identification, and adopted the concept of species based on the production of like offspring.

The Swedish scientist, Carl von Linné (Carolus Linnaeus) is usually considered the "father" of taxonomy. He founded the hierarchic system of arranging organisms into series of groups or categories, in which each category encompasses one or more of the categories next lower in the scale. Each higher category embraces all the characteristics of the immediately subordinate categories so that (when these number more than one) it serves to systematize them into a higher but broader group. Linnaeus set up five categories in the hierarchy. In descending sequence these are Class, Order, Genus, Species, and Variety. He used "variety" as a convenience to express various individual differences, but his hierarchy was based on genus and species. Each kind of organism was given two names: one to denote the species and one the genus—a system called *binomial nomenclature*. Linnaeus also named many new species and refined the use of keys.

Linnaeus did not use the categories of phylum and family, which together with kingdom bring the hierarchy for animal species in use today to a minimum of seven levels. (Variety is no longer considered part of this series.) Additional categories, formed by division of existing ones or by adding new intermediate ones, are in frequent use, especially to get greater precision in species relationships. The phylum deserves special consideration since it is universally used to pigeonhole larger groups of animals. It is a relatively stable category based on morphological features, but subjective judgment allows divergent placement for groups with less distinct features, with features overlapping those of other groups, or about which there is insufficient information.

To define taxonomy or systematics as the science of classification is to oversimplify. Simpson (1961) expresses it this way: "Systematics is the scientific study of the kinds and diversity of organisms and of any and all relationships among them." Taxonomy cannot be limited to classification, but must draw upon the entire broad spectrum of science; this becomes obvious if one tries to describe an organism without using any actual or implied relatedness to the physical world.

Zoological taxonomy then is concerned with the diversities and affinities of animals, their relationships in space and in time, their ordered arrangement into groups, and their designation by distinctive names. Nomenclature is a necessary complement or corollary to taxonomy and classification.

Nomenclature takes its official start with the publication of Linnaeus' tenth edition of *Systema Naturae* in 1758, which established the binomial system as the standard. Each species of plant or animal is given a scientific name composed of a capitalized generic name preceding a specific designation, as *Gallus domesticus* (domesticated chicken), *Musca domestica* (house fly), or *Plasmodium vivax* (malarial organism). The generic name is broader in concept and may encompass related species, such as *Plasmodium vivax, Plasmodium falciparum, Plasmodium ovale,* and *Plasmodium malariae.* Each of these species has the characteristics of the genus, *Plasmodium;* each has specific attributes listed in a published description of the species in question, and each incidentally causes a form of malaria in man. For precise designation the name of the describer or its abbreviation and the date of the description are added to the scientific name according to established rule, e.g., *Ascaris lumbricoides* Linnaeus, 1758. Similar rules govern the usage of subgeneric and subspecific names as well as the procedure for substituting a new generic name for one previously published.

The regulations governing the determination and application of names to animals have the following full title: *The International Code of Zoological Nomenclature adopted by the XV International Congress of Zo-* *ology, London, 1958.** It supersedes the Rules (Règles, since previously French was the sole official language) published in 1905 after approval by the V International Congress in 1901. The 1958 Code involved the preparation of elegant dual texts in French and in English so that either language supplies the official version. Its aim is to promote permanence, universality, and stability of zoological nomenclature without restricting freedom of taxonomic practice.

The present Code is composed of eighty-seven Articles. Those that seem of interest and that students majoring in zoology have asked about are as follows (some in abbreviated form):

Art. 1. Zoological nomenclature is the system of scientific names applied to taxonomic units of animals (taxa; singular: taxon) known to occur in nature, whether living or extinct.

Art. 2. Zoological nomenclature is independent of other systems of nomenclature in that the name of an animal taxon is not to be rejected merely because it is identical with the name of a taxon that does not belong to the animal kingdom.

Art. 5. The name of a species consists of two words (binomen) and that of a subspecies of three words (trinomen) . . .

Art. 11b. The name must be either Latin or latinized, . . .

Art. 11f. A genus-group name must be a noun in the nominative singular or be treated as such.

Art. 18a. A genus- or species-group name, once established, cannot afterwards be rejected, even by its own author, because of inappropriateness.

Art. 23. The valid name of a taxon is the oldest available name applied to it . . . (Certain exceptions and considerations are allowed to this Law of Priority.)

---

*Published by the International Trust for Zoological Nomenclature, 14 Belgrave Square, London S.W.1, and obtainable at the Trust price of $3.00 post free.

Art. 28. Names of the family- and genus-groups must be printed with a capital initial letter and names of the species-group with a lower-case initial letter.

Art. 29. A family-group name is formed by the addition, to the stem of the name of the type genus, of -IDAE in the case of a family and -INAE in the case of a subfamily.

Art. 61. The "type" affords the standard of reference that determines the application of a scientific name. Nucleus of a taxon and foundation of its name, the type is objective and does not change, whereas the limits of the taxon are subjective and liable to change. The type of a nominal species is a specimen, . . .

When a new specimen is discovered, its similarity to existing species is examined. If the similarity is sufficiently close, it is placed in an already existing genus, in which case the generic portion of the scientific name is automatically established; if it has many differences, a new genus is erected for it. Related genera are grouped into families; families with shared characteristics constitute an order; orders with similar features are placed in a class; classes showing anatomical affinity constitute a phylum. Occasionally groups exhibit relationship intermediate between the already mentioned categories, and these are designated by appropriate prefix, e.g., subclass, superfamily, or by such names as cohort or tribe. Practice rather than rule governs naming and the endings of categories other than those stated in Article 29, but the Code now recommends that the suffixes -OIDEA and -INI be adopted for superfamilies and tribes respectively.

The concept of type is defined in Article 61. The designation of types provides an objective yardstick, which is needed because the limitations of a genus or other category are set by subjective judgment. The type specimen serves as the point of reference for the name of the new group and therefore stabilizes the nonobjective factors. The Code recommends, and practice dictates, that a single specimen be designated as the type (or holotype). The type specimen is placed in Institutional custody to insure safekeeping and availability. A type-specimen is only a sample of the taxon it represents, and the probability is against its possessing typical or average characteristics of the population to which it belongs. Only on Noah's Ark would a taxonomist have had little worry about the variations composing a taxon.

Suppose a zoologist discovers a new species, but he finds that his specimens have too many variant characters for inclusion in any existing genera. He then erects a new genus for the specimen, stating his reasons in his published description. This new genus turns out to be intermediate in characteristics between two existing genera composing part of a family. Therefore the new genus becomes a part of that family, which however already has a name derived from the root of the previously designated type-genus plus the suffix -IDAE.

WHAT IS A SPECIES

The concept of what constitutes a "species" is relative. No absolute definition is available. In the plant kingdom, many instances of "ploidy" further confuse the development of any statement equally applicable to the animal kingdom. Let us examine some variants in definitions:

1. "A species may merely be said to be a well-defined, autonomous and persistent organic unit, living in a free state of nature, not grading freely into any other unit, and generally of less perfect fecundity outside than inside its limits. A species moreover differs from all other species not only morphologically, but also in its physiological manifestations, and in its 'psychic' behavior." Ales Hrdlicka in *Human Biology and Human Welfare,* E. V. Cowdry, editor.

2. "A species is a group of individuals of common descent, with certain constant specific characters in common which are represented in the nucleus of each cell by constant

and characteristic sets of chromosomes carrying homozygous specific genes, causing as a rule intra-fertility and inter-sterility." Attributed to the late Alfred Huettner.

3. "A species is that stage of the evolutionary process at which the once actually or potentially interbreeding array of forms becomes segregated into two or more separate arrays which are physiologically incapable of interbreeding." Th. Dobzhansky, 1937.

4. "Species are groups of actually or potentially interbreeding natural populations, which are reproductively isolated from other such groups." Ernst Mayr, 1949.

Such definitions of species have a common feature which suggests sterility as the principal criterion distinguishing species. However, Mayr points out that sterility and fertility in the ordinary sense are not applicable terms, since two animals in nature with overlapping habitats may never breed, but the same animals limited by confinement may breed freely in captivity and produce fertile offspring. Related species are separated in nature by a physiological and behavioral divergence which effectively prevents breeding. This is reproductive isolation and is probably the chief criterion differentiating related species. Obviously it can be applied only to forms that are contemporary and with overlapping distribution. For geographically or chronologically isolated groups, the degree of reproductive isolation or crossability has to be surmised from morphological and physiological data.

In those species of overlapping habitat, where the criterion of reproductive isolation can be invoked, morphological variations provide supportive evidence separating species. Thus the degree of morphological variation can serve as a key to indicate the separation of species, when reproductive isolation cannot be determined. At best such a morphological scale is relative and, as Mayr points out, "will differ in every family and genus." For the complexities of the problem the student should check some of the comprehensive works on taxonomy.

ANIMAL DISTRIBUTION

Distribution of Animals in Space

Biology is the study of life. Many species of animals and plants lived in the past and are now extinct; their study is the special province of paleontology. Since extinct animals either represent dead-end branches or are ancestors of living forms, their comparative structure is of concern to the biologist. The paleontologist has formulated a classification of fossil organisms in terminology often strange to the biologist. On the other hand, biology often utilizes physiological and ecological data in studies of taxonomy and phylogeny, and this introduces terms foreign to the student of paleontology. In the study of evolution, the two sciences are interdependent.

Paleontology as a special field of geology provides a history of the chronological sequence of fossils. There are many blanks in the record, since generally only those animals with hard parts left any extensive remains. Undoubtedly many soft-bodied ancestors of living organisms have left no discernible trace. Frequently in the systematic account of a phylum, and occasionally in the discussion of phylogeny, references will be made to geologic eras and periods. Figure 1-1 is a representation of the geologic time scale which should be useful for reference.

Distribution of Animals in Space

Ecology is a study of the relationships of organisms to the environment. Such study provides information on the interrelationships of animals and plants, both competitive and otherwise. Geography contributes data on accesses or barriers to the spread of species and the effect of topography as it modifies barometric pressure, temperature, rainfall, light, and tides.

Invertebrate animals occur in practically all known environments, at least within the area including and encompassed by the earth's atmosphere. They occur in the air, on and in the soil, and in aquatic habitats: fresh-water, brackish water, and marine. Animal adaptation to the unlimited diversities of the environment has resulted in the appearance of new species, a process that is continuing apace.

The marine or ocean environment deserves special emphasis. For one thing, salt water covers more than seventy per cent of the surface of the earth and covered even more in earlier geologic ages.

Since the salt content of sea water approaches the concentration in body fluids for many animals, adverse osmotic pressures are less of a problem, both for adults and for larval stages. Salt water contains all the essential minerals for protoplasm, as well as most others. The presence of salt modifies the physical properties in several important ways. Buoyancy is increased, which favors the suspension of smaller nonswimming organisms and decreases the problem of body support for larger animals. The freezing point of sea water is lower than that of fresh water and the temperature is more uniform. Colder water is able to hold more oxygen in solution than warmer water. Ocean currents, both horizontal and vertical, aid in dispersal of smaller nonswimmers or poor swimmers and also contribute to distribution of suspended food and oxygen in solution.

Geologic Time Scale						
Rough estimates of :			Sequence table, older below and younger above			Some features of the life record
Millions of years since beginning	Duration in millions of years		Eras	Periods	Epochs	
0.025	1	0.025	Cenozoic	Quaternary	Recent	Man
1		1			Pleistocene	
12	75	11			Pliocene	Mammals and birds numerous / Flowering plants / Bony fishes numerous
28		16		Tertiary	Miocene	
39		74	11		Oligocene	
58		19			Eocene	
75		17			Paleocene	
135	130	60	Mesozoic	Cretaceous	(Epoch divisions not necessary for present purposes)	Birds arise / Mammals arise / Reptiles numerous
165		30		Jurassic		
205		40		Triassic		Crisis in marine life
230	300	25	Paleozoic	Permian		Amphibians numerous / Archaic coal forests
255		25		Pennsylvanian		
280		25		Mississippian		Aquatic vertebrates numerous, rise of true fishes, rise of land animals and plants
325		45		Devonian		
360		35		Silurian		First vertebrates
425		65		Ordovician		All basic types of aquatic animals appear
505		80		Cambrian		First abundant fossils
2000	1500		Pre-Cambrian	Period divisions not well established		Fossils few and obscure / Origin of life (not recorded)
?	?		(Unknown ages, before formation of rocks now exposed in crust of the earth)			

The tidal zone is subject to much greater change, owing not only to tides but to the effect of wave action on the shore and the admixture of fresh water from rivers. Water outside the low-tide mark is also affected by the tides. The submerged so-called continental shelf, which precedes the drop to deep water, is affected by tide action and is intermediate in environmental variability between the tidal zone and deep water. Stability of the environment in deep water decreases species radiation, and it is here that many primitive animal species are found.

The ocean environment is divided into a number of overlapping life zones (Fig. 1-2). The *littoral* or tidal zone is subject to an alternating environment that affects food gathering, respiration, reproductive patterns, and osmotic adaptation. Between the low-tide mark and the 600-foot (100 fathoms) depth is the *neritic* zone, in general equivalent to the continental shelf. The width of the shelf varies; it is, for example, much wider on the Atlantic coast of North America than on the Pacific coast. The tidal and neritic zones have the greatest variety of invertebrate species, correlated with the intensive environmental fluctuations. Between the continental shelf and the 1000-fathoms depth is the *bathyal* zone. Because of insufficient light, photosynthesis would be limited to upper layers. Organic debris from the plants and animals occupying these upper layers contributes one of the important links in the food-chain of the numerous inhabitants of the bathyal zone. The *abyssal* zone includes all of the deeper portions of the ocean. In general, the number of species diminishes from the low-tide line into deep water.

Invertebrates living in or on the ocean floor constitute the *benthos*. Microscopic and minute organisms that are free-floating or poor swimmers are called *plankton,* while strong swimmers are collectively called the *nekton*. The plankton and nekton together constitute pelagic organisms, which are independent of the ocean bottom. Larval stages of many benthonic and nektonic animals are frequently planktonic—an important factor in species dispersal.

HOMOLOGY

Morphological data contribute significant and sometimes sole evidence establishing species relationships. Species may show a fundamental similarity when structural correspondence is due to descent from common ancestry (homology) or a misleading resem-

Fig. 1-2 Diagram showing the different types of life and the life zones in the ocean. It should be noted that the littoral, neritic, bathyal, and abyssal realms are actually depth zones. After Shrock and Twenhofel 1953, courtesy of the McGraw-Hill Book Company.

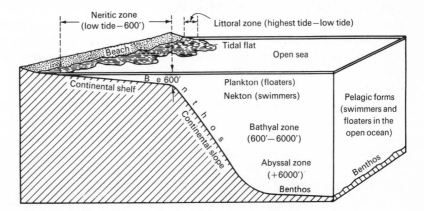

blance due to a chance similarity in adaptation (convergence). Since homology is a useful tool in the study of phylogeny, it is important to assay its validity.

Hanson (1964) outlines Remane's criteria for establishing homology. There should be a close correspondence in site or location of the structure at issue for the species in question. There should be close similarity in the number, shape, and function of the components of that structure. When two species possess structures that are similar, the probability of homology is increased if other species with a similar structure exhibit a graded series between them. If the components of one structure show probable homology between two species, the likelihood of relationship by common descent is increased if other organs can be shown to possess close similarities. Although homology is most closely affiliated with macroscopic morphology, it is being applied to unicellular forms, physiological processes (since they are often correlated with structural similarities), and correspondence in molecular structure for such molecules as the respiratory pigments, fatty acids, and enzymes.

SYMMETRY

Animal form is as responsive to physical laws as are inanimate objects. Symmetry appears in the animal kingdom in a somewhat restricted number of types. Only a few animals lack a consistent symmetry. Many Porifera and amoeboid protozoa are the chief examples of asymmetry.

A few planktonic protozoa possess a spherical type of symmetry. Planes passing through the center of such forms in any direction produce equivalent halves.

Some actively swimming and many sessile animals possess a cylindrical or subspherical body form with unlike ends. Any plane transecting the animal along any radius of the axis will result in equal halves. This type of symmetry is termed radial, and implies a

rather uniform environment with biotic stresses equally distributed. Some of the simpler sponges and many Cnidaria and Echinodermata exhibit radial symmetry as adults, but for the last-named group this radial symmetry is superimposed upon the primary bilateral symmetry of the larvae.

In Ctenophora and some Cnidaria, several structures have a bilateral arrangement. A plane through the longitudinal axis bisecting such structures will produce two equal halves, and a plane at right angles to the first one will also produce two equivalent halves, but a moiety produced by the first transection is different from one produced by the second. The symmetry, called biradial, shows two planes of symmetry. It arose from a partial bilateral condition superimposed upon the primary radial symmetry.

Most animal phyla possess bilateral symmetry, which in Aschelminthes seems to be superimposed upon radial symmetry. Such animals have a single plane of symmetry which lies along the anterior-posterior axis perpendicular to the planes of the dorsal and ventral surfaces. Such a plane is termed median sagittal, and it will divide the animal with bilateral symmetry into symmetrical halves.

CLEAVAGE PATTERNS

The mitotic division of the egg in the embryology of an animal is called cleavage or segmentation. The amount of the reserve food supply, yolk, is one of the factors affecting size of the cleavage cells, which are termed *blastomeres*. When there is marked difference in size of the blastomeres at division, the larger are designated macromeres and the smaller, micromeres. When the egg contains evenly distributed yolk, it is *homolecithal*; when eccentrically located, *telolecithal*; and it is termed *centrolecithal* when after the initial central cleavages, the blastomeres move to the periphery to leave the undivided yolk centrally situated. Cleavage in which the entire egg mass divides is called *holoblastic*. In centrolecithal and the more extreme telolecithal eggs, most or all of the yolk fails to divide. Such cleavage is called *meroblastic*. Insecta and some Crustacea produce centrolecithal eggs; scorpions and Cephalopoda produce telolecithal eggs and have *discoidal* cleavage resembling that of the chick; and holoblastic eggs are generally characteristic of Mollusca (other than Cephalopoda), a few Crustacea, and the rest of the metazoan phyla.

A number of cleavage patterns correlated with symmetry relationships occur in holoblastic eggs. *Radial* cleavage is the regular alternation of meridional and equatorial segmentations around a polar axis, which results in a series of tiers of blastomeres with a blastocoele appearing centrally. Porifera, Cnidaria, Brachiopoda, most Echinodermata, and some Hemichordata undergo radial cleavage.

A unique kind of cleavage occurs in Ctenophora. At the end of the third cleavage a slightly curved rod of four pairs of cells is formed. The longitudinal axis through this embryo corresponds with one of the axes of the future adult. This type of cleavage is called *dissymmetrical*.

Bilateral cleavage is associated with a bilateral symmetry which has been determined in the eggs of many animals prior to segmentation. In a typical case, the first division is in the median plane to delineate right and left halves. The next cleavage is also meridional and approximately at right angles to produce two slightly smaller anterodorsal cells. With variations in rhythm of division and blastomere size, particularly in later fissions, this type of cleavage is characteristic of most Aschelminthes and some Hemichordata.

Spiral cleavage is characteristic of a number of phyla, and it serves as one of the criteria separating the two main branches of the diphyletic tree. Some of these phyla include Platyhelminthes, Nemertina, Acanthocephala, Entoprocta, Annelida, and Mollusca (except Cephalopoda). After the first two meridional furrows, the third cleavage is oblique and unequal. The quartet of micromeres produced lie in a position rotated 45° from the vertical and rest above the grooves between the four macromeres.

Particularly associated with spiral cleavage is the determination of potential fate of the blastomeres. In the one-celled egg of numerous animals, areas of the protoplasm are already predestined to develop into specific structures in subsequent normal embryology, and cell-lineage studies have traced these areas and their subsequent localization in blastomeres to their respective fates. To illustrate, some embryos with blastomeres separated at the two-cell stage will develop half or partial embryos; that is, their potential is already restricted to the half which they would have represented normally. Such eggs have *determinative cleavage*. They have already undergone protoplasmic differentiation. At the other extreme are embryos in which, during early embryology, one cell can take the place of any other. These cells have great ability to regulate or adapt, and their fate depends upon their location. They are *totipotent* at this stage. Separated at the two-cell stage, each blastomere forms a complete embryo. Such eggs have *indeterminate* cleavage. Their fate becomes restricted relatively late as differentiation sets in, so that eventually they become determinate. The classical examples of determinate spiral cleavage include Mollusca and Annelida, while the Tunicates have determinate bilateral cleavage. Most vertebrates, echinoderms, many arthropods, and cephalopods are illustrative of animals with indeterminate cleavage.

LARVAL TYPES

Among invertebrates, the marine representatives commonly have distinctive larvae, whereas fresh-water species usually have direct development. Often these marine larvae form part of the plankton. Food is readily available, osmotic stresses are minimal; and currents are unlikely to transport these larvae to an unfavorable environment. At the same time, such larvae favor species dispersion. Fresh-water habitats are much less uniform, currents in streams would carry unattached eggs or larvae away, quite possibly to a deleterious environment, and body salt content of the animal would cause water ingress osmotically.

Opinions differ on the evolutionary significance of invertebrate larvae. Parallel and convergent evolution may account for some of the similarities, and certainly such larvae have undergone adaptive modifications to the environment. Also it should be generally recognized that these larvae may resemble the *larvae* of ancestors and not the adults.

Study of the larval stages must continue in the search for phylogenetic relationships and for criteria distinguishing homologous and convergent similarity. Attention is directed briefly to some of these larvae, keeping in mind that the factor of larval size and the physical limitations of the environment, whether for benthonic or pelagic developmental stages, allow only a limited number of responses.

Part of the evidence for considering the Porifera as a blind branch on the evolutionary tree is the inversion of the flagellated cells of the *amphiblastula* from the outer surface of this larva to the gastrodermal lining in the adult. This is a unique performance among metazoa, although a nearly identical process occurs in the colonial protozoan, *Volvox.* The Cnidaria develop from a mouthless, ciliated stereogastrula, which has been named *planula.* The planula may well be a stemform, giving rise to the cnidarian-ctenophoran branch on the one hand and leading to Bilateria on the other. The parasitic ctenophoran, *Gastrodes,* has a typical planula larva relating this phylum to Cnidaria.

In the change to bilateral symmetry, several theories have been advanced. One of these involves the planula stem-form leading to the Acoela, which are small primitive turbellarians with mouth but lacking an intestinal lumen. An acoeloid form was ancestral to other turbellarians, including the Polyclads, which have determinate spiral cleavage and develop through a stereogastrula to a type of larva called *trochophore,* atypical in this group. The generalized trochophore is an elliptical or more commonly a biconical larva, usually with circumferential bands of cilia of which the most constant encircles the equator (Fig. 1-3). The trochophore appears repeatedly in a group of Bilateria termed *Protostomates,* because of the correlated orientation of the larval blastopore and the adult mouth. In an alternate group of Bilateria including Echinodermata, Hemichordata, and Chordata, the adult anus arises from or in the region of the blastopore. These phyla constitute the *Deuterostomates.* In general, only the Protostomata, supported by additional features reserved for later discussion, appear to be a cognate group.

Trochophore or trochophore-like larvae occur in the following protostomate groups. *Müller's larva* of polyclad turbellarians has eight flattened ciliated lobes, and another

Fig. 1-3 Trochophore of *Polygordius. A,* anus; *dLM,* dorsal muscles; *ED,* hind gut; *J,* stomach; *J₁,* intestine; *Mstr,* mesodermal band; *n,* nerves; *Neph,* protonephridia; *O,* mouth; *Oe,* oesophagus; *oeLM,* oesophageal muscle; *SP,* apical plate; *vLM,* ventral muscle; *vLN,* lateral nerve; *Wkr, wkr,* pre- and post-oral zones of cilia; *WS,* apical cilia; *wz,* adoral cilia. Redrawn from R. Hertwig (after Hatschek), *A Manual of Zoology* (translated and edited by J. S. Kingsley) 1902, Holt, Rinehart & Winston, Inc.

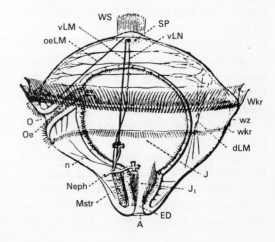

larva in this group has four. The *pilidium* is a helmet-shaped larva with a pair of lobes or lappets. It bears little resemblance to a trochophore, but belongs to a group (Nemertina) which on other grounds is related to flatworms. Nearly identical trochophores occur in the polychaete annelids and among Mollusca, groups in which the adults are structurally very diverse. Other trochophore versions appear in Sipunculoidea, Ectoprocta, and in Phoronida in which the larva is called an *Actinotrocha*. Adult rotifers are structurally not unlike the trochophore, and the determinate cleavage, in some cases approaching spiral patterns, of these and related groups suggests affinity.

Deuterostomate Bilateria possess no common larval type. Among living Echinodermata, there is marked similarity between the *auricularia* of the Holothuroidea and the *bipennaria* of the Asteroidea. In the Hemichordata, the *tornaria* larva bears marked resemblance to echinoderm larvae and has been mistaken for one. The *dipleurula* larva represents a hypothetical echinoderm embryo, invented to coordinate the early embryology of the various subgroups (Fig. 1-4).

Fig. 1-4 Diagrammatic reconstruction of hypothetical Dipleurula. Redrawn from various sources.

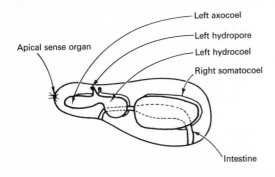

Apical sense organ
— Left axocoel
— Left hydropore
— Left hydrocoel
— Right somatocoel
Intestine

NEOTENY AND PAEDOMORPHOSIS

The fourth law of von Baer states that the embryonic stages of an animal do not repeat the adult phase of ancestors but will be comparable to embryonic stages of those ancestors. This rule opposes Haeckel's recapitulation theory. Garstang pointed out two antagonistic competitions in the ontogeny of marine animals. One of these involved the extension of embryonic life as a floating or swimming larva which served to distribute the species widely, and the other was the impetus to become sexually mature in order to reproduce the species maximally. Natural selection influences larval stages as well as adults, and it frequently appears to have resulted in a kind of compromise of the competitive forces.

Neoteny (approximately equivalent to *paedogenesis*) is the attainment of sexual maturity in a larval form or the retardation in development of some prospective adult structures as compared with the organs of reproduction. Many cases of neoteny are cited in the literature (deBeer, 1958). If mutation worked to favor larval adaptation, such change could be introduced into adult descendants by the process of neoteny. This concept for the production of phylogenetic change and subsequent radiation of the modified line is *paedomorphosis*. Such a process may well be one of the main causes for branching in the phylogenetic tree.

REFERENCES

Embryology and Evolution

Ax, Peter, Die Entdeckung neuer Organisationtypen im Tierreich. Wittenberg (East Germany): Ziemsen, 1960.

deBeer, G. R., Embryos and Ancestors (3rd ed.). London: Oxford, 1958.

Dougherty, E. C., Z. N. Brown, E. D. Hanson, and W. D. Hartman, eds., The lower

Metazoa: comparative biology and phylogeny. Berkeley: U. of California, 1963.

Garstang, W., The theory of recapitulation: a critical restatement of the biogenetic law. J. Linn. Soc. London Zool., 35:81, 1922.

Hanson, E. D., Animal diversity (2nd ed.). Englewood Cliffs, N.J.: Prentice-Hall, 1964.

Korschelt, E., and K. Heider, Lehrbuch der vergleichenden Entwicklungsgeschichte der wirbellosen Tiere. Jena: Fischer, 1893-1909. Second edition and English translation by Bernard and Woodward. New York: Macmillan, 1936.

MacBride, E. W., Textbook of embryology, Vol. I, Invertebrata. London: Macmillan, 1914.

Richards, A., Outline of comparative embryology. New York: Wiley, 1931.

Ross, H. H., A synthesis of evolutionary theory. Englewood Cliffs, N.J.: Prentice-Hall, 1962.

Yonge, C. M., Evolution and adaptation in the digestive system of the Metazoa. Biol. Rev., 12:87, 1937.

Taxonomy

Dobzhansky, Th., What is a species? Scientia, 280, 1937.

Mayr, E., Systematics and the origin of species. New York: Columbia, 1942.

————, E. G. Linsley, and R. L. Usinger, Methods and principles of systematic zoology. New York: McGraw, 1953.

Simpson, G. G., Principles of animal taxonomy. New York: Columbia, 1961.

Marine Biology

MacGinitie, G. E., and N. MacGinitie, Natural history of marine animals. New York: McGraw, 1949.

Yonge, C. M., The sea shore. London: Collins, 1949.

Paleontology

Shrock, R. R., and W. H. Twenhofel, Principles of invertebrate paleontology (2nd ed.). New York: McGraw, 1953.

Treatise on invertebrate paleontology (R. C. Moore, ed.). Lawrence, Kansas: Geol. Soc. Amer. and U. of Kansas (in process since 1952).

Physiology

Physiological adaptation (C. L. Prosser, ed.). Washington: American Physiol. Soc., 1958.

Prosser, C. L., and F. A. Brown, Jr., Comparative animal physiology (2nd ed.). Philadelphia: Saunders, 1961.

Major Treatises on the Invertebrates

Bronn, H. G., Klassen und Ordnungen des Tierreichs. Leipzig: Akad Verlag, 1873-. (This work, still being published, has a monumental coverage on many invertebrate groups.)

Cambridge natural history (S. F. Harmer and A. E. Shipley, eds.). London: Macmillan, 1895-1909. (Reprinted 1959 by Wheldon and Wesley, Ltd., Codicote, England.)

Handbuch der Zoologie: eine Naturgeschichte der Stämme des Tierreiches (W. Kükenthal and T. Krumbach, eds.). Berlin: Walter de Gruyter, 1923-.

Hyman, L. H., The invertebrates: Vol. I, Protozoa through Ctenophora; Vol. II, Platyhelminthes and Rhynchocoela; Vol. III, Acanthocephala, Aschelminthes, and Entoprocta; Vol. IV, Echinodermata; Vol. V, Smaller coelomate groups; others in process. New York: McGraw, 1940-1959.

Lankester, E. R. (ed.), A treatise on zoology. London: A. & C. Black, 1900-. (This important work was never completed.)

Traité de zoologie: anatomie, systématique, biologie (P. Grassé, ed.). (First eleven volumes are on the invertebrates.) Paris: Masson et Cie, 1948-.

2

PROTOZOA

The single-celled microscopic animals known as protozoa were first seen by the Dutch lens maker, Leeuwenhoek, in the latter part of the seventeenth century. Although this monumental discovery evoked great interest and study at the time, these animalcules were thought then to differ from larger animals primarily in size. The actual recognition and establishment of protozoa as a phylum of single-celled organisms postdated the cell theory of 1839. The cell theory, based primarily on study of multicellular organisms, probably hastened the appreciation of protozoa as a special group. Protozoa are commonly thought of as *unicellular,* but (following Hyman) if they are defined as animals whose body protoplasm is not subdivided into cells, the term *acellular* is more appropriate. This concept accomplishes a real service in emphasizing the unique qualities of the protozoan, its individuality, and the survival and generative processes not duplicated generally for the cells of metazoa. However, cytologists emphasize the very great similarity in cell organelles between the protozoan and the metazoan cell, and, if it be accepted that protozoa are ancestral to metazoa, we can accept protozoa as being highly evolved cells conducting themselves as total organisms. Since one prominent theory derives metazoa from ciliates, it is of interest to note that one metabolic enzyme system (of glyconeogenesis) appears to be restricted to protists (the ciliate, *Tetrahymena pyriformis*) and to germinating seeds of higher plants (Holz, 1964).

A typical protozoan is a microscopic, uninucleate animal which as a unit carries on all life functions. Frequently a number of like individuals are joined to form a colony, and bi- or multinucleate species are common. Such a description serves to differentiate the protozoan from the macroscopic animal, but the separation from other microscopic forms is less clear. Characteristics of multicellular organisms served as the principal criteria allocating living organisms to the two traditional groups: the plant and animal kingdoms. Many microorganisms do not readily fall in either group, but have evolved by protoplasmic differentiation within the cell rather than undergoing the division-of-labor specialization into tissues as in multicellular organisms. In 1866, Haeckel proposed the erection of a third kingdom, which he named *Protista,* for the inclusion of those organisms transitory or intermediate between the two classical kingdoms.

Stanier (1959) gives a brief summary of the Protista and the four major groups it encompasses. These are the algae, fungi, protozoa, and bacteria. The first three of these are similar to the cells of higher organisms, with chromatin usually located within a nucleus which is delimited by a membrane from the cytoplasm. The surface layer of cytoplasm is differentiated into a plasma membrane and encloses various formed protoplasmic components called *organoids* as well as food reserves and other nonliving materials. Ehret (1960) suggests the alternate name of *envelops* for the plasma and nuclear membranes and points out that bacteria appear to be single-envelop systems more or less homologous to the nucleus of a typical cell. The substitute term is proposed

Fig. 2-1 Various protozoa; (a) *Amoeba*; (b) foraminiferan; (c) *Paramecium*; (d) tintinnid ciliate; (e) same extended; (f) *Noctiluca* (flagellate); (g) *Peridinium* (dinoflagellate); (h) *Ceratium* (dinoflagellate). 1, pseudopodium; 2, collar cells; 3, spore cells; 4, spicule; 5, contractile vacuole; 6, gullet; 7, cilia; 8, trichocysts; 9, flagellum; 10, cup or lorica. After MacGinitie and MacGinitie 1949, courtesy of the McGraw-Hill Book Company.

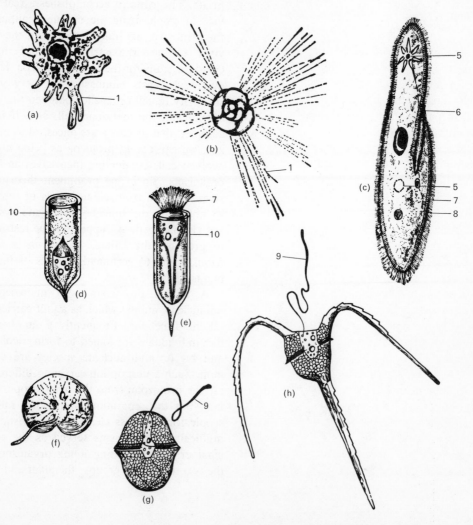

as part of a more specific terminology for the revolutionary concepts developing from study of the ultrastructure revealed by the electron microscope. Bacteria as well as blue-green algae never have the nucleus and cytoplasm separated by a nuclear membrane. This and other distinctions between bacteria and the other Protista are discussed by Stanier, Doudoroff, and Adelberg (1963). The term Protista recognizes the relatedness of algae and protozoa and emphasizes the comparative simplicity of their biological organization; the presence of transitional forms between the animal and plant kingdoms; the relative lack of differentiation into tissues, and the origin of multicellularity from unicellular forms.

ORGANIZATION OF THE PROTOZOA

Protozoa occur in an infinite variety of shapes (Fig. 2-1). These minute animals occur in all sorts of aquatic habitats, and though mostly free-living are well represented in parasitic and commensal relationships with both plants and animals. Individual and species survival are dependent upon obtaining food, upon structural protection against unfavorable conditions, upon tropistic mechanisms that provide recognition of favorable and unfavorable environment and correlated pursuit or evasion responses, and upon reproductive potential sufficient to balance the hazards of survival. Structural protoplasmic modifications called *organelles* developed in protozoa are somewhat analogous to tissues and organs of multicellular animals. For instance, surface modifications are fundamental to locomotor adaptation; to sensory function; in production of protective cysts in unfavorable situations; and in participation in sexual and asexual reproductive processes.

The term organelles has long been applied to functional specializations of the protozoan protoplasm, even though fundamental vital characteristics are performed in many cases by apparently undifferentiated protoplasm. Organelles have permanent or recurring structural modifications so consistent as to be subject to prediction, and they can be described as definite entities (Fig. 2-2). Common examples are locomotor organelles such as cilia or flagella, protective organelles such as trichocysts, attachment devices in sessile forms, and modifications for water balance and osmotic exchange.

Cytoplasm and Surface

The protozoan body is divisible into cytoplasm and nuclear material. The cytoplasm is commonly differentiated into two layers of apparently different colloidal consistency, ectoplasm and endoplasm. The more hyaline and usually more homogeneous

Fig. 2-2 Composite flagellate structure. After Beck and Braithwaite, *Invertebrate Zoology Laboratory Workbook* 1962, courtesy of the authors and Burgess Publishing Co. (Copyright held by authors.)

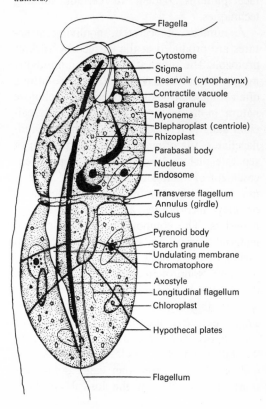

Flagella
Cytostome
Stigma
Reservoir (cytopharynx)
Contractile vacuole
Basal granule
Myoneme
Blepharoplast (centriole)
Rhizoplast
Parabasal body
Nucleus
Endosome
Transverse flagellum
Annulus (girdle)
Sulcus
Pyrenoid body
Starch granule
Undulating membrane
Chromatophore
Axostyle
Longitudinal flagellum
Chloroplast
Hypothecal plates
Flagellum

surface layer is termed ectoplasm. The relative gelation of this layer is primarily responsible for body shape, especially in typical amoeba and some flagellates, in which the cortical layer is not highly differentiated. In many protozoa, however, the zone near the surface is sharply defined and permanent. It contains a variety of inclusions such as contractile and noncontractile fibrils, mitochondria, and granules. In the ciliates and flagellates, the surface layer of the cortex is set off as a distinct peripheral membrane called the *pellicle* or *periplast*. The cell surface in *Paramecium* (Ehret and Powers, 1959) appears to be composed of packed hexagonal organelles called ciliary corpuscles, provided with a spindle-shaped cleft externally, from which the cilia emerge in a linear series. Deeper-lying trichocysts extend into the intracorpuscular space between adjacent corpuscles in line with the cilia. The symmetrically packed organelles account for the rhomboidal and polygonal surface patterns evident in certain staining techniques.

A number of secreted, nonliving structures are produced at the surface by various protozoa. The simplest of these is a nonliving membrane called the *cuticle*. A close-fitting, often somewhat flexible covering of cellulose nature more or less impregnated with calcium salts is termed a *theca*. Among Dinoflagellates it is often secreted in a pattern of separate plates. A more loosely applied encasement of analogous nature is the *shell* or *test*. It may be a homogeneous secreted layer or may incorporate a variety of foreign materials. The composition of the secreted material varies. In some species, calcium carbonate is the basic material. Silica is used by a few. Nonprotein chitin occasionally, and the glucoprotein pseudochitin more frequently, are the organic materials utilized. A single-apertured, loosely applied conical or vase-shaped shell which may terminate in the stalk in attached species is called a *lorica,* and usually the protozoan can extend portions of its body out the lorical aperture.

Among some test-producing protozoa a layer of cytoplasm covers the shell.

Chromoplasts are relatively common organelles among protozoa. Chlorophyll is responsible for the green color in species which utilize photosynthesis, although other pigments occurring in plastids may mask the green color. In a few forms a red pigment, hematochrome, occurs diffuse in the cytoplasm rather than contained in plastids. Commonly correlated with the occurrence of chloroplasts are bodies called *pyrenoids,* whose probable function is related to carbohydrate synthesis, or reserve storage.

Various kinds of vacuoles occur among protozoa. Contractile vacuoles are common in fresh-water forms, but generally absent in marine and parasitic protozoa, except ciliates, in which they apparently function to remove metabolic water. Fluid enters the vacuole to be later more or less rhythmically discharged to the animal's exterior. These vacuoles appear to be concerned with osmotic or hydrostatic equilibrium. Number and position of contractile vacuoles is variable, but is more fixed in highly organized forms. A vacuole of somewhat similar appearance in Dinoflagellates is not contractile, but apparently functions for the intake of fluids from the external medium. Gaseous vacuoles formed in Radiolaria, particularly in the outer cytoplasm, apparently act as depth regulators for these organisms.

Food vacuoles are common in many protozoa. These are due primarily to inclosure of food masses by the cytoplasm for digestion. They are not organelles in a precise sense, but physical manifestations which result in an interface at the boundary produced by the juncture of materials of different properties.

Locomotor Organelles

A variety of locomotor organelles occur among the protozoa. Types of such structures serve to demarcate the phylum into groups, although many individual life cycles exhibit more than one kind of locomotor organelle. Among some of the Sporozoa, a type of gliding locomotion does not seem to be associated with any specific type of organelle, unless it be contractile *myonemes.* Among Sarcodina and some Sporozoa, amoeboid movement occurs with the aid of surface projections called pseudopodia, while the Flagellata and Ciliophora utilize the beating of filamentous hairlike structures, flagella and cilia, respectively.

A number of types of pseudopodia occur. These have some taxonomic value normally, but in some instances modification of the ecological habitat has resulted in temporary substitution of a nontypical form. Pseudopodia with blunt, rounded margins which frequently exhibit demarcation between ectoplasm and endoplasm are called *lobopodia.* Several types of slender projections occur, some of which anastomose to form branching networks. *Filopodia* are thin, tapered pseudopodia, hyaline and nongranular in nature. *Myxopodia* tend to form extensive networks and characteristically exhibit active flow of granules (Fig. 2-3). *Axopodia* are semipermanent pseudopodia occurring as individually radiating fibers in the Actinopoda. They possess an axial rod surrounded by a thin layer of cytoplasm.

Recent electron-microscope studies indicate that the gross structure of cilia and

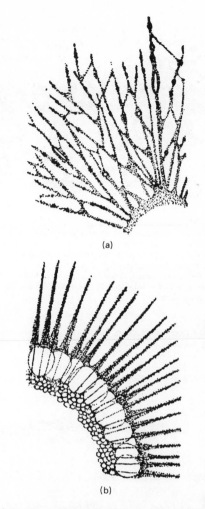

(a)

(b)

Fig. 2-3 (a) Myxopodia and (b) Axopodia. From Hall, *Protozoology* 1953, courtesy of Prentice-Hall, Inc.

Fig. 2-4 Diagrammatic transverse section of a flagellum. The line ∝ indicates the axial plane of the outer fibre. From I. R. Gibbons and A. V. Grimstone, *J. Biophys. Biochem. Cytol.* (July), 1960, Vol. 7, No. 4, 697-715. Reprinted by permission of the Rockefeller University Press.

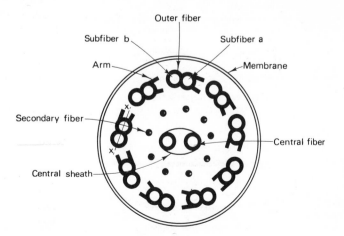

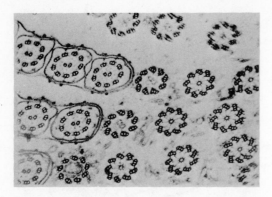

Fig. 2-5 Transverse sections through basal bodies and flagella in the anterior body-region of *Pseudotrichonympha,* including the transition from the former to the latter. At top are flagellar grooves, and at the bottom are sections through the proximal ends of the basal bodies, X 95,000. From I. R. Gibbons and A. V. Grimstone, from *J. Biophys. Biochem. Cytol.* (July), 1960, Vol. 7, No. 4, 697-715. Reprinted by permission of the Rockefeller University Press.

Fig. 2-6 Diagrams of ciliary movement and metachronal action along a ciliary row. After Jahn and Jahn 1949, courtesy of H. E. Jaques and Wm. C. Brown Co., Publishers.

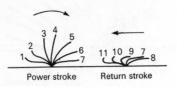

Power stroke   Return stroke

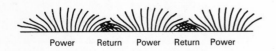

Power   Return   Power   Return   Power

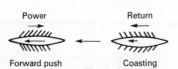

Power   Return

Forward push   Coasting

Action of oars in Roman galley

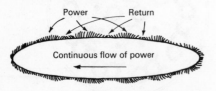

Power   Return

Continuous flow of power

Action of cilia of large holotrich

flagella is nearly identical, although the latter may bear one or more lateral finlike flimmers and additional spiral fibers. The basic structure of both flagella and cilia is a core composed of two fibers surrounded by a sheath of nine fibers. Gibbons and Grimstone showed in the flagellate *Pseudotrichonympha* that each outer fiber of the sheath is actually a doublet with one subfiber bearing arms projecting toward the next outer fiber in the ring. Just within the doublets there is a circle of nine smaller fibers. The helically disposed central fibers are encased in a common sheath (Fig. 2-4). The doublets, joined by a third subfiber to produce a cylinder of triplets, form the basal body (*basal granule, kinetosome),* where phosphate reserves appear to be concentrated (Fig. 2-5). In *Pseudotrichonympha* the flagella occur in rows and arise from deep grooves in the cell surface of this protozoan. Some of these can be seen in section in Fig. 2-5. Flagella are effective because of a spiral undulation which begins at the attached end and moves to the free end. As a result often the flagellate pursues a spiral course as it advances. For monoflagellates generally, the cell body trails the single flagellum as the animal swims.

Cilia are in general smaller and more numerous than flagella. Their more rapid beat (Fig. 2-6), synchronized with adjacent cilia, results in a wave action which propels the animal. Cilia may be fused actually or functionally into finlike plates which form a type of undulating membrane, or they may be fused conically into cirri. Another type of undulating membrane occurs in flagellates in which the proximal portion of the flagellum courses along the edge of a thin sheet of cytoplasm.

For both flagella and cilia, the longitudinal fibers fuse and enter the cell body to join the *basal granule* or *kinetosome.* The older name for the basal granule of a flagellum was *blepharoplast.* Fibers called *rhizoplasts* connect it with the nucleus and frequently in parasitic species, and in some free-living flagellates, with another structure of un-

known function, called the *parabasal body,*
which usually lies near the nucleus. In many
flagellates a presumably supportive "rod" of
hyaline protoplasm called *axostyle* runs from
the basal granule through the interior of the
cytoplasm. Its staining reactions are not uniform for different species.

The kinetosome of a cilium does not connect with the nucleus, but from its right side
a thread or strand called a *kinetodesma*
winds forward (except in *Stentor* in which
it runs posteriad) to spiral with those arising from other cilia in the same linear series.
The connecting kinetosomes and kinetodesma form a functional and structural unit
called a *kinety* (plural: kineties), but are
not connected to other kineties (Fig. 2-7).
The kineties as a group make up the *infraciliature.* It is of extreme significance that flagellates at cell division cleave parallel to the
kineties, while among ciliates the cleavage
plane crosses kineties. Figure 2-8 indicates
that the pellicle includes the organization of
the kineties, plus the ciliary corpuscles enveloping the base of a ciliary unit of one to
four cilia, plus an alternating system of *trichocysts.* A parasomal sac of unknown function occurs on the right side of each ciliary
corpuscle. The polygonal patterns produced
by the ciliary corpuscles in apposition probably acounts for some of the so-called silver-
line staining systems. Longitudinally, the

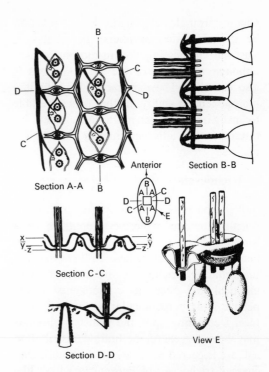

Fig. 2-7 Interpretative diagrams of a ciliary corpuscle and of
idealized sections of it in *Paramecium.* The guide lines adjacent
to the diagram define planes of sections described in earlier
figures. Planes of sectioning are shown on the outline of the
cell in the center of the figure. After Ehret and Powers 1959,
courtesy of Academic Press, Inc.

Fig. 2-8 A reconstruction of the pellicle system as it would appear
in perspective view. The relationships of the kinetodesma and
trichocysts to the hexagonally packed ciliary corpuscles that form
the outer surface of *Paramecium* are also shown. After Ehret and
Powers 1959, courtesy of Academic Press, Inc.

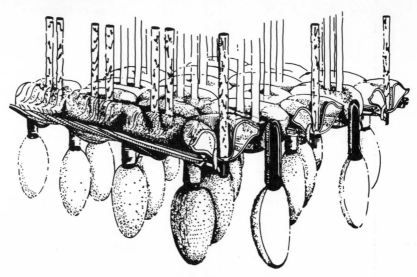

ciliary corpuscles are rigidly bound together by the kinetodesmal fibers. In ciliates at least the kineties function in morphogenesis, although a portion of the macronucleus is also essential. They appear to have limited morphogenetic ability, in that some are able to instigate formation of a new gullet, for instance, while adjacent kineties form typical pellicle.

Trichocysts

Protozoa possess certain structures which function by the explosive propulsion of a thread or fiber. These include trichocysts and nematocyst-like organelles. In *Paramecium,* undischarged trichocysts are more or less elliptical and occur as components of the pellicle lying perpendicular to the body surface. Depending upon the genus, trichocysts may have a general or limited distribution and are triggered by a variety of stimuli. Discharged trichocysts of *Paramecium* look like elongate golf tees and exhibit fine transverse striations on the shaft. In *Dileptus,* the trichocyst appears to be an elongated vesicle containing toxic fluid. The orientation of this vesicle is reversed at discharge (Fig. 2-9).

Fig. 2-9 Trichocysts of *Dileptus anser,* (a) before and (b) after discharge. After Hayes 1938, *Trans. Amer. Microsc. Soc.,* Vol. 57, No. 11.

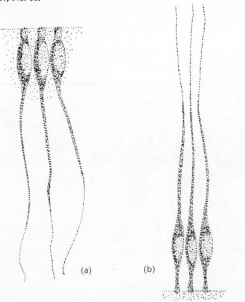

(a)   (b)

Basal granules of the pellicle or possible macronuclear materials are responsible for replacement of trichocysts. Among some Dinoflagellates are nematocyst-like organelles, which contain a coiled thread. Among the Cnidosporidia, polar capsules contain coiled filaments. These organelles have been variously described as anchoring mechanisms or as functioning in offense or defense.

Group Associations

In many protozoa, reproductive processes of fission or budding give rise to an association of individuals called a colony. Such groupings may be spherical, discoidal, or arboroid, and they generally are stable and typical enough to possess taxonomic value. Other colony-like formations occur. Sometimes budding gives rise to a chain of protozoa because of delayed separation. Another formation involves production of a syncytial group by union of uninucleate forms. Such a group is called a *plasmodium.* Some flagellates form temporary and nonuniform groupings of nonflagellate stages. The term *palmella* is applied to them.

NUTRITION AND FOOD RESERVE MATERIALS

Types of Nutrition

Various types of nutrition, not necessarily mutually restrictive, occur among protozoa. In those forms possessing chlorophyll, part or all of the nutrition is autotrophic or holophytic. This process of photosynthesis results in the formation of complex carbohydrate materials from common inorganic ones, just as occurs in green plants. Subsequently, both plants and autotrophic protozoa must obtain nitrogen for protein synthesis. Another group of protozoa require organic food. They do not ingest solid materials, but absorb soluble or predigested nutrients. This type of nutrition is saprozoic

and is typical of parasitic protozoa and colorless, free-living flagellates. Many protozoa are holozoic. They ingest solid and formed nutrients which undergo some sort of digestion before utilization. Such food might consist of bacteria, yeasts, and algae as well as minute animal material, both protozoan and metazoan. This pattern of nutrition has led to the development of food-capturing and food-ingesting organelle systems of varying degrees of complexity. Most Sarcodina simply envelop the food with pseudopodia which close to form food vacuoles. These are transient containers lost with the egestion of indigestibles. In other protozoa, partly or completely holozoic, specialized surface areas serve for food capture and ingestion. *Euglena* possesses a small infolded pouch or pit enclosing the base of the flagellum. This pit is often referred to as a cytopharynx or even as a

gullet, but it seems probable that holozoic nutrition does not occur in *Euglena*. However, the pit does function as a discharge site for contractile vacuoles. In many flagellates and in most Euciliates, a definite region called a mouth or cytostome is evident. It opens to a passage of varying shape, called the cytopharynx. While this represents the more primitive condition, in many ciliates a preoral chamber occurs adjacent to the mouth. This chamber is called a *vestibule* when lined with cilia or a *buccal cavity* if it contains membranelles. In *Paramecium,* a vestibule precedes a buccal cavity.

Sometimes the term *peristome* has been used as equivalent to buccal cavity, and sometimes in a more general sense for the area around the mouth. In many ciliates (Fig. 2-10) cilia functionally or morphologically fused into rows surround the cytostome

Fig. 2-10 Various ciliates: (a) *Didinium*, (b) *Coleps*, (c) *Stentor*, and (d) *Stylonychia*. After Beck and Braithwaite, *Invertebrate Zoology Laboratory Workbook* 1962, courtesy of the authors and the Burgess Publishing Co. (Copyright held by authors.)

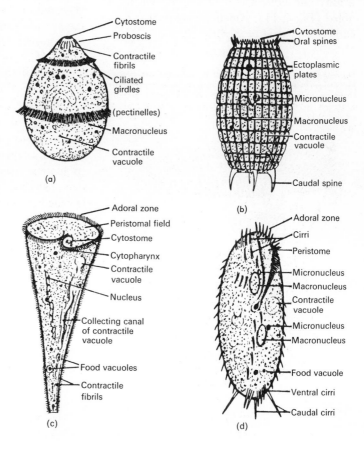

and spiral toward the cytopharynx to direct food-containing currents. *Stentor* has an adoral zone of membranelles, each individual of which is composed of three parallel rows of cilia which have coordinated action but which are not confined by a limiting membrane. These cilia have fine hairlike protuberances. Below the kinetosomes of these cilia, root fibrils converge medially to form a bundle for each membranelle and these lead to a zig-zag basal fiber common for the entire series of membranelles.

Some ability to reject nonnutritive particles has been demonstrated for such well-known protozoa as *Paramecium* and *Stentor*. Food moved to the inner end of the cytopharynx is "pushed" into and engulfed by the endoplasm, where commonly a spherical vacuole forms around it. As this food vacuole is carried through the endoplasm, changes in acidity and liquefaction of solids have been noted (Fig. 2-11). A definite acid pH occurs earlier, a neutral or slightly alkaline pH oc-

Fig. 2-11 Diagram showing the digestion within the food vacuoles in *Carchesium polypinum*. *a*, digestion area; *b*, region of little change; *c*, region of acid reaction; *d*, region of neutral reaction; *e*, area of defecation. From Kudo (after Greenwood), *Protozoology*, 3rd Ed., 1950, courtesy of Charles C Thomas, Publisher, Springfield, Illinois.

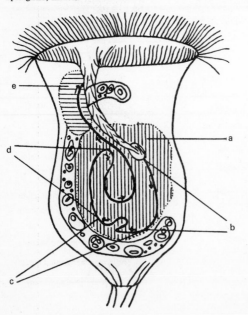

curs in the vacuole at later stages in most protozoa investigated. Indigestible materials are usually egested through a somewhat specialized cortical zone called cytopyge in typical flagellates and ciliates.

Digestion and Food Reserves

Digestion of proteins and carbohydrates has been repeatedly demonstrated. Of specific interest is the ability of a number of symbiotic protozoa to digest cellulose. Digestion of fats is less clearly validated, but fats and lipoids are common food reserves in many protozoa, so that the circumstantial evidence for the presence of lipases is very strong. In some forms, oil droplets may serve as mechanisms which aid in floating, aside from the probable nutritional aspects. Some chlorophyll-bearing species store starch, but glycogen or paraglycogen is a more common reserve for protozoa generally. Some flagellates store a glycogenlike, refractile material called *leucosin*. An iodine-negative polysaccharide not soluble in hot water can be hydrolyzed to glucose. This carbohydrate, called *paramylum* or sometimes *paramylon*, is common in some Mastigophora. A number of protozoa store spheres or crystals of material of protein nature. One kind of nitrogenous reserve which occurs as granules demonstrable by special staining techniques is called *volutin*. Normally a number of these reserve food materials have characteristic size and shape for the species in which they occur, but of course are subject to change under adverse conditions.

Nuclei

The nucleus has a nuclear membrane enclosing nucleoplasm or nuclear sap, plastin, and chromatin. This last substance is chromophilic, staining readily with basic dyes and giving a positive Feulgen reaction indicative of the presence of deoxyribonucleic acid (DNA), a material responsible for continuity of hereditary information to successive generations, including the composition of specific proteins. Intranuclear bodies called *endosomes* or *karyosomes* are entirely or partly composed of chromatin. The material, plastin, shows staining reactions similar to cytoplasm. It stains faintly with acidic dyes and gives a negative Feulgen response. Within the nucleus it commonly occurs in discrete bodies called nucleoli or *plasmosomes,* sometimes on the inner surface of the nuclear membrane and as more or less irregular strands in the nucleoplasm. Distinction between nucleoli and endosomes is often difficult, since the latter may be partly composed of plastin. In many nuclei, chromatin also occurs as granules in the nucleoplasm and as granules adsorbed on the endosomal surface. In some protozoa, the endosome disappears during the mitotic cycle, while in others it persists and undergoes division. Some nuclei lack endosomes, and their nucleoli may or may not disappear during mitosis. Additional study is needed to establish the significance of these intranuclear structures.

Protozoan nuclei exhibit great variety in structure, but they can be separated roughly into two kinds, one called *vesicular* and the other *compact* or massive. Many intermediate forms grade between the two types. The vesicular nucleus is the common type for Mastigophora, Sarcodina, and Sporozoa. It is usually rounded with considerable nucleoplasm, localized chromatin, and one or more intranuclear bodies. In those organisms with more than one nucleus, little apparent difference occurs in the different nuclei. In the Ciliophora, which exhibit nuclear dimorphism, the micronuclear structure is frequently vesicular.

The compact or massive nucleus contains a great deal of chromatin and relatively little nucleoplasm. Macronuclei of Ciliophora are typical of the compact type. In these groups of protozoa the macronuclei show great variation in shape and size as well as in number. The name is derived from the compact or

dense massing of the chromatin. Some staining techniques exhibit slightly different staining affinities for chromatin of the micro- and macronuclei, but the latter themselves may show similar differential staining. At binary fission, in many Ciliophora the macronucleus divides *amitotically*.

Cyst Formation

The metabolic period in a protozoan life cycle in which feeding and activity are the paramount manifestations is called the vegetative stage or *trophozoite*. Commonly it reproduces asexually under favorable conditions. In less favorable circumstances a process called *encystment* occurs. In early precystic stages the organism tends to become more spherical. Surface organelles, particularly those associated with locomotion and food-getting, become obliterated. Surface cytoplasm changes in appearance, often becoming alveolar. Commonly, food reserves increase. With loss of fluid, the precystic sphere decreases in size. Secreted material of carbohydrate or protein nature forms around the spherical surface, although sometimes inorganic material is utilized. Cysts have been classified as protective and reproductive types, although these functions may often occur mutually. The actual causes of encystment are not known, but modification of the activity of metabolic enzyme systems occurs, probably instigated by any of a number of adverse environmental conditions. Encystment is commonplace among fresh-water and parasitic species except Sporozoa.

REPRODUCTIVE PHENOMENA

Asexual Processes

Protozoa reproduce both asexually and sexually. The usual method of asexual reproduction is *binary fission* (Fig. 2-12), and

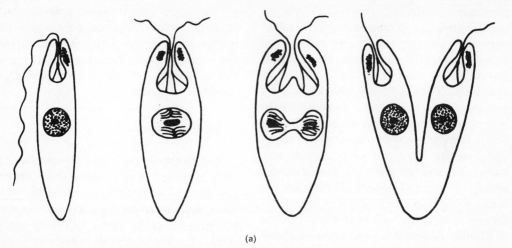

(a)

Fig. 2-12 Comparison of fission in *Euglena* and *Paramecium*. (a) Fission in *Euglena*. After Jahn and Jahn 1959 (after Hall), courtesy of H. E. Jaques and Wm. C. Brown Company, Publishers. (b) Fission in *Paramecium*. From Kudo, *Protozoology* 3rd Ed. 1950, courtesy of Charles C Thomas, Publisher, Springfield, Illinois.

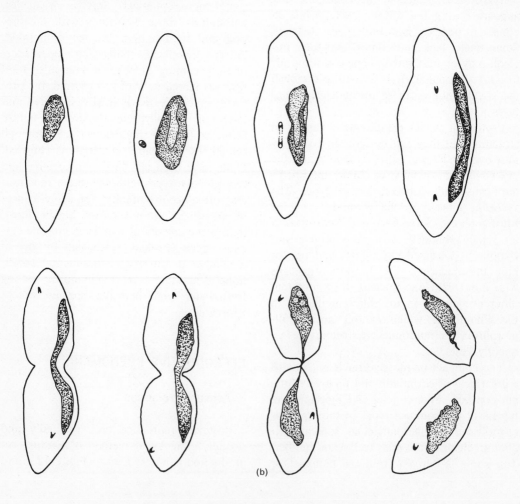

(b)

it may occur in either vegetative or cyst stage for some protozoa, although usually it is the trophozoite which undergoes fission. In flagellates the cleavage line is longitudinal and hence parallel to the kineties, while in ciliates the cleavage line cuts transversely across the kineties (Fig. 2-13). The former is termed *symmetrogenic;* the latter, *homothetogenic* fission. Binary fission involves the division of the protoplasm into two approximately equal masses. For uninucleate protozoa undergoing simple fission, the nucleus divides mitotically. In the Ciliata the micronucleus undergoes mitotic division while an amitotic process divides the macronucleus.

The process of budding suggests an inequality in the size of the daughter organisms, but this is not always true. A better criterion is that the bud lacks the differentiation characteristic of both daughter cells following simple fission. Budding, whether internal or external, as a reproductive method is common only in the Suctoria.

Multiple fission is a kind of internal budding in which many fission products are split off simultaneously, commonly leaving behind

Fig. 2-13 Homothetogenic and symmetrogenic fission in protozoa; (a) as in a ciliate, *Tetrahymena*; (b) as in a phytoflagellate such as *Euglena*. After Corliss 1961, courtesy of the Pergamon Press.

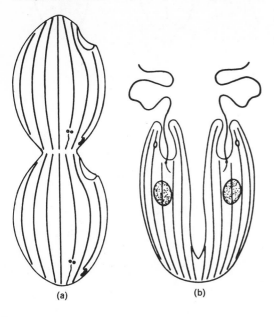

(a)   (b)

a residual core of protoplasm. This type of reproduction may occur in more than one stage of the life cycle, and additional terminology has sprung up to identify it. When this multiple fission occurs during the asexual cycle and results in fission products which change into adults directly, the term *schizogony* is used. *Agamogony* is a synonym for multiple fission when gametocytes (gamete-producing cells) are not formed. Occasionally some of the adults produced by schizogony are physiologically changed and give rise at multiple fission, not to another generation of like adults, but to gametocytes. The gametocytes may undergo *gamogony,* a multiple fission in which the end products are gametes. After union of gametes in pairs (*syngamy*) the resulting diploid zygote or sporont may give rise by a multiple fission called *sporogony* to sporozoites. The latter become adult to start the asexual part of the life cycle once more.

Multinucleate protozoa may reproduce asexually by budding or fission. In some Sporozoan life cycles, uninucleate stages undergo nuclear division to become multinucleate amoeboid forms called *plasmodia,* which then reproduce by multiple fission. A somewhat similar process called *plasmotomy* occurs with some multinucleate protozoa. In the last instance, nuclei are distributed to daughter organisms by subdivision of the syncytial organism.

Indirect nuclear division is characteristic of protozoa generally, except for the macronucleus in the Ciliophora which divides amitotically. However, the mitotic process shows great variation. Many protozoa undergo a process closely similar to cell division in metazoan cells, although probably the achromatic figure is a nuclear rather than a cytoplasmic product. In this process, called *eumitosis,* the sequence of chromosomal behavior follows the familiar pattern with definite prophase chromosomes, longtitudinal splitting, and equatorial placement on the spindle. Polar organization of the achromatic figure is variable. Centrioles may or may not be present. When they are present they may have originated from the nuclear membrane or from an endosome. Another variant of the eumitotic pattern is entirely intranuclear with a persistent nuclear membrane. In some processes which have a rather typical achromatic figure, typical chromosomes are not apparent, but the entire chromatin mass appears on the equatorial plate and is subsequently divided in two. This process has been called *cryptomitosis,* but intermediates grade into typical eumitosis.

In many cases, chromosomal behavior is markedly different. Neither prophase nor metaphase stages are typical of metazoan nuclear division. Only one end of the threadlike chromosome contacts the equatorial plate. This end represents the last junction of the longitudinally separating chromosome, and its eventual rupture suggests incorrectly a transverse division of the chromosome.

This pattern of indirect cell division is termed *paramitosis.*

Sexual Processes

Sexual reproduction probably occurs generally among Protozoa, although in some species it has never been observed. In some Sporozoa it forms an essential sequence of the life cycle, but in many protozoa it occurs at erratic intervals. Typically, the sexual process involves the fusion of gametic products from unlike parents, a process called *exogamy,* although in *Paramecium* and a few other forms, *autogamy* involving the fusion of haploid nuclei within a single organism has been reported.

Sexual reproduction can be separated into two categories. In *syngamy,* haploid sex cells fuse to form a zygote. The fusing gametes may be alike (isogametes) or unlike (aniso-

Fig 2-14 Conjugation in *Paramecium.* After Jahn and Jahn 1949, courtesy of H. E. Jaques and Wm. C. Brown Company, Publishers.

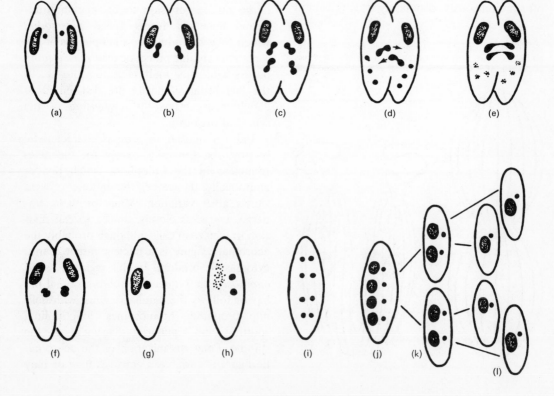

gametes). The second category is *conjugation* (Fig. 2-14). In this process, haploid nuclear material is exchanged between two adhering individuals, which subsequently separate to undergo reorganization and restoration of the normal nuclear complement. Sometimes, but not always, this involves fission. Sometimes the conjugants are equal (*Paramecium*), sometimes unequal as in *Vorticella* (Fig. 2-15).

A process of endomixis with nuclear reorganization and reassembly approximating those in conjugation, but occurring in individual paramecia without opportunity for nuclear exchange, has been described in textbooks for decades. Endomixis is no longer considered to occur, while the phenomena observed are interpreted as autogamy, with fusion of two haploid nuclei to begin a revitalized life cycle. In the absence of autogamy or of conjugation in *Paramecium*

aurelia, the line becomes senescent and death results.

Sexual reproduction is characteristic of most organisms, both plant and animal. Essential to it is the process of meiosis, which results in reduction of the chromosome number to haploid for the fusion nuclei. Typically, the reduction occurs at gamete formation. Resultant gamete fusion restores the diploid condition, which persists through the greater part of the life cycle for many protozoa. Among some Sporozoa, gametic fusion is followed almost immediately by meiosis, so that in these forms, the organism is haploid during the greater extent of the life cycle. In Euciliata and Suctoria, meiosis occurs during conjugation. Typically, the first two divisions of the micronucleus are meiotic, one being reductional and the other equational. The sequence of these two divisions differs in various species.

Fig. 2-15 Various conjugative pairings: (a) *Nyctotherus* (heterotrich); (b) *Pleurotricha* (hypotrich); (c) *Ancistrocoma* thigomotrich); (d) *Cycloposthium* (entodinimorph); (e) *Scyphidia* (peritrich); (f) *Vorticella* (peritrich); (g) *Euplotes* (hypotrich). From Hall (after various sources). *Protozoology*, 1953, courtesy of Prentice-Hall, Inc.

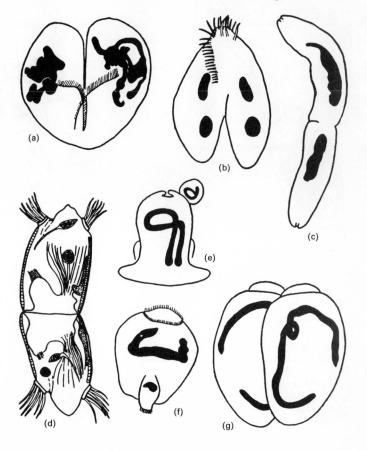

HIGHER SUBDIVISIONS IN PROTOZOAN CLASSIFICATION

Subphylum Plasmodroma

In these protozoa, locomotion is amoeboid or flagellate, or locomotor organelles are lacking. When more than one nucleus is present, the nuclei are morphologically similar.

Class I Flagellata or Mastigophora. Flagella or, rarely, cilia (Order Opalina) serve for locomotion during at least part of the life cycle.

Fig. 2-16 Some photosynthetic flagellates: (a) *Chlamydomonas*; (b) *Euglena*; (c) and (d) *Gymnodinium* and *Ceratium* (dinoflagellates); (e) *Chloromeson* (also capable of amoeboid movement). *f*, flagellum; *c*, chloroplast; *n*, nucleus; *e*, eyespot; *w*, wall; *p*, pellicle. From Stanier, Doudoroff, and Adelberg, *The Microbial World*, 2nd Ed., 1963, courtesy of Prentice-Hall, Inc.

SUBCLASS PHYTOMASTIGINA Typically these flagellates possess chloroplasts (Fig. 2-16) which are secondarily lost in a few forms. Sexual stages in the life cycles are frequent. Rarely more than two flagella are present.

SUBCLASS ZOOMASTIGINA These lack chloroplasts and carbohydrate reserves (Fig. 2-17). Syngamy is not common in this group. Usually there are more than two flagella. The Zoomastigina is considered to be a rather heterogeneous assemblage.

Class II Rhizopoda (Sarcodina). These are mostly free-living, pseudopod-producing forms with binary fission. The production of flagella is frequent. A definite pellicle is lacking, but some produce tests or shells (Fig. 2-18).

SUBCLASS ACTINOPODA These are floating or sessile forms which usually produce axopodia and rarely flagella. Shelled forms are common.

SUBCLASS RHIZOPODA Pseudopodia other than the axopodial type are characteristic. The

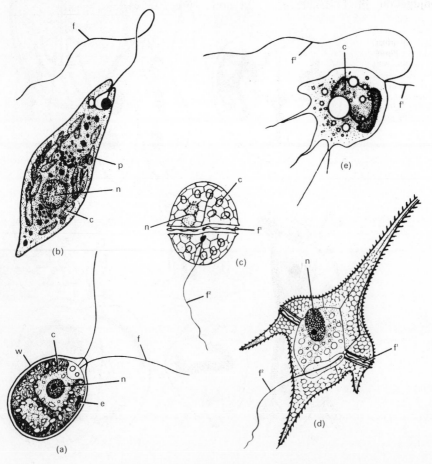

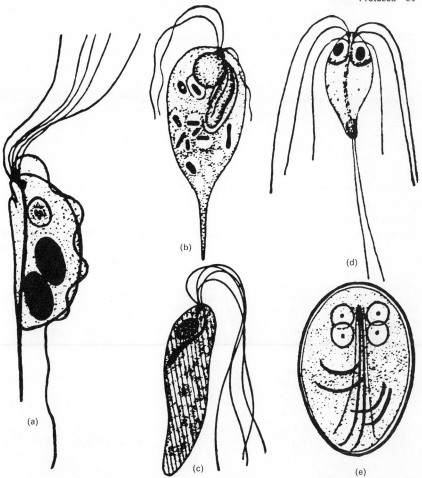

Fig. 2-17 Some intestinal flagellates. (a) *Trichomonas hominis*, from man; (b) *Chilomastix mesnili*, from man; (c) *Polymastix bufonis*, from the toad; (d) *Hexamita salmonis*, from the salmon; (e) *Giardia lamblia* cyst, from man. From Hegner (after various authors) 1933, courtesy of The Macmillan Company.

Fig. 2-18 Foraminifera, (a) *Globigerina*; (b) *Rotalia*; and (c) *Nummulites* (megalospheric form). From Hegner (after various authors) 1933, courtesy of The Macmillan Company.

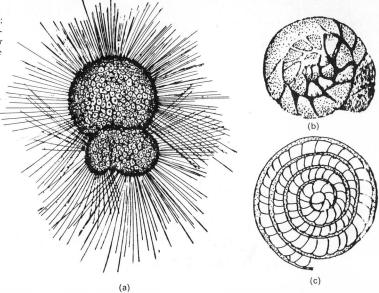

peripheral cytoplasm is not highly vacuolated. A multinuclear condition is frequent, and a number produce tests.

Class III Sporozoa. These obligate endoparasites lack contractile vacuoles and locomotor organelles, although microgametes often are flagellate. Asexual reproduction is by multiple fission, and walled spores are commonly produced after syngamy. Spores, absent in blood-inhabiting forms, serve as the transmission stage to a new, usually specific host.

SUBCLASS TELOSPORIDIA In this group reproduction occurs both by multiple fission and by sporogony, producing spores which lack polar capsules (Fig. 2-19).

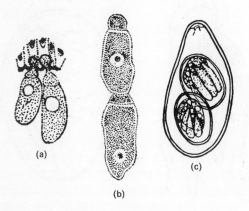

(a)

(b)

(c)

Fig. 2-19 (a) Telosporidia, (b) Gregarinida, and (c) Coccidia (*Isospora hominis* oocyst containing two spores, each with four sporozoites). From Hegner (after various authors) 1933, courtesy of The Macmillan Company.

Fig. 2-20 (a) Diagrammatic representation of a generalized *Paramecium* and (b) of a trophozoite of a parasitic ciliate, *Balantidium*. Adapted from various sources.

SUBCLASS CNIDOSPORIDIA In this group each spore contains one or more polar capsules which, upon extrusion, may function as organelles of attachment or may provide tubular channels for infection of the epithelial cell by the sporoplasm or generative cell contained in the spore. A polar capsule contains a coiled filament and bears a resemblance to a nematocyst. The zygote fails to undergo typical sporogony, but modifies into one or more trophozoites.

SUBCLASS HAPLOSPORIDIA In this group the oval spores are commonly operculate and lack polar filaments. There is a single order (Haplosporidia), a group parasitic in fish and in invertebrates.

Subphylum Ciliophora

These protozoa, which are never amoeboid, possess cilia as permanent or transitory organelles. Nuclei are dimorphic, with macronuclei being somatic and micronuclei, generative. Nutrition is holozoic generally, saprozoic in a few parasitic species. In most forms a cytostome is present. Reproduction is commonly by conjugation and homothetogenic binary fission.

Class Ciliata. The single class has the characteristics of the subphylum.

SUBCLASS HOLOTRICHA This large group has a uniform distribution of cilia and lacks cirri (Fig. 2-20).

SUBCLASS SPIROTRICHA These generally sparsely ciliated Ciliophora are characterized by the adoral zone bearing prominent membranelles of fused cilia disposed in a clockwise spiral from the distal end.

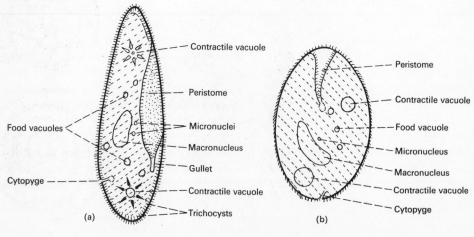

(a)
- Contractile vacuole
- Peristome
- Micronuclei
- Macronucleus
- Gullet
- Contractile vacuole
- Trichocysts

Food vacuoles
Cytopyge

(b)
- Peristome
- Contractile vacuole
- Food vacuole
- Micronucleus
- Macronucleus
- Contractile vacuole
- Cytopyge

The resume of the orders in each of the protozoan classes will follow the discussion of the class concerned.

CLASS FLAGELLATA

Flagellata or Mastigophora typically possess one to many flagella (or rarely cilia as in Order Opalina) as locomotor organelles. In some species the flagella are transitory, appearing only during certain stages of the life cycle. Flagella also occur among representatives of both Sarcodina (Fig. 2-26) and Sporozoa, and on the other hand a number of flagellates utilize pseudopodia for locomotion or food-gathering.

The Flagellata usually do not exhibit sharp demarcation between cortical protoplasm and endoplasm, but a thin restraining envelop called the pellicle is a common feature, responsible in part for the shape of the animal. The forward-projecting flagellum in uniflagellate forms propels the animal by an undulating beat which moves from base to tip.

Nutrition is typically holophytic among the Phytomastigina, which utilize the chlorophyll of chromatophores in photosynthesis. In most of the subdivisions of this subclass, colorless species occur and nutrition is saprozoic. Some green forms can survive with saprozoic nutrition, when the chlorophyll is destroyed by keeping the animal in the dark. In some cases the presence or absence of chromatophores seems to be the only morphological differentiation between genera, if indeed they are different—e.g. *Euglena* and *Astasia* or *Chlamodomonas* and *Parapolytoma.* Very frequent binary fission also may have accounted for achloritic forms, if one of the daughter cells failed to receive chloroplasts at division. Finally a number of chlorophyll-bearing species are holozoic, utilizing amoeboid ingestion. Various types of plastids have been reported from flagellates. In addition to chloroplasts, there are occasionally colorless leucoplasts as well as chromoplastids containing yellow and red pigments. Commonly associated with chloroplastids are bodies called pyrenoids around which polysaccharides such as starches and paramylum accumulate and which may be responsible for their synthesis.

In the subclass Zoomastigina, chromatophores are absent. Nutrition is holozoic or saprophytic with glycogen and lipoid food reserves occurring commonly. Starch and paramylum are lacking. Formation of tests or shells is uncommon among Zoomastigina.

Flagellate life cycles are usually simple, but dimorphic or polymorphic patterns occur, particularly in the Phytomastigina. The occurrence of amoeboid stages in some flagellate life cycles seems particularly significant. Typically, reproduction is asexual by longitudinal binary fission. In the Phytomastigina sexual reproduction occurs in *Volvox* and other Phytomonadida and a few instances have been reported from the Zoomastigina. A hologamic sexual fusion occurs in *Scytomonas (Copromonas) subtilis.*

In the family Volvocidae (Phytomonadida) the life histories show asexual as well as sexual reproduction. In some species daughter colonies may be produced by any member of the colony, but in the more spherical colonies, *Eudorina, Pleodorina,* and *Volvox,* this ability is limited to cells in the posterior hemisphere. The cells divide to form a spherical group called a *plakea,* which in *Volvox* retains an opening or pore. The future anterior ends of the cells in the daughter colony face centrally. Later an extroversion occurs, the plakea turning inside out through its pore. The daughter colony becomes spherical again and continues its development within the mother colony, from which it ultimately escapes by dissolution of some surface cells of the latter, or by a pore in this wall.

Various degrees of isogamy and anisogamy occur in family Volvocidae. In *Volvox aureus,* some zooids enlarge greatly to become macrogametes. In the genera *Eudorina, Pleodorina,* and *Volvox* these ova are

Fig. 2-21 Diagram of *Volvox* illustrating asexual reproduction and gamete formation. After Beck and Braithwaite, *Invertebrate Zoology Laboratory Workbook*, 1962, courtesy of the authors and Burgess Publishing Co. (Copyright held by the authors).

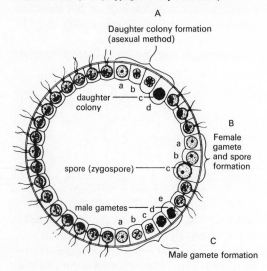

A

Daughter colony formation
(asexual method)

daughter
colony

B
Female
gamete
and spore
formation

spore (zygospore)

male gametes

C
Male gamete formation

fertilized in situ, rather than when free. Biflagellate sperm arise by fission in zooids (Fig. 2-21). In *Volvox,* sperm enter the female colonies in dioecious species and subsequently penetrate the macrogametes. The resultant zygote encysts, and in many species the cyst wall show a characteristic spiny surface. This zygote may serve as an overwintering stage, escaping from the disintegrating parent colony. Later under favorable circumstances it will hatch to give rise to a new colony.

In subclass Zoomastigina the family Trypanosomidae, which is parasitic in the vascular system of vertebrates, is of special in-

Fig. 2-22 Structural differences and sequential relationships in Trypanosomatidae. After Jahn and Jahn 1949, courtesy of H. E. Jaques and Wm. C. Brown Company, Publishers.

TRYPANOSOMIDAE

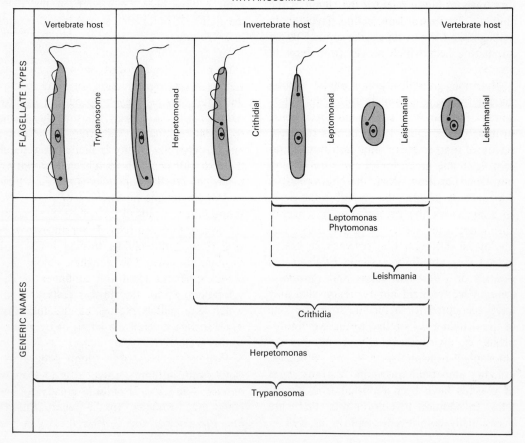

terest. Pathogenecity of these parasites is obvious only in man and domesticated animals, and most species are geographically limited to tropical climates by habitat of the blood-sucking invertebrate host. The life cycle is commonly polymorphic, and ranges from an ovoid, nonflagellate form (Leishman body) through an ovoid, flagellate form (Leptomonas) and a Crithidial form possessing an undulating membrane between nucleus and flagellate-bearing end to the Trypanosome form with undulating membrane arising beyond the nucleus (Fig. 2-22). Not all species exhibit the complete morphological series, and this serves as a basis for the recognition of six genera. The nonpathogenic *Trypanosoma lewisi* (Fig. 2-24B), utilizing rat and flea hosts, is the classical cycle. The life cycles of parasitic Trypanosomidae can be found in any textbook of animal parasitology as well as those of such parasitic flagellates as *Giardia* and *Trichomonas* (Fig. 2-24). Cleveland has monographed the Hypermastigid symbionts (e.g., *Trichonympha)* of termites and other wood-eating insects (Fig. 2-23).

Before leaving the Mastigophora, mention should be made of the "choanoflagellates." These Protomastigid protozoa are represented by both solitary and colonial forms. Many of them possess a collar whose function and apparent structure is closely paralleled by the choanocytes of sponges.

Proterospongia (*Protospongia*) has been described as a sponge remnant. Actually, it is a colonial flagellate with a misleading convergence that suggests a close but questionable phylogenetic relationship (Fig. 2-25).

Resume of the Orders of Class Flagellata

The first seven Orders belong in Subclass Phytomastigina, and the rest are in the Zoomastigina. Some authorities place the opalinid group with the ciliates.

Order 1 Chrysomonadida These flagellates have no transverse groove or gullet. They have brown or yellow chromoplasts and often oil reserves. Starch is lacking, although leucosin is sometimes present. These protozoa occur in salt and fresh water. *Ochromonas, Chromulina, Dinobryon.*

Order 2 Heterochlorida These possess two unequal flagella. The surface is a flexible periplast. Yellow chromatophores are present and leucosin and lipid reserves are characteristic. *Chloromeson, Mysochloris.*

Order 3 Cryptomonadida These marine and fresh-water protozoa commonly have green, yellow, or brown chromoplasts and starch reserves. These flagellates are very rarely amoeboid. *Chilomonas, Cryptomonas.*

Order 4 Dinoflagellida These protozoa, often armored, typically possess a prominent transverse groove in which one of the two flagella courses. These flagellates form starch and oil reserves and most of them are marine. *Ceratium, Noctiluca, Peridinium.*

Fig. 2-23 Some parasitic flagellates, (a) a trypanosome; (b) *Trichomonas,* and (c) *Trichonympha.* From Stanier, Doudoroff, and Adelberg, *The Microbial World,* 2nd Ed., 1963, courtesy of Prentice-Hall, Inc.

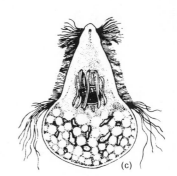

(a)　　　(b)　　　(c)

Order 5 Phytomonadida Green chromatophores and starch reserves are typical and many also store lipids. None are holozoic, and a gullet is lacking. These mostly fresh-water protozoa have many colonial species. *Chlamydomonas, Pandorina, Volvox.*

Order 6 Euglenida These primarily fresh-water protozoa typically have one or two flagella, a stigma, and a gullet or reservoir. Many species have chloroplasts; lipids and carbohydrates (paramylum) are stored reserves. *Euglena, Phacus, Astasia.*

Order 7 Chloromonadida These possess green chromatophores or are colorless. Fat storage is common. *Vacuolaria, Chattonella, Gonyostomum.*

Order 8 Rhizomastigida These are amoeboid forms with one to four flagella. *Histomonas, Mastigamoeba.*

Order 9 Protomastigida These occur in fresh or salt water and are mostly small and with two flagella. Many are parasitic. Multiple fission is common. *Codosiga, Trypanosoma, Leishmania, Bodo, Proterospongia.*

Order 10 Polymastigida These delicately pellicled forms have three to eight flagella and one to many nuclei, and many are parasitic or commensal. Cyst formation is common in the life cycles. *Retortomonas, Tetramitus, Chilomastix, Giardia.*

Order 11 Trichomonadida These parasitic and commensal protozoa have one or many nuclei but are never binucleate. Three to six flagella communicate with the rodlike axostyle. *Descovina, Trichomonas, Coronympha.*

Order 12 Hypermastigida These are obligate symbionts living in the intestine of termites and roaches. They are uninucleate but possess multiple flagella. *Lophomonas, Trichonympha.*

Fig. 2-24 Trypanosome life histories. (A) *Trypanosoma gambiense* is transmitted to man by the tsetse flies (genus, *Glossina*). It is the causative agent of one variety of African sleeping sickness. (a) Man; (b) other mammalian hosts; (c) trypanosome in blood; (d) to (g) development of trypanosome in gut and salivary glands of *Glossina*; (h) infective form of trypanosome; (i) man, exposed to bite of infected *Glossina*; (j) other mammals, exposed to bite of infected *Glossina*. The central figure shows the location of the several developmental stages of the trypanosome in the gut and salivary glands of *Glossina*. From Belding, *A Textbook of Clinical Parasitology*, 1942 (2nd Ed., 1952) by permission of Appleton-Century-Crofts. (B) *Trypanosoma lewisi* is a parasite or commensal of rats. After Jahn and Jahn 1949, courtesy of H. E. Jaques and Wm. C. Brown Company, Publishers.

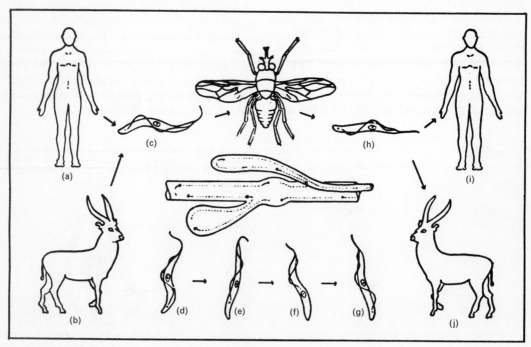

(A)

Order 13 Opalina These flattened, ciliated protozoa lack a cytostome and are bi- or multi-nucleate with all nuclei alike. Fission is usually symmetrogenic and conjugation does not occur. These protozoa are internal parasites of Anura. *Protoopalina, Opalina, Zelleriella.*

Fig. 2-25 *Protospongia* (*Proterospongia*). After Jahn and Jahn 1949, courtesy of H. E. Jaques and Wm. C. Brown Company, Publishers.

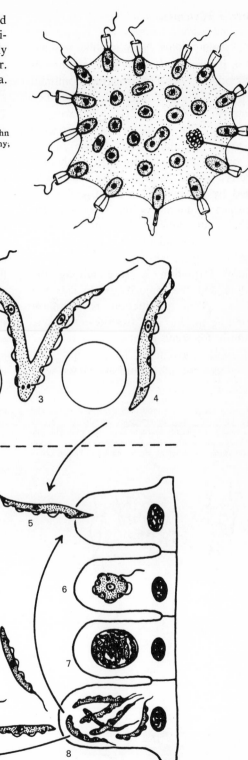

In rat

In flea

Trypanosoma lewisi

Rectum

Stomach

(B)

CLASS SARCODINA

This group, which includes the familiar amoeba, is characterized by the presence of pseudopodia, at least during the dominant part of the life cycle. Many show flagellate characteristics (Fig. 2-26) regularly or occasionally. The body form of Sarcodina tends to be irregular except during encystment or in those forms with spherical symmetry (Fig. 2-27). The discipline afforded by the pellicle in Mastigophora is not present among Sarcodina. The cytoplasm usually shows optical differentiation into ectoplasm and endoplasm, but exhibits fluctuations during activity.

Colony formation is rare among the Sarcodina and the majority of species are free-living. Shell production is common both among marine and fresh-water forms, particularly for some groups.

Amoeboid movement is perhaps best described as a special feature associated with the colloidal nature of protoplasm with reversible changes occurring between a viscous liquid stage called a sol and a semi-solid stage called a gel. In amoeba, the ectoplasm has been considered to have an elastic surface layer called *plasmolemma*. Inside the plasmolemma, the ectoplasm and adjacent zone of entoplasm are in a state of gelatin and this zone is named *plasmogel*, possibly separated from the plasmolemma by a hyaline fluid. The remainder of the entoplasm is composed of the more liquid *plasmosol*. Metabolic by-products may be responsible for the sol-gel reversibility. Upon attachment of the plasmolemma to the substrate, the adjacent plasmogel becomes liquefied or changes to plasmosol. Contraction of the posterior plasmogel forces the fluid core of plasmosol into a bulge to initiate the pseudopodium. At the lateral periphery of the bulge, the plasmosol gelates to produce a continually advancing tube of plasmogel, while at the physiological posterior end of the

Fig. 2-26 *Naegleria gruberi*, a protozoan showing flagellate and amoeboid stages. (a) Unusually elongated amoeba; (b) amoeba with four nuclei; (c) and (d) flagellate stages; (e) cyst with one nucleus; (f) cyst with three nuclei; (g) amoeba leaving cyst. From Hall (after Wilson) *Protozoology*, 1953, courtesy of Prentice-Hall, Inc.

Fig. 2-27 Some variations in amoeboid protozoa, (a) an amoeba; (b) a foraminiferan; (c) a radiolarian. From Stanier, Doudoroff, and Adelberg, *The Microbial World*, 2nd Ed. 1963, courtesy of Prentice-Hall, Inc.

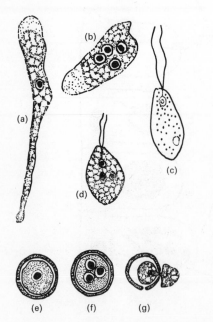

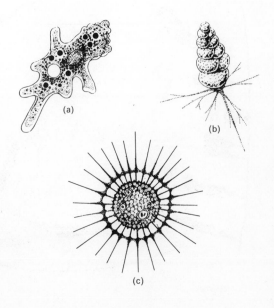

amoeba, the inner layer of plasmogel is being simultaneously converted to plasmosol core which continues to be pushed forward by the contracting plasmogel (Fig. 2-28). The resultant movement of the liquid plasmosol has been called "fountain streaming."

Nutrition in the Sarcodina is holozoic with ingestion performed by pseudopodia. A variety of minute plant and animal organisms including small metazoans serve as food. Food is engulfed by pseudopodia, which close to form a food vacuole. Protein-splitting enzymes have been demonstrated as has glycogen, the latter resulting from carbohydrate storage. Fat digestion has been demonstrated in *Amoeba,* and lipoid reserves are common. Egestion of nondigestible material occurs by the animal's "flowing away" from material as it reaches the amoeba surface.

Among Sarcodina, asexual processes of various kinds serve as the principal mode of reproduction. Binary fission is a common method. Cytoplasmic changes occur in *Amoeba proteus* during fission, correlated with the nuclear changes of mitosis (Fig. 2-29). In the early stages the surface of the amoeba is studded with minute pseudopodia, which become larger during later mitosis,

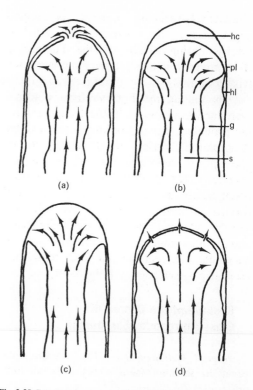

Fig. 2-28 Cytoplasmic movement in a pseudopodium *g* plasmogel; *hc,* hyaline cap; *hl,* hyaline layer; *pl,* plasmolemma; *s,* plasmosol. From Kudo (after Mast) *Protozoology,* 3rd Ed., 1950, courtesy of Charles C Thomas, Publisher, Springfield, Illinois.

Fig. 2-29 External cytoplasmic changes in *Amoeba proteus* during division. From Kudo, (after Chalkley and Daniel) *Protozoology,* 3rd Ed., 1950, courtesy of Charles C Thomas, Publisher, Springfield, Illinois.

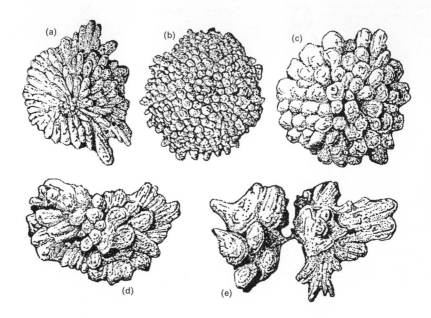

ultimately assuming normal pseudopod appearance as the organism splits. Nuclear history during fission of the Heliozoan, *Acanthocystis*, is illustrative of the eumitotic type of mitosis.

Only among the Foraminifera is sexual reproduction common. Typically isogametes are produced. Several of this group exhibit dimorphic life cycles with the production of two types of shells, microspheric or megalospheric, which in some species are sharply distinguished by the size of the initially formed chamber or *proloculum*. Megalospheric adults (gamonts) are uninucleate and produce gametes, while the microspheric agamonts are multicellular and reproduce asexually by schizogony (Fig. 2-30).

Resume of the Orders of Class Rhizopoda (Sarcodina)

Order 1 Helioflagellida These Actinopoda occur in sea and fresh water. One to four flagella are characteristic as are typical axopodia. *Actinomonas, Dimorpha.*

Order 2 Heliozoida These are chiefly freshwater actinopods with radiating axopodia which appear to contain granules. Test production is common. *Actinophrys, Actinosphaerium, Monomastigocystis.*

Order 3 Radiolarida These marine actinopods have a long geologic history. A skeletal, lacunar membrane separates the protoplasm into inner and outer (more vacuolated) layers. Sometimes axopodia are missing. One to many nuclei occur in the inner protoplasmic layer. *Dorotaspis, Thalassicolla, Castanidium.*

(The following orders do not have axopodia.)

Order 4 Proteomyxida This group of uncertain position is parasitic in eel grass (a marine flowering plant), in some algae, and in volvocid flagellates. Both uninucleate amoeboid and plasmodial forms occur and some cycles includes a flagellate stage. *Pseudospora, Vampyrella, Actinocoma.*

Order 5 Mycetozoida This and the preceding order have some similarity to fungi and are

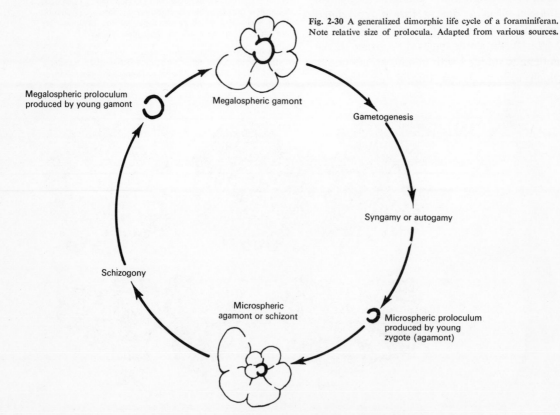

Fig. 2-30 A generalized dimorphic life cycle of a foraminiferan. Note relative size of prolocula. Adapted from various sources.

Megalospheric proloculum produced by young gamont

Megalospheric gamont

Gametogenesis

Syngamy or autogamy

Microspheric proloculum produced by young zygote (agamont)

Microspheric agamont or schizont

Schizogony

included in the so-called slime molds. They occur in soil and vegetable mold, and some are parasitic in roots and underground stems. *Dictystellum, Plasmodiophorina.*

Order 6 Amoebida Representatives of this group occur in marine, fresh-water, or moist soil habitats and as parasites in the intestine of invertebrates and vertebrates. Formation of lobopodia is typical, as is binary fission. A few exhibit a flagellar stage. *Dimastigamoeba, Naegleria, Amoeba, Entamoeba, Endolimax.*

Order 7 Testacida These fresh-water Rhizopoda produce a single-chambered and single-apertured test which may include foreign bodies in the test wall. Creeping is accomplished by filopodia or lobopodia, and the body can be withdrawn into the shell. *Arcella, Euglypha, Difflugia, Placocista.*

Order 8 Foraminifera This group is chiefly marine and produces calcareous and/or siliceous tests surrounded by a layer of cytoplasm. The shell may be uni- or multi-chambered. Species are sessile or creep slowly by myxopodia. More species are extinct than recent. *Elphidium, Discorbina, Spirillina, Allogromia.*

CLASS SPOROZOA

This class of protozoa are all parasitic, and as parasites they are represented in all animal phyla. Infective stages are ingested as spores or enter the host by inoculation, where they occur as intra- or intercellular parasites. In the case of inoculative transfer, organisms are not enclosed by a spore wall, but occur as naked sporozoites. In general, the members of this class exhibit a high degree of host specificity.

Specific locomotor organelles are generally lacking among the Sporozoa, although microgametes may possess flagella. A number of forms show a transitory amoeboid stage during the life cycle, so that some locomotion is accomplished in an amoeboid manner. Among the gregarines a peculiar gliding motion, probably accomplished with the aid of successively contracting myonemes, serves for locomotion.

Nutrition is saprozoic typically, although

Fig. 2-31 Reproduction by budding. (A) Budding in the sporozoan *Myxidium lieberkuhni*, from Kudo, R.R., *Protozoology*, 3rd Ed. 1950, courtesy of Charles C Thomas, Publisher, Springfield, Illinois. (B) Budding in the suctorean, *Ephelota*. N = nucleus. From Hertwig, *A Manual of Zoology* (translated and edited by J. S. Kingsley) 1902, Holt, Rinehart & Winston, Inc.

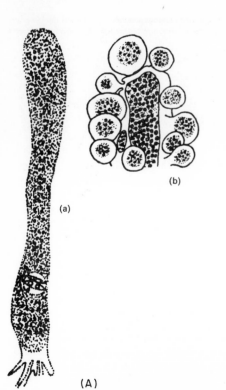

(a)

(b)

(A)

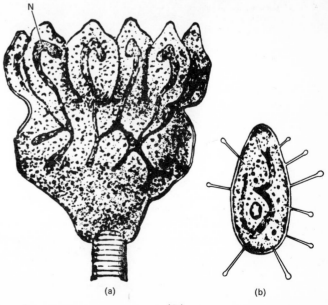

(a)

(b)

(B)

some Microsporidia have been reported as able to ingest solid particles. Although saprozoic nutrition occurs by absorption over the entire body surface, among some gregarines absorption seems to be specialized at the anterior end.

Among the Sporozoa, typical life cycles exhibit both sexual and asexual reproduction. The latter may involve repeated binary fission as in malarial organisms or in *Aggregata,* resulting in production of many daughter individuals. The Myxosporidian, *Myxidium* (Fig. 2-31), undergoes multiple division through the simultaneous production of external buds, a process preceding schizogony. Most sporozoa exhibit multiple fission in both sexual and asexual phases, although asexual schizogony is lacking among the Eugregarines. In *Monocystis* (Fig. 2-32) the trophozoites modify into gametocytes (gamonts) and no schizogony (agamogony or merogony) occurs. These gamonts adhere in pairs (syzygy) which

become enclosed within a cyst wall. Such a structure with its gametocytes is called a gametocyst. The syzygid gamont undergoes a peripheral sporogony (gamogony) which is a multiple fission producing gametes. These gametes fuse in pairs to form encysted zygotes (oöcysts). Each zygote becomes a spore, within which eight sporozoites are produced. Many of these occur in a single gametocyst. These sporozoites, upon release from the spore case, serve as the infective stage. Released in the intestine of the host (earthworm for common species), they migrate to infect the cells of the seminal vesicles.

Among the Coccidia, multiple division occurs during both asexual and sexual phases. *Eimeria schubergi* parasitizes the intestinal cells of the centipede, *Lithobius.* Infective sporozoites invade epithelial cells of the host. Schizogony produces many merozoites which are freed to invade new cells. Periodically, the invading coccidians do not

Fig. 2-32 Life cycle of *Monocystis*, parasitic in male organs of the earthworm. Adapted from various sources.

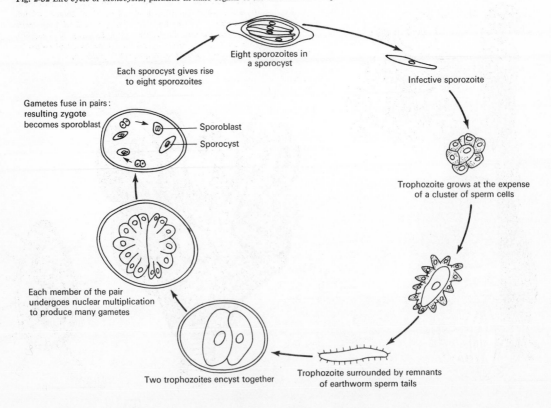

Eight sporozoites in a sporocyst

Each sporocyst gives rise to eight sporozoites

Infective sporozoite

Gametes fuse in pairs: resulting zygote becomes sporoblast

Sporoblast

Sporocyst

Trophozoite grows at the expense of a cluster of sperm cells

Each member of the pair undergoes nuclear multiplication to produce many gametes

Two trophozoites encyst together

Trophozoite surrounded by remnants of earthworm sperm tails

undergo schizogony, but modify into macro- and microgametes. After a macrogametocyte extrudes nuclear material, it changes directly into a female gamete. The microgametocyte undergoes division to produce many flagellate microgametes. After gamete fusion, the resultant zygote secretes a membrane to becomes an oöcyst. First-stage sporogony results in four sporoblasts, and each sporo-

blast undergoes fission to produce two sporozoites, so that a second stage of sporogony occurs. The mature oöcysts pass from the host. After ingestion by a new host, the sporozoites are freed to initiate the cycle again.

In *Aggregata eberthi,* metagenesis as well as alternation of hosts occurs in the life cycle (Fig. 2-33). Intracellular schizogony oc-

Fig. 2-33 The life cycle of *Aggregata eberthi.* (a) A mature spore; (b) germination of spore; (c) to (f) schizogony; (g) a merozoite, swallowed by *Sepia;* (h) to (j) development of microgametes; (k) to (l) development of macrogamete; (m) fertilization; (n), (o) first zygotic division, chromosomes reduced in number from 12 to 6; (p), (q) development of sporoblasts, each of which develops into a spore with three sporozoites. This coccidian is parasitic in a cuttlefish (*Sepia*) which gets the infection by eating infected crabs (*Portunus*). Schizogony occurs in the crab. Gamete formation and fertilization occur in the cuttlefish. Compare this life cycle with that of the malarial organism. From Kudo, *Protozoology,* 3rd Ed., 1950, courtesy of Charles C Thomas, Publisher, Springfield, Illinois.

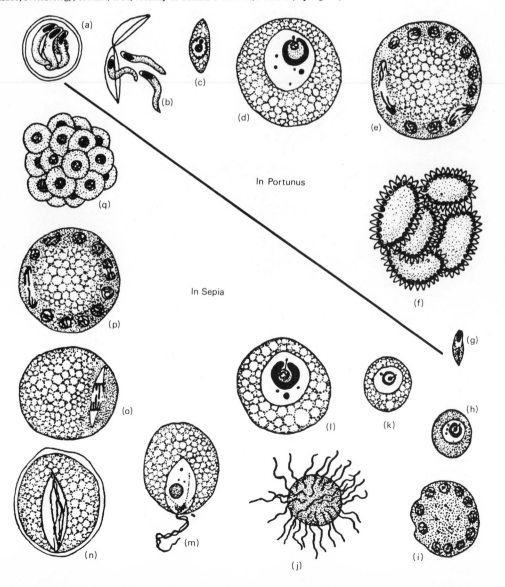

(a)

(b)

(c)

(d)

(e)

(q)

In Portunus

(f)

(p)

In Sepia

(g)

(o)

(l)

(k)

(h)

(n)

(m)

(j)

(i)

Fig. 2-34 Life cycle of malarial parasite. In this diagram *Anopheles quadrimaculatus* (note wing spots) and *Plasmodium falciparum* (note shape of gametocytes) are being used to demonstrate the life cycle.

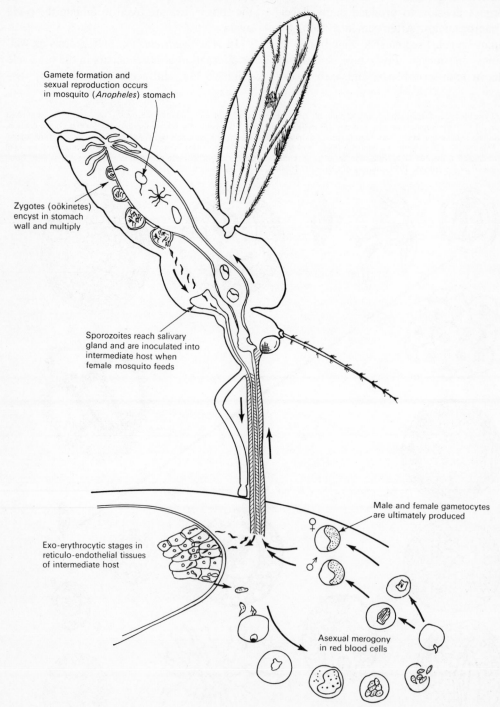

Gamete formation and
sexual reproduction occurs
in mosquito (*Anopheles*) stomach

Zygotes (oökinetes)
encyst in stomach
wall and multiply

Sporozoites reach salivary
gland and are inoculated into
intermediate host when
female mosquito feeds

Male and female gametocytes
are ultimately produced

Exo-erythrocytic stages in
reticulo-endothelial tissues
of intermediate host

Asexual merogony
in red blood cells

curs in the crab, *Portunus*. When the cephalopod, *Sepia,* devours the crab host, merozoites are freed to penetrate the gut wall. These modify into macro- and microgametocytes. The zygotes undergo sporogony, and the resultant spores serve as the infective stage for the intermediate host. Another coccidian, *Ovivora thalassemae,* exhibits merogony and sporogony in the same host, and anisogamy which is characteristic of the entire class.

The life cycle of the hemosporidian, *Plasmodium* (Fig. 2-34), parasitic in man and in other animals, exhibits host alternation, multiple fission in both sexual and asexual phases, and anisogamy. In the human malarias, naked sporozoites are inoculated into the circulatory system of man by the bite of infected *Anopheles* mosquitoes. The sporozoan enters cells of the reticuloendothelial system where it undergoes schizogony to produce merozoites, which eventually enter red blood corpuscles. These merozoites change into amoeboid trophozoites, which typically modify into signetring stages within the corpuscle. Growth and schizogony result in the production of more merozoites, which are freed into the plasma by hemolysis of the corpuscles. These merozoites infect other red blood corpuscles to repeat the asexual erythrocytic cycle. The periodic chills and fever are coincident with the termination of repeated schizogonic cycles. Eventually some of the merozoites modify into macro- and microgametocytes (gamonts). These are the stages that must be ingested by the mosquito for completion of the life cycle. In the stomach of the arthropod host, the microgametocyte divides into flagellate sperm cells while macrogametocytes mature to eggs. Fertilization results in a motile zygote called an *oökinete,* which penetrates to encyst in the outer stomach wall of the mosquito. This encysted zygote *(oöcyst)* undergoes sporogony to produce many sporozoites. These migrate to the salivary glands to be discharged when the mosquito feeds.

The Cnidosporidia produce spores with polar capsules. These bear considerable resemblance to nematocysts. They erupt a thread or tube that serves as attachment or communication with the intestinal wall. Many Cnidosporidians are fish parasites, in which they produce large cystlike masses. In general, spore formation appears to be the principal method of reproduction. The spore hatches and the uninucleate amoeboid zygote is released. It multiplies to become a syncytial mass. Cells called pansporoblasts are budded off endogenously, perhaps in a process akin to plasmotomy. For *Myxobolus,* parasitic in fresh-water fish, the pansporoblast divides to form two large and two small cells. The subsequent fate of the latter is obscure, but each of the large cells multiplies to form a group of six nuclei with adjacent cytoplasmic masses. Two of the six become valve cells of the spore; two are associated with polar capsules; and two become isogametes. The isogametes will subsequently fuse to form the uninucleate zygote or sporoplasm. It is apparent for *Myxobolus* that each pansporoblast gives rise to two spores and that the spores are complex muticellular units. In some rare cases, a schizogony may precede the nuclear multiplication producing the syncytium.

Resume of the Orders of Class Sporozoa

The two principal subclasses are the Telosporidia and Cnidosporidia, the latter group characterized by polar capsules in the spores. The first three orders belong to the Telosporidia.

Order 1 Gregarinida These are typically parasitic in the body spaces of invertebrates, early development occurring in tissue cells. *Schizocystis, Gregarina, Monocystis.*

Order 2 Coccidia These telosporidians are intracellular parasites in epithelial cells of vertebrates and higher invertebrates. *Hepatozoon, Aggregata, Eimeria, Isospora.*

Order 3 Hemosporidia These are intracellular parasites of red blood corpuscles or reticulo-endothelial tissues of vertebrates. Schizogony and gametocyte production occur in the vertebrate, while syngamy and sporogonic reproduction are in the invertebrate host. *Plasmodium, Babesia.*

Order 4 Myxosporida These are mostly parasitic in cold-blooded vertebrates, particularly fish. Bivalve spores with one, two, or four polar capsules are produced. *Myxobolus, Myxobilatus, Leptotheca.*

Order 5 Actinomyxida In this group, uninucleate sporoplasms fuse into pairs. Subsequently, the spore becomes three-rayed, or develops three valves and three polar capsules. *Triactinomyxon, Sphaeractinomyxon.*

Order 6 Microsporidia In these intracellular parasites of arthropods and fish, the small simple spores have minute polar capsules. *Nosema, Stempellia, Bacillidium.*

Order 7 Helicosporidia This order is represented by a single genus parasitic in Diptera and in mites. *Helicosporidium.*

SUBPHYLUM CILIOPHORA

As the name of this subphylum indicates, these protozoa are characterized by the presence of cilia, as in the familiar laboratory genus, *Paramecium.* Among most of them (Class Ciliata) the cilia are persistent throughout the life of the organism, but in Class Suctoria, cilia are present only during immature stages. Cilia provide the sole means of locomotion for the group; in many instances they also function in food-getting. An additional function may be as thigmotactic organelles. The distribution and arrangement of cilia are taxonomically important. Cilia are frequently fused into tufts called cirri, while the cilia of a row may be fused to form a finlike membranelle. Cilia bear close resemblance structurally to flagella.

Most Ciliata are solitary and free-swimming, but some are variously attached, and colonial forms occur among the latter. *Vorticella,* an attached form with a contractile stalk, was the first protozoan to be accurately described. Leeuwenhoek found it nearly three centuries ago. Many of its near relatives are colonial forms. The body form of the Ciliates is persistent, determined largely by a definite but thin pellicle. The ectoplasmic layer gives rise to the infraciliature, including trichocysts and cilia, and the endoplasm contains dimorphic nuclei and contractile vacuoles as well as other organelles. The trichocysts are explosive organelles, whose primary function is anchorage by the tube or rod produced; but some, called toxicysts, appear to produce a toxic fluid that is an offensive and defensive weapon.

Ciliates are typically holozoic, although the few parasitic forms may be partly or completely saprozoic. Coordinate with holozoic nutrition is the specialized development of the food-procuring apparatus (Fig. 2-35). It occurs in two general patterns: raptorial and ciliary feeding. In the former, the cytostome may be strengthened by a stockade of trichites. In some species the cytostome can be closed. Among ciliary feeders, the mouth may be at the bottom of a funnel or vestibule;

Fig. 2-35 *Vorticella*, showing adoral circlets of cilia. The inner ciliary row continues into the vestibule along the latter's lesser curvature while the outer enters along the greater curvature. Adapted from various sources.

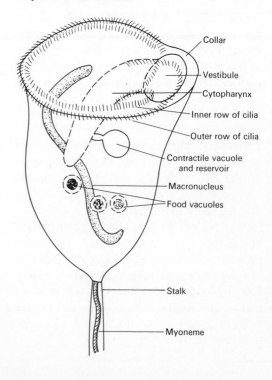

Collar

Vestibule

Cytopharynx

Inner row of cilia

Outer row of cilia

Contractile vacuole and reservoir

Macronucleus

Food vacuoles

Stalk

Myoneme

and usually a groove, the peristome, spirals into the vestibule and is emphasized by membranelles or cirri.

Typically among Ciliophora there is a binary fission pattern of asexual reproduction in which the division cuts across the kinetodesmata of the infraciliature system. However, in Peritrichida, the order to which *Vorticella* belongs, the fission is longitudinal. Encystment, common among Ciliophora, is the only period some species undergo asexual division. In asexual division, the micronuclei divide by a modified type of eumitosis, while the macronucleus divides amitotically.

Sexual reproduction among most Ciliophora involves a temporary sexual union called conjugation. Two ciliates adhere by oral surfaces, and nuclear exchange of gametic material occurs. Fusion of gametes occurs in each conjugant, and after separation the fusion nuclei divide a number of times and give rise to both macronuclei and micronuclei. Cytoplasmic division is often necessary to restore the normal complement of micro- and macronuclei.

Suctorians (sometimes placed in Class Suctoria = Suctorea) are widely distributed in fresh and salt water and are devoid of cilia in the adult stage, which is typically attached and sometimes is ectocommensal. A few species are parasitic. Suctorians lack a cytostome, and holozoic nutrition is accomplished by means of suctorial tentacles. Asexual reproduction is limited to endogenous or exogenous budding. The budded offspring exist as ciliated embryos responsible for species distribution (Figs. 2-36 and 2-31B). Nuclear behavior is mitotic for micronuclei, amitotic for the macronucleus as in other ciliates.

In sexual reproduction, nearby Suctorians may conjugate in a process very similar to that in *Paramecium;* but in some cases the sexual union becomes permanent, with one of the conjugants incorporated within the other. The Suctorians bear closest resemblance to ciliates of the Order Holotrichida.

Fig. 2-36 Sessile and migratory stages of the suctorial, *Tokophyra quadripartita.* After Jahn and Jahn 1949, courtesy of H. E. Jaques and Wm. C. Brown Company, Publishers.

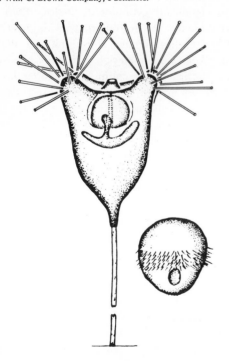

Resume of the Orders of Class Ciliata

Order 1 Gymnostomatida These holotrichs lack ciliation around the oral area, but often embedded around the cytostome is a stockade of rods called trichites. *Actinobolina, Coleps, Dileptus, Loxodes, Prorodon.*

Order 2 Trichostomatida The vestibular funnel or groove leading to the cytostome is ciliated. Ciliation is generally symmetrical. *Colpoda, Tillina, Balantidium.*

Order 3 Chonotrichida The body has a protruding, more or less cone-shaped funnel which may be spiraled and which contains rows of cilia. Cilia are usually lacking in other areas on these protozoa, which are ectocommensal on crustaceans. *Trichochona, Spirochona.*

Order 4 Suctorida Attached by a noncontractile stalk, the mature stage lacks cilia but retains kinetosomes. Tentacles appear at time of attachment. *Acineta, Ephelota, Podophrya.*

Order 5 Apostomatida These holotrichs have a minute ventral cytostome and nearby a distinctive "rosette" containing a number of vertical septa. These typically marine protozoa are parasitic or symbionts. Ctenophores and sea anemones may serve as one host, and crustaceans as a second host. *Foettingeria, Pericaryon.*

Order 6 Astomatida Found principally in oligochaete annelids, these large holotrichs are uiformly ciliated and lack a cytostome. *Mesnilella, Haptophrya, Anoplophrya.*

Order 7 Hymenostomatida These are small, uniformly ciliated holotrichs with a ventral buccal cavity supplied with an undulating membrane, sometimes reduced. *Anophrys, Colpidium, Tetrahymena, Paramecium.*

Order 8 Thigmotrichida These marine and fresh-water holotrichs are ectocommensal or parasitic, mostly on gills and mantle of bivalve molluscs. The group is characterized by an anterior zone of thigmotactic cilia. *Thigmophrya, Sphenophrya.*

Order 9 Peritrichida These protozoa are mostly attached, often by a contractile stalk. The enlarged terminal peristome bears two or more rows of cilia. Some stalked peritrichs are colonial. *Vorticella, Epistylis, Zoothamnium.*

Order 10 Heterotrichida These are probably the most primitive spirotrichs, since they tend to have a uniform body ciliation unless encased in a lorica. *Stentor, Nyctotherus, Blepharisma.*

Order 11 Oligotrichida Body ciliation in these spirotrichs is reduced or absent. There are usually two zones of membranelles, a shorter oral group and a longer spiraled row. *Halteria, Strombidium.*

Order 12 Tintinnida These cone-shaped, mostly marine protozoa are encased in a lorica, but are nevertheless motile. *Tintinnus, Tintinnopsis.*

Order 13 Entodiniomorphida These spirotrichs are found in the alimentary canal of herbivores. The pellicle is thick and may be extended as posterior spines. *Diplodinium, Entodinium.*

Order 14 Ctenostomida Eight membranelles are characteristic of the oral surface. The body is somewhat wedge-shaped, has a reduced ciliation, and is supplied with a carapace. *Discomorpha, Epalxis, Saprodinium.*

Order 15 Hypotrichida These spirotrichs have cilia on the ventral surface compounded into cirri. Commonly there is a conspicuous zone of membranelles spiraling from the cytostome. *Euplotes, Uronychia, Oxytricha, Stylonychia.*

PHYLOGENETIC CONSIDERATIONS

Protozoa exhibit marked diversity in form and in complexity, not only in the phylum but also in the major classes and subclasses into which it is divided. Because contemporary species exist in each class with unique combinations of features not readily graded into a single taxonomic series, the hypothesis of polyphyletic origins seems reasonable and can be applied broadly.

The geological record is sparse except for the Radiolarians and the Foraminifera, and neither of these groups has undergone marked change. In the former, most Cambrian species have been placed in genera current now. The Radiolarida are strictly marine, while a few Foraminifera occurring in fresh water are primitive or degenerate. Their significance to the petroleum industry has stimulated the study of Foraminifera. The morphology, composition, and apertures of their shells provide a much more complete and significant evolutionary history than is the case for the Radiolarians. Composition of the earliest known Foraminiferan shells was of chitinous material, and many present-day species retain chitin in the inner layer of the young test. Pre-Cambrian records of insufficient confirmation have been made for both Radiolaria and Foraminifera. The unique geologic history of these two groups does not imply that they are ancestral to most other modern protozoa but that the diversity of the protozoan classes occurred in very ancient times.

Among the protozoa photosynthetic forms appear to stand at the base of protozoan phylogeny, and the protozoa may be polyphyletic. This consideration of nutrition places the Flagellates as the most primitive protozoa. It is unlikely that a single archetype was ancestral to the chlorophyll-bearing forms leading to algae on the one hand and to holozoic and saprozoic protozoa on the other. The path of evolution runs from the simple or primitive to the complex with ultimate specialization. Specialization, with its loss of plasticity, undoubtedly spelled the doom of many organisms. Sometimes saprozoic and parasitic modes of life led to degeneration. Loss of or extreme modification of intermediates leaves no clearly delineated pathway of descent. However, some subgroups of protozoa exhibit combinations of features that probably place them in the line of descent.

The Chrysomonad Phytomastigina lack a restrictive cell wall; they often show amoeboid activity; and they lack starch, although fat and the carbohydrate, leucosin, occur as food reserves. Some of this group show alternate flagellate and amoeboid stages, while some have flagella and pseudopodia simultaneously. Furthermore, some species carry on holozoic as well as holophytic nutrition. The unequal apportionment of chromatophores during fission has resulted in colorless individuals dependent upon other than holophytic nutrition for survival. These characteristics suggest that the Chrysomonadida may be ancestral not only to other Flagellata but to some lines of Sarcodina. Since other Phytomastigina that carry on photosynthesis also have colorless near relatives, they may be ancestral to some of the Zoomastigina.

Zoomastigina lack chloroplasts and starch reserves. Many are amoeboid. Nutrition is commonly holozoic or saprozoic. The group is ancestral to many lines of Sarcodina, among whom are species that produce flagellate young. The Foraminifera are closely related to the Testacida, which produce a single-chambered test. Radiolarida and Foraminifera both produce flagellated stages called swarmers, which also suggests a probable flagellate ancestry.

In the class Sporozoa, only the Telosporidia appear to form a real phylogenetic sequence indicated by life-cycle similarities. Of this group the Gregarinida are most primitive. The presence of flagellated microgametes in the Sporozoa ties them to the flagellates, and quite probably the Protomastigida. The Cnidosporidia are quite dissimilar from the Telosporidia. They possess capsules containing a coiled filament which has been likened to a flagellum to suggest a mastigophoran relationship. On the other hand, they produce small plasmodial amoeboid young, and a relationship to the Mycetozoida of the Rhizopoda has been advanced. The Acnidosporidia of older classifications include a group of very uncertain phylogenetic position, including the placing of some of them as fungi.

The Ciliophora are sharply set off from the other protozoa, but except for length, a cilium is morphologically very similar to a flagellum. Also, a number of species have an elongated bristle somewhat resembling a flagellum. The Holotrichida are considered as most primitive. They lack the specialization of an adoral zone and have a more uniform distribution of cilia. They are probably ancestral to the other Ciliates as well as to the Suctoria.

In general, surface modification among the protozoa has produced some extreme specialization leading to Hypermastigida among flagellates and to Peritrichida and Chonotrichida in the Ciliophora. Probably the formation of a firm ectoplasm represented the initiation of surface changes. One taxonomic scheme divided the phylum upon the occurrence or absence of firm ectoplasm, separating the Sarcodina from the other groups, but this results in an artificial separation contradicted by other comparative features. However, it is certain that the change from a highly plastic surface to one disciplined by a firm ectoplasm stimulated evolutionary invention, particularly for modes of locomotion and for food-catching apparatus, to provide the gamut from attached ciliary feeders to raptorial predators. The Protozoa constitute a large phylum of great diversity, with many genealogical secrets lost in antiquity, and so their phylogenetic history must be estimated largely from the biology of highly evolved present-day descendants.

REFERENCES

Allen, R. D., Amoeboid movement. Scient. Amer., 206:112, 1962.

Corliss, J. O., The opalinid infusorians: flagellates or ciliates? J. Protozool., 2:107, 1955.

———, The ciliated protozoa: characterization, classification and guide to the literature. New York: Pergamon, 1961.

Deflandre, Georges, Rhizopoda and Actinopoda. In (W. T. Edmondson, ed.) Ward and Whipple's Fresh-water biology (2nd ed.). New York: Wiley, 1959.

Ehret, C. F., Organelle systems and biological organization. Science, 132:115, 1960.

———, and E. L. Powers, The cell surface of Paramecium (pp. 97-133). In (G. H. Bourne and J. F. Danielli, ed.) Internat. Rev. Cytol., Vol. VIII. New York: Academic, 1959.

Gibbons, I. R., and A. V. Grimstone, On flagellar structure in certain flagellates. J. Biophys. Biochem. Cytol., 7:697, 1960.

Grassé, P. P., Phylogénie; Protozoaires: généralites, flagelles, Tome I, Fasc. 1 (1952), and Protozoaires: Rhizopodes, Actinopodea, Sporozoaires, Cnidosporidies, Tome I, Fasc. 2 (1953). In (P. Grassé, ed.) Traité de zoologie. Paris: Masson et Cie, 1952-1953.

Grimstone, A. V., Fine structure and morphogenesis in Protozoa. Biol. Rev., 36:97, 1961.

Hall, R. P., Protozoology. Englewood Cliffs, N. J.: Prentice-Hall, 1953.

Hawes, R. S. J., The emergence of asexuality in Protozoa. Quart. Rev. Biol., 38:234, 1963.

Holz, G. G. Jr., Nutrition and Metabolism of ciliates. In (S. H. Hutner, ed.) Biochemistry and physiology of Protozoa, Vol. III. New York: Academic, 1964.

Hutner, S. H., and L. Provasoli, The phytoflagellates. In (A. Lwoff, ed.) Biochemistry and physiology of Protozoa, Vol. I. Philadelphia: Academic, 1951.

———, Comparative biochemistry of flagellates. In (S. Hutner and A. Lwoff, ed.) Biochemistry and physiology of Protozoa, Vol.

II. Philadelphia: Academic, 1955.

Hyman, L. H., The invertebrates: Protozoa through Ctenophora, Vol. I. New York: McGraw, 1940.

———, The invertebrates: smaller coelomate groups, Vol. V. New York: McGraw, 1959. (The literature since Vol. I for Protozoa and other groups is reviewed in the final chapter.)

Jahn, T., and F. F. Jahn, How to know the Protozoa. Dubuque, Iowa: Wm. C. Brown Company, 1949.

Kudo, R. R., Protozoology (4th ed.). Springfield, Ill.: Charles C Thomas, 1954. (A fifth edition is dated 1966.)

Lackey, James B., Zooflagellates. In (W. T. Edmondson, ed.) Ward and Whipple's Fresh-water biology (2nd ed.). New York: Wiley, 1959.

———, Morphology and biology of a species of Protospongia. Trans. Amer. Microsc. Soc., 78:202, 1959.

Manwell, R. D., Introduction to protozoology. New York: St. Martins, 1961.

Marcus, E., On the evolution of the animal phyla. Quart. Rev. Biol., 33:24, 1958.

Noland, L. E., Ciliophora. In (W. T. Edmondson, ed.) Ward and Whipple's Fresh-water biology (2nd ed.). New York: Wiley, 1959.

Pennak, R. W., Fresh-water invertebrates of the United States. New York: Ronald, 1953.

Pitelka, D. R., Electron-microscopic structure of Protozoa. New York: Pergamon, 1963.

Stanier, R. Y., Introduction to the Protista. In (W. T. Edmondson, ed.) Ward and Whipple's Fresh-water biology (2nd ed.). New York: Wiley, 1959.

———, M. Doudoroff, and E. A. Adelberg, The microbial world (2nd ed.). Englewood Cliffs, N.J.: Prentice-Hall, 1963. (Contains a discussion of the Protista.)

Tarter, V. The biology of Stentor. Oxford and New York: Pergamon, 1961.

Wichterman, R., The biology of Paramecium. New York: Blakiston, 1953.

3

MULTICELLULAR ORIGIN AND ORGANIZATION

Multicellular animals arose from protozoa, but the path by which this was accomplished is not certain, and in fact it may well be lost in the antiquity of unfossilized ancestors. Nevertheless, hypotheses have been and will be developed to explain the origin or origins of the metazoa or multicellular animals. Such hypotheses are fruitful because they stimulate the search for evidence of relationships. Findings accumulate as circumstantial evidence, which as in a court of law indicates a probable solution.

ORIGIN OF THE METAZOA

There are two main hypotheses on the evolution of the unicellular to the multicellular (or the acellular to the cellular) condition: (1) the colonial hypothesis, and (2) the compartmentalization or cellularization hypothesis.

The colonial theory supposes that a colonial aggregate of acellular forms eventually achieves a division of labor so that the colony begins to function as a unit. Peripheral cells on a discoidal or a morular colony of protozoa show locomotor specialization by the retention of flagella. Surface cells would also develop a sensitivity to the environment. Nervous and locomotor functions would begin to show specialization for these cells. More deeply embedded cells might become specialized in food storage, digestive, and reproductive functions. While morular colonies of flagellate protozoa do not exhibit this latter specialization of function, many of the simple metazoans show it markedly. In some spherical colonies such as *Volvox,* sexual reproduction becomes limited to certain surface cells. A *Volvox* colony has developed a polarity manifest by locomotion in which one side is always in the lead. Since the reproductive cells tend to be at the other or posterior side of the colony, a morphological polarity is also commonly evident.

The colonial theory has several variants, but all are based on ancestry from colonial flagellates. The flagellates appear to be ancestral to the other protozoa and probably to plants. A Volvox-like progenitor exhibits polarity, functional differentiation of cells, and sexual reproduction. Haeckel postulated such an organism, which he called a blastaea, to be a phylogenetic stage parallel to the blastula of embryology. He went on to invent a two-layered organism which he called a gastraea, formed by invagination of the posterior wall of the blastaea. Such an organism would be two-layered or diploblastic and generally similar to hydrozoan Cnidarians (Coelenterates). But this phylum does not ordinarily undergo gastrulation by the simple invagination postulated by Haeckel, and other workers substituted an inward migration of cells to give rise initially to a solid gastrula (stereogastrula), a stage parallel with the important larval stage of Cnidaria called a planula.

The sponges (Parazoa or Porifera) are a unique group of animals which probably arose independently from the Protozoa. Corliss considers them to be derived from the Zoomastigina rather than the Phytomastigina, which in the colonial theory is ancestral to the other metazoa. A characteristic sponge cell called a choanocyte has a very similar counterpart in the Zoomastigina. *Proterospongia* is provided with choanocytes and has been considered to be a regenerating sponge fragment, although more recently it is acclaimed as a colonial protozoan. Sponges probably evolved from a colonial protozoan, but not through the Haeckelian blastaea-gastraea line.

The second theory of metazoan origin is the compartmentalization or cellularization hypothesis. In this theory, the progenitor is considered to be a multinuclear or *polyenergid* protozoan (an energid is considered to be a physiologically integrated unit of cytoplasm and nuclear material). In this theory, the Ciliophora are usually regarded as the protozoan line ancestral to the metazoa. The path here goes directly from the polyenergid ciliate to the acoelous or rhabdocoelous turbellarian. Similarities involve size, presence of cilia, hermaphroditism, transfer of gametic material, and the comparison of ciliate trichocysts with sagittocysts in acoelous turbellarians. Hansen (1958) calls attention to electron-microscope studies of the cytoplasmic reticulum or network of animal cells, which indicate a continuity with the cell membrane. It is theorized that this reticulum is the primordium of the cell membranes that must form between the polyenergids in the development of metazoa.

It is obvious that the Cnidaria and the related Ctenophora are by-passed if evolution of the metazoa went from the ciliates to the turbellarians directly. Hadži, supported by other investigators, derives the Cnidaria from Rhabdocoel Turbellaria. Hadži considers the Anthozoa to be the most primitive Cnidaria. This premise, supported by Hansen (1958), involves a number of problems. Hadži believes that the macrophagous Anthozoa inherited this condition from the Rhabdocoelida, but Hand (1959) contends that the presence of nematocysts in the endodermal tissues of Anthozoa involves a specialization rather than a primitive condition. In general, the Hydrozoa are more variable than are Anthozoa. Hand also points out that hermaphroditic, free-living flatworms would give rise to dioecious, attached Anthozoa on the basis of this theory, although generally sessile animals tends to be monoecious. The Hadži theory holds that the bilaterality exhibited in Anthozoa is primitive and that the radial symmetry is superimposed on it. Hyman (1959) points out the rarity of a change of symmetry from radial to bilateral and the frequency of change from bilateral to radial. Another argument against the Hadži theory involves the loss of the excretory system, which would be remarkable in an animal as complex as an Anthozoan, a reduction in specialization of the reproductive system, and the complete lack of any sign of spiral cleavage among Coelenterates. Finally, the geologic history is much older for medusoid coelenterates than is evident for the Anthozoa. These features are discussed pro and con among the papers cited in the references.

The Ctenophora have long been considered as related to polyclad turbellarians. The unique segmentation pattern with determinative cleavage seems closer to the polyclads than to any Cnidaria. Some early theories suggested that the Ctenophora were ancestral to the Polycladida, but the presumed intermediate animal has since been shown to be a modified ctenophoran. Hadži reverses the relationship by considering the ctenophore to be developed from the polyclad embryo (Müller's larva) through neoteny. However, the ctenophores have several features in common with the Cnidaria including the tetraradiate symmetry, the mesogloea, the nervous system, and the radial canals. *Euchlora rubra,* a ctenophore recently discovered to produce nematocysts—a feature previously thought limited to Cnidaria—provides additional evidence for a cnidarian-ctenophoran relationship, and makes a polyclad connection even more improbable.

ORGANIZATION OF THE METAZOA

The metazoa are animals composed of many cells in which the cells are organized into tissues arranged in layers holding some degree of functional specialization. In the lower metazoans, the body wall is composed of two epithelia contiguous (except in the hydrozoan coelenterates) with an intermediate fluid layer called *mesogloea* or *mesenchyme,* supplied with some wandering amoeboid cells and usually with fibers. In the three phyla (Porifera, Cnidaria, and Ctenophora) the mesogloeal layer is relatively unformed and never develops nor permanently contains organs. The outer epithelium was named *ectoderm* and the inner, *entoderm.* Since these phyla had only two discrete layers of cells, they were designated as *diploblastic.* However, many years prior to this nomenclature, it was recognized by embryologists that the vertebrate embryo

developed through a pattern of three parallel layers and that a considerable degree of correspondence existed for the fate of these layers in various ontogenies. The outer and inner layers were thought to correspond with the ectoderm and entoderm of Cnidaria and were called by the same names, while the intermediate layer was called *mesoderm.* In the bilateral eumetazoa, not only is this layer cellular, but specific organs and cavities develop from it. Phyla with three such well-defined layers are considered to be *triploblastic.* The three embryonic layers (ectoderm, mesoderm, and entoderm) are the *germ layers* of embryology, but the implied homology is only broadly applicable.

All triploblastic animals pass through a diploblastic stage known as the gastrula. The endoderm forms the archenteron or primitive intestine with an anticipated function of digestion, and the only functions that can be attributed with certainty to the ectoderm at this stage are protective, sensory, and usually locomotor. In the formation of the gastrula, surface cells of the blastula make their way inward in various patterns. In the familiar invagination or emboly a group of cells pushes inward as a pocket. This reduces the cavity of the blastula (blastocoele or primary cavity), which later in many animals will be completely obliterated by development of mesoderm. The cavity that frequently develops within the mesoderm is the secondary body cavity or coelom. It is characteristically lined by its own epithelium, called mesothelium. Gonads arise in the coelomic mesoderm, and the coelomic cavity usually communicates with the exterior through coelomoducts. In some metazoa, both primary and secondary cavities are retained.

The principal body cavity in Arthropoda is a hemocoele, and since arthropods arose from annelid stock characterized by a prominent coelom, a comparison of body cavities for these phyla is interesting (Fig. 3-1). In such cases, the primary cavity or blastocoele may function as a hemocoele with circulatory fluid and function. The hemocoele never communicates with the exterior. However, a hemocoele may arise secondarily, so the term is not a synonym of the blastocoele. In other animals a coelom never develops, but the blastocoele may be retained as the principal cavity between the gut and the body wall. This cavity is known as a pseudocoele. In other animals no cavity appears between gut lumen and the exterior. It is apparent that in triploblastic animals the phyla can be subdivided on the basis of acoelomate, pseudocoelomate, and coelomate structure.

Coelomate animals fall into two major groups. In protostomates the coelomic cavity usually appears by the development of a split in paired solid bands of mesoderm. Because of such origin, this type of coelom is called a schizocoele. In the other major group (deuterostomates) the coelom arises as originally or subsequently paired outpockets of the archenteron. These evaginations close. A coelom formed by this process is called an enterocoele.

REFERENCES

de Beer, G. R., The evolution of Metazoa (pp. 24-33). *In* (J. Huxley, A. C. Hardy, and E. B. Ford, ed.) Evolution as a process. London: G. Allen, 1954.

Carter, G. S., On Hadži's interpretation of animal phylogeny. Syst. Zool., 3:163, 1954.

Hadži, Jovan, An attempt to reconstruct the system of animal classification. Syst. Zool., 2:145, 1953.

Hand, Cadet, On the origin and phylogeny of the coelenterates. Syst. Zool., 8:191, 1959.

Hansen, E. D., On the origin of the Eumetazoa. Syst. Zool., 7:16, 1958.

————, Animal diversity, 116 pp. Englewood Cliffs, N.J.: Prentice-Hall, 1961.

Hyman, L. H., The invertebrates, Vol. II. New York: McGraw, 1951.

————, The invertebrates, Vol. V (Retrospect chapter). New York: McGraw, 1959.

Lackey, J. B., Morphology and biology of a species of *Protospongia*. Trans. Amer. Microsc. Soc., 78:202, 1959.

Fig. 3-1 Diagrams to show the relations of the cavities of the body and their condition in annelids as compared with arthropods. From J. A. Ramsay, *A Physiological Approach to the Lower Animals*, 1952, The Syndics of the Cambridge University Press.

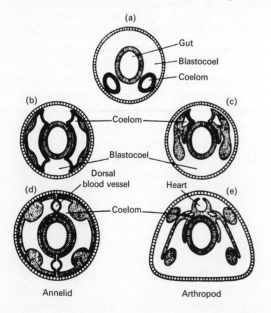

(a)
Gut
Blastocoel
Coelom

(b)
(c)
Coelom
Blastocoel
Dorsal blood vessel
Heart
(d)
(e)
Coelom
Annelid
Arthropod

4

PHYLUM PORIFREA (Parazoa)

The Porifera or sponges are typically attached animals with a primary radial symmetry often modified by branching and folds into asymmetrical masses. Most Porifera are marine, or occur in very brackish waters, but a single family (Spongillidae) occurs only in clean fresh water. The basic sponge form is that of a cylinder or vase (Fig. 4-1), whose wall is perforated by pores and channels through which water flows into a single central cavity, the *spongocoel*. Water leaves the latter chamber through a single osculum, propelled by the beat of choanocyte flagella. *Choanocytes* possess a protoplasmic collar in the form of a membrane which encircles the base of the single flagellum. In more complex sponges, choanocytes are limited to radial pockets of the central cavity or to discrete chambers in the water channels of the body wall. Electron-microscope studies indicate that the choanocyte collar is composed of abutting or apposed rods or tentacles, not encased in a common sheath, but sometimes joined by bridges.

Sponges lack organs and organ systems. This includes absence of a mouth and of nervous tissue. Although histological findings suggest the presence of nerve cells, Jones points out that this is not substantiated by the biochemical and physiological evidence and that a state of excitation can be transmitted by the contractile tissue.

MORPHOLOGY

The body wall consists of an outer epithelium or sometimes a syncytial epidermis, lacking in Hexactinellida, composed of flattened cells called pinacocytes; an inter-

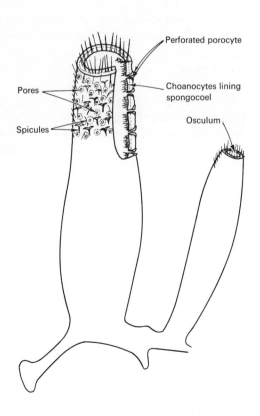

Perforated porocyte

Pores

Choanocytes lining spongocoel

Osculum

Spicules

Fig. 4-1 Diagrammatic representation of part of a *Leucosolenia* colony; a genus having ascon structure. Adapted from various sources.

mediate gelatinous matrix, called mesogloea, containing various cells and skeletal elements; and an inner epidermis which lines the spongocoel and is composed either of choanocytes or, when they have retreated, of pinacocytes derived from external surfaces. In some sponges, the spongocoel is obliterated and the analogous excurrent channels are lined by pinacocytes. Reproduction occurs by asexual as well as sexual processes. In the latter case the ovum develops into a free-swimming, flagellated larva before it becomes attached for sessile adulthood.

Respiration is an aerobic process and occurs through surface cells in sponges. It is related to the amount of water circulating

Fig. 4-2 Olynthus stage. After Schechter 1959, courtesy of Prentice-Hall, Inc.

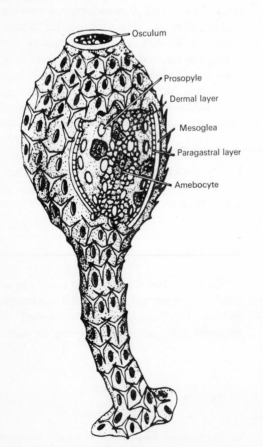

- Osculum
- Prosopyle
- Dermal layer
- Mesoglea
- Paragastral layer
- Amebocyte

through the sponge, which in turn is dependent upon the activity of the choanocyte flagella, and to the size of oscula and pores for those species partly able to regulate these apertures. Ammonia is a common nitrogenous waste material for animals in an environment allowing rapid diffusion and dilution in circulating water. Ammonia has been demonstrated for some sponges, whereas urea and uric acid were not found, the latter being particularly adapted to terrestrial animals where water balance must be protected.

The asconoid type of sponge structure is simplest and is seen in an immature stage called *olynthus* (Fig. 4-2), which occurs briefly in the life cycle of some calcareous sponges. The outer epithelium is composed of flattened pinacocytes; choanocytes form the epithelium lining the spongocoel; the intermediate mesogloeal layer contains wandering cells and skeletal elements in the gelatinous matrix; and the pores are direct channels through single porocytes in the body wall. The syconoid sponge structure (Fig. 4-3) differs principally by the presence of a more complicated wall. Outpockets radiate from the spongocoel and the choanocytes are limited to these channels, called radial canals. Their apertures to the spongocoel are internal ostia. Folds in the external wall produce an inpocketing of definite recesses or channels, called incurrent canals, lying adjacent and parallel to the radial canals with which they communicate laterally by pores called prosopyles. The perforations seen in the external surface of a syconoid sponge opening to the incurrent canals are termed dermal ostia and are therefore not homologous with the pores seen in olynthus or *Leucosolenia*. Thickening of the cell layers external to the blind ends of radial canals may allow for the formation of subdermal spaces between dermal ostia and incurrent canals in some syconoid sponges.

The leuconoid type of sponge structure (Fig. 4-3) exhibits a more extreme modification of the canal system, but it can be derived from the simpler types. The choanocytes are limited to little pockets or cham-bers which receive the incurrent water through the prosopyles and discharge it to excurrent channels through openings called apopyles. The leuconoid structure may be further complicated by canals intervening between incurrent canal and flagellated chamber, or excurrent canal and flagellated chamber, or both. A cortical layer with or without subdermal spaces is common for this type of sponge. In addition to the compli-cated canal system with small flagellated chambers, in the leuconoid sponge the spongocoel is obliterated as a well-defined cavity; many oscula mark the apertures of excurrent canals; and the entire sponge be-comes asymmetrical in form and irregular in structure.

Although the leuconoid structure may have evolved through ascon and sycon inter-mediaries, in most instances it appears to have developed directly from a *rhagon* stage. This is a low, cone-shaped form with prominent spongocoel and a single osculum at the apex. Choanocytes do not line the spongocoel, but occur in pouches or diverti-cula opening broadly to the spongocoel. These pouches develop direct pore connec-tion from the exterior, which is not folded as in the syconoid type. Subdivision of the

primary pouches with concurrent develop-ment of excurrent canals leads directly to the leuconoid structure.

Spicules and Spicule Formation

Rigid sclerites or spicules of various typical shapes are characteristic of most sponges and are utilized in most taxonomic schemes. Spicules are classified on the basis of their distribution or location. Larger spicules that form the principal framework of the sponge are called *macroscleres*. They often occur in bundles and frequently pro-trude from the body wall. Smaller spicules distributed singly through the flesh of the sponge are called *microscleres*. These may be similar in shape to macroscleres, but spheres, variously spined asters, curved rods, and other types of microscleres are common (Fig. 4-4). A third site for spicules is in the wall of gemmules in fresh-water sponges, where they occur as rough rods or am-phidiscs often radially disposed.

Spicule terminology is largely based on the number of axes and the number of rays (Fig. 4-4). For example, a triaxon spicule possesses three axes which cross each other at a common point to produce a sclerite of six rays (Hexactinellida). In addition to the

Fig. 4-3 Morphological types of sponges. (a) Ascon; (b) Sycon; and (c) Leucon. After Van Cleave 1931, courtesy of the McGraw-Hill Book Company.

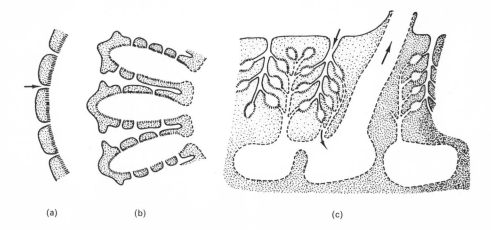

(a)   (b)   (c)

triaxon form, a number of other basic types occur. The monaxon spicule has a single straight or curved axis. If the two ends are similar, the spicule grew in both directions and is actually diactinal, in contrast with unidirectional growth to produce a monactinal monaxon, also called a style. All sorts of tapered as well as rounded, smooth, knobbed, or spiny knobbed ends occur. Curvature may be in one plane or spirally twisted, or sharply hooked. An extensive terminology has been formulated to describe these modifications. In the tetraxon spicule, four rays in different planes grow from a common intersection. Although occasionally all rays are of equal length, more commonly one ray is elongated with the three short ones situated symmetrically at one end. These are termed triaenes. Many types are described in the literature. Sometimes a simple or toothed disc or knob replaces the short rays. Such a formation at both ends of the long ray axis

produces an amphidisc or birotular spicule. Commonly scattered in the mesogloeal layer are sclerites with equal rays arising from a common center. These are polyaxon asters, and the rays may be shorter or longer than the diameter of the common center. Finally there is a form of sclerite that develops concentrically to form a sphere.

In the Hexactinellida the skeleton is composed of six-rayed spicules made primarily from opaline silicic acid and containing small amounts of an organic material called spiculin. This type of spicule is restricted to this class. Spicule fusion is a feature of the group, and the terms lyssacina and dictyonina are used to describe it. In the former, triaxon spicules are formed separately with interlacing and later fusion providing a somewhat less rigid irregular network. In the dictyonine type, all six rays are fused at formation with neighboring spicules to provide a three-dimensional uniform latticework

Fig. 4-4 Various sponge spicules. (a) to (d) Monaxons; (e) triaxon; (f) tetraxon; (g) to (i) asters; (j) to (m) birotular spicules or amphidiscs; (n) hexactine. Adapted from various sources.

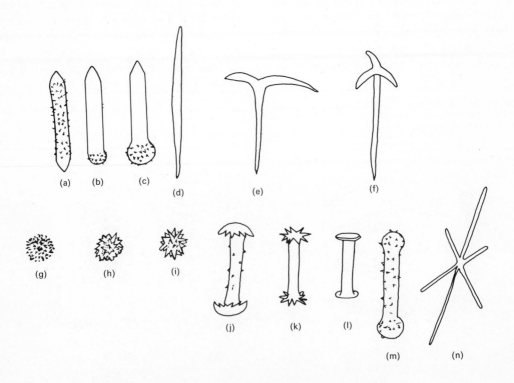

(Fig. 4-5). The latter type has been derived repeatedly from the lyssacine and does not indicate different origin. In addition to these fusion complexes, numerous free spicules occur. Prostalia spicules project from the sponge, and are described by location. Spicules associated with outer and inner surfaces are respectively dermalia and gastralia, while those characteristic of the trabecular net are called parenchymalia.

Most spicules are composed of calcium carbonate or silica deposited around a central organic core by amoebocytes of the mesogloea. Such sclerite-producing cells are called scleroblasts, or more specifically calcoblasts or silicoblasts, depending upon the composition of the resulting sclerite. Silicon spicules appear to form completely within a single silicoblast, or for larger spicules, within a syncytial mass. The formation of calcareous spicules is better established. Here calcium carbonate is deposited around an

organic core between the nuclei of a binucleate scleroblast. Growth of the spicule continues as the nuclei move apart. Eventually the cytoplasm separates. The deeper scleroblast called the *founder* is principally responsible for the continued development of the spicule as the cell proceeds more deeply into the mesogloea (Fig. 4-6). At the outer end the second cell, called the *thickener,* deposits additional calcium carbonate as it too moves inward along the spicule. For multirayed calcareous spicules, as many scleroblasts come together as there will be rays. Each scleroblast begins the division that will ultimately give rise to a founder and a thickener for each ray. Each scleroblast produces a minute spicule between the separating nuclei. The various spicules fuse centrally and the thickeners continue to add calcium carbonate to strengthen and thicken the junction. Meanwhile the founders, as they move toward the tips, are forming and lengthening

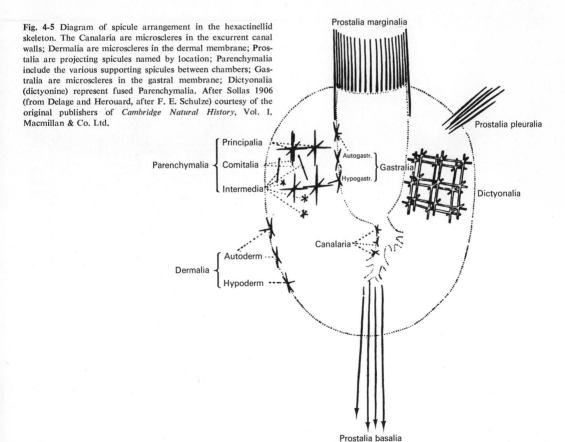

Fig. 4-5 Diagram of spicule arrangement in the hexactinellid skeleton. The Canalaria are microscleres in the excurrent canal walls; Dermalia are microscleres in the dermal membrane; Prostalia are projecting spicules named by location; Parenchymalia include the various supporting spicules between chambers; Gastralia are microscleres in the gastral membrane; Dictyonalia (dictyonine) represent fused Parenchymalia. After Sollas 1906 (from Delage and Herouard, after F. E. Schulze) courtesy of the original publishers of *Cambridge Natural History*, Vol. I, Macmillan & Co. Ltd.

the spicules. Finally both founders and thickeners return to the mesogloea.

The second skeletal element consists of spongin, which is a tough, flexible, somewhat elastic organic material of protein nature. This forms a branching and interlocking network of fibers which may help to support the spicular skeleton, or which may be the sole skeleton. The bath sponge *(Spongia* or *Hippospongia)* is an example of the latter. Modified amoebocytes called spongioblasts secrete the spongin fibers internally, and ultimately these fibers fuse with those of adjacent spongioblasts. After spongin production, these cells degenerate.

Classification of the Porifera

Class I Calcarea   In this group the skeleton is composed of monaxonal and tri- and tetractinal spicules of calcium carbonate. The members of this class are typically shallow-water marine forms. The choanocytes are of large size. This class has commonly been separated into orders based on whether the structure is asconoid or more advanced. In the future it may be divided on an embryological basis, with one group arising from a parenchymula (stereogastrula) larval type and the other from a stomoblastula-amphiblastula sequence, with the latter exhibiting a transitory cross of cells suggesting a tetraradiate symmetry. *Clathrina, Sycon, Leucosolenia.*

Class II Hexactinellida   These are deep marine forms with radial symmetry and small choanocytes. The body wall is a constant and distinctive feature of the class. The thimble-shaped flagellated chambers (Fig. 4-7) are regularly spaced and lie in a trabecular net formed by the syncytial fusion of the pseudopod elongations of modified amoebocytes. Mesogloea is almost non-existent as is true epidermis. Water in the subdermal trabecular spaces enters the flagellated chambers through

Fig. 4-6 Diagram illustrating formation of a triradiate spicule. After Schechter 1959, courtesy of Prentice-Hall, Inc.

Fig. 4-7 Portion of the body-wall of a hexactinellid, (*Walteria*) showing thimble-shaped flagellated chambers below the dermal membrane. After Sollas 1906, courtesy of the original publishers of *Cambridge Natural History*, Vol. I, Macmillan & Co., Ltd.

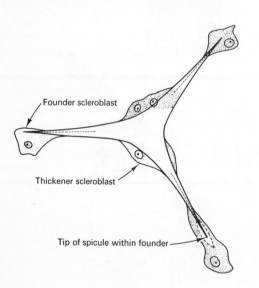

Founder scleroblast

Thickener scleroblast

Tip of spicule within founder

ostia and is propelled through subgastral trabecular spaces more or less defined as excurrent canals into the spongocoel.

Among the smaller sclerites in the Hexactinellida are two types that do not occur simultaneously. One of these is the amphidisc, and the other is the hexaster with six regular rays variously branched or surmounted with discs. Their respective distribution separates this class into two orders:

Order 1 Hexacterophora These have hexasters but the amphidiscs are lacking. Flagellated chambers are generally regular. *Euplectella.*

Order 2 Amphidiscophora These possess amphidiscs but not hexasters. Flagellated chambers exhibit more diversity. *Hyalonema.*

Class III Demospongiae In this class the skeleton is composed of siliceous spicules or spongin fibers or both, but the sclerites are never triaxon. Both flagellated chambers and choanocytes are small. Only the leuconoid canal system occurs in this group, and it arose from a rhagon larval type. Generally, members of the class are rather solid and more or less rounded in contour. Lévi (1953, 1957) suggests a diphyletic origin of this group based principally on embryological development. He proposes the following division:

SUBCLASS CERACTINOMORPHA This group is somewhat more homogeneous than the other subclass. These form a completely flagellated parenchymula, which invaginates after attachment and becomes a rhagon. The fresh-water family, Spongillidae, belongs here. *Halisarca, Aplysilla, Spongia, Hippospongia, Spongilla.*

SUBCLASS TETRACTINOMORPHA In the embryology of this subclass, a solid, externally flagellated parenchymula (stereogastrula) larva changes to an amphiblastula by dispersion of the interior cells. *Oscarella, Plakina, Plakortis.*

FOOD-GETTING AND DIGESTION

Sponges are attached animals which must obtain food from the water drawn through them by action of the collar cells. Carter points out that, although the movement of a flagellum is slow (the tip may move 1.2 mm per second), the combined effect of the activity of all flagella is sufficient to displace a volume of water equivalent to the volume of the sponge every minute. The distance water is propelled from the osculum varies inversely with the size of the oscular aperture. Bidder showed that this jet is important in dispersal of excreta to reduce its chances of again circulating through the sponge.

Minute food particles are brought into the sponge along with water through the incurrent channels. Food particles adhere to the outer surfaces of the choanocyte collars. The food is ingested by the choanocytes; in the calcareous sponges with large collar cells digestion begins here, but subsequently much of the food is transferred to adjacent amoebocytes. In sponges with small choanocytes the food is passed immediately to amoebocytes. It is probable that soluble nutrients will diffuse directly to the mesogloea, without prior ingestion by choanocytes. All digestion is intracellular. Indigestible material is egested by the amoebocytes and swept away in the excurrent channels. Food reserves are stored in special cells called thesocytes, possibly modified from amoebocytes. It is interesting to note that unique fatty acids with unusually large numbers of carbon atoms have been isolated from sponges. Glycogen and material of protein nature have also been demonstrated in the thesocytes.

REPRODUCTION, EMBRYOLOGY AND REGENERATION

Certain amoebocytes thought to be persistent embryonic cells are called *archaeocytes* and have been considered responsible both for production of sex cells and for initiating regeneration. Recent investigations, however, have confirmed some earlier studies, indicating the production of oogonia and of spermatogonia from choanocytes by transformation. The egg mother cell appears in the wall of the radial canals just beneath the layer of choanocytes. It grows by nourishment supplied by nurse cells which are transformed choanocytes. The sperm is transported to the egg by a modified choano-cyte, which also has acted as a nurse cell.

The fertilized egg undergoes maturation and holoblastic cleavage, giving rise to a 16-cell embryo in which the cells occur in two layers of eight each. The eight cells next to the choanocyte layer are destined to become epidermis, while the deeper layer is ancestral to choanocytes. The latter cells continue cleavage which results in a hollow ball of smaller cells, capped by a group of eight epidermal cells. Flagella have developed on the side of the small cells facing the blasto-coele. Now an opening or "mouth" appears medially in the eight large cells. Material from adjacent maternal cells is ingested. This larval stage (Fig. 4-8) is called a stomo-blastula. When it attains full growth it turns inside out, in a process similar to what occurs in *Volvox*. This inversion brings the flagella to the outside to form one hemisphere, with the epidermal cells which have begun to multiply massed at the other pole. A small cavity remains somewhat eccentrically be-tween the two cell masses. This larval stage

escapes from the parent sponge through excurrent channels. It swims with the flagella forward. This free-swimming larva is called an amphiblastula (Fig. 4-9). Four of the cells at the anterior end are somewhat modi-fied and form a cross which suggests a tetraradiate symmetry. The amphiblastula settles to the bottom and attaches by the flagellar end which invaginates, aided by overgrowth of the cells of the nonflagellated pole. A gastrula forms, lined by flagellated cells and possessing a blastopore. The devel-oping sponge becomes more cylindrical and at the free end an aperture appears which becomes the osculum. With the appearance of pores, in some Calcarea an olynthus stage results, while in Demospongiae a modified pattern gives rise to a rhagon.

Other sponges exhibit a somewhat differ-ent early embryology. In these, the fertilized egg undergoes cleavage to produce a coelo-blastula composed of slender, externally flagellate cells, except at one end where flagella are lacking. These, as well as many of the adjacent flagellated cells, migrate to

Fig. 4-8 Stomoblastula of *Grantia*, within embryonic chamber of parent. After Van Cleave (from Dendy) 1931, courtesy of the McGraw-Hill Book Company.

Fig. 4-9 Amphiblastula of *Sycandra*. After Richards (after Schulze) 1931, courtesy of John Wiley & Sons, Inc.

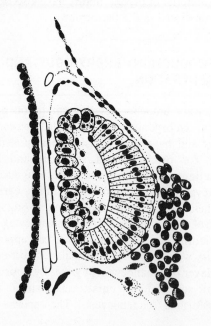

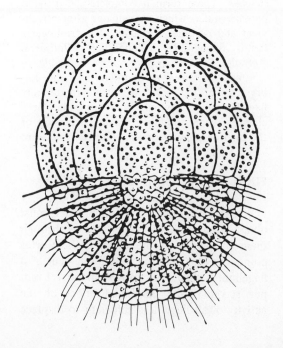

the interior, where the flagella are lost and the cells, assuming an amoeboid character, more or less fill the central cavity. This solid, flagellated larva is called a parenchymula or stereogastrula. After a short free life, this larva becomes sedentary and the outer flagellated cells migrate centrally to give rise to choanocytes. The cells formerly central become the surface epidermis, a central spongocoel develops, and the osculum forms. This embryological pattern also produces an intermediate asconoid olynthus stage.

In the fresh-water sponges (Spongillidae) and in some marine sponges an asexual reproductive process called gemmulation occurs. Particularly in the fresh-water species, winter and desiccation survival is dependent upon *gemmule* formation. Internal buds or gemmules begin as an aggregation of generalized amoebocytes. Through the agency of other amoebocytes, called trophocytes, the mass of amoebocytes develop food reserves. Still other amoebocytes become arranged around the mass in a circumferential columnar layer which later secretes on its inner face

a rather hard, thick membrane (Fig. 4-10). Subsequently, a thin membrane is secreted on the outer face. In many fresh-water species, amphidiscs secreted elsewhere are placed radially between the two secreted membranes, replacing the columnar amoebocytes, which may add to the outer membrane before dispersal. The gemmule is supplied with a pore canal called a micropyle. When the parental tissue degenerates, the gemmules remain or fall to the bottom. When environmental conditions are again favorable, they germinate. Many of the food-laden amoebocytes of the gemmule are multinuclear. In the process of germination, these undergo cytoplasmic division to produce uninucleate cells which exit through the micropyle, whereupon they aggregate. Cell differentiation and rearrangement gives rise to a young sponge. In marine sponges, gemmule formation begins by clumping of similar undifferentiated amoebocytes, and a thin membrane forms around the aggregation. Later, surface cells become flagellated except at one pole. This larva has a free-swimming existence

Fig. 4-10 Sponge gemmule, diagrammatic. From Schechter 1959, courtesy of Prentice-Hall, Inc.

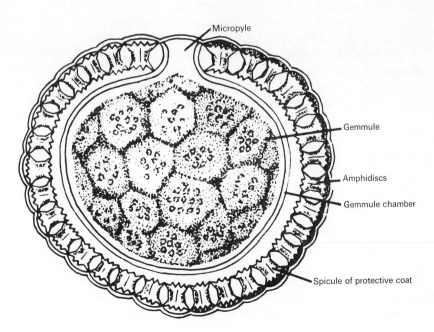

Micropyle

Gemmule

Amphidiscs

Gemmule chamber

Spicule of protective coat

before attaching at the nonflagellated end. Subsequent differentiation and reorientation of existing cells produces a young sponge.

Among both marine and fresh-water sponges a somewhat abbreviated survival process occurs. It involves the formation of reduction bodies by aggregation not of generalized amoebocytes more or less totipotent, but rather of the cell types characteristic of the species in question. In a favorable environment these reduction bodies reorganize as complete sponges.

The ability to regenerate is so well developed in sponges that it constitutes a phase of reproduction. Isolated pieces, particularly if they contain varied cell types, will readily produce a new sponge. A sponge passed through bolting cloth and fragmented into single cells and cell aggregates, can reassemble. Cell masses of one species will not aggregate with those of another species. For some sponges, a single or group of choanocytes cannot regenerate a complete sponge, indicating that the ability to return to generalized totipotent cell types capable of regeneration is not uniform for all species.

Fibrous sponges (those lacking spicules) have been used for centuries by man, not only for bathing, but for scrubbing and, in olden days, as padding in armor. A great deal of water can be held in the minute interstices of the spongin network as well as being absorbed by the fibers, and spongin itself is a tough material that can stand hard usage. Only a few kinds of sponges are important commercially; these are collected from relatively shallow waters of warm seas such as areas adjacent to Florida and the West Indies as well as the Mediterranean Sea. In good years, a thousand tons of sponges are collected by various methods including dredging, the use of long-handled hooks, and by divers. After collection, the spongin skeleton must be freed of the living organic matter. Sponges are slow growers and bath sponges take many years to reach fair size. The sponge industry is sufficient to warrant "seeding" or sponge culture, in which sponge pieces are "planted" in suitable waters, to utilize sponge regenerative ability.

PHYLOGENETIC CONSIDERATIONS

The Porifera represent a very ancient group that already showed diversity in the Cambrian. The earliest Paleozoic records reveal spicule fusion into the frameworks characteristic of each of the Recent classes of sponges. Shrock and Twenhofel point out that "spicules made by Cambrian sponges are indistinguishable from similar ones in recent sponges." Down through the geologic ages this phylum has demonstrated a limited but uniform persistence.

The Porifera possess some characteristics of distinction. Choanocytes are represented throughout the group, in which they occur as lining of internal cavities. Such cells are reminiscent of some flagellate protozoans, but direct descent from choanoflagellates seems improbable since none of the sponge larval types show external collared cells. Aggregates of choanocytes have been pictured as representing sponge fragments or described as colonial flagellates, but in either case do not represent a phylogenetic precursor of the sponges. Lack of a mouth and retention of intracellular digestion fail to align the Porifera with any other metazoa. Recent biochemical studies indicate the presence in sponges of fatty acids which have a unique number of carbon atoms. Such data may emphasize further the phylogenetic isolation of the Porifera.

Presence of flagella, simplified reproductive procedures, and intracellular digestion are indicative of protozoan ancestry. The presence of an external and an internal epidermis separated by a gelatinous layer containing cells; radial symmetry, and sessile habit are similar to cnidarian biology, but the "inversion" embryology of the sponges prevents homologizing the body layers, and radial symmetry is a common corollary of fixed habitat. In addition the primitive cnidarian was probably a swimming medusoid form. Both Porifera and Cnidaria may have a possible similar ancestry, as indicated by some embryological features. A stereogastrula occurs in both groups; parenchymula in the sponges and planula in Cnidaria. The presence of four altered cells at the flagellar end of the amphiblastula larva of calcareous sponges suggests a primitive tetraradiate symmetry seen in many Cnidaria.

The interrelationships among the classes of Porifera are not clear-cut. The asconoid olynthus type of structure is common for Calcarea. The leuconoid structure probably arose independently many times. One group of Hexactinellida has spicules reminiscent of calcareous sponges, while amphidiscs occur in both classes of siliceous sponges. Canal systems undoubtedly were subject to extensive evolutionary modification, but such systems are not preserved among fossils.

As a group, the sponges have evolved from colonial flagellate ancestors. Whether or not they emerged from the same or different mastigophoran ancestors, they have diverged sharply from the more productive primitive metazoans, but have not been successful in radiation leading to other phyla.

REFERENCES

Bidder, G. P., The relation of the form of a sponge to its currents. Quart. J. Microsc. Sci., 67:293, 1923.

Carter, G. S., A general zoology of the invertebrates. London: Sidgwick and Jackson, 1951.

Dendy, A., On the origin, growth, and arrangement of sponge spicules. Quart. J. Microsc. Sci., 70:1, 1926.

Hyman, L. H., The invertebrates: Protozoa through Ctenophora (pp. 284-364). New York: McGraw, 1940. (For material since 1940, see Retrospect chapter in Vol. V.)

Jones, W. C., Is there a nervous system in sponges? Biol. Rev., 37:1, 1962.

Lévi, C., Sur une nouvelle classification des Démosponges. Compt. rend. acad. sci., Paris, 236:853, 1953.

———, Ontogeny and systematics in sponges. Syst. Zool., 6:174, 1957.

Pavans de Cecatty, M., Les structures cellulaires de type nerveux de type musculaire d'éponge siliceuses *Tethya lyncurium*. Compt. rend. acad. sci., Paris, 251:1818, 1960.

Rasmont, R., Ultra-structure des choanocytes d'Éponges. Proc. 15th Internat. Congr. Zool., London, 707-708, 1958.

———, J. Bouillon, P. Castiaux, and G. Vandermeersche, Ultrastructure of the choanocyte collar-cells in fresh-water sponges. Nature, 181:58, 1958.

Schechter, Victor, Invertebrate zoology. Englewood Cliffs, N.J.; Prentice-Hall, Inc., 1959.

Sollas, I. B. J., Porifera (sponges) (pp. 163-242). In (S. F. Harmer and A. E. Shipley, eds.) Cambridge natural history, Vol. I. London: Macmillan, 1906. (There is a 1959 reprint edition.)

Tuzet, O., The phylogeny of sponges (pp. 129-148). In (Dougherty, E. C., Z. N. Brown, E. D. Hanson, and W. D. Hartman, eds.) The lower Metazoa. Berkeley: U. of California, 1963.

5

CNIDARIA

The phylum Cnidaria constitutes a large and varied group of animals of considerable economic import, for coral reefs occur in suitable tropical waters distributed over an area of some sixty-eight million square miles (Wells 1957). Biologic interest is especially focused on the group, because the onset of tissue differentiation marked the inception of the nervous system in the animal kingdom. Studies of the nervous system not only provide some answers about the physical basis of impulse transmission, but even more about the behavioral responses with implications for adaptation and phylogeny.

The Cnidaria is a phylum with a primary radial symmetry, with the body form basically that of a double-walled cup in which the cellular layers are separated by a gelatinous stratum varying in its cellular and fiber content, with tentacles encircling the cup aperture and with an armature of so-called stinging or nettle cells called *nematocysts*. Cnidaria are all aquatic and predominantly marine. They may be permanently or transitorily attached or they may be free-floating or active swimmers. An alternate name for this phylum is Coelenterata, although in a less restricted usage that term includes the Ctenophora.

The Cnidaria are divided into three classes. Class Hydrozoa includes the familiar *Hydra* of beginning biology courses, as well as the polymorphic marine siphonophores such as the frequently pictured Portuguese man-of-war *(Physalia)*. Some Hydrozoa produce massive calcareous skeletons and contribute to coral reef formation. This is the only cnidarian class with fresh-water representatives. Pennak lists two genera and eleven species of hydra in inland waters of the United States, and a fresh-water "jellyfish," *Craspedacusta sowerbii,* of sporadic and unpredictable distribution. Other fresh-water medusae have been described from Africa, India, and China. One colonial hydrozoan *(Cordylophora)* occurs in estuaries on the Atlantic coast as well as from inland rivers of the lower Mississippi drainage basin. The hydras are common in unpolluted waters of ponds and streams and in shallow water along lake shores, where they are attached to vegetation and other underwater objects.

The second cnidarian class is the Scyphozoa, familiarly called medusae or jellyfish. They occur in the open ocean, but a number are common in such estuaries as those of Chesapeake Bay. Some jellyfish, of which *Haliclystus* of the Pacific coast is a well-known example, attach to vegetation by an adhesive disc on the end of a stalk. These attached jellyfish occur in coastal waters and inlets in colder climates. Although they are unable to swim, some of them can detach and move about in an end-for-end manner somewhat like an inchworm. The largest cnidarian known is a jellyfish *(Cyanea arctica),* which may reach a diameter of nearly two meters. Purples, blues, and browns are common in these translucent animals.

The third class is the Anthozoa, and it includes about two-thirds of the known species of coelenterates. These exclusively marine cnidarians are solitary or colonial. In addition to sea anemones and most corals, the sea fans and sea pens occur in this class. The sea fans (and sea feathers) are typically colonies branching in one plane from a single stem or in all directions to produce a fan or bushy shape. In the sea fans, the skeleton contains a horny protein substance. This group is very colorful with yellows, oranges, and purples common. The precious red coral of jewelry occurs here.

Sea pens are a group of brilliantly colored colonial Anthozoa which have an elongate stalk with small secondary feeding individuals developing laterally on the upper end. The lower end of the stalk, which serves as an anchor, can burrow into soft substrate in the warmer coastal waters where these Anthozoa are found. The sea pens are outstanding among coelenterates for their ability to produce luminescent granules. While most sea pens are under a half meter in length, a few species may be much longer.

Sea anemones differ from most other Anthozoa in lacking a skeleton. These cnidarians are most common in relatively shallow coastal waters in tropical seas, where the species are more numerous and the individuals often larger than in colder zones. Many anemones attach to hard, rocky substrates, but a number live in or on mud, and some small species remain attached to seaweed. White and various tans and greens are common colors, but some anemones are a brilliant orange or blue. The largest species of anemones may reach nearly a meter in diameter, but most are much smaller.

The corals, including those Hydrozoa and Anthozoa which produce substantial calcareous skeletons, are the ones most important in formation of reefs. In any major reef formation a great many species of corals occur. Yonge reports Crossland found 174 species belonging to 54 genera in one small section of the Great Barrier Reef of Australia.

The more common types of reefs are fringing reefs, barrier reefs, and atolls. Fringing reefs form near land, separated from the shore by a relatively shallow channel. Barrier reefs are separated from the land by wide and relatively deep water. Atolls are somewhat ringlike formations of coral encircling relatively shallow lagoons, almost as if the coral developed along the rim of a submerged extinct volcano.

Since reef corals grow in shallower water (approximately 175 feet represents the lower limit for living coral, and a somewhat similar depth appeared to be maximal for extinct corals), one explanation for the great vertical thickness of coral reefs (borings have gone over 1,000 feet without reaching the bottom) is that reef building started on submerged surfaces when the ocean was lower, owing to water loss to glaciers during the glacial epochs. As the ocean level rose with the retreat and melting of glaciers, new coral grew on the coral already laid down. So-called solitary corals grow at greater depth and over a wider range of latitude.

Living coral has a protective armament of nematocysts, and its enemies are relatively few. One polychaete annelid *(Hermodice)* is a known predator, and a few fish occasionally browse on living coral. Many other marine animals utilize the interstices in dead coral; a number of these are able to penetrate deeper by boring. Some molluscan gastropods and bivalves *(Lithophaga)* and barnacles are among the borers. Sponges, anemones, sipunculids, tubiculous annelids, crabs, various echinoderms, and a number of fish species are common and characteristic of coral formations.

GENERAL MORPHOLOGY AND SPECIAL FEATURES

The body form of Cnidaria exhibits many variations; hence the phylum is referred to as polymorphic. Two principal variants predominate. One of these, the polyp, is a cylindroid, sessile organism attached to the colony or to the substrate at the aboral end. The lumen of this cylinder is called the gastrovascular cavity, a name indicative of a dual function of digestion and food distribution (Fig. 5-1). The external opening of this cavity is at the oral end of the polyp. In some polyps, the gastrovascular cavity is continuous with cavities in the tentacles. In solitary species, the gastrovascular cavity ends blindly; in colonial forms it may be continuous with the cavity of the common stalk.

In some colonial forms division of labor is correlated with structural change in the polyp. A typical individual is a feeding polyp with tentacles, mouth, and digestive system and is called a *gastrozooid*. Sometimes the polyp is elongated into a slender, fingerlike structure which has lost the typical tentacles and digestive organs but is provided with an armature of nematocysts, and which serves as a protective and food-procuring unit. Polyps modified for the production of medusa buds, or gonophores, are called *gonozooids* or *blastostyles*. While these represent common modifications of polyps, not all colonies possess all the variant structures.

The second main body form generally characteristic of the Cnidaria is the *medusa* or jellyfish. The name is derived from the mythological monster whose head was covered with hissing serpents rather than hair, a fancied resemblance to the ring of tentacles on the medusa rim. Instead of being cylindroid with a long oral-aboral axis, the oral and aboral surfaces are fused into the shape of a concave disc or bell, thickened with an extensive development of mesogloea. The shape (Fig. 5-2) has been likened to that of an umbrella. The usually convex aboral surface is called the exumbrella, while the oral surface is concave and is the subumbrella. The gastrovascular cavity is a central pouch continuous to the rim of the bell as tetra-

Fig. 5-1 *Hydra,* suspended from a gas bubble secreted at its base. From Schechter 1959, courtesy of Prentice-Hall, Inc.

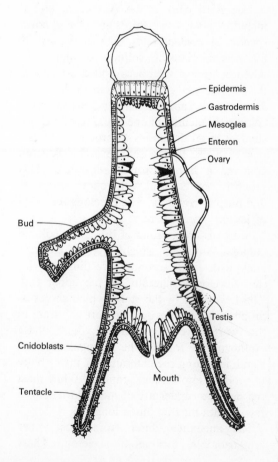

Epidermis

Gastrodermis

Mesoglea

Enteron

Ovary

Bud

Testis

Cnidoblasts

Mouth

Tentacle

merically disposed radial canals which enter a peripheral ring canal. Externally tentacles occur along the bell margin, and in some medusae a shelf called the *velum* projects inward from the subumbrellar rim. In addition to a number of variations that are still recognizably medusoid in form, attached medusae in some colonial forms (Portuguese man-of-war, *Physalia,* and its near relatives) show extensive polymorphic variation (Fig. 5-3). Some of these include pneumatophores which provide buoyancy for the colony, muscular nectophores which provide locomotion, and shield- or leaflike hydrophyllia which apparently are protective.

Polymorphic development in coelenterates is often correlated with a process termed *metagenesis,* usually considered to be that life-cycle pattern in which an asexually-derived generation alternates with a sexually-derived one. This alternation of generations among Cnidaria involves an asexually-producing polyp which gives rise by budding to a medusoid generation in which sperm and eggs are produced. Acceptance of the sexually-reproducing medusa as the ancestral form relegates the polyp to a derived or secondary generation. Hyman (1959) reiterates the argument that the polyp is a persistent

Fig. 5-2 *Rhopalonema,* a trachyline medusa. Redrawn from Hertwig, *A Manual of Zoology* (translated and edited by J. S. Kingsley) 1902, Holt, Rinehart & Winston, Inc.

larval form in which the ability to multiply asexually by budding was developed. The phenomenon of regeneration or replacement of injured or lost parts is frequently better

Fig. 5-3 Diagram of siphonophore colony to show polymorphism. *a,* float or pneumatophore; *b,* swimming bells; *c,* protective and digestive individual (dactylozooid); *d,* tentacles armed with nematocysts; *e,* generative medusoid (gonozooid); *f,* feeding polyp (gastrozooid); *g,* cut end of colony. Broken lines indicate continuity of gastrovascular cavity. Adapted from Hertwig, *A Manual of Zoology* (translated and edited by J. S. Kingsley) 1902, Holt, Rinehart & Winston, Inc.

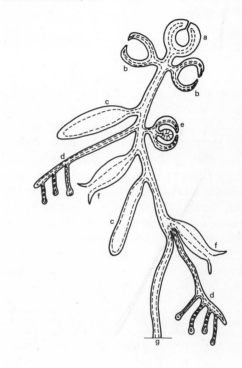

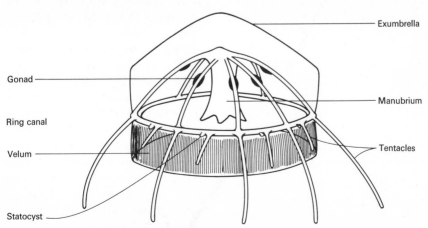

developed in larval than in adult organisms. The related process of asexual reproduction is frequent among immature stages of many invertebrate animals. Regenerative ability is well developed among Cnidaria, and the process has been extensively studied.

While coelenterates are considered to have a primary radial symmetry, this symmetry is frequently modified by superimposed bilateral or biradial features. In the Anthozoa, a cnidarian class which is structurally limited to a polypoid body form, a section cut through the oral-aboral axis along one diameter divides the animal into two halves which cannot be duplicated by a similar section through any other diameter. This is true because the elongation of the aperture to the gastrovascular cavity occurs in one plane through the oral-aboral axis. A similar biradial symmetry is seen in the related phylum, Ctenophora. The basic radial symmetry of many Cnidaria shows marked inclination to be subdivided into quadrants (Fig. 5-4). This tetramerous relationship is evidenced by distribution of gonads and the radial canal subdivision of the gastrovascular cavity in medusae, and by the septa characteristic of Anthozoa, although some of the latter exhibit

a hexamerous condition. Tetramerous symmetry is shared by the Ctenophora.

The body wall of the typical coelenterate is composed of two well-defined cellular layers of epithelia separated by a gelatinous layer called mesogloea. In Scyphozoa and Anthozoa, this layer normally contains fibers and various cells, many of a stellate, amoeboid shape. Especially in the Anthozoa, the mesogloea is lamellate with fibers running obliquely right and left in alternate sheets. Such a structure allows for considerable reversible extensibility in the living animal. In the Hydrozoa, cells are usually absent from the mesogloeal layer, but mechanical properties indicate a fibrous, nonhomogeneous structure. Pantin (1952) points out that in all coelenterates the muscular, sensory, and nervous systems are spread out in a single sheet at the bases of the respective epithelial layers. With the attachment of the sheets of muscle fibers to the mesogloeal surfaces, tension can be applied to this fibrous complex.

Typical cells of the ectoderm and entoderm (gastrodermis) in Cnidaria are cuboidal to columnar in shape, and in most of the Hydrozoa the bases of these cells possess contractile elements or myonemes. These so-called epithelio-muscular cells have their muscular elements disposed at right angles to the radii of these coelenterates. Some realization of the effectiveness of the epithelio-muscular-mesogloeal complex is indicated by Pantin's citation that tentacles of some hydras can contract to less than five per cent of their extended length.

In the Scyphozoa and Anthozoa the epidermal muscle is usually composed of fibers independent of the epithelium, and these may sink into the mesogloea instead of having only surface connections. Among Hydrozoa, the nervous system in *Hydra* is best known. Lentz and Barrnett from electron-microscope studies point out that several types of nerve cells occur in hydra in a well-developed but diffusely organized system. These types with their processes are called ganglion, neurosecretory, and sensory nerves. The ganglion

Fig. 5-4 Diagram of *Obelia* medusa, oral view, showing tetraradiate features. From Schechter 1959, courtesy of Prentice-Hall, Inc.

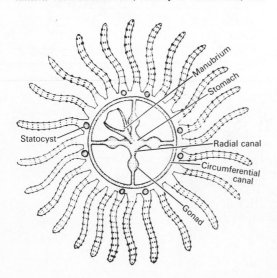

cells occur adjacent to the bases of the epithelio-muscular cells. Some of their processes were traced to cnidoblasts and to epithelio-muscular processes. Neurosecretory cells are similar in size, shape, and location, but contain accumulations of dense granules thought to be neurosecretory in nature, encompassed by membranes. The sensory cells are elongate cells whose axes lie radially in epidermis and gastrodermis. Within a deep indentation at the distal end, these cells give rise to a single cilium.

The normal reflex action has been demonstrated for *Hydra*. An animal in a nonnutrient solution has its mouth closed and tentacles extended and relatively motionless. With introduction of a specific stimulant, glutathione, tentacle tips move toward the mouth, which opens, and into which the tentacle tips may be inserted (Lenhoff).

Pantin (1965) reiterates that the most advanced nerve net occurs in hydromedusae and that at least histologically the simplist sensory-neuro-muscular system is found in the Anthozoa. A great deal of study has occurred on these more robust cnidarians. There appears to be a single nerve net and a single muscle sheet under the epithelium at either boundary of the mesogloea. In *Actinia* this nerve net in the peristome appears to be divided into a superficial and a deeper layer. Communication between the two layers occurs at the pharynx, where the layers meet, and probably through pores called *cinclides* in those species which have them. Pantin (1952) points out that a number of reflex systems are clearly differentiated in Anthozoa. Three of these include a through-conduction reflex system with emphasis on motor response; a local reflex system in the disc; and an action system in the column generalized for a number of functions. The complexity of this relatively simple nervous system is shown by the evident coordination of the various systems in the anthozoan. Robson demonstrated a pacemaker system in the sea anemone, *Stomphia*, that initiated the parieto-basilar muscle ac-

tions of rhythmic swimming activity. This pacemaker is located in the middle third of the column wall. Passano points out that hydromedusae have rhythmic activity regulated by pacemakers, while scyphomedusae do not. Josephson studied pacemaker coordination in the hydroid *Tubularia*.

In the Scyphozoa, Horridge showed that the nerve net of *Aurelia* ephyra and (in earlier work) adults is a double synaptic reticulum acting like a continuous net. Mackie (1963) showed the functional separation of two conduction routes associated with swimming forward or backward respectively in the nectophores of siphonophores. This same author in 1965 demonstrated occurrence of conduction in nerve-free epithelium in this same hydrozoan group.

Noncellular elements distinctive for Cnidaria are the *nematocysts,* or so-called stinging or nettle cells. Actually they are not cells, but *organoids* produced by cells called cnidoblasts. The root, cnido-, means nettle and is the source of the phylum name. Nematocysts tend to be ovoid or flask-shaped capsules, each containing a coiled hollow filament attached to the capsule at one end. Upon adequate stimulation, these filaments are eversibly and explosively discharged through the external end of the capsule.

Cnidoblasts arise from interstitial cells, which are undifferentiated wandering cells occurring in the epithelium. The cnidoblasts carrying the developing nematocysts are oriented ultimately in the surface epithelium at a suitable site. It was previously thought that nematocysts originated at points far removed from their definitive functional site and that they entered entodermal cells prior to a sojourn in the gastrovascular cavity, from which they were picked up by pseudopodia of the gastrodermis and delivered to the tentacles. More recent investigations indicate their origin in loci near the base of the tentacles, at least in some coelenterates.

Chapman and Tilney in studies illustrated by beautiful electromicrograms have shown that the hydra nematocyst capsule is enclosed in a stockade of rodlike structures, and that the capsule has an operculum and is provided with a trigger bristle called a *cnidocil*. The cnidocil in cross section has a core surrounded by nine fibrils, suggesting a similarity to a flagellum. Westfall reports on nematocysts in the sea anemone, *Metridium*. The trigger bristle in these animals actually is a flagellum, and three flaps occur instead of an operculum. In addition the capsule is supported by fibrous bands instead of rods. A special type of nematocyst in *Metridium* and other Anthozoa is called *spirocyst*. It differs from typical nematocysts in having a single-walled capsule and no flagellum or cnidocil.

The cnidocil or the anthozoan flagellum associated with nematocysts suggests mechanical discharge, but this is not the sole factor. For some nematocysts, chemical stimulation due to the presence of food activates the stinging cell or lowers its mechanical threshold, thereby increasing the efficiency of these food-procuring nematocysts. While this suggests that nematocysts are independent effectors, Lentz and Barrnett found nerve-cell processes in close association with the base of cnidoblasts, and Westfall points out the probability that spirocysts are under the influence of the nervous system. Another factor which suggests at least an inhibitory effect of the nervous system is that nematocysts which respond to food stimuli, fail to

Fig. 5-5 Diagram of stenotele type of nematocyst with cnidoblast. (a) Undischarged; (b) discharged, but not released from cnidoblast. Greatly modified, principally after Schulze 1917 and after Schneider 1890.

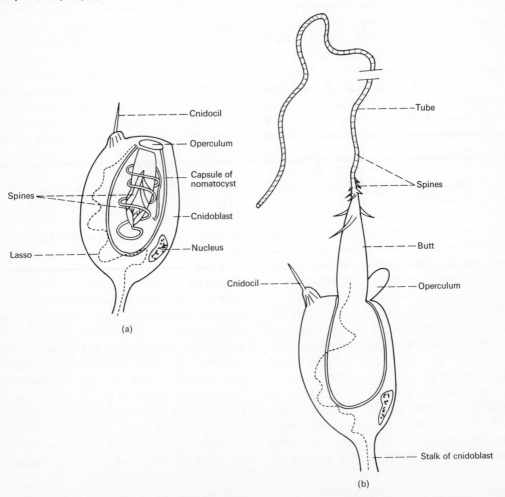

(a)

(b)

do so when the coelenterate is satiated with food.

Seventeen kinds of nematocysts have been described, and their distribution among coelenterates is a taxonomic aid. Four kinds occur in hydras. *Desmonemes* or volvents coil or spiral around available projections on the potential prey. *Stenoteles* or penetrants (Fig. 5-5) act by piercing with an accompanying discharge of toxic substances. Two types of *isorhizas* or glutinants, upon discharge by mechanical stimulation, adhere to smooth surfaces and apparently provide purchase for the tentacles in locomotion.

As protective, anchoring, or food-procuring devices, nematocysts are particularly abundant on tentacles and, in many polyps, around the oral pole. In Anthozoa and some Scyphozoa they are often abundant on special filaments and on the modified edges of mesenteries within the gastrovascular cavity.

HYDROZOA

In the class Hydrozoa the phenomena of metagenesis and polymorphism are well illustrated, but some representatives are restricted to a polypoid structure (*Hydra*) and others (some Trachylina) have only a medusoid form. The polyp or hydranth of a solitary hydrozoan possesses a basal plate or pedal disc provided with adhesive glands for intermittent attachment to the substrate. In some forms this adhesive disc is at the end of a stalk. At the free end of the stalk, or continuous with the pedal disc in stalkless forms, the hydranth occurs as a vaselike or cup-shaped body enclosing the gastrovascular cavity by a wall of two cellular layers: the inner gastrodermis or entoderm and the outer ectoderm. Terminally the gastrovascular cavity or enteron opens by a mouth at the end of a more or less expansible hypostome or pharynx. Tentacles primitively are distributed irregularly over the hydranth surface, as in the brackish or fresh-water colonial *Cordylophora* or the marine, *Podo-*

coryne (Fig. 5-6). In most Hydrozoa the tentacles have a regular distribution which may involve an aboral ring series at the base of the hydranth, and a second more distal or oral ring around the mouth as in *Tubularia* (Fig.5-7), or the tentacles may be reduced to a single ring at the hypostome base as in the familiar *Hydra* and *Obelia*.

Fig. 5-6 *Podocoryne.* Portion of a colony showing irregular distribution of tentacles on the hydranth with a gonophore containing a medusa. Modified from Hertwig (after Agassiz) *A Manual of Zoology* (translated and edited by J. S. Kingsley) 1902, Holt, Rinehart and Winston, Inc.

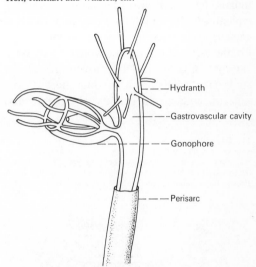

Fig. 5-7 Diagram of *Tubularia* hydroid.

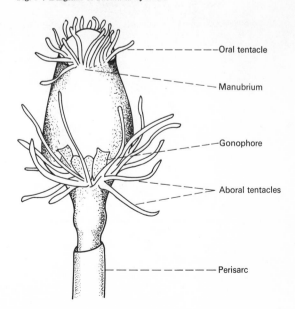

As characteristic of all cnidarians, Hydrozoa are carnivorous. Hydras are known to feed on many different kinds of living animals. These include annelid and nematode worms, crustacea, arachnids, insect larvae, and even small vertebrates such as newly hatched fish or tadpoles. Food is captured when it comes in contact with tentacles and nematocysts and is engulfed through the expansible pharynx. At first digestion is extracellular in the enteron. Later, particles are engulfed by pseudopodial action of lining cells. The mouth also functions for egestion of unusable material. The vascular function of the gastrovascular cavity is accomplished by the beating of flagella which occur on a number of cells, and by movements of the hydranth, which has a stirring effect on the enteron contents in solitary Hydrozoa, and on distribution through the stalk enteron to nonfeeding elements in colonial species. The nerve net, already discussed, has some tendency to concentrate into radial cords which join a nerve ring at the bell margin in medusoid forms. Statocysts and ocelli are special sense organs occurring on the bell margin.

Reproduction in Hydrozoa occurs both sexually and asexually. While both of these occur in the familiar *Hydra,* this is not considered to be primitive. In the colonial *Obelia,* the body is protected by a secreted surface layer, the perisarc. The perisarc expanded as a cup around a hydranth is here called hydrotheca. A more cylindrical covering of the same origin around a *blastostyle* is the gonotheca. In *Obelia* the blastostyle produces medusa buds asexually. Hydromedusae typically have a velum, reduced however in *Obelia.* In this genus, free-swimming medusae occur with gonads on the radial canals. Fertilization occurs in sea water, and development proceeds through a ciliated planula (Fig. 5-8), which becomes sessile to give rise to a polyp which further multiplies by branching.

In the athecate colonial hydroid, *Tubularia,* the asexual buds (gonophores) develop as hollow stalks from the hydranth between oral and aboral tentacles. Each gonophore develops a medusa devoid of tentacles, which remains attached. Sexes are separate, and

Fig. 5-8 Section through *Aurelia* planula, *ap*, aboral pole; *en*, entoderm; *et*, ectoderm; *gv*, gastrovascular cavity; *m*, mesolamella; *mo*, mouth; *n*, cell nuclei; *op*, oral pole; *yg*, yolk granules. After Waterman (after Hein), *Selected Invertebrate Types*, 1950 (F. A. Brown, Jr., ed.) courtesy of John Wiley & Sons, Inc.

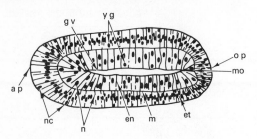

Fig. 5-9 Diagram of *Tubularia* gonophore with developing larvae. Adapted from various sources.

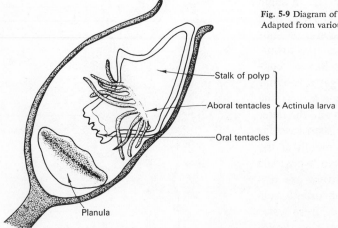

within the female medusa after fertilization, development occurs, including planula and an advanced larval type called *actinula* (Fig. 5-9). This larva bears more resemblance to a small polyp with a single ring of tentacles than it does to a medusa. In some of the Trachylina, a group generally characterized by an inconspicuous or absent polyp stage, the life cycle involves a planula and an actinula which metamorphoses to a medusa. In some of the Limnomedusae, including *Gonionemus* and the fresh-water jellyfish, *Craspedacusta sowerbii* (Fig. 5-10), the planulae become sessile and form polyps which reproduce by branching into colonies. Buds separate to form the genesis of new colonies, and medusae bud directly from the polyps. The actinula, with its propensity for budding either polyps or medusae, supports the thesis that the medusa was the primitive body form in Hydrozoa.

Craspedacusta sowerbii was discovered in 1880 in a botanical tank of the Royal Botanical Gardens at Kew in London. This tank had been planted with water lilies brought from Brazil. *Craspedacusta* has been found since in numerous other places in Europe and other continents. In the United States it has been described from most states east of the Rocky Mountains as well as in the western coastal states. This jellyfish, which averages between one and two centimeters in diameter, has a sporadic, apparently discontinuous existence in both natural and artificial bodies of water and is found most frequently in late summer. Its life cycle alternates with an inconspicuous, nontentacled hydroid stage that initially was described as the genus *Microhydra ryderi,* until elucidation of the life cycle showed it to be the branching hydroid stage of *Craspedacusta*.

The order Siphonophora deserves special mention. These colonial floating or swimming colonies exhibit the highest degree of polymorphism among Cnidaria, a subject mentioned earlier. Nectophores are able to pulsate in some siphonophores to effect some locomotion as in *Physalia*. Most siphono-

phores have an inverted medusoid member modified to form a float, and change of gas content within this pneumatophore allows some vertical change, but neither *Physalia,* the Portuguese man-of-war, nor the more aberrant *Velella,* known as the by-the-wind-sailor, is able to do so. The *Velella* float is a flattened disc containing concentric chitinous air chambers. Across the upper surface of the disc a translucent purple sail stands erect. This cnidarian is propelled by wind action. *Physalia,* which is typically a bluish color, has an elongate balloon-shaped float surmounted by a crest. Glands produce gas to fill the float.

These large siphonophores are dangerous to man. *Physalia* may have a float nearly a foot long with tentacles trailing as much as forty feet. Water extracts of portions of these tentacles can produce anaesthesia and death in small animals. Nematocyst stings of this species can send a strong man to the hospital in great pain. Although *Physalia* is more common in warmer waters, in some years it has appeared in sufficient numbers on the

Fig. 5-10 *Craspedacusta.* (a) Diagrammatic representation of medusa; (b) hydroid with developing medusa bud. Adapted from Payne 1924 and from Reisinger 1957.

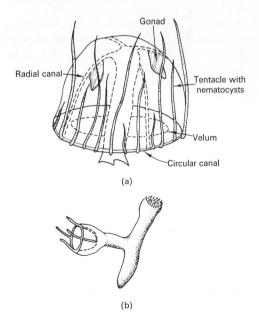

(a)

(b)

New York and New Jersey coasts to require closing of beaches.

Symbiotic and commensal relationships frequently involve Cnidaria. One of the most interesting is that of a small fish, *Nomeus gronovii,* which is commonly found among the trailing tentacles of *Physalia* in the Gulf of Mexico. *Nomeus,* which appears to be immune to these nematocyst toxins, is not only protected from enemies, but may act as a decoy to bring other fish into contact with the tentacles, and both partners profit from this food supply. *Nomeus,* however, is not adverse to taking nips of tentacles as a food supplement.

Classification of Hydrozoa

Class I Hydrozoa Both polyp (hydranth) and medusa body forms occur. The usually small medusae are craspedote (i.e., provided with a velum). The gastrovascular cavity of the polyp is nonseptate and lacks nematocysts. The mesogloea is acellular.

Order 1 Anthomedusae (Gymnoblastea) In these Hydrozoa no theca incloses either hydranth or gonophore. Medusae are elongate on the oral-aboral axis or lacking. *Hydra, Bougainvillia, Cordylophora, Tubularia, Podocoryne.*

Order 2 Leptomedusae (Calyptoblastea) Both hydranths and gonophores possess thecae. Medusae are usually somewhat flattened. *Obelia, Sertularia.*

Order 3 Limnomedusae The polyps are reduced and sessile, and some are without tentacles. Tentacles on the medusae are hollow and may be provided with suckers; additional stalked suckers are sometimes present. The radial canals are four or six in number and are sometimes branched. *Gonionemus, Craspedacusta, Proboscidactyla, Limnocnida.*

Order 4 Trachylina The polyp is reduced or absent. Tentacles often arise from the exumbrella instead of the medusa rim. *Geryonia, Liriope, Rhopalonema.*

Order 5 Hydrocorallina The minute polyps are dimorphic, sessile, and colonial and protrude through pores in an extensive calcareous skeleton. Medusae are minute or absent. *Mille-pora, Stylaster, Stylantheca, Allopora, Astylus.*

Order 6 Siphonophora These are highly developed polymorphic floating colonies. The atypical medusae are usually attached. *Physalia, Velella.* (Because of unusual structure, *Velella* is some times placed in a separate order.)

SCYPHOZOA

This class generally is recognized for its medusoid characteristics. These medusae lack a velum; the enteron develops four lateral pouches within which occur the gonads and nematocyst-bearing gastric filaments. Four peristomial pits indent into the subumbrella. The mesogloea is an extensive layer and contains cells indicative of the triploblastic nature of these Cnidaria.

The gastrovascular cavity opens from the subumbrellar side by a four-cornered mouth situated at the end of an endodermally lined prolongation: the *gullet* or *manubrium.* The manubrium opens into a centrally placed stomach, from which four radial gastric pouches protrude laterally. The radial canals arising from the gastrovascular cavity join at a peripheral ring canal. In *Aurelia,* the four perradial canals lie on the same radii as the gastric pouches and branch before reaching the ring canal (Fig. 5-11). In each quadrant between adjacent perradial canals there is a branched interradial canal, and between each interradial and perradial canal there is an unbranched adradial canal. The flagellated cells of the gastrodermis in the canals act to create an outgoing current of digested products in the eight adradial canals, and an ingoing current in the branched canals. Digestion is extracellular, aided by glands in the gastric filaments, and intracellular as available materials are absorbed by the gastrodermis.

The scyphozoan nervous system is a subumbrellar plexus that appears to be a nonpolarized synaptic system behaving like a nerve net. This network is not condensed into a nerve ring at the rim of the bell, but is concentrated into eight rhopalial ganglia into which the perradial and interradial canals project. A *rhopalium* (Fig. 5-12) is a concentration of sense organs, including a reduced tentacle (*tentaculocyst*) functioning for equilibrium, an ocellus, and two sensory pits of presumed olfactory nature. Discharge of nematocysts is due not to the nerve net, apparently, but to an intrinsic receptor-effector system within the individual nematocyst.

The best-known life cycles are in the order Semaeostomeae. In *Aurelia,* and most other genera of this order, the sexes are separate. The gonads occur in the floor of the gastric pouches and fertilization occurs in this vicinity, sperm being drawn in through the manubrium. The eggs undergo early development in recesses among the fringes of the oral arms. Eventually, a planula is freed. This larva attaches at one end and modifies into a polyplike stage called a *hydratuba* or

Fig. 5-11 Subumbrellar view of young *Aurelia,* showing circulation in the radial canals. After Schechter 1959, courtesy of Prentice-Hall, Inc.

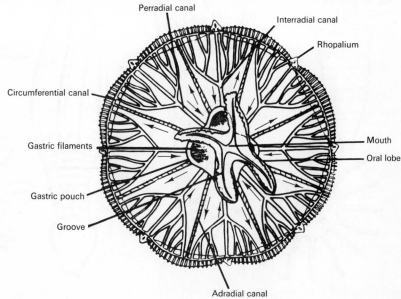

Fig. 5-12 Diagram to show tentaculocyst or rhopalium on a section of the umbrellar margin. After Schechter 1959, courtesy of Prentice-Hall, Inc.

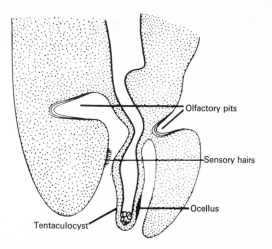

Fig. 5-13 Stages in the life history of *Aurelia*. Top row shows growth of planula to scyphistoma and subsequent strobilation in later stages below. An oral view of scyphistoma is shown in the lower left and two ephyrae in lower right. After Hertwig (from Leuckart), *A Manual of Zoology* (translated and edited by J. S. Kingsley) 1902, Holt, Rinehart & Winston, Inc.

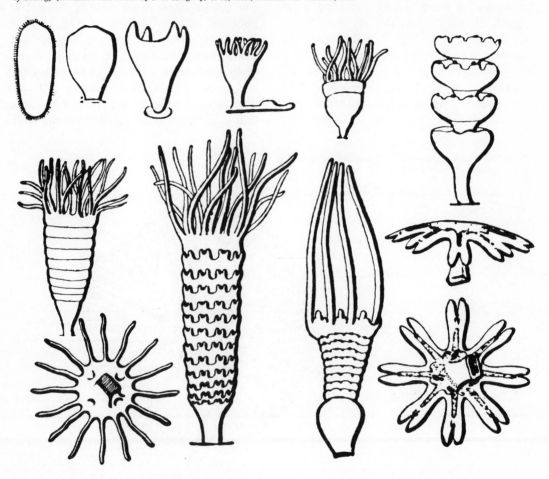

Fig. 5-14 Diagrams of the arrangement of primary mesenteries or septa in Anthozoa. Figures (a) and (b) represent the octamerous arrangements in subclass Alcyonaria. The more primitive condition is illustrated in (a) in which there is a pair of directive mesenteries (distinguished by location of the muscle bands) at either end of the pharynx. In (c), the hexamerous condition characteristic of subclass Zooantharia is illustrated. On the directives the muscle bands are drawn in solidly. Adapted from various sources.

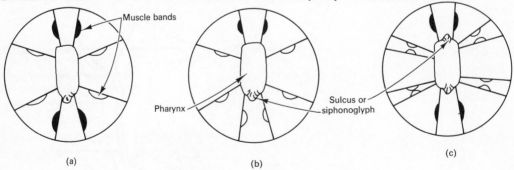

scyphistoma (Fig. 5-13). Other scyphistoma may bud from the base of the hydratuba. In the following late-winter season, each scyphistoma develops transverse constrictions, either singly or in series. In the latter case, this kind of segmentation is termed *strobilation*. Each segment is a developing larva called an *ephyra*. The terminal scyphistome tentacles disappear. Eight lobes develop from the rim of the ephyra, each bearing a rhopalium. With development, the series of ephyra is held intact by muscle strands between successive larvae. Eventually these strands break to free the ephyra one at a time. The ephyra develop into typical medusae by filling in the notches between the lobes. These notches are adradial in position. In some Scyphozoa, the planula metamorphoses to an ephyra with the development of tentacles, at which stage it bears some resemblance to an actinula.

Classification of the Scyphozoa

Class II Scyphozoa These acraspedote (velum is absent) medusae are typically free-swimming. They have a marked tetraradiate symmetry and possess tentacles around the mouth. The polyp generation is reduced or absent. Scyphozoa are exclusively marine.

Order 1 Stauromedusae These are vase-shaped medusae with a fluted margin typically bearing eight multitentacled lobes. These animals are attached by an adhesive disc, usually at the end of an aboral stalk. *Lucernaria, Haliclytus.*

Order 2 Cubomedusae These cube-shaped medusae are free-swimming. The bell margin turns inward to form a false velum. *Carybdea.*

Order 3 Coronatae The medusa bell has a circumferential groove separating a scalloped margin bearing tentacles. *Linuche, Nausithoe.*

Order 4 Semaeostomeae The mouth is prolonged as four fringed lobes. Tentacles are marginal or extending into the subumbrella as V-shaped groups. *Pelagia, Aurelia, Cyanea.*

Order 5 Rhizostomae The mouth is obliterated, but secondary openings occur on the four fused oral lobes. Tentacles are absent. *Cassiopeia, Rhizostoma.*

ANTHOZOA

The body form of Anthozoa is restricted to the polyp type, but it differs from the polypoid structure in the Hydrozoa by the presence of an ectodermally lined gullet or stomodaeum and by the presence of septa or mesenteries growing radially from the body wall. Some or all of these septa join the stomodaeal invagination. The elongate mouth opens in the middle of the tentacled oral disc. The gullet or stomodaeum also tends to be oval in cross section. Frequently the wall is thrown into folds. Commonly, one or both of the narrow ends is developed as a flagellated groove. Such a groove is called a *siphonoglyph* or *sulcus*. Lesser flagella are common on most of the gullet surface. The gullet opens into the gastrovascular cavity, and below this point the septa are free along their inner borders.

The Anthozoa are divided into two subclasses. The Alcyonaria are octamerous, with a single siphonoglyph which as a convenience is called ventral (Fig. 5-14). The longitudinal retractor muscle bands are on the surfaces of the septa facing the siphonoglyph. The subclass Zoantharia are typically hexamerous, usually have siphonoglyphs visible externally at one or both ends of the mouth, and the retractor muscles on those septa abutting on siphonoglyphs lie on the outer or distal face of those mesenteries. The septa always occur in a mirror-image relationship on either side of the long axis of the gullet, so that in keeping with the dorsoventral convenience, they appear as bilaterally symmetrical. The paired septa which join the narrow ends of the gullet are called directives, whether or not a siphonoglyph is present. Since the retractor muscles are on the outside of the directives (Fig. 5-14), these muscles on the so-called ventral directives face away from, rather than toward the ventral siphonoglyph, in contrast with the orientation in Alcyonaria. *Metridium* has a septal pattern characteristic of Zoantharia.

In addition to the two pairs of directives, there are four other pairs of septa reaching the stomodaeum (i.e., primary mesenteries). In the space between each two primary pairs, a secondary pair extend from the body wall. Eventually these may be flanked by smaller pairs of tertiaries, and quarternaries may finally develop lateral to each pair of tertiaries. Except for the directives as already stated, the retractor muscles face each other on each pair of mesenteries.

Digestion in the Anthozoa is both extracellular and intracellular. In the Alcyonaria, the so-called dorsal septa of the gastrovascular cavity subserve a vascular function by the beating of their flagella. The other septa have digestive glands along their lower edges which fail to reach the aboral end of the enteron. In the sea anemones of subclass Zoantharia (Fig. 5-15) the free inner edges of the septa carry a rod or piping of glandular cells and nematocysts, and in the region just aboral to the inner end of the stomodaeum the central glandular piping is flanked by two flagellated ridges with circulatory function. Some Zoantharia feed exclusively by ciliary action of tentacles, oral disc, and stomodaeal lining. All Anthozoa are carnivorous.

The nervous system of Anthozoa, in keeping with the sessile mode of life, is most evident at the active end of the polyp and near the septal bands of muscle. It appears to be an unpolarized synaptic plexus.

Gonads in Anthozoa are located on the septa. Fertilization occurs in the gastrovascular cavity or in sea water, and in some forms the young develop within the body of the parent to a planula or a tentaculate stage. Externally developing young become ciliated planulae, and anemone larvae modify to a free-swimming, polyplike stage. Tentacles appear after attachment. Some Anthozoa are hermaphroditic. Cleavage in Cnidaria is holoblastic and a hollow blastula is formed. Gastrulation is by polar ingression or migration of cells in Hydrozoa, but emboly or

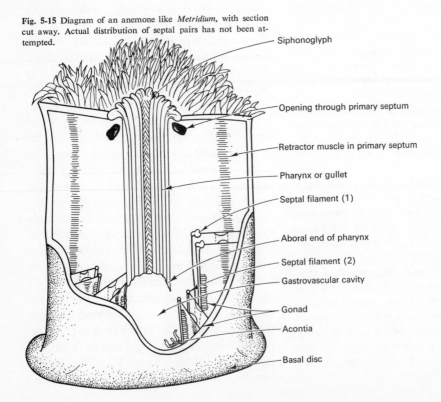

Fig. 5-15 Diagram of an anemone like *Metridium*, with section cut away. Actual distribution of septal pairs has not been attempted.

Siphonoglyph

Opening through primary septum

Retractor muscle in primary septum

Pharynx or gullet

Septal filament (1)

Aboral end of pharynx

Septal filament (2)

Gastrovascular cavity

Gonad

Acontia

Basal disc

invagination appears in the other two classes. A planula, which is sometimes hollow, is characteristic of all classes.

The order Madreporaria (Scleractinia) in Class Zoantharia constitutes the true corals. It is this group that is responsible for the formation of coral reefs and atolls. There are about 500 described genera in this order, containing about 2,500 Recent species. At least twice this number of fossil species are known, of which many belong in the Order Rugosa (Tetracoralla), known from the Ordovician Period throughout most of the Paleozoic Era. The Rugosa tend to have a conical or cylindrical shape, and the outer calcareous wall is variously wrinkled or rugose. Six asymmetrically placed primary septa occur in the early development. Four of these form a kind of template of irregular quadrants in which subsequent major septa develop into four areas. For an account of the Rugosa, paleontological sources should be consulted.

Living corals are produced by hexamerous polyps. The skeleton is primarily calcium carbonate accumulated by an unknown secretory process on the ectodermal surface at the aboral end of the polyp. On the young polyp, the first external skeleton formed is a basal plate. As the young polyp elongates, the calcareous plate thickens and also extends upward at the periphery to form a cup called the *prototheca*. The prototheca (Fig. 5-16) early shows ridges radiating from its center, where the calcium carbonate accumulates to form a central rod or *columella*. These ridges alternate with the mesenteries or fleshy septa of the coral polyp, and they are called *sclerosepta*. With continued growth, the young skeleton is composed of six sclerosepta radiating from the columella to the outer wall or theca. The sclerosepta may continue growth external to the theca with the formation of a new circular wall called *epitheca*, and additional sclerosepta may arise in the spaces between primary and secondary mesenteries of the polyp. Coral polyps may reproduce asexually by budding within the area of the oral disc, or by budding in fleshy areas between adjacent oral discs. The living portion of the coral is represented by the peripheral layer of polyps, and the entire

Fig. 5-16 Development of coral. In (a) coral is shown in black; in (b) coral is white and the mesogloea is black. *a*, theca; *b*, mesenteries; *c*, costa; *d*, basal plate; *f*, sclerosepta; *r*, directives; and *s*, gullet. From Hertwig, *A Manual of Zoology* (translated and edited by J. S. Kingsley) 1902, Holt, Rinehart & Winston, Inc.

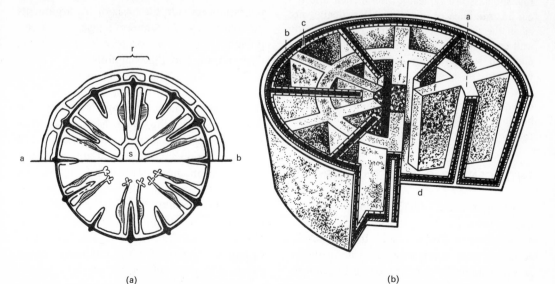

(a)   (b)

skeleton of the coral whether solitary or colonial is the *corallum*. Its structure serves as the basis of classification. The Porosa group have the various calcareous walls perforated; the Aporosa lack such perforations, and the fungian corals do not develop an epitheca so that the sclerosepta protrude as sinuous lamellate ridges.

Classification of the Anthozoa

Class III Anthozoa   These marine Cnidaria are solitary or colonial polypoid forms with hollow tentacles on an oral disc. The opening to the septate gastrovascular cavity is through a stomodaeum (ectodermally lined gullet). Gonads are on the gastrovascular septa, which have nematocyst-bearing free edges.

SUBCLASS 1 ALCYONARIA   The distinctive feature of this group is the presence of eight pinnately branched tentacles and the presence of eight septa or mesenteries radially disposed and connecting the body wall and stomodaeum. The Alcyonaria are colonial forms, with an internal skeleton composed of separate spicules or tubular aggregates. This subclass is commonly divided into six orders and includes *Alcyonium,* one of the soft corals; *Tubipora,* the organpipe coral; and *Corallium,* the red coral of jewelry.

SUBCLASS 2 ZOANTHARIA   The tentacles in this subclass are typically unbranched and occur in multiples of six. Characteristically, not all of the radial septa projecting from the body wall connect with the stomodaeum. Both colonial and solitary forms occur. The skeleton, when present, is never limited to isolated spicules. Usually this subclass is divided into five orders and includes sea anemones and reef-building corals. *Metridium, Edwardsia, Astrangia, Fungia, Meandra.*

PHYLOGENETIC CONSIDERATIONS

All three classes of Cnidaria have recognized ancestors dating from the Lower or Mid-Cambrian Periods, and it is generally accepted that cnidarians are a primitive group structurally near the dawn of eumeta-zoan phylogeny. Of course it must be recognized that evolution was in progress prior to the Cambrian with its cnidarian record. Despite the limitations, hypotheses have been advanced attempting to explain the relationships of the various classes to each other, and to other phyla. Hadži's interpretation of the compartmentalization theory (see Chapter 3) derives Cnidaria from bilateral flatworms in an anthozoan-scyphozoan-hydrozoan sequence. The older and more widely accepted theory emphasizes radial symmetry leading from colonial flagellates to hydrozoans, which in turn gave rise to the other two classes. The latter sequence seems more probable at present.

Two morphological types (polyp and medusa) occur in the Hydrozoa. The older view considered the polyp to be the original type form; but the more generally accepted view considers the motile, dioecious medusa to be nearer the ancestral type. Examination of cnidarian life cycles revealed the common presence of a ciliated planula. This larval type is not restricted to the Cnidaria, but appears also in the divergent Porifera, as well as in Ctenophora and Platyhelminthes. However, Greenberg contends that the planula represents an environmental response of the developing embryo rather than indicating homology. On the basis of his arguments on symmetry, Greenberg suggests a polyphyletic origin from protozoa for Cnidaria, Ctenophora, and Platyhelminthes.

Within the Cnidaria, the Anthozoa are restricted to a polyp form, but in the other two classes a medusoid stage is common or dominant in the life cycle. Many Hydrozoa have a regular alternation between the sexually produced polyp and the asexually produced medusa. In many hydrozoan species the planula changes to a second larval type, the *actinula,* with development of tentacles. The actinula bears some resemblance to a small polyp. The Trachylina is a hydrozoan group primarily medusoid with a polyp stage reduced or absent. The occurrence of two kinds of nematocysts in Trachylina, but not in the same suborder, is indicative that two divergent branches exist. In the Trachylina, medusae arise by budding of the actinula. In the Limnomedusae, medusae are budded off from a primitive polyp which itself can multiply to form a small colony of polyps. In *Tubularia,* we have seen the actinula developing within an attached medusa from which it is eventually freed to produce a new colonial polyp. The actinula larva appears to be close to the stem-form which gave rise to the two classes (Hydrozoa and Anthozoa) which are predominately or completely polyploid and even more closely related to the medusoid Scyphozoa, particularly if this stem-form was itself medusoid. Rees at a symposium on cnidarian evolution stated that the ancestral form was a fertile actinula. It should be stated that Berrill pointed out earlier that there is no evidence that the actinula was ever an adult form. He finds a correlation between egg size and degree of polar organization and the appearance of an actinula stage, thereby suggesting a convergence or parallel evolution resulting from the developmental situation.

A major problem in the anthozoan corals exists for the origin of the Madreporaria. The fossil record of this group dates from the middle Triassic, while the Rugosa (Tetracoralla) did not exist after the mid-Permian. If the former group descended from the latter, an unknown late Permian form must have bridged the gap. Another hypothesis suggests a much earlier common origin, based on the supposition that Paleozoic Madreporaria had not evolved a recognizable skeleton.

REFERENCES

Allman, G. J., Monograph of the gymnoblastic or tubularian hydroids. Ray Society, 1872.

Berrill, N. J., Development and medusa-bud formation in the Hydromedusae. Quart. Rev. Biol., 25:292, 1950.

Chapman, G. B., and L. G. Tilney, Cytological studies of the nematocysts of *Hydra.* J. Biophys. Biochem. Cytol., 5: Part I 69-78; Part II 79-84; 1959.

Crowell, S., and Editorial Board (eds.), Behavioral physiology of Coelenterates. Amer. Zoologist, Vol. V, No. 3, 1965.

Garstang, W., The morphology and relations of the Siphonophora. Quart. J. Microsc. Sci., 87:103, 1946.

Greenberg, M. J., Ancestors, embryos, and symmetry. Syst. Zool., 8:212, 1959.

Hand, C., On the origin and phylogeny of the Coelenterates. Syst. Zool., 8:191, 1959.

Hill, Dorothy, Rugosa (pp. 233-324). *In* (R. C. Moore, ed.) Treatise on invertebrate paleontology, Part F, Coelenterata. Lawrence, Kansas: U. of Kansas and the Geol. Soc. Amer., 1956.

Horridge, G. A., The nervous system of the ephyra larva of *Aurelia aurita.* Quart. J. Microsc. Sci., 97:59, 1956.

Hyman, L. H., Phylum Cnidaria (pp. 365-661). *In* The invertebrates: Protozoa through Ctenophora, Vol. I. New York: McGraw, 1940.

———, Phylum Cnidaria (pp. 718-731). *In* The invertebrates: smaller coelomate groups, Vol. V. New York: McGraw, 1959.

Josephson, R. K., The coordination of potential pacemakers in the hydroid *Tubularia.* Amer. Zool., 5:483, 1965.

Leghiss, S., Nervous organization and the problem of the synapse in *Actinia equina.* Amer. Zool., 5:411, 1965.

Lenhoff, H. M., Activation of the feeding reflex in *Hydra littoralis* (pp. 203-229). *In*

(Lenhoff and Loomis, eds.) The biology of *Hydra*. Coral Gables, Florida: U. of Miami, 1961.

Lentz, T. L., and R. J. Barrnett, Fine structure of the nervous system of *Hydra*. Amer. Zool., 5:341, 1965.

Mackie, G. O., Analysis of locomotion in a siphonophore colony. Proc. Roy. Soc. London (B), 159:366, 1964.

———, Conduction in the nerve-free epithelia of siphonophores. Amer. Zool., 5:439, 1965.

MacGinitie, G. E., and N. MacGinitie, Coelenterata (pp. 117-143). *In* Natural history of marine animals. New York: McGraw, 1949.

Pantin, C. F. A., Behavior patterns in lower invertebrates. Symposia Soc. Exp. Biol., No. IV. New York: Academic, 1950.

———, The elementary nervous system. Proc. Roy. Soc. London (B), 140:147, 1952.

———, Capabilities of the coelenterate behavior machine. Amer. Zool., 5:581, 1965.

Passano, L. M., Pacemakers and activity patterns in medusae: Homage to Romanes. Amer. Zool., 5:465, 1965.

Payne, Fernandus, A study of the fresh-water medusa, *Craspedacusta ryderi*. J. Morphol., 38:387, 1924.

Pennak, R. W., Coelenterata (pp. 98-113). *In* Fresh-water invertebrates of the United States. New York: Ronald, 1953.

Rees, W. J., Evolutionary trends in the classification of capitate hydroids and medusae.

Bull. Brit. Mus. (Nat. Hist.) Zool., 4:1, 1957.

———, Cnidaria and their evolution. Nature, 207 (4995):359, 1965.

Reisinger, E., Zur Entwicklungs geschichte und Entwicklungs mechanik von *Craspedacusta* (Hydrozoa, Limnotrachylina). Zeitsch. für Morph. u. Ökol. Tiere Bd 45:656-698, 1957.

Robson, E. A., The swimming response and its pacemaker system in the anemone, *Stomphia coccinea*. J. Exp. Biol., 38:685, 1961.

Schneider, K. C., Histologie von *Hydra fusca* mit besonderer Berüchsichtigung des Nervensystem der Hydropolypen. M. Schulze, Arch. f. mik Anat., 35:321, 1890.

Schulze, Q., Neve Bieträge zu einer Monographie der Gattung *Hydra*. Arch. Biontologie, 4:33, 1917.

Shrock, R. R., and W. H. Twenhofel, Phylum coelenterates (pp. 98-179). *In* Principles of invertebrate paleontology (2nd ed.). New York: McGraw, 1953.

Wells, John W., Scleractinia (pp. 328-444). *In* (R. C. Moore, ed.) Treatise on invertebrate paleontology, Part F, Coelenterata. Lawrence, Kansas: U. of Kansas and the Geol. Soc. Amer., 1956.

———, Coral reefs. Mem. Geol. Soc. Amer., 1(67):609, 1957.

Yonge, C. M., The biology of coral reefs (pp. 209-260). *In* (F. S. Russell, ed.) Advances in marine biology. London: Academic, 1963.

6

PHYLUM CTENOPHORA

The typical ctenophoran has a spherical or inverted pear shape, floats or swims feebly in surface waters of the ocean, and displays considerable luminescence. It is transparent, and the outer surface is marked by eight meridional bands which terminate short of either pole, and which are composed of short transverse plates or strips of cilia. The cilia of each plate are fused together and are reminiscent of some of the membranelles among the ciliophoran protoza. The phylum name is derived from these ciliary plates which resemble combs. A pair of retractile tentacles usually occurs on opposite sides of the animal.

The Ctenophora share a number of features with the Cnidaria. The primary symmetry of these groups is radial or biradial and is organized around an oral-aboral axis. The space between the entodermal lining of the gastrovascular cavity and the epidermis contains no body cavity but is filled with a gelatinous material called mesogloea. The gastrovascular cavity has regularly spaced tubular branches lying in the mesogloeal layer. These and other structures indicate a tetramerous division of the original radial symmetry. These groups share with the Parazoa a singular lack of development of organ systems.

Ctenophora are placed in two classes. Most of the eighty-odd species have tentacles and are placed in Class Tentaculata. The order Cydippida are the oval or spherical forms and appear to have maintained a more generalized structure. The characteristic larval stage called the *cydippid larva* is common for members of other orders as well, but the modified adults are variously lobate or flattened.

Classification of the Ctenophora

Class I Tentaculata Tentacles are present.
Order 1 Cydippida These are ovate or spherical animals with a pair of tentacles retractile into sheaths. The meridional and

pharyngeal canals do not communicate orally.

Order 2 Lobata The body is slightly compressed in the tentacular plane and prolonged into lobes orally in the stomodaeal plane. The tentacles lack sheaths. Some of the meridional canals join with the pharyngeal canals orally to communicate by a ring canal.

Order 3 Cestida Extreme elongation of the body in the stomodael plane produces a ribbon-like form. The comb-rows immediately adjacent to the tentacle sheath are rudimentary. Anastomosis of meridional and pharyngeal canals occurs orally.

Order 4 Platyctenea These are greatly modified ctenophores, flattened in the oral-aboral plane to produce creeping forms. Meridional canals are missing. Comb-rows occur in the larva only in most species.

Class II Nuda Ctenophores that are without tentacles.

Order 5 Beroidea These are thimble-shaped animals markedly compressed in the tentacular plane. Pharynx lumen is large, occupying most of the body interior. Meridional canals anastomose through numerous branches.

GENERAL AND SPECIAL FEATURES

The planes of symmetry through the oral-aboral axis need to be recognized. In the Cydippida, two tentacles are characteristic, arising from tentacular sheaths on opposite sides of the animal. The plane (Fig. 6-1) bisecting the tentacle sheaths is called the tentacular, lateral, or transverse plane. The stomodaeum or pharynx is flattened at right angles to the tentacular plane. The long axis of the stomodaeum lies in the stomodaeal, median, or sagittal plane. The comb-rows lie in the quadrants cut by these two planes and are referred to as subtentacular or subsagittal rows, according to the plane to which they are adjacent.

Less typical Tentaculata include the Cestida. In *Cestum veneris* (Venus' girdle), extreme elongation in the stomodaeal plane results in a gelatinous ribbon that may reach a length of over four feet. Hence, the subsagittal comb-rows are very long, while the

Fig. 6-1 Diagrammatic cross-section of cydippid ctenophore through pharynx and tentacular sheaths to show the relationship of the primary planes to the canals and to the gonads. Subsagittal costae are those adjacent to the sagittal plane, and the subtentacular costae are those adjacent to the transverse plane.

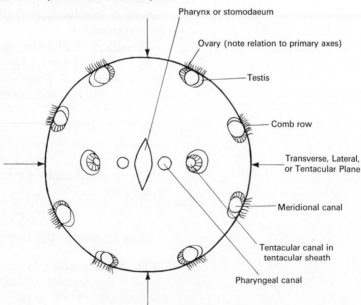

Pharynx or stomodaeum

Ovary (note relation to primary axes)

Testis

Comb row

Transverse, Lateral, or Tentacular Plane

Meridional canal

Tentacular canal in tentacular sheath

Pharyngeal canal

Sagittal, Median, or Stomodaeal Plane

subtentacular comb-rows are reduced. The gastrovascular canals are modified to reach the extremities, with the subsagittal pairs lying aborally, the subtentacular pairs medially, and the pharyngeal canals forking to provide a pair of canals orally in each half of the ribbon. In the order Platyctenea (Fig. 6-2), the animals are orally-aborally flattened. They are creeping in habit. They have comb-rows, a statocyst, and tentacles at least in the cydippid larval stage. The genus *Gastrodes* is parasitic in a tunicate during part of its larval existence. While a parasite, it goes through a metamorphosis which includes a cydippid larval type. When this parasite leaves the host, it changes into a creeping type of organism which is probably the adult. It gives rise to a larval stage that is a typical *planula,* and this is the only known occasion that this cnidarian type of larva appears among the Ctenophora.

The genus *Beroe* is the principal representative of Class Nuda. *Beroe* (Fig. 6-3) is nearly cylindrical, with a slight flattening in the transverse (tentacular) plane. It is characterized by a greatly enlarged pharynx, a reduced mesogloeal layer, no tentacles, and numerous side branches of the meridional gastrovascular canals. At the oral end these canals loop to join the pharyngeal canals.

Food-getting and Digestion

The digestive system of the cydippid ctenophore (Fig. 6-4) opens at the oral sur-

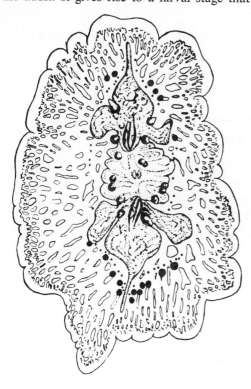

Fig. 6-2 *Coeloplana* adult. After Van Cleave (redrawn from Komai) 1931, courtesy of the McGraw-Hill Book Company.

Fig. 6-3 (a) Adult *Beroe* and (b) polar view to show flattening. 1, branched papillae of polar fields; 2, meridional canals; 3, pharyngeal canal; 4, canal along mouth rim; 5, mouth. After Mayer, from Hyman, Vol. I, 1940, courtesy of the McGraw-Hill Book Company.

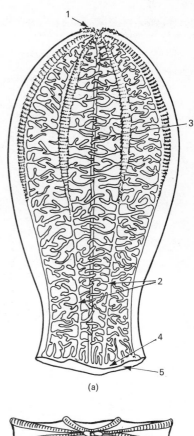

(a)

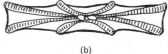

(b)

face into the stomodaeum or pharynx, which is the physiological stomach. Partly digested food moves aborally into a chamber called the stomach for distribution to the various canals. Aborally this morphological stomach continues as the aboral or infundibular canal to the aboral pole where tetramerous division results in four small canals, two of which open to the exterior through anal pores and function in egestion. On either side of the stomach in the tentacular plane a large perradial canal passes horizontally. It gives rise to two interradial canals before turning orally as the tentacular canal to end blindly in the tentacle sheath. The interradial canals bifurcate to form adradial canals, two of which appear in each quadrant. Each of the eight adradial canals continues to join a meridional

canal which lies in each costa just beneath the respective comb-row. From the oral side of the stomach, a pair of blind pharyngeal (stomodaeal) canals proceeds orally in the tentacular plane along either side of the pharynx.

All of the Ctenophora are carnivorous and eat a variety of plankton organisms. These are caught by the extended tentacles (in those which have them) which are armed with colloblasts (adhesive or lasso cells). Prey, sticking to these colloblasts, is transferred to the mouth. In the order Lobata, *Leucothea,* which has reduced nonextensile tentacles, captures food by the aid of extensile surface papillae equipped with sticky suckers. In related species, food is caught in surface mucus and passed along by short

Fig. 6-4 Cydippid ctenophore with aboral end tilted forward. Comb-rows and tentacle are shown on the right, meridional canals are on the left, and the gastrovascular system is cross-hatched.

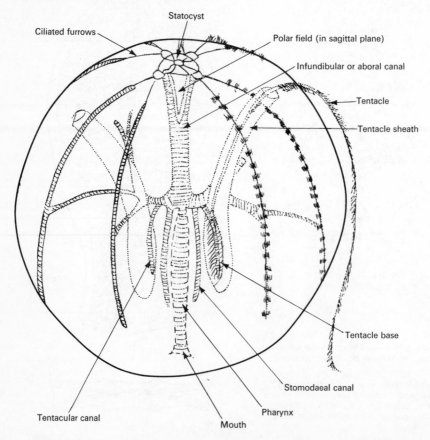

Statocyst

Ciliated furrows

Polar field (in sagittal plane)

Infundibular or aboral canal

Tentacle

Tentacle sheath

Tentacle base

Stomodaeal canal

Tentacular canal

Pharynx

Mouth

tentacles toward the mouth. Extracellular digestion occurs mainly in the pharynx. Material is moved to the meridional canals of the gastrovascular system principally by ciliary action. Food is picked up by some of the cells for intracellular digestion, while indigestible material is thrown off through the mouth or anal pores.

Nervous System and Sense Organs

The nervous system is similar to that of the Cnidaria. It is a diffuse plexus with no real centralization and no concentration into ganglia. It is reported to be synaptic. The network is more concentrated immediately beneath the comb-rows and under the ciliated furrows leading to the statocyst. Some concentration of the plexus also occurs around the mouth.

The aboral *statocyst* or apical organ (Fig. 6-5) functions to coordinate the beat of the comb-rows, two of which occur in each quadrant. The floor of the statocyst is composed of a slightly concave mass of ciliated cells. Four interradial clumps of fused cilia called balancers protrude to support a spherical mass of small concretions. This mass is the statolith or otolith. From the periphery of the base, fused cilia produce a transparent dome cover. From the base of each interradial ciliary clump, two ciliated grooves extend to the aboral ends of the two comb-rows in that quadrant. A ciliated depression extends from the floor of the statocyst in either direction in the stomodaeal plane. These are called *polar plates*. Their sensory function appears to be more significant when the animal is swimming.

Horridge has investigated some of the receptor-conductor-effector systems in Ctenophora. Presumed photoreceptor cells occur in the base of the apical organ or statocyst. If nonmotile cilia surrounding the apical organ are touched, this structure is retracted from its normally projected position. Balancer cilia are individually encased in a bounding membrane to which the cilium is attached by

Fig. 6-5 Sagittal section through ctenophoran statocyst. From Hertwig, *A Manual of Zoology* (translated and edited by J. S. Kingsley) 1902, Holt, Rinehart & Winston, Inc.

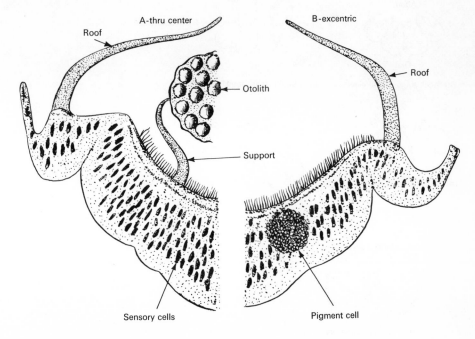

what appears in electromicrograms to be two pairs of membranes somewhat analogous to the gut suspension by mesenteries seen in vertebrate embryology. With regularity, one of the balancer cilia beats toward the center of its group. This beat initiates a wave which is transmitted along the ciliated groove to the polar plates and then to the comb-plates, where the wave of ciliary movement travels normally toward the oral end. Despite two systems of presumed conductive elements present in the ciliated grooves, Horridge was not able to demonstrate synapses and suggests that conduction is not nervous, but a cell-to-cell transmission. His studies of ctenophores indicate that such responses as feeding movements, tentacle and apical organ retraction, and inhibition of ciliary beat are coordinated by separate pathways, whose separation may be only functional.

Reproduction and Embryology

Ctenophores are hermaphroditic. The gonads are embedded under the epithelium of each meridional canal with the ovary in each case adjacent to the principal plane (Fig. 6-1) and the testis on the opposite side of each canal. Fertilized eggs escape through the surface adjacent to the meridional canals generally, although among some Platyctenea, sperm ducts occur, and some species brood their young.

The first two cleavages are meridional and result in four equal blastomeres. The first cleavage furrow corresponds to the stomo-

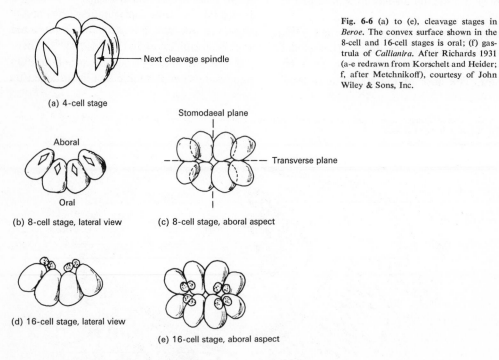

Fig. 6-6 (a) to (e), cleavage stages in *Beroe*. The convex surface shown in the 8-cell and 16-cell stages is oral; (f) gastrula of *Callianira*. After Richards 1931 (a-e redrawn from Korschelt and Heider; f, after Metchnikoff), courtesy of John Wiley & Sons, Inc.

(a) 4-cell stage

Next cleavage spindle

Aboral

Oral

(b) 8-cell stage, lateral view

Stomodaeal plane

Transverse plane

(c) 8-cell stage, aboral aspect

(d) 16-cell stage, lateral view

(e) 16-cell stage, aboral aspect

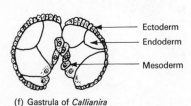

Ectoderm

Endoderm

Mesoderm

(f) Gastrula of *Callianira*

daeal plane of the adult, while the second corresponds to the tentacular plane. Experimental separation of these blastomeres produces asymmetrical larvae, indicating that cleavage is determinative or mosaic, but higher powers of regeneration in the adult suggest later reduction in determinative influence. The third cleavage is unequal and somewhat diagonal and results in a curved plate of eight cells. (Fig. 6-6) separated into two rows of four by the tentacular plane. The concavity of this plate is aboral. The eight blastomeres give off two successive groups of micromeres, and the latter continue to divide to produce a ring of micromeres at the aboral pole destined to produce the epidermis. The macromeres become the endoderm. The micromeres proliferate and envelop the macromeres with a single layer of cells. The macromeres invaginate simultaneously after giving rise to small cells at the oral pole. Thus gastrulation in the ctenophores includes epiboly and emboly. The small cells are carried in with the macromere invagination and form part of the gastrovascular system, probably the tentacular canals. In the cydippid forms, the stomodaeum and paired tentacle sheaths arise from ectodermal invaginations and the latter give rise to the tentacles. The cells of the mesogloea arise from ingression of ectodermal cells, particularly from oral and stomodaeal regions. The stomodaeum eventually will become continuous with an axial cavity formed by the macromeres and which becomes the stomach and infundibular or aboral canal.

A primary tetramerous condition is exhibited in two ways. The stomach becomes somewhat constricted into four radial pouches, each of which will ultimately give rise to two meridional canals, while on the surface, four radial epidermal thickenings will give rise to the two comb-rows characteristic of each quadrant. At the aboral pole, ectodermal derivatives will produce the statocyst. In class Tentaculata, typical cydippid larvae occur, although modified in adults in some of the orders later. Except for the ten-

tacles, a cydippid type of larva also occurs in Class Nuda.

PHYLOGENETIC CONSIDERATIONS

The ctenophoran level of development has stimulated many theories concerning its phylogenetic position. With the Cnidaria the Ctenophora share a number of important features, and are frequently placed with them in phylum Coelenterata. Both groups show a radial symmetry modified by a tetrameric condition; a branching gastrovascular system as the sole body cavity; a noncentralized synaptic nerve net; and a gelatinous mesogloeal layer containing occasional cells. On the other hand, the Ctenophora stand apart with increased bilaterality, comb plates, colloblasts (Fig. 6-7), determinative cleavage of unique type, and a highly developed aboral sensory region.

Apparent similarity of some Ctenophora to Polyclad Turbellarians has suggested the opposite views that the former are ancestral to the Platyhelminthes (Lang) or degenerate from them (Hadži). No strong evidence exists for either hypothesis.

In addition to the general features above, the following isolated instances apparently tie the Ctenophora to the Cnidaria and

Fig. 6-7 Colloblast or glue cell characteristic of Ctenophora. From Hertwig (after Samassa), *A Manual of Zoology* (translated and edited by J. S. Kingsley) 1902, Holt, Rinehart & Winston, Inc.

especially to the Hydrozoa. The parasitic ctenophoran, *Gastrodes,* produces a planula larva; *Hydroctena* is a craspedote, bell-shaped hydrozoan medusa with two laterally situated tentacles provided with sheaths. It also possesses an aboral statocyst. The ctenophore, *Euchlora rubra,* has long been known to carry nematocysts. Formerly, these were thought to have been obtained by ingestion, but Picard (1955) reports that they are produced in the tentacle bases; that they do not appear in the gastrovascular cavity; and that they are all the atrichous iso-rhizal type which is found in Scyphozoa and Alcyonaria, but also occur in the same hydrozoan sub-group to which *Hydroctena* belongs.

The Ctenophora seem to have arisen from the Hydrozoa, exhibit some features parallel with Scyphozoa and Anthozoa, and evolved some unique features hinting a bilaterality but not leading to the higher phyla with this fundamental type of symmetry.

REFERENCES

Coonfield, B. R., Coordination and movement of the swimming plates in *Mnemiopsis.* Biol. Bull., 66:10, 1934.

——, Apical dominance and polarity in *Mnemiopsis.* Biol. Bull., 71:421, 1937.

deBeer, G. R., The evolution of the Metazoa (pp. 24-33). *In* (Julian Huxley *et al.,* eds.) Evolution as a process. London: G. Allen, 1954. (Discussion of Hadži.)

Heider, Karl, Vom Nervensystem der Ctenophoran. Zeitschrift für Morphologie und Ökologie der Tiere, 9:638, 1927.

Horridge, G. A., Relations between nerves and cilia in ctenophores. Amer. Zool., 5:357, 1965.

Komai, Taku, A note on the phylogeny of the Ctenophora (pp. 181-188). *In* (Dougherty, E. C., Z. N. Brown, E. D. Hanson, and W. D. Hartman, eds.) The lower Metazoa. Berkeley: U. of California, 1963.

Mayer, A. G., Ctenophores of the Atlantic Coast of North America. Carnegie Inst. Wash. Publ. No. 162, 58 pp., 1912.

Picard, J., Les nématocysts du cténaire *Euchlora rubra.* Recueil Trav. Stat. Marine Encoume, Bull. No. 9, Fasc. 15:99, 1955.

Totton, A., Egg-laying in ctenophores. Nature, 174:360, 1954.

7

PLATYHEL-MINTHES AND MESOZOA

The phylum Platyhelminthes is composed of bilaterally symmetrical, soft-bodied animals, commonly called flatworms. These contain no body cavity, the area between digestive canal, if present, and body wall being occupied with an irregular network composed either of massed cells or a syncytium. This mesenchymal tissue is called *parenchyma*. The digestive tract typically has a single orifice, the mouth, which therefore functions for egestion as well as ingestion. Flatworms have a protonephridial excretory system. They are typically hermaphroditic with complex reproductive systems, and cross-fertilization is characteristic. Protandry or structural adaptations reduce or prevent self-fertilization in most cases.

Platyhelminths are commonly divided into three classes, one of which with rare exceptions is free-living while the other two are strictly parasitic. The free-living class is named Turbellaria and undoubtedly is ancestral to the parasitic classes, Trematoda and Cestoda. The presence of various adhesive and holdfast organs among Turbellaria was one of the important factors favoring the development of parasitism. The parasitic classes differ from each other fundamentally by the complete lack of a digestive tract among cestodes.

Some 10,000 species of flatworms have been described, but authorities call attention to the relatively sparse knowledge about Turbellaria in many areas of the United States.

CLASS TURBELLARIA

The Turbellaria are predominantly free-living flatworms with a typically ciliated epidermis. Most of them are less than one quarter of an inch long, although a few reach a length of well over one foot. Most turbellarians are depressed (dorsoventrally flattened), but this shape grades into forms that are cylindroid. The sides of the body may be parallel or tapered from the midpoint in both directions or from either end. Some turbellarians bear one or more pairs of tentacles at the anterior end.

Turbellaria are bilaterally symmetrical (Fig. 7-1). The mouth opens along the midventral line usually near the middle of the body. The symmetry is visible externally in the paired condition of various structures such as ocelli, adhesive organs, and various projections such as tentacles and caudal lobes. In turbellarians not uniformly ciliated (Fig. 7-2) the dorsal surface may lack cilia.

Adhesive organs function by the localized production of sticky secretions. In more complex types the edges of protrusible projections facilitate contact with prey or substrate. Such organs are of use in the capture of food as well as in locomotion.

An epidermal feature common to many turbellarians is the presence of *rhabdites* (Fig. 7-2). These are formed, rod-shaped secretions of epidermal or mesenchymal gland cells and may occur either in epidermis or the underlying parenchyma. In the epidermis they occur at right angles to the surface and are frequently most numerous along the periphery of the flattened body and on the dorsal surface. Such a distribution suggests a protective function. Under adverse conditions, rhabdites discharge to form a sticky encasement about the animal. Such an ad-

Fig. 7-1 Composite diagrams to illustrate some turbellarian structures. (a) Dorsal view with nerve trunks indicated by broken lines; (b) ventral view with male reproductive system depicted on the left and female system on the right. Space between organs indicated on the cross-section in (a) is filled with connective tissue. Adapted from various sources.

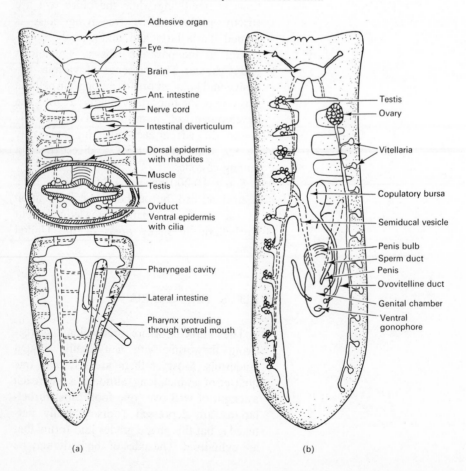

(a)   (b)

hesive layer might deter enemies by its physical consistency and might also have a repellent or toxic action. Rhabdites commonly are less frequent on the ventral surface where the production of a heavy adhesive layer would retard locomotion as an escape mechanism. The formation of a gelatinous layer may also be a prelude to encystment in response to unfavorable environmental conditions. Some related structures produced by glands in turbellarians are included with rhabdites under the name of *rhabdoids*. It is of phylogenetic interest that rhabdites occur in the other acoelomate phylum, Nemertina.

Most turbellarians are marine; this is apt to be forgotten because of the usual study of fresh-water forms in general biology. Turbellaria originated in the sea, and two of the five orders into which the group is usually subdivided are strictly marine, while the

others are largely marine or at least well represented in that environment. Terrestrial species have evolved from fresh-water species, but another radiation includes forms that have invaded brackish water or returned to a marine habitat.

A benthonic habitat on hard bottom surface is generally characteristic for more robust species; small ones are found more commonly on sand or soft substrate. Most marine species occur in littoral waters, although a few are found in deeper water. Some marine forms are pelagic in warmer seas, and many kinds occur in the animal communities in masses of seaweeds. Most fresh-water turbellarians occur in running waters, and where these streams freeze or dry up, these flatworms have definite seasonal cycles. Some turbellarians can adjust to a considerable temperature range, but others are restricted. Pennak points out that one European species restricted to cold streams has an optimum water temperature of 7° centigrade and generally disappears when the temperature reaches 12°. Some genera are adapted to both running and standing waters, with smaller more active species correlated with the former. Whereas most turbellarians are restricted to a single environment, *Macrostomum* (a rhabdocoel) has species in fresh-water, brackish, and marine environments. One North American triclad group is composed of eyeless cave dwellers, and there is an unusual correlation between the cave or group of nearby caves and the species endemic to it.

In the United States, in the area east of the Mississippi the triclad genera are reasonably well known and the other orders to a lesser degree, but in the western half of the United States Turbellaria have been sparsely studied. The distribution generally of fresh-water flatworms in this country suggests efficient overwintering practices and behavior effective in survival and dissemination of the species.

Among marine turbellarians a number are commensal with various invertebrates such

Fig. 7-2 Sections through the dorsal and the ventral wall in a fresh-water planarian. Compare for cilia and rhabdites. 1, rhabdites; 2, epidermis; 3, nuclei (epidermis); 4, basement membrane; 5, circular muscle layer; 6, pigment; 7, diagonal muscle layer; 8, longitudinal muscle layer; 9, fixed nuclei (mesenchyne); 10, free nuclei (mesenchyne); 11, rhabdite-forming gland cell; 12, parenchymal muscles; 13, basal bodies of cilia. After Hyman, Vol. II, 1951, courtesy of the McGraw-Hill Book Company.

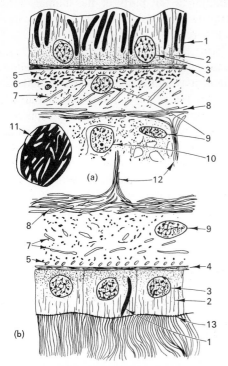

as molluscs and echinoderms. *Bdelloura* is a well-known ectocommensal on the horseshoe crab, *Limulus*. Turbellarians of the Family Fecampiidae of the European coast include some of the few entoparasitic species. These flatworms grow to sexual maturity in the hemocoele of marine crustaceans.

Digestive System

The turbellarian digestive system is a caecal type with mouth, pharynx, and one or more blind intestinal pouches. Rarely anal pores are present but even here the mouth continues to function for most egestion. The ventrally situated mouth is median and usually midway from the ends, although in lower orders particularly it tends to be more anterior. In many worms of the order Acoela the mouth constitutes the sole development of the digestive system.

The structure of the pharynx is of considerable taxonomic value. The primitive or simple pharynx is equivalent to an invaginated portion of the body wall and histologically is similar to it. It is typical of acoels, lower rhabdocoels, and is represented in the alloeocoel order of turbellarians. A more effective food-getting pharynx involved the development of a well-defined ring or bulb of muscle, ensheathed from the parenchyma and located adjacent to the mouth. This bulbous portion of the pharynx can be everted in many turbellarians. Inversion is accomplished by a surrounding framework of diagonal muscles attached to the nearby body wall. The deeper portion of this pharynx is a thin-walled tube, whose lumen may act as a storage space for the recessed muscular bulb.

In the higher orders (Tricladida and Polycladida) a large space called the pharyngeal cavity develops adjacent to the mouth. In both of these orders, diverticula of the intestine commonly extend both caudad and cephalad from the ventral mouth. The pharyngeal cavity opens to the intestine through an elongate rim which extends in triclads as a cylinder and in many polyclads as a broader pleated skirt into the pharyngeal cavity. This rim, commonly known as a proboscis, can be inverted through the mouth, and its orifice functions for ingestion. This type of pharyngeal structure is called plicate, and because of its length is often folded when retracted.

The intestine arises directly from the pharynx or via a short esophagus. In the lower groups, the intestine tends to be a simple sac running caudally from the anterior mouth and may have a slightly folded surface. In triclads the esophagus leads into an intestine with three branches, one extending forward in a median position and a pair running caudally on either side of the pharyngeal cavity (Fig. 7-3). This pair may communicate with each other at the posterior end. Each of these three main pouches commonly gives off lateral diverticula. Among Polycladida, there is a main intestine lying medially, all or a major part of which extends caudally from the opening of the pharynx. The name Polycladida is derived from the presence of many lateral branches radiating to all parts of the animal. A few members of this order have one or more anal pores.

Turbellaria are almost uniformly carnivorous, although some members of the lower orders may utilize algae. Most turbellarians capture living prey, but some rhabdocoels and many polyclads and triclads supplement the diet by scavenging. Jennings has studied feeding in free-living flatworms, and most of this account comes from his papers.

One species of acoel turbellarian, *Convoluta paradoxa,* feeds on various marine life such as diatoms, protozoa, and small crustaceans. Small prey is captured by the

Fig. 7-3 Diagrams comparing turbellarian digestive tracts. (a), (b), and (c) are rhabdocoel variants; (d) is an Alloeocoel; (e) is a triclad, and (f) to (i) are polyclad variants. 1, mouth; 2, pharyngeal cavity; 3, pharynx; 4, pharyngeal glands; 5, intestine; 6, proboscis; 7, ciliated pits; 8, cerebral eye cluster; 9, tentacular eye cluster; 10, main intestine; 11, male gonopore; 12, female gonopore; 13, adhesive disc. After Hyman, Vol. II, 1951, courtesy of the McGraw-Hill Book Company.

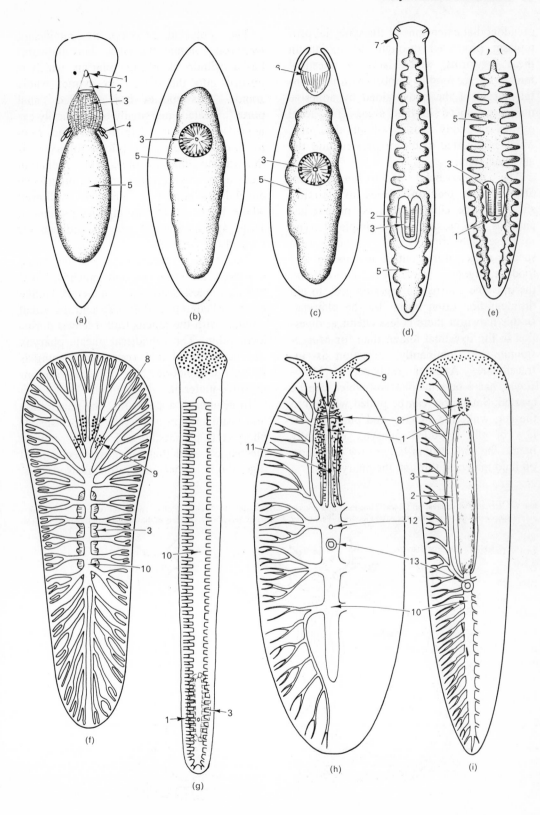

(a)   (b)   (c)   (d)   (e)

(f)   (g)   (h)   (i)

pseudopodial extensions of the syncytial protoplasm protruded through the mouth in these flatworms, which lack an intestinal lumen. Larger food is grabbed with the frontal margin of the body, aided by adhesive mucus produced in that area. This acoel presses its body closely about the prey, which is ingested whole or pressed into the gut syncytium.

The rhabdocoels, *Macrostomum* and *Stenostomum,* feed on various invertebrates such as large ciliates, rotifers, nematodes, annelids, and crustacea. The simple pharynx in these flatworms is not provided with special musculature, but is distensible and food is ingested whole. In *Stenostomum,* the intestine churns the ingested prey to aid disintegration often begun by the pharynx. In this flatworm there is less chemical digestion in the intestinal lumen than for *Macrostomum.* Predominantly, digestion is intracellular. Another rhabdocoel, *Mesostoma,* has a bulbous pharynx which can be everted. Small prey can be pulled whole into the gut, while the sucking and pumping action of the extruded pharynx eventually breaks the body wall of larger prey to suction off fluid materials through the pharynx.

The polyclad, *Cycloporus papillosus,* feeds on colonial tunicates. This flatworm has a cylindrical, plicate pharynx which is pushed into the colony to extract whole zooids. This species has so-called "anal pores" located marginally on laterally-extended gut diverticula. In the polyclad, *Leptoplana,* the retracted plicate pharynx is thrown into ruffles or folds. This turbellarian feeds upon small crustaceans and polychaete annelids. While small prey is swallowed whole, larger animals are ingested piecemeal. Dead animal material may be utilized for food also.

The triclad, *Polycelis,* feeds on small crustacea, insect larvae, and annelids, but it will also ingest dead animal material. Unlike most turbellarians, *Polycelis* entraps small animals with the mucus trail it leaves during locomotion. The cylindrical plicate pharynx can be extruded and (once an opening is forced) it penetrates the prey to withdraw nutritive material.

In general, it appears that the penetration and disintegration of prey by the protrusible pharynx is principally and perhaps entirely mechanical, and that for most species most digestion is intracellular in the gastrodermis.

Fig. 7-4 Excretory structures; (a) typical flame-bulb in a polyclad (after Lang); (b) flame-bulb of a cestode; (c) typical solenocyte of a polychaete annelid. All diagrammatic. After Goodrich 1945, *Quart. J. Microsc. Sci.,* 86:113, courtesy of the Company of Biologists Limited.

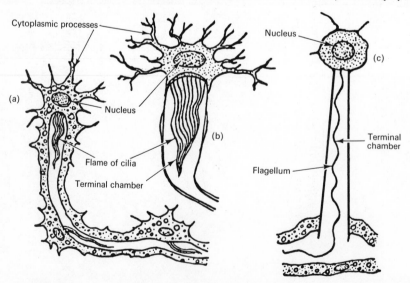

In *Cycloporus,* however, digestion occurs principally within the intestinal lumen. *Polycelis* is known to store fats, carbohydrates, and proteins, the latter in so-called sphere cells in the gastrodermis. For other turbellarians, fat storage is well documented, but storage of other food products is less well known.

Excretion

Excretion is accomplished presumably by the generally distributed flame-bulb nephridia (Fig. 7-4), but primarily these organs may have an osmoregulatory function since, analogous with other groups, marine species are less endowed with them. Among Acoela, which lack nephridia, injected vital dyes have accumulated in the cells of the mesenchyme and appear to be thrown off through the mouth. There is some evidence that the intestinal wall may have an excretory function for other turbellarians also.

Nervous System

This system illustrates a probable mode of origin from ancestors with a nerve network and a radial pattern of longitudinal nerves. Gradations occur from a generalized network with practically no concentration to

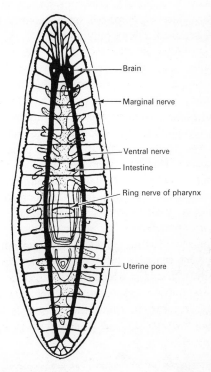

Fig. 7-5 Digestive and nervous systems of *Syncoelidium,* a triclad commensal on *Limulus,* the horseshoe crab. From Hertwig (after Wheeler), *A Manual of Zoology* (translated and edited by J. S. Kingsley) 1902, Holt, Rinehart & Winston, Inc.

Fig. 7-6 Diagrams of cross-sections to show distribution of longitudinal nerves in (a) alloeocoel, (b) marine triclad, (c) freshwater triclad, and (d) land planarian. 1, lateral nerve cord; 2, dorsal nerve cord; 3, ventral nerve cord; 4, epidermis; 5, subepidermal nerve net; 6, subepidermal musculature; 7, submuscular nerve net; 8, ventrolateral nerve cord; 9, commissure between dorsal and ventral cords; 10, ventral nerve plate; 11, simulated ventral cords in the ventral nerve plate. After Hyman, Vol. II, 1951, courtesy of the McGraw-Hill Book Company.

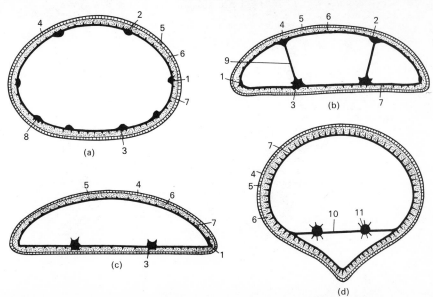

a series of longitudinal paired tracts joined by regular commissures (Fig. 7-5). The pair of longitudinal cords lying ventrally are most persistent (Fig. 7-6). However, among higher turbellarians, emphasis on a network has been retained among polyclads.

The brain or cerebral ganglia lie at the anterior end in close affinity with the chemo-, tacto-, and photoreceptors that are variously present in turbellarians. In the lower orders, sensory organs for dorso-ventral orientation are commonly associated with the cerebral ganglia. These organs are *statocysts*. They are composed of a cell with a thin layer of protoplasm surrounding a large mineral inclusion or concretion lying free in a small cavity or vesicle lined with sensory epithelium.

Both acoelomate phyla (Platyhelminthes and Nemertina) exhibit a gradation from primitive groups in which the principal nerve net lies outside the body wall musculature to higher forms in which this muscle is immediately external to the principal nerve system, although many may retain or develop a secondary network externally.

Reproduction and Embryology

With very few exceptions turbellarians are monoecious. Copulation with cross-fertilization is the usual but not the absolute rule as indicated by isolation experiments. Some species develop parthenogenetically.

The male organs include paired testes which connect through paired vasa deferentia or sperm ducts with the ejaculatory duct into which small so-called prostate glands empty. Sometimes conjoined or separate enlargements called spermiducal vesicles occur distally on the sperm ducts and function to store sperm. Commonly, in the absence of spermiducal vesicles, sperm are stored in a muscular enlargement of the ejaculatory duct termed the seminal vesicle. The terminal portion of the ejaculatory duct can be protruded or everted as a copulatory organ called the cirrus or penis (Fig. 7-7).

Fig. 7-7 *Anoplodium graffi* Monticelli; a turbellarian parasite in echinoderms. After Westblad 1953, courtesy of the Arkiv för Zoologi.

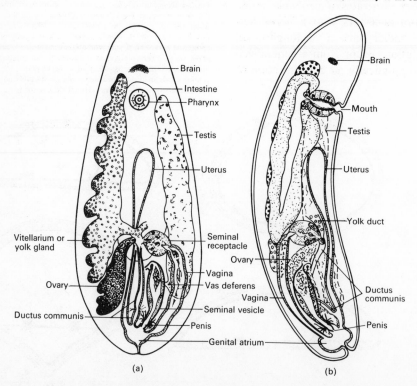

(a)   (b)

The female organs consist of paired ovaries, yolk glands (vitellaria), and their respective ducts leading to the common genital atrium to which a saclike outpocket called the copulatory bursa is joined by a canal. This latter organ receives sperm at copulation either through its canal to the genital atrium or through a separate opening to the exterior. Occasionally the bursa may have an additional and direct connection to the distal part of the oviduct which is enlarged as a seminal receptacle for subsequent storage of sperm from the copulatory partner.

Many variations occur in the reproductive system. These include the primitive conditions of hypodermic insemination through the body wall and the situation in which ovary and vitellarium form a single gland complex. Other features include the presence or absence of fusion of oviduct and vitelline duct, enlargements of oviducts to form a so-called uterus, separate male and female genital pores, and the frequent presence of a genito-intestinal canal between part of the female complex and the intestine.

Spiral determinative cleavage is characteristic of polyclad turbellarians and bears great resemblance to this process in annelids and molluscs. The first two cleavages result in a plate of four cells. At the next cleavage each of these cells develops a spindle whose longitudinal axis is at an angle of 45 degrees, so that the quartet of smaller blastomeres (*micromeres*) which are produced at the animal pole lie obliquely to the first quartet now called *macromeres*. At the next cleavage each macromere spindle is at right angles to the axis of the preceding one, so that a second quartet of micromeres is formed between the two existing quartets. Spiral cleavage is not so much actually spiral as it is a regular alternating series of cleavages following the original oblique split.

Three quartets of micromeres are given off toward the animal pole by successive division of the macromeres, and a fourth quar-

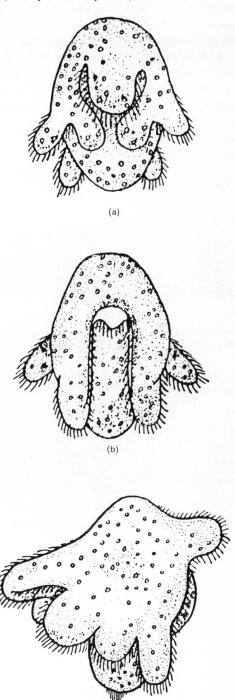

Fig. 7-8 (a) Dorsal, (b) ventral, and (c) lateral views of free-swimming (Müller's) larva of the polyclad, *Yungia*. After Richards 1931, courtesy of John Wiley & Sons, Inc.

(a)

(b)

(c)

tet is subsequently produced at the vegetal pole. The first micromere quartet and its daughter cells form ectoderm, including the nervous system. The next two quartets and their offspring produce ectoderm and some ectomesoderm. A single cell, enumerated as the 4d cell of the fourth micromere quartet, is responsible for endoderm and endomesoderm. The latter constitutes the principal mesoderm of the turbellarian. The other cells of the fourth quartet together with the now smaller macromeres apparently disintegrate or serve as reserve food material. Among many polyclads, a free-swimming larval stage known as *Müller's larva* (Fig. 7-8) occurs briefly, and is characterized by eight ciliated caudal lobes.

Asexual Reproduction and Regeneration
A number of turbellarians reproduce occasionally, regularly, or solely by transverse fission (Fig. 7-9). Each of the developing daughter organisms is known as a *zooid*. In some forms, because of the extensive differentiation of zooids before separation, a condition of pseudometamerism or linear colonization exists temporarily. Regeneration is a phenomenon particularly well developed in turbellarians that possess ability to repro-

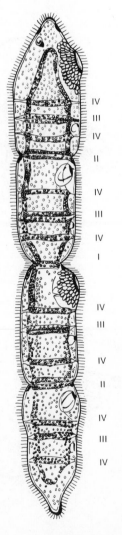

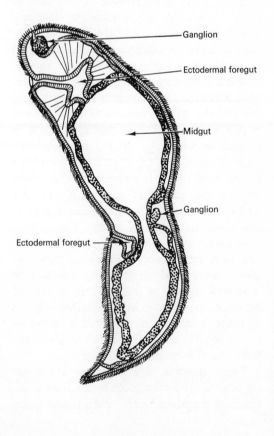

Fig. 7-9 (a) Rhabdocoele turbellarian (*Microstomum*) in process of fission into sixteen zooids with roman numerals indicating the order of the fission planes and (b) section through *Stenostomum* undergoing fission. (a) From Van Cleave (after von Graff) 1931, courtesy of the McGraw-Hill Book Company; (b) from Hertwig, *A Manual of Zoology* (translated and edited by J. S. Kingsley) 1902, Holt, Rinehart & Winston, Inc.

Ganglion

Ectodermal foregut

Midgut

Ganglion

Ectodermal foregut

duce asexually; there is an extensive literature on this subject. Relatively small pieces
of worm will regenerate complete animals.
In general, regenerative ability decreases
from the anterior end along the longitudinal
axis and this is paralleled by a decrease in
metabolic or oxidative activity. The name of
metabolic or axial gradient is applied to this
phenomenon.

Orders of Turbellaria

Order Acoela These primitive marine flatworms typically lack an intestinal lumen; this
space is occupied by cells. The pharynx is absent in many Acoela. Discharge of both excretory materials and reproductive cells occurs
through the mouth, and there are no structurally specialized organs for either of these systems. *Convoluta, Nemertoderma, Polychoerus.*

Order Alloeocoela This is a group that
structurally appears to grade between the
Acoela and the Tricladida. Unlike Acoela they
possess nephridia and an intestine. The
pharynx may be simple, as in Acoela, or bulbous or plicate as in higher turbellarians. Most
Alloeocoels are marine. *Allostoma, Hofstenia,
Prorhynchus.*

Order Rhabdocoela In this group the mouth
tends to be anterior and the intestine is a simple
sac sometimes thrown into shallow folds. The
pair of ventral nerve cords predominate. Usually
they possess paired protonephridia. Rhabdocoels
occur in marine, fresh-water, and terrestrial
habitats. *Catenula, Mesostoma, Stenostomum.*

Order Tricladida The triclads are characterized by a mouth midway between the ends, a
plicate proboscis, and an intestine with three
principal branches, one of which is directed forward and two backward. Distinct yolk glands
and a common gonopore are characteristic. Representatives of this order are generally studied
in the undergraduate laboratory. *Bdelloura,
Dugesia, Planaria, Syncoelidium.*

Order Polycladida In these marine turbellarians there is a single main pouch of the intestine, but it is provided with many prominent
lateral diverticula. Several pairs of longitudinal
nerve cords have retained prominence, as has a
nerve network. Yolk glands are absent; male

and female gonopores open separately. *Euplana,
Notoplana, Stylochus.*

CLASS TREMATODA

The Trematoda, commonly referred to as
"flukes," are internal or external parasites,
have no cilia in the adult stage, and possess
a cuticular body surface. The presence of a
digestive system differentiates them from the
other class of parasitic flatworms, Cestoda.
A sharp sexual dimorphism occurs in the few
trematodes that are dioecious, but most of
the approximately 6,000 known species are
hermaphroditic. The patterns of the flame-
bulb excretory system have had considerable
taxonomic value. Holdfast organs, called
suckers, are characteristic features and were
utilized in some older systems of classification.

The trematodes fall into two major
groups: Monogenea and Digenea. The
Monogenea generally have simple life cycles
which involve only a single host. Adult monogenetic trematodes have a well-developed
posterior sucker, often with multiple adhesive organs (Fig. 7-10). Although these
suckers are imperforate, the rounded contours suggest mouth openings. The name
Polystoma is derived from this feature and
is applied to the more populous order. The
Digenea have a single postoral sucker on
the ventral surface, lacking in some forms.
The name Digenea is derived from the complicated life cycles characteristic of the
group. There is a metagenesis or alternation
of sexual and asexual generations, and two
to four hosts are involved in the course of
completion of the cycle. With two exceptions occuring in annelids, all digenetic
trematodes utilize molluscs in the asexual
phase. One small group of trematodes called
Aspidobothrea (Aspidocotylea) are prob-
lematic since some of their characteristics
seem to suggest an overlapping with the
other groups. Most of them have a single

large posterior sucker, often rectangularly subdivided. They do not show metagenesis, but some of them have alternation of hosts. The larval stage hatching from the egg bears close similarity to digenetic larvae and is unlike those of the Monogenea. Aspidobothrea are parasites of molluscs and at least some of them utilize a vertebrate for the second host. Since Monogenea are parasites of low-er vertebrates and do not appear in molluscs, their life cycles differ sharply from the Digenea and Aspidobothrea. The latter group will not be discussed further.

Although adhesive organs occur at the anterior end of monogenetic trematodes, the mouth does not open through a sucker as is characteristic of the Digenea (Fig. 7-11). There is a muscular bulbous pharynx simi-

Fig. 7-10 *Polystomum integerrimum nearcticum*; (a) bladder generation and (b) gill generation. From Paul, 1938, *J. Parasitol.*, 24; 489.

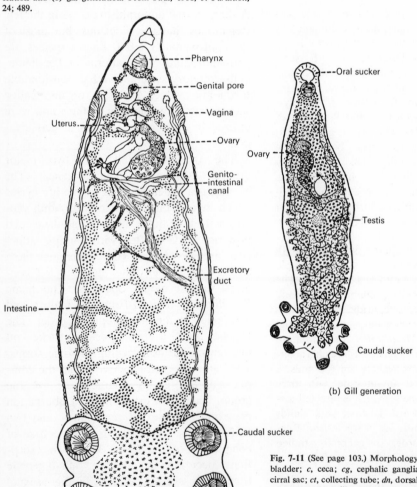

(a) Bladder generation

(b) Gill generation

Fig. 7-11 (See page 103.) Morphology of a typical trematode. *b*, bladder; *c*, ceca; *cg*, cephalic ganglia; *cl*, cilia; *cr*, cirrus; *crs*, cirral sac; *ct*, collecting tube; *dn*, dorsal nerve trunk; *e*, esophagus; *ec*, excretory capillary; *ep*, excretory pore; *fc*, flame-cell; *ga*, genital atrium; *go*, genital opening; *lc*, Laurer's canal; *ln*, lateral nerve trunk; *mg*, Mehlis' gland; *n*, nucleus; *oöt*, oötype; *os*, oral sucker; *ov*, ovary; *p*, pharynx; *pg*, prostatic gland; *s*, spines; *sr*, seminal receptacle; *sv*, seminal vesicle; *t*, testis; *u*, uterus; *vd*, vas deferens; *ve*, vas efferens; *vn*, ventral nerve trunk; *vs*, ventral sucker; *vt*, vitellaria; *vtd*, vitelline duct. From Belding, *Textbook of Clinical Parasitology*, 1942 (2nd Ed., 1952), by permission of Appleton-Century-Crofts.

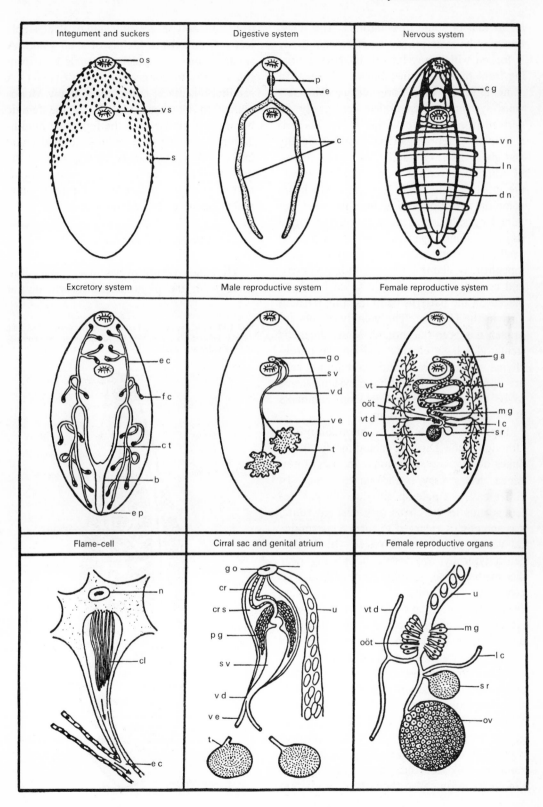

Integument and suckers	Digestive system	Nervous system
Excretory system	Male reproductive system	Female reproductive system
Flame-cell	Cirral sac and genital atrium	Female reproductive organs

lar to that of some turbellarians. The intestine may be a simple sac or more commonly is forked with many lateral diverticula arising from the two main pouches or caeca. In some Digenea, anal pores occur. The nervous system of trematodes can easily be derived from the turbellarian types. There is a pair of cerebral ganglia joined medially and giving rise to a number of paired nerves, of which the ventral pair running caudally are most prominent. Monogenea, which are commonly ectoparasitic, usually have retained eyes, whereas only free-living larval stages of some digenetic trematodes possess ocelli. All trematodes possess paired protonephridial flame-bulb excretory systems and considerable taxonomic value has been placed on the patterns of branching, particularly in the Digenea. The validity of this approach has been questioned. Many digenetic trematodes have channels within the parenchyma, within which fluid-containing cells are apparent. This lymphatic system seems to be a structure persisting from remnants of a larval excretory system.

Typically trematodes are hermaphroditic, although some Digenea including the blood flukes of man are dioecious. In the Monogenea, testes vary from one to many. In either case a single sperm duct or vas deferens runs to the cirrus or penis. En route, it is sometimes enlarged to form a spermiducal vesicle or a seminal vesicle. In the Digenea typically two testes, both lying near the median line, communicate through a common sperm duct, with the extrusible cirrus lying within an oval cirrus sac. A prostate gland is often associated with this portion of the male system.

The female organs in Monogenea include a single, elongate ovary, an oviduct, a pair of laterally disposed yolk glands whose ducts sometimes join to form a yolk reservoir, and a common ovovitelline duct leading to the genital atrium. This latter duct connects with a genito-intestinal canal near the entry of the common yolk duct and is provided with a slight expansion called the ootype. Radiating

from the ootype are unicellular glands collectively called the Mehlis or shell gland. A single or paired copulatory canals lead from the surface to connect with the oviduct. A seminal receptacle is present in many Monogenea. In Digenea (Fig. 7-12) the female organs are similar with the following modifications: absence of a genito-intestinal canal and of copulatory canals, enlargement of the ovovitelline duct to form an elongate tubular uterus, and the presence of Laurer's canal which opens to the dorsal surface.

Life Cycles of Trematoda

The study of life cycles among parasites, aside from the phylogenetic information it

Fig. 7-12 *Opisthorchis* (*Clonorchis*) *sinensis*. After Goodchild, *Selected Invertebrate Types*, 1950 (F. A. Brown, Jr., ed.) courtesy of John Wiley & Sons, Inc.

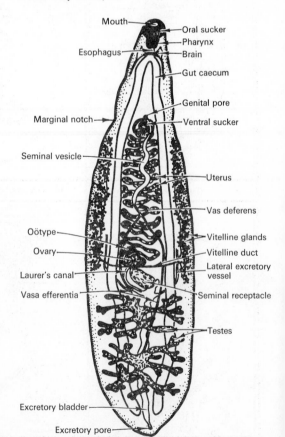

supplies, provides the only sound basis for combating parasitic infestation. Although the life cycle of *Polystoma integerrimum* is atypical for Monogenea, it provides an interesting combination of ecto- and endoparasitism. Adult polystomes occur in the urinary bladder of frogs and produce eggs which pass to the exterior when the frogs breed in the spring. The developing larva is protected by a shell. In a few weeks the larva hatches, swims with the aid of ciliary bands, and attaches by hooklets to gills of tadpoles. If attachment is on the external gill, the larva matures sexually within a few weeks to produce viable eggs. If the larva is attached more internally on the gill, at metamorphosis of the amphibian it migrates over the body surface and through the intestine to reach the urinary bladder where it becomes a typical adult in about three years.

Digenetic trematodes with two exceptions utilize molluscs as the first intermediate host (Fig. 7-13). After asexual reproduction the new generation of larvae reach the definitive host directly or indirectly through a second and sometimes a third intermediate host. The definitive or final host is defined as the one in which the parasite achieves sexual maturity.

In general, operculated or capped eggs are passed from the final host, then hatch to ciliated, free-swimming *miracidia,* which enter a molluscan intermediate host (usually a specific snail genus) and metamorphose to a hollow bladder form known as a *sporocyst.* Internally the sporocyst produces a new-generation larva called *redia,* which differ from the sporocyst by the presence of a pharynx (Fig. 7-14). Similarly the redia give rise to a new larval stage called *cercaria,* which typically leaves the snail and is motile by means of a tail. Depending upon the life cycle, the cercaria may encyst on vegetation as a *metacercaria* to be ingested accident-

Fig. 7-13 Life cycle of *Opisthorchis (Clonorchis) sinensis.* (a) Man infected with adult worm; (b) animal reservoir host; (c) ovum in feces; (d) metamorphosis in snail (d₁, miracidium after hatching in intestine of snail; d₂, sporocyst; d₃, redia; d₄, cercaria); (e) free-swimming cercaria; (f) fresh-water fish with encycted metacercariae; (g) man infected by eating raw or insufficiently cooked fish; (h) resevoir animal host infected in similar manner. From Belding, *Textbook of Clinical Parasitology* 1942 (2nd Ed., 1952), by permission of Appleton-Century-Crofts.

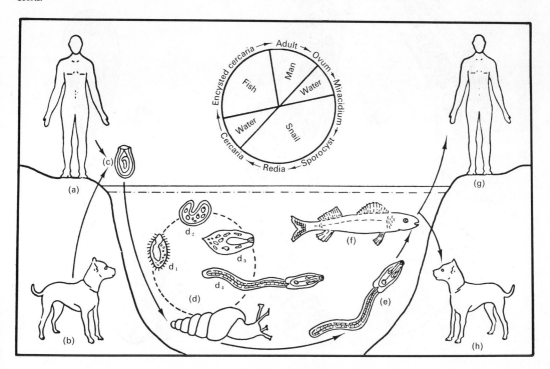

ally by the definitive host, or it may become a metacercaria in a second intermediate host, or it may actively penetrate the definitive host. Variations in this life cycle may occur by the addition of an extra sporocyst or an extra redial generation.

Various parasites reach man as the definitive host through each of these life-

Fig. 7-14 Developmental stages of *Fasciola hepatica*. (a) young larva; (b) sporocyst from the lung of *Limnaera*; (c) older sporocyst with rediae; (d) redia which has produced rediae internally; (e) redia with cercariae; (f) cercaria; (g) encysted *Fasciola. A,* eye spot; *D,* digestive tract; *Dr,* glands; *Ex,* ciliated lobules and main trunks of excretory system; *G,* birth opening; *Kz,* germ cells; *N,* nervous system. From Hertwig (from Korschelt and Heider, after Leuckart), *A Manual of Zoology* (translated and edited by J. S. Kingsley) 1902, Holt, Rinehart & Winston, Inc.

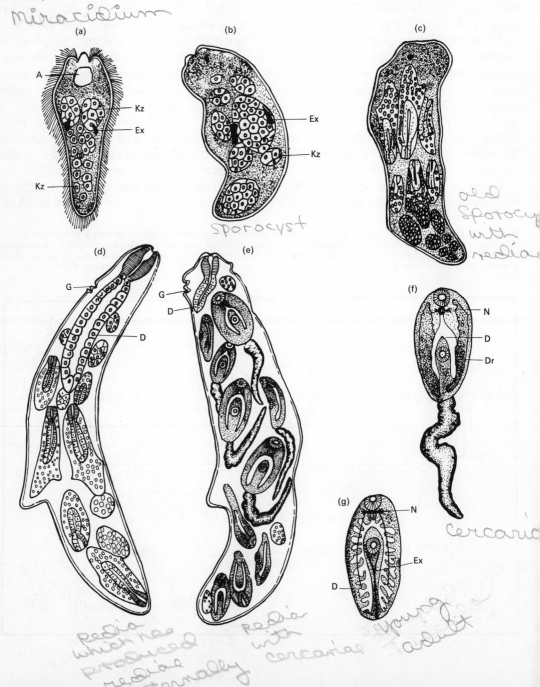

cycle patterns. The sheep liver fluke, *Fasciola hepatica,* which is an occasional parasite of man, reaches the definitive host as a metacercaria on vegetation. *Opisthorchis* (= *Clonorchis*) *sinensis,* another trematode which lives in the liver, reaches man through metacercariae in fish. *Paragonimus westermani,* a lung parasite of human beings, reaches the final host when certain uncooked infested crustaceans are eaten, while the notorious blood flukes of man (genus, *Schistosoma*) are dioecious forms (Fig. 7-15) living in the mesenteric veins around the urinary bladder or rectum, after active penetration by their fork-tailed cercariae.

Classification of Trematoda

Following Stunkard (1962) the trematodes are divided into two subclasses. Subclass

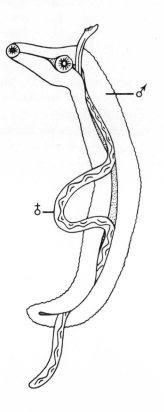

Fig. 7-15 A dioecious trematode, *Schistosoma*; diagrammatic. From Schechter 1959, courtesy of Prentice-Hall, Inc.

Pectobothridia: These are mostly ectoparasites of lower vertebrates (*Polystoma* is an exception), which do not have alternation of generations. The suckers tend to be firm and rigid and are frequently armed. The group is divided into two orders, based primarily on whether the posterior sucker is single or multiple. The other subclass is the *Malacobothridia,* which are generally endoparasitic, typically use a mollusc as the first host, and usually have alternation of generations. The suckers tend to be flexible. The Aspidobothrea are placed here as an order, and the second order is Digenea, of which nearly 5,000 species are known.

The Aspidobothrea include a small number of genera which never exhibit metagenesis or asexual reproduction and which have relatively simple life cycles. While these worms normally reach sexual maturity in molluscan hosts, they can occur as incidental parasites in some predators feeding on these hosts. The typically very large posterior sucker is subdivided into compartments by septa. The Digenea constitute a large group of trematodes in which the life cycle is characterized by alternation of generations, with asexual reproduction occurring in a molluscan host and sexual reproduction in a vertebrate host. Several successive larval stages occur, and additional intermediate hosts may be utilized between the molluscan and the vertebrate host.

CLASS CESTODA

The Cestoda are commonly known as tapeworms. Most of them are divided serially into segments called proglottids, and the adults typically possess some sort of holdfast organs on the anterior terminal unit, which is called the *scolex*. As is characteristic of trematodes, the body is clothed by a cuticle lying adjacent to the circular muscle that marks the edge of the parenchyma. The cuticle is secreted by goblet-shaped cells embedded in the peripheral area of the parenchyma. Deeper in the mesenchyme, a zone of predominantly longitudinal muscle separates the parenchyma into cortical and medullary zones. Cestodes differ from trematodes primarily because the former exhibit no evidence of endoderm or of any digestive tract. Because of this latter feature, adult tapeworms are restricted to a habitat where food can be obtained by absorption. Consequently, they are intestinal parasites of vertebrates or rarely of such adjoining ducts as

Fig. 7-16 *Echinococcus gramulosus*, a tapeworm typically with three proglottids: one young, one mature, and one gravid. From Belding, *A Textbook of Clinical Parasitology*, 1942 (2nd ed., 1952). By permission of Appleton-Century-Crofts.

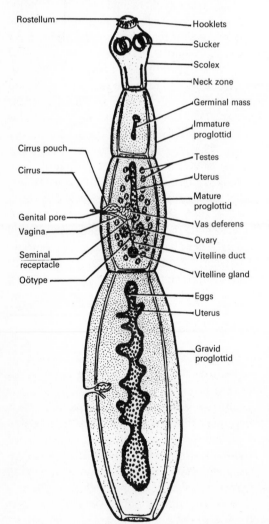

Rostellum

Hooklets

Sucker

Scolex

Neck zone

Germinal mass

Immature proglottid

Cirrus pouch

Cirrus

Testes

Uterus

Mature proglottid

Genital pore

Vagina

Vas deferens

Ovary

Vitelline duct

Seminal receptacle

Oötype

Vitelline gland

Eggs

Uterus

Gravid proglottid

those of the liver and the pancreas.

In general, tapeworms can be divided into a number of body regions (Fig. 7-16). The scolex or anterior end is usually followed by a narrow unsegmented neck. In the posterior body, divided into proglottids and called a *strobila,* three regions grade almost imperceptibly into each other. Since new proglottid differentiation is at the posterior region of the neck, the proglottids immediately caudad exhibit a gradually increasing definition of body organs, the most prominent of which are for reproduction. Usually the male system achieves prominence first, anatomically indicating a condition of protandry in tapeworms. Further back, both reproductive systems as well as other organs reach a definitive mature condition. Accumulation of eggs in the uterus for some tapeworms becomes noticeable, and mature proglottids gradually become gravid proglottids in which the uterus as a storage organ enlarges, usually with production of lateral diverticula. In these same tapeworms the so-called eggs are really embryonated larvae called *onchospheres,* characterized by six hooks. In essence, gravid proglottids are simply egg sacs, and in many of the common tapeworms sections of the gravid area of the strobila are broken off to pass out with the excreta. In some of the more primitive tapeworms the strobila is not dehisced, since the uterus has an external ventral pore and eggs do not accumulate, but are passed off continuously from mature proglottids.

The tapeworm scolex (Fig. 7-17) is a slight angular, spherical, or elongate enlargement anterior to the narrow neck. It contains a nerve ring, nerve cords, and the anterior portion of the excretory system. Externally it is characterized by one of three types of suckerlike holdfast organs and, in some forms, various hooks.

The suckerlike organs can be roughly classified into three types. Some of the more primitive tapeworms have elongate groove-like structures called *bothria* with poorly developed musculature. The other types are sharply defined and set off from the parenchyma by a muscular sheath. The *acetabulum* is provided with strong radial muscles to provide an efficient sucking cup. The *bothridia,* which may be stalked or sessile, are characterized by leaflike marginal expansions and frequently have secondary sucking cups. Hooks are common on the anterior end of the scolex, and a single or double ring of hooks may encircle the somewhat protrusible end of the scolex, called a *rostellum.* In some forms, the rostellum may be cone-shaped with small hooks disposed over

its surface. Occasionally, the suckers themselves may be armed. One entire order is characterized by eversible *proboscides* bearing small hooks or spines (Fig. 7-17). The efficiency of these structures for attachment has resulted in de-emphasis of the suckers, so that the musculature development approaches that of bothria.

As many as five pairs of longitudinal nerve trunks may be retained by tapeworms (Fig. 7-18). The most prominent pair extend from paired cerebral ganglia in the scolex, lie near the lateral margins of the strobila, and are joined by at least one ring

Fig. 7-17 Diagrammatic representations illustrating various cestode scolexes. (a) Tetraphyllidea; (b) Diphyllidea (modified from Borradaile, *et al*; (c) Trypanorhyncha; (d) Pseudophyllidea (*Diphyllobothrium*); (e) Pseudophyllidea (*Caryophyllaeus*). (a) and (c) after Linton, (d) after Hertwig and (e) after M. Schultze, all modified from Hertwig, *A Manual of Zoology* (translated and edited by J. S. Kingsley) 1902, Holt, Rinehart & Winston, Inc.

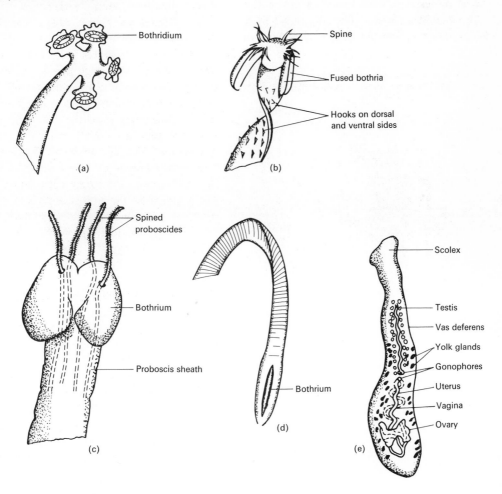

commissure in each proglottid. This connective is situated near the posterior margin of the segment. Two accessory longitudinal nerves lying above and below accompany each lateral nerve trunk. The cerebral ganglia are joined by a broad connective, and commonly a nerve ring encircles the scolex in the vicinity of the cerebral ganglia.

The excretory system is composed of flame bulbs in the mesenchyme which join excretory canals running lengthwise in the strobila. The principal canals lie laterally just within the medullary mesenchyme. Because of their origin, these are recognized as the ventral pair, and they are frequently accompanied by the dorsal pair of vessels which are actually apt to lie just mediad to the ventral pair. The dorsal and ventral vessel on each side are joined in the scolex, and sometimes the two sides are joined there by a plexus. Near the posterior margin of

Fig. 7-18 Nervous system of the cestode, *Moniezia expansa*. After Tower, 1900, *Zoologische Jahrbücher*, Abt. Anat., Band 13:359, courtesy of Gustav Fischer Verlag.

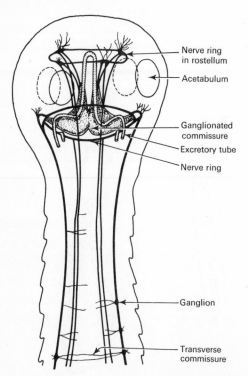

each proglottid a transverse vessel joins the pair of ventral vessels. Another feature associated with excretion in some tapeworms is the deposit of solid calcareous bodies in the cortical parenchyma.

With one exception *(Dioecocestus,* whose generic name is formed by combining the roots of the words, dioecious and cestode), tapeworms are hermaphroditic. The male reproductive system in monoecious tapeworms consists of testes, usually very numerous, situated near the upper side of the medullary parenchyma. From the testes small ducts join to form the vas deferens, which leads to the ejaculatory duct and cirrus within the cirrus sac. The cirrus sac opens to a recess called the common genital atrium, ventrally situated on tapeworms in the order Pseudophyllidea, laterally disposed on most other tapeworms (Fig. 7-19). The female reproductive organs consist of a typically bilobed ovary, oviduct, vitellaria or yolk glands, oötype with shell glands, vagina, and uterus. The vitellaria are peripherally, laterally, or caudally distributed in the proglottid. The vagina leads from the common genital atrium to join the oviduct, which also receives the vitelline duct. The oviduct is then enlarged to form the oötype provided with the Mehlis or shell gland. Fertilized eggs move from the oötype into the uterus, which may be a relatively straight or highly coiled tube, opening ventrally in most tapeworm orders (Fig. 7-20) but ending as a blind pouch usually with extensive lateral diverticula in the familiar tapeworms of the order Cyclophyllidea. Some members of this order have double sets of genitalia in each proglottid.

Relatively little is known of the early embryology of tapeworms, but life-cycle studies are extensive. The first larval stage develops within the shell to a six-hooked embryo called an *onchosphere* or *hexacanth larva.* In cyclophyllidean tapeworms this occurs in the uterus of the gravid proglottid. When these passed proglottids ultimately disintegrate, the shelled onchospheres are

Fig. 7-19 Diagrams showing the fundamental plan of organization of sexual organs in (a) trematodes and (b) cestodes. After Van Cleave 1931, courtesy of the McGraw-Hill Book Company.

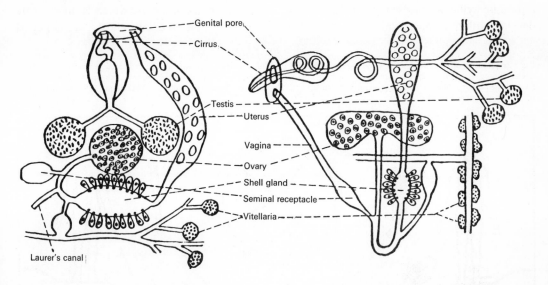

Fig. 7-20 Proglottid of *Diphyllobothrium latum*. Note uterine pore. *cb*, cirrus sheath opening with the vagina; *dg*, vitelline duct; *dt*, vitellarium, *h*, testes; *od*, oviduct; *ov*, ovary; *sd*, shell gland; *u*, uterus ; *va*, vagina; *vd*, vas deferens (dark-lined); *w*, excretory canal. From Hertwig, *A Manual of Zoology* (translated and edited by J. S. Kingsley) 1902, Holt, Rinehart & Winston, Inc.

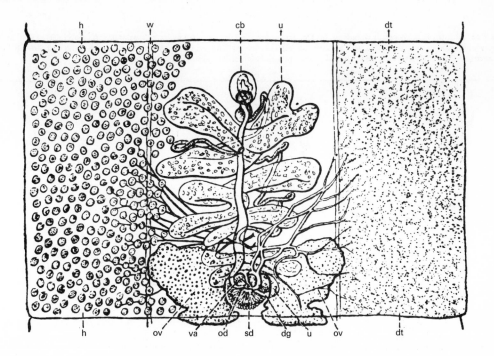

freed to contaminate food of the intermediate host. In *Diphyllobothrium latum* (Fig. 7-21), a pseudophyllidean tapeworm, onchospheres develop within an operculate egg discharged from the proglottid through the uterine pore. This egg hatches to a free-swimming ciliated larva called *coracidium,* which is ingested by the first intermediate host, a copepod

Fig. 7-21 Life cycle of *Diphyllobothrium latum.* (a) man infected with adult tapeworm; (b) ovum passed in feces; (c) coracidium or ciliated free-swimming larva; (d) copepod ingests larva; (e) procercoid larva in copepod; (f) fish infected by ingesting copepod; (g) plerocercoid larva in fish; (h) man infected by eating raw fish. From Belding, *Textbook of Clinical Parasitology* 1942 (2nd ed., 1952). By permission of Appleton-Century-Crofts.

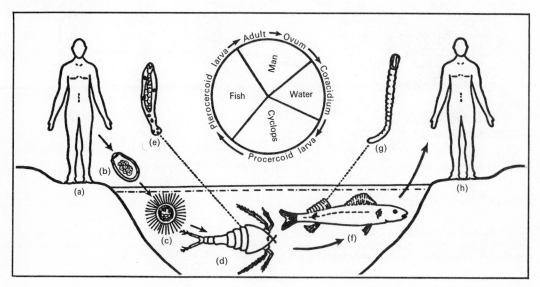

Fig. 7-22 Life cycle of *Echinococcus granulosus.* (a) Dog infected with adult worm; (b) ovum in feces of dog; (c) man infected with hydatid cyst; (d) herbivorous animal infected with hydatid cyst; (e) hydatid cyst in tissues; (f) dog infected by eating hydatid cyst. From Belding, *Textbook of Clinical Parasitology,* 1942 (2nd ed., 1952) by permission of Appleton-Century-Crofts, Inc.

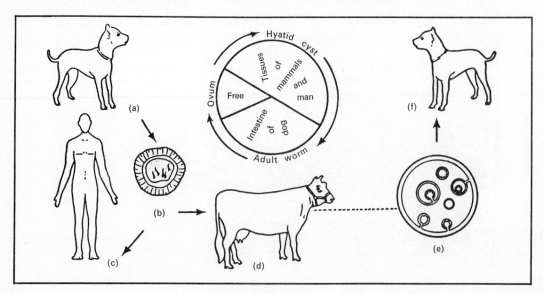

crustacean. The parasite penetrates to the body cavity bearing the six hooks at the posterior end and is now called a *procercoid*. When the copepod is eaten by suitable freshwater fish, the procercoid bores through the intestinal wall and becomes an encysted wormlike larval stage called *plerocercoid* or *sparganum*. Fish-eating mammals including man are definitive hosts for this large tapeworm. In man, infestation with this parasite often shows correlation with the development of pernicious anemia.

In cyclophyllidean tapeworms, arthropods are common intermediate hosts. Onchospheres are ingested by this host. In the case of *Dipylidium caninum*, flea larvae devour the tapeworm larvae in their food. *Cysticercoid* larvae develop in the flea tissues. This larva has a solid body with a small scolex retracted into an anterior recess. Dogs, cats, and frequently children accidentally ingest

infected fleas to become definitive hosts. In the Taeniidae family, the intermediate host is a mammal, and carnivorous habits of the final host are essential to completion of their life cycles. In the intermediate host, the infective stage reached by the parasite is called a bladder worm or *cysticercus*. The scolex is inverted into the fluid-filled bladder in these forms. The human tapeworms, *Taenia saginata* and *Taenia solium,* reach the definitive host by the eating of insufficiently cooked beef or pork respectively. *Echinococcus granulosus,* a member of this family, reaches adult stage in the intestine of dogs (Fig. 7-22). There is relatively little host specificity for the larval stage, which is commonly found in herbivorous hosts and in such omnivorous animals as pigs, rats, and man. The larval stage is a serious parasite and undergoes asexual reproduction by the formation of secondary bladders with multi-

Fig. 7-23 Diagram of the life cycle of *Hymenolepis nana*. Note that no intermediate host is necessary. From Faust, *Human Helminthology*, 1929, courtesy of Lea and Febiger.

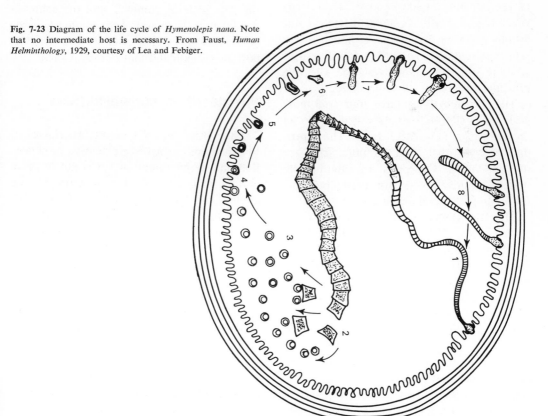

ple scolices. The lack of host specificity, the tremendous production of scolexes asexually, and the often considerable disability of the intermediate hosts, serve to insure survival of this minute species of tapeworm. Another small tapeworm *(Hymenolepis nana)* is a common parasite of man in the southern United States (Fig. 7-23).

Classification of Cestoda

The Cestoda can be conveniently divided into two subclasses. Subclass *Cestodaria* (excellent diagrams in Hyman, Vol. II) are unsegmented tapeworms. The body lacks a scolex, has a single set of reproductive organs, and develops through a larval stage with ten hooks. Subclass *Cestoda* (or *Eucestoda)* is characterized by a body segmented into proglottids, a holdfast organ called the scolex, typically with multiple sets of reproductive organs, and a larval stage which is armed with six hooks. Most classifications agree on five orders, although divergent representatives have been transferred to separate orders in some systems. The five principal orders are included here.

The **Tetraphyllidea** have four well-muscled, often stalked suckers called *bothridia* on the scolex (Fig. 7-17 (a)). The reproductive system has a uterine pore. Eggs are not operculate. Copepods are intermediate hosts; definitive hosts are elasmobranchs, fishes, amphibia and reptiles.

The **Diphyllidea** is an order set up for a single genus, *Echinobothrium*. It includes small tapeworms parasitic as adults in elasmobranchs. The scolex is provided with two poorly musculatured *bothria,* apparently degenerated from four, and several rows of spines on the elongate neck (Fig. 7-17 (b)). The larval stage, a cysticercoid, is found in decapod crustaceans in some species.

The **Trypanorhyncha** as adults occur in elasmobranch and ganoid fishes. A plerocercoid larva is found in a number of invertebrates and in fish. This is the last larval stage; an earlier larval stage, procercoid, occurs in some life cycles. Structurally, the scolex is unique with four, usually armed, eversible proboscides and four weakly musculatured lappetlike bothria (Fig. 7-17 (c)).

The **Pseudophyllidea** usually have two poorly musculatured bothria on an unarmed, ill-defined scolex (Fig. 7-17 (d), (e)). Genital pore and uterine pore are usually ventral on the proglottid. Coracidium, procercoid, and plerocercoid larvae occur in the life cycle. Adult tapeworms usually occur in fresh-water fish, although one species occurs in birds, and *Diphyllobothrium latum* occurs in mammals including man.

The **Cyclophyllidea** are the common tapeworms which mostly utilize birds and mammals as definitive hosts. These strongly segmented tapeworms have a scolex with four efficient suckers called *acetabula* and, terminally, a protrusible rostellum usually armed with hooks. The uterus ends blindly, the yolk gland is compact, and the common genital pore is lateral. *Dipylidium, Echinococcus, Hymenolepis,* and *Taenia* are important cyclophyllid tapeworms of man.

PHYLOGENETIC CONSIDERATIONS

Parasitism characteristic of two classes of Platyhelminthes involves extensive modification and degeneration, and it is not in these groups that evidence for ancestry of the phylum as a whole is likely to be found. But within the classes some interrelationships are apparent. Genera have been grouped into families not only by structural and embryological similarity but by strong parallels in ecology. The evolution of the parasite shows a correlation with the evolution of the host (Stunkard, 1957). Tapeworm families particularly show a parallel distribution in the bird families they parasitize. Parasitism is very ancient. In the tapeworms, the widespread parasitism among elasmobranchs is probably indicative of a parasitism that evolved with these ancient chordates.

With two exceptions, all digenetic trematodes utilize molluscan hosts. It is generally accepted that molluscs represent the original hosts for these trematodes and that later hosts were superimposed. More recently evidence has been advanced that some trematodes can foreshorten the life cycle and undergo sexual reproduction in the snail host. This supports the conclusion that the mollusc was the original definitive host.

Host specificity is well established among parasitic flatworms. The well-adapted parasite, indicating a long association with a given host, is less apt to produce deleterious effects leading to a host reaction terminating the relationship. To do so would be detrimental to a completion of the parasitic life cycle. Trematodes show marked host specificity for snail hosts as well as for definitive hosts. Hargis (1957) discusses the host specificity of marine Monogenea and its implications for phylogeny. Among tapeworms of man, *Bertiella studeri* can reach maturity in some other primates. *Taenia saginata* can develop only in man. *Diphyllobothrium latum* adults and *Echinococcus granulosus* larvae probably have a long history as mammalian parasites but either is apt to cause considerable host reaction in man, perhaps indicative of the lesser adjustment associated with lower host specificity.

Monogenea and Digenea probably both arose from rhabdocoele turbellarians, but they well may have developed independently. Structurally, Monogenea appear to be less modified from turbellarian ancestry, but the more complex life cycle of Digenea makes direct comparison difficult.

Among cestodes, Tetraphyllidea are probably most primitive and closer to a turbellarian ancestor. The Tetraphyllidea probably gave rise to Pseudophyllidea and Trypanorhyncha on one hand and to Cyclophyllidea on the other.

Examination of ciliated, free-living turbellarians provides the best evidence for ancestral relationship for the phylum Platyhelminthes. Hyman, who is a world authority on the Turbellaria, considers the Acoela as the primitive group ancestral to the other groups. Alloeocoela, Polycladida, and Rhabdocoela evolved from the acoels directly while the triclads represent a further radiation of the Alloeocoela.

MESOZOA

This group of minute parasitic animals is characterized by a presumed simple structure in which an outer cellular or syncytial layer covers a core of reproductive cells. Hyman (1940, 1959) supported by Dodson (1956) considers the Mesozoa to be primitively simple in structure, and they are placed as a phylum below the Porifera (Parazoa). They are considered to have a planula-like structure, but there are some remarkable differences. Planulae have a syncytial or cellular epithelium overlaying a core of phagocytic and reproductive cells, whereas the surface layer in the Mesozoa is phagocytic and the interior cell or cells are strictly reproductive (Fig. 7-24). It has been pointed

Fig. 7-24 Generalized drawing of a young dicyemid mesozoan. After McConnaughey 1951, courtesy of the *Univ. Calif. Publ. Zool.*

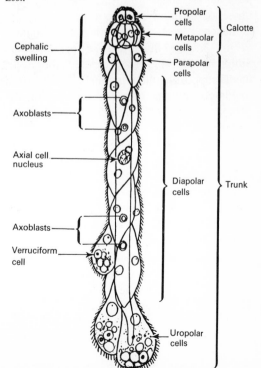

out that the Mesozoa structurally are at a pregastrular stage since they do not exhibit an endodermal migration to the interior. In support of the position that Mesozoa are primitively simple, Hyman points out their similarities to protozoa. These include the presence of cilia, the internal position of reproductive elements in some protozoa, and the metagenesis characteristic of some parasitic protozoa.

On the other hand, the molluscan parasitism of the dicyemid mesozoans is an example of host specificity of long duration. It is here, rather than with the orthonectid mesozoans (which have been found as parasites in turbellarians, nemerteans, annelids, echinoderms, and molluscs), that affinity for platyhelminths is more likely to be found. The digenetic trematodes are parasites of molluscs. In the embryology of Digenea, the egg undergoes segmentation to a two-celled stage. One of these cells is ancestral to somatic cells. Successive division of the other cell line produces daughter cells, half of which become reproductive cells. The reproductive cells remain in the interior of the developing embryo and become the progenitors of the next larval stage following the metamorphosis of the *miracidium* to a sporocyst in the molluscan host. An analogous situation occurs in the life cycle of orthonectids. Stunkard (1954) has presented the arguments supporting the relationship of Mesozoa to Platyhelminthes. It seems certain that the Mesozoa are not primitively simple, but neither can they be placed as a class of Platyhelminthes, although their structure and life cycle suggest some affinity with that phylum.

A brief resume of a life cycle in each of the two orders (Dicyemida and Orthonectida) follows. The life cycle of dicyemids is incompletely known. In the renal organs of very young cephalopods (a group that includes the octopus and squid), minute but elongate ciliated larvae called *nematogens* (Fig. 7-25) are commonly present. Most of these contain a row of three elongate axial

cells surrounded by layers of ciliated cells constant in number. This larval stage is the stem-nematogen. Each axial cell contains a vegetative nucleus and *agametes* which arose by repeated fission of a generative nucleus. No meiosis occurs in these fissions. The agametes possess cell walls, and these cells develop into a new generation of nematogens which soon are freed into the kidney fluid. Within these nematogens (Fig. 7-26), a new generation of nematogens arises. Eventually, and correlated with sexual maturity of the host, the last nematogen generation gives rise to a slightly different larval stage, either from agametes or by metamorphosis. This new larval stage is called a *rhombogen*. In rhombogens, only a few of the generative cells within the axial cell continue to develop, and these undergo meiosis to form hermaph-

Fig. 7-25 Young stem nematogen of *Dicyemia*, showing three axial cells each containing several germ cells. After McConnaughey 1951, courtesy of the *Univ. Calif. Publ. Zool.*

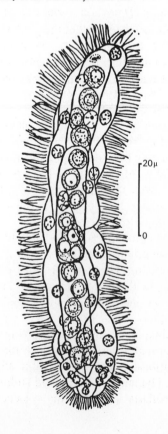

20μ

0

roditic cell aggregates called infusorigens with oocytes surrounding the male element. Upon fertilization, the zygotes develop into infusoriform larvae (Fig. 7-27), which are somewhat cone-shaped, ciliated stages characterized by two large refractile globes at the nonciliated anterior end. A cup-shaped urn formed consistently of four interior cells containing germinal nuclei has a cavity which opens to the surface. Infusoriform larvae leave the host and sink to the ocean floor. The life history (Fig. 7-28) is unknown from this point until the infection reappears in baby cephalopods.

The orthonectids, parasitic in the tissues of various invertebrates, occur as amoeboid, multinucleate masses called plasmodia, which reproduce asexually by unequal division. Some nuclei in the plasmodium develop as

agametes into males or females, although a few species are hermaphroditic. These are oval or somewhat elongate ciliated forms with a core of reproductive cells. Copulation occurs in sea water, and larvae develop ovoviviparously. These ciliated larvae leave the mother and reinfect the host species.

Fig. 7-27 Infusoriform larva of *Dicyemmenea abelis*. After Stunkard 1954, courtesy of the *Quart. Rev. Biol.*

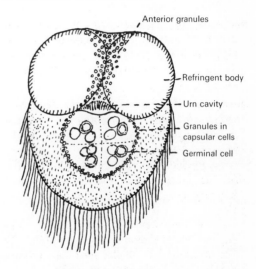

Fig. 7-26 Vermiform larva inclosed in the axial cell of a nematogen. After McConnaughey 1949, courtesy of the *Univ. Calif. Publ. Zool.*

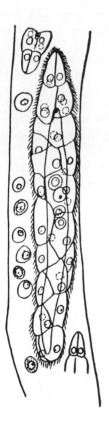

Fig. 7-28 Diagram of the dicyemid life cycle. After McConnaughey 1951, courtesy of the *Univ. Calif. Publ. Zool.*

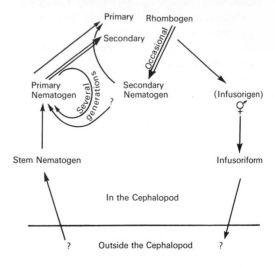

REFERENCES

Benham, W. B., The Platyhelmia, Mesozoa, and Nemertini. *In* (E. R. Lankester, ed.) A treatise on zoology, Part IV. London: A. & C. Black, 1901.

Dodson, E., A note on the systematic position of the Mesozoa. Syst. Zool., 5:37, 1956.

Hargis, W. J. Jr., The host specificity of monogenetic trematodes. Exp. Parasitol., 6:610, 1957.

Hartmann, M., Mesozoa. *In* (W. Kükenthal and T. Krumbach, ed.) Handbuch der Zoologie—eine Naturgeschichte der Stämme des Tierreiches, 1:996-1014. Berlin: Walter de Gruyter, 1925.

Hyman, L. H., Phylum Mesozoa (pp. 233-247). *In* The invertebrates: Protozoa through Ctenophora, Vol. I. New York: McGraw, 1940.

———, Phylum Platyhelminthes (pp. 52-458). *In* The invertebrates: Platyhelminthes and Rhynchocoela, Vol. II. New York: McGraw, 1951.

———, Phylum Mesozoa (pp. 713-715) and Phylum Platyhelminthes (pp. 731-738). *In* The invertebrates: smaller coelomate groups, Vol. V. New York: McGraw, 1959.

———, and E. R. Jones, Turbellaria (pp. 323-365). *In* (W. T. Edmondson, ed.) Ward and Whipple's Fresh-water biology. New York: Wiley, 1959.

Jennings, J. B., Studies on feeding, digestion, and food storage in free-living flatworms (Platyhelminthes: Turbellaria). Biol. Bull., 112:63, 1957.

———, Further studies on feeding and digestion in triclad Turbellaria. Biol. Bull., 123:571, 1962.

La Rue, G. R., The classification of the digenetic Trematoda, a review and a new system, Exp. Parasitol., 6:305, 1957.

McConnaughey, B. H., The life cycle of the dicyemid Mesozoa. Univ. Calif. Publ. Zool., 55:295, 1951.

Nouvel, H., Les Dicy'emides, Part I. Arch. Biol., 58:59, 1947.

———, Les Dicy'emides, Part II. Arch. Biol., 59:147, Turbellaria (pp. 114-141), 1948.

Pennak, R. W., Fresh-water invertebrates of the United States. New York: Ronald, 1953.

Smyth, J. D., The physiology of tapeworms. Biol. Rev., 22:214, 1947.

Stunkard, H. W., Studies on North American Polystomatidae, Aspidogastridae, and Paraamphistomidae. Ill. Biol. Monogr., 3:1, 1917.

———, Interrelationships and taxonomy of the digenetic trematodes. Biol. Rev., 21:148, 1946.

———, Life history and systematic relations of the Mesozoa. Quart. Rev. Biol., 29:230, 1954.

———, Host-specificity and parallel evolution of parasitic flatworms. Zeitschr. Tropenmed. u. Parasitol., 8:254, 1957.

———, Taeniocotyle nom. nov. for *Macraspis* Olsson, 1869, preocccupied, and systematic position of the Aspidobothrea. Biol. Bull., 122:137, 1962.

Wardle, R. A., and J. A. McLeod, The zoology of tapeworms. Minneapolis: U. of Minnesota, 1952.

8

NEMERTINA OR RHYNCHOCOELA

This group of acoelomate worms stand apart from Platyhelminthes (which are probably their nearest relatives) because of the more refined development of some structures and the presence of some innovations. In the nemertines the nervous system reaches a greater degree of concentration, both in the cerebral ganglia and in the longitudinal nerves. Among free-living flatworms, as many as five pairs of longitudinal trunks become reduced to three pairs. In nemertines, a single pair of lateral trunks are strongly developed. Commonly there is also a middorsal nerve and occasionally a median ventral nerve. An increasing tendency to develop ganglia at intervals along the length of some of these nerve trunks occurs among nemertines. Another significant feature in this group is the increased identity of the body wall as a distinctive organ. The development of a posterior exit to the digestive tract marks still another advance over the blind caecal pattern of flatworms.

A common name for nemertines is ribbon worms. MacGinitie and MacGinitie relate that *Cerebratulus lacteus,* common along the Atlantic Coast of the United States, may reach a length of 35 feet and a width of one half inch when extended. This same worm can contract to a somewhat cylindrical three feet. *Cerebratulus* is not the largest nemertine. Species of *Tetrastemma,* some of which are commensal in Tunicates, are among the smallest, being less than one quarter inch in length. Not only are ribbon worms very extensible, but the eversible proboscis can be projected several feet in the larger species. Because of shape and extensibility, nemertines can move through small openings, and many are excellent burrowers in sand or mud.

Some nemertines are drably colored in whites and browns, but many are irregularly striped or uniformly colored in reds, oranges and greens. In general, the anterior region is apt to be more vividly colored than the posterior.

Two features that are peculiarly distinctive for nemertines are the closed circulatory

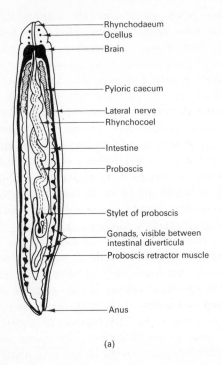

- Rhynchodaeum
- Ocellus
- Brain
- Pyloric caecum
- Lateral nerve
- Rhynchocoel
- Intestine
- Proboscis
- Stylet of proboscis
- Gonads, visible between intestinal diverticula
- Proboscis retractor muscle
- Anus

(a)

Fig. 8-1 (a) Adult nemertean, *Prostoma rubrum* showing organ systems. After Coe 1943, courtesy of Conn. Acad. Arts & Sci. (b) Sagittal view of *Prostoma graecense*. After Reisinger 1926, courtesy of Gebrüder Borntraeger, Berlin, editors of *Biologie der Tiere Deutschlands*.

system and the eversible proboscis. From this latter feature the alternate phylum name of *Rhynchocoela* has been derived. The lymphatic system characteristic of some parasitic flatworms has a circulatory function but can scarcely be considered as ancestral to the well-defined circulatory system of Nemertina. On the other hand, Hyman considers the anterior protrusible organ characteristic of some rhabdocoel turbellarians to be a definite forerunner to the nemertine proboscis.

Nemertina are predominately marine, nonparasitic worms which lack external pseudometamerism. They are usually rather uniformly elongate animals (Fig. 8-1), somewhat ovoid in cross section and without conspicuous appendages. The skin is uniformly ciliated and provided with glands which secrete a mucus at the surface. Only about a dozen species of some 600 described are not marine. One of these, *Prostoma rubrum* is widely distributed in fresh waters in the United States. Of the marine forms, a few are commensal or possibly parasitic. Commensal partners of nemertines include

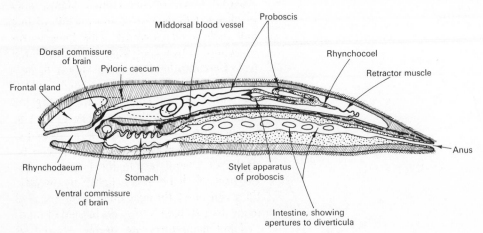

- Middorsal blood vessel
- Proboscis
- Dorsal commissure of brain
- Rhynchocoel
- Pyloric caecum
- Retractor muscle
- Frontal gland
- Rhynchodaeum
- Anus
- Stomach
- Stylet apparatus of proboscis
- Ventral commissure of brain
- Intestine, showing apertures to diverticula

Note that proboscis is hollow and stylet is attached to *one* side only

(b)

tunicates, anemones, bivalve molluscs, and crabs.

An important feature of rhynchocoels is the development of the muscle in the body wall. The more primitive forms have an outer circular and an inner longitudinal layer, a condition which parallels that for some primitive turbellarians. Other nemertines have three prominent layers, but they do not fall into a monophyletic group since some have two layers of circular muscle separated by a longitudinal stratum and others have a contrary arrangement. A classification system utilizing Dimyaria and Trimyaria, indicating the number of muscle layers, is therefore artificial.

The Nemertina are commonly divided into two subclasses. Subclass Anopla includes those rhynchocoels in which the brain lies in front of the mouth and the proboscis has no armature other than some nematocystlike structures. In the Anopla, the longitudinal nerve cords lie in a more primitive position within or external to the body-wall musculature. In the class Enopla, the brain is at the same level or behind the mouth, the

proboscis secretes one or more piercing thornlike structures called stylets (Fig. 8-2), and the body-wall musculature is external to the longitudinal nerve cords.

Marine nemertines are widely distributed along coasts in regions of temperate climate, and a number of genera are common in both arctic and antarctic regions. In general, rhynchocoels occur in deeper water in warmer oceans and nearer the surface in colder waters. A number of genera of enoplan rhynchocoels are pelagic. These are well known from the more southern regions of the North Atlantic, where they are most common below a thousand meters. Some of these are good swimmers; others with less developed musculature are floaters. The enoplan genus, *Geonemertes,* is a terrestrial group found under adequate cover on subtropical shores in both the Atlantic and the Pacific.

While some nemertines can swim by undulating body action sometimes aided by fins, for most of them locomotion is confined to crawling on suitable substrate. Most of this locomotion is parallel to that in Turbel-

Fig. 8-2 *Amphoporus griseus*, (a) head, showing arrangement of ocelli, (b) central stylets and bases, and (c) middle chamber of proboscis with armature. After Coe 1943, courtesy of Conn. Acad. Arts & Sci.

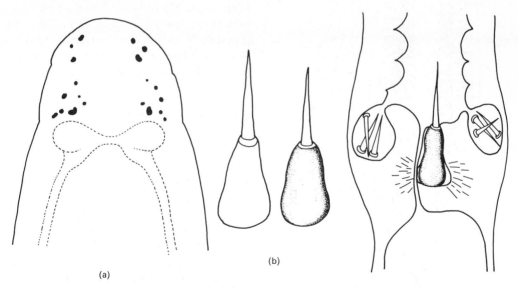

(a)

(b)

(c)

laria, with slime or mucus production providing purchase for ciliary action.

DIGESTIVE SYSTEM

The alimentary canal may be a relatively uniform tube throughout its length from the anterior opening to the anus. The mouth opens ventrally in more primitive nemertines, but in many of the group it has no external orifice but connects with the proboscis canal near the proboscis pore. Frequently, the digestive canal shows a varying diameter and the foregut is a relatively simple tube, sometimes differentiated zonally by constrictions into successive regions and an elongate intestine with one large cephalad-projecting caecum and many lateral caeca (Fig. 8-3).

Fig. 8-3 *Plionemertes plana*, showing proboscis, and digestive and nervous systems from ventral surface. After Coe 1926, courtesy of the Mus. Comp. Zool. Harvard.

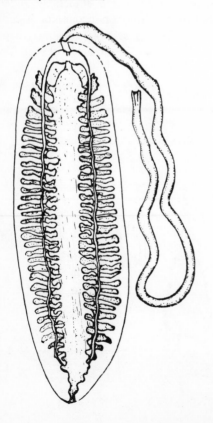

Nemertines are carnivorous, and the proboscis functions in obtaining food as well as in a defensive capacity. It is a hollow organ which upon extrusion is turned inside out by the hydrostatic action of musculature upon the fluid contained within the proboscis sheath or rhynchocoele. The proboscis is withdrawn into the proboscis sheath by retractor muscles, and since it is frequently longer than the pseudocoele, it may be folded upon itself within the sheath dorsal to the digestive canal.

Annelids constitute the most common food of nemertines, although crustaceans are utilized by some genera. When a nemertine finds the trail of an annelid, the proboscis follows the trail (even into the burrow) and spirals closely around the prey. Adhesive mucus is utilized to hold the annelid, which may be pierced repeatedly by the proboscis stylet in armed nemertines. While there is some indication of toxic or anesthetic effects of proboscis secretions, Jennings has shown for *Lineus* that the prey, which is swallowed whole, is killed by acid secretions in the foregut of this rhynchocoel. These acid secretions appear to be associated with the presence of carbonic anhydrase in acidophil gland cells of the buccal cavity and foregut. Digestion is begun in the intestinal lumen by proteolytic enzymes, and completed intracellularly by the gastrodermis. Lipase has been identified in the phagocytic cells and carbohydrases are almost certainly present.

CIRCULATORY SYSTEM

The blood-vascular system is considered to be a closed system, the blood propelled by the contraction of circular muscle present in larger vessels. Various smaller thin-walled vessels and lacunae occur in the system. The principal tubes are longitudinal and consist of a middorsal and a pair of lateral vessels joined by transverse connectives. Colorless corpuscles are generally characteristic of the blood, but some species have corpuscles provided with the respiratory pigment, hemo-globin and colors other than red occur.

EXCRETORY SYSTEM

Flame-bulb protonephridia occur laterally and empty through one or more pairs of nephridiopores. Flame-bulbs are commonly dispersed in close continuity with the lateral blood vessels.

NERVOUS SYSTEM

Two pairs of ganglia connected dorsally and ventrally by commissures surround the proboscis sheath. A dorsal and paired lateral nerve cords arise from this complex (Fig. 8-4). Connecting these cords are net-works in more primitive nemertines, but reg-ular commissures replace the networks in many species. The ventral connectives of the lateral nerve trunks pass below the digestive canal. Various chemo-sensory and tactile sense organs occur principally at the ante-rior end. A varying number of paired eyes are common in the Nemertina.

Fig. 8-4 Diagram of the nervous system of *Neuronemertes auran-tiaca* showing the dorsal and ventral (cerebral) ganglia and most of the left lateral nerve cord. The cerebral ganglia are connected above and below to form a ring around the rhynchodaeum. *dg*, dorsal ganglia; *vg*, ventral ganglia; *dc, vc*, corresponding com-missures; *n*, cephalic nerves; *pn*, origin of proboscidial nerves; *dn*, dorsal nerve entering the *pa*, the posterior anastomosis of the lateral nerves at the caudal extremity but terminating anteriorly some distance behind brain; *ln*, lateral nerve, with *dp*, metameric dorsal; *lp*, lateral; and *vp*, ventral peripheral nerves; *dln*, dorso-lateral nerve, with delicate communicating branches both with the dorsal nerve and with the dorsal peripheral branches of the lateral nerve; *g*, gastric nerve; *cn*, caudal nerves. After Coe 1926, courtesy of the Mus. Comp. Zool. Harvard.

REPRODUCTION AND EMBRYOLOGY

Most nemertines are dioecious, with the gonads tending to be pseudosegmentally ar-ranged between the lateral caeca of the in-testine (Fig. 8-1). Each ovary or testis is provided with its own pore; these tend to lie laterodorsally. In the females, the gonopores may be transitory. Freshly deposited eggs are connected by a gelatinous matrix. Fer-tilization is typically external and spawning is an annual occurrence.

Fig. 8-5 Optical section of a pilidium of *Micrura caeca* to show the wide mouth opening to a large esophagus which leads to a small spherical midgut. After Coe 1943, courtesy of Conn. Acad. Arts & Sci.

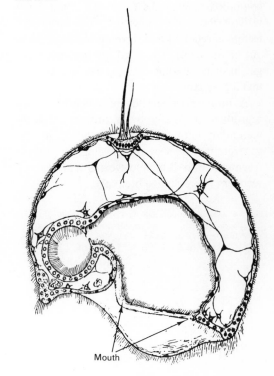

Mouth

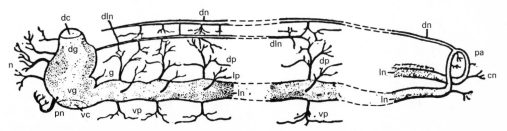

Spiral determinative cleavage is characteristic of Nemertina. Development is direct in most nemertines, but in one order of the probably more primitive subclass (Anopla) metamorphosis occurs through either *Desor's larva* or a *pilidium* (Fig. 8-5). The free-swimming ciliated pilidium frequently has a resemblance to a helmet, with a pair of oral lobes which might be thought of as ear-flaps and a narrow plume of long cilia at the apex.

Metamorphosis of the pilidium is initiated by the formation of a series of paired and median discs which invaginate from the larval ectoderm. Later, most of these discs become hollow, and upon coalescence their combined inner walls form the initial body wall of the adult nemertine. The larval intestine is retained and develops into the midgut of the adult. The hind gut and the foregut in at least some forms arise by ectodermal inpocketing.

A number of species of nemertines can reproduce asexually by a process of fragmentation (Fig. 8-6). Strong ability to regenerate is shown by the development of the fragments into complete worms and also by recovery from chance breakage.

Fig. 8-6 Asexual reproduction by fragmentation is shown in *Lineus socialis* in (a), (b), and (c). (d) is an enlarged section of an adult worm to show fission zones. After Coe 1943, courtesy of Conn. Acad. Arts & Sci.

REFERENCES

Benham, W. B., The Platyhelmia, Mesozoa, and Nemertini (pp. 159-195). *In* (E. R. Lankester, ed.) A treatise on zoology, Part IV. London: A. & C. Black, 1901.

Coe, W. R., The pelagic nemerteans. Mem. Mus. Comp. Zool., Harvard, 49:1, 1926.

———, Biology of the nemerteans of the Atlantic coast of North America. Trans. Conn. Acad. Arts Sci., 35:129, 1943.

Hyman, L. H., The invertebrates: Platyhelminthes and Rhynchocoela, Vol. II (pp. 459-531). New York: McGraw, 1951.

Jennings, J. B., A histochemical study of digestion and digestive enzymes in the rhynchocoelan, *Lineus ruber* (O. F. Müller), Biol. Bull., 122:63, 1962.

MacGinitie, G. E., and N. MacGinitie, Natural history of marine animals. New York: McGraw, 1949.

Reisinger, E., Nemertini, Schnurwürmer. Biol. Tiere Deutschlands, Lief 17, Teil 7:1, 1926.

Wheeler, J. F. G., Notes on *Gorgonorhynchus bermudensis*. Ann. Mag. Natur. Hist., Ser. II, 6:433, 1940.

Wilson, C. B., Habits and early development of *Cerebratulus lacteus*. Quart. J. Microsc. Sci., 43:97, 1900.

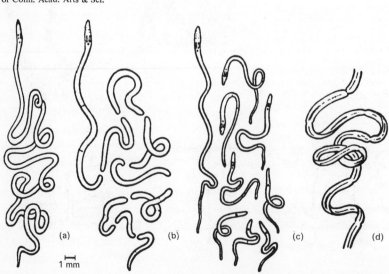

(a)   (b)   (c)   (d)

1 mm

9

PHYLUM ASCHELMINTHES

In a number of animal groups, of which the phylum Aschelminthes is a prominent member, a more or less extensive space called a *pseudocoele* occurs between the outer body wall and the alimentary tract and other organs. Mesenteries do not support the contained organs and there is no continuous peritoneal lining characteristic of a true coelom. Fluid is present in the pseudocoele and occasionally the space is bridged by the anastomosis of delicate processes of amoeboid cells. Embryologically, the pseudocoele usually represents a persistent blastocoele, which is obliterated in development in the typical coelomate animal.

Another feature shared by most pseudocoelomates (Endoprocta seem to be an exception) is the condition of relative *eutely* or nuclear constancy. In cellular or nuclear constancy (the latter term is better, since there is a tendency to form syncytia) the ability of nuclei to divide is lost or restricted about hatching time. Sometimes tissues in adults show a constant or nearly constant number of nuclei for each organ; any subsequent growth is due to increase in amount of cytoplasm in individual cells or in the syncytium. In some animals that exhibit eutely, not only number but location of nuclei seems predetermined. If the vegetative functions of nuclei are kept in mind, it is not surprising that most animals that have nuclear constancy have determinate cleavage. Another relationship occurs between eutely and the ability for regeneration, or for asexual reproduction by such a process as budding. Germinal tissue usually retains its ability to divide, although this is not true for the ovary in mature Rotifera, which constiutes one of the classes of Phylum Aschelminthes.

This phylum includes five groups of animals, sometimes placed in separate phyla on the basis of their divergencies, but which nevertheless share generally a number of characteristics indicative of close phylogenetic relationship. These features include a cuticle which is often striated or annulated, a fluid-filled pseudocoelom, pseudometamerism, somatic musculature of the body wall (mainly longitudinal), a proctodaeum lined with cuticle, and a lack of circulatory and respiratory systems. The Aschelminthes have determinative cleavage and often exhibit eutely. Some additional features are unevenly distributed among the groups composing this phylum. The intestinal musculature is poorly developed; the pharynx is prominent; the excretory system usually has protonephridia and lateral canals; and a foregut with triradiate lumen is frequent. The five groups which will be included as classes are Rotifera, Gastrotricha, Nematoda, Nematomorpha, and Kinorhyncha. The Priapulida, included in Aschelminthes by Hyman (albeit with recognition of their diversities), is removed because of the detection of the coelomic nature of their body cavity (Shapeero, 1961).

CLASS ROTIFERA

These microscopic, usually transparent Aschelminthes are mostly less than half a millimeter long. Although a few rotifers are marine, and some are parasitic, most occur in fresh water as free-swimming, sessile, or creeping forms (Fig. 9-1). The typical form is cylindrical, tapering slightly to a truncated anterior end bearing one or two rings of cilia. At the other extremity the trunk narrows and the movable foot or tail protrudes from it. Frequently a pair of movable toes extends from the trunk. Many variations in body form occur among the approximately 1500 known species. The shape may vary from a broad cone to a spheroid. The cuticle may be thickened to produce a slightly flexible armor called a *lorica*. The trunk may be curved into a slight arc, and it may be

Fig. 9-1 Composite diagram showing some of the features seen in the genus, *Asplanchna*. Adapted from various sources.

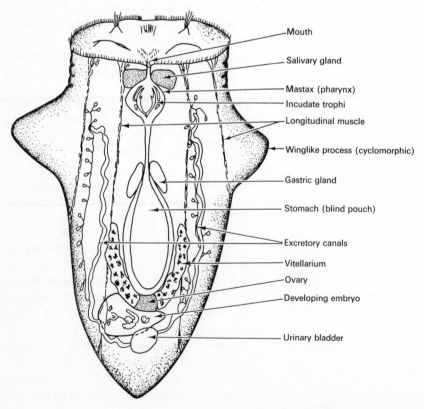

Mouth

Salivary gland

Mastax (pharynx)

Incudate trophi

Longitudinal muscle

Winglike process (cyclomorphic)

Gastric gland

Stomach (blind pouch)

Excretory canals

Vitellarium

Ovary

Developing embryo

Urinary bladder

flattened, especially on the ventral side. Various lobations of the ciliary anterior rings occur as well as spines and other projections from the trunk. The foot may be modified as a stalk, reduced, or absent. The number of toes may vary.

Characteristic of Aschelminthes, there is no well-defined head. The mouth opens at the broader anterior end and bears functional relationship to the cilia located there. The somewhat asymmetrical anterior surface bears the ciliary apparatus distinctive of rotifers. This apparatus is called the *corona*. The cilia occur in one or two rings and, when the cilia are beating, the more or less circular lobations of the corona common in some rotifers suggest the motion of a wheel —hence the name of wheel animalcule.

Variations in the corona are best understood if the projected evolutionary development is explained as described in Hyman after de Beauchamp. This hypothesis might be explained as follows: A primitive creeping rotifer possessed a mouth situated in the middle of a broad ciliated ventral zone; from this area a band of cilia encircled the anterior end of the animal, so that the total ciliated area somewhat resembled a signet ring; and reduction of cilia around the mouth and retention of cilia on one or both edges of the band could lead to the structure characteristic of many free-swimming rotifers. Among rotifers with two rings of cilia in the corona, the outer ring is known as the *cingulum* and the inner as the *trochus*. The mouth is located between these two rings toward the ven-

Fig. 9-2 Composite diagram of *Epiphanes senta*. Adapted from various sources.

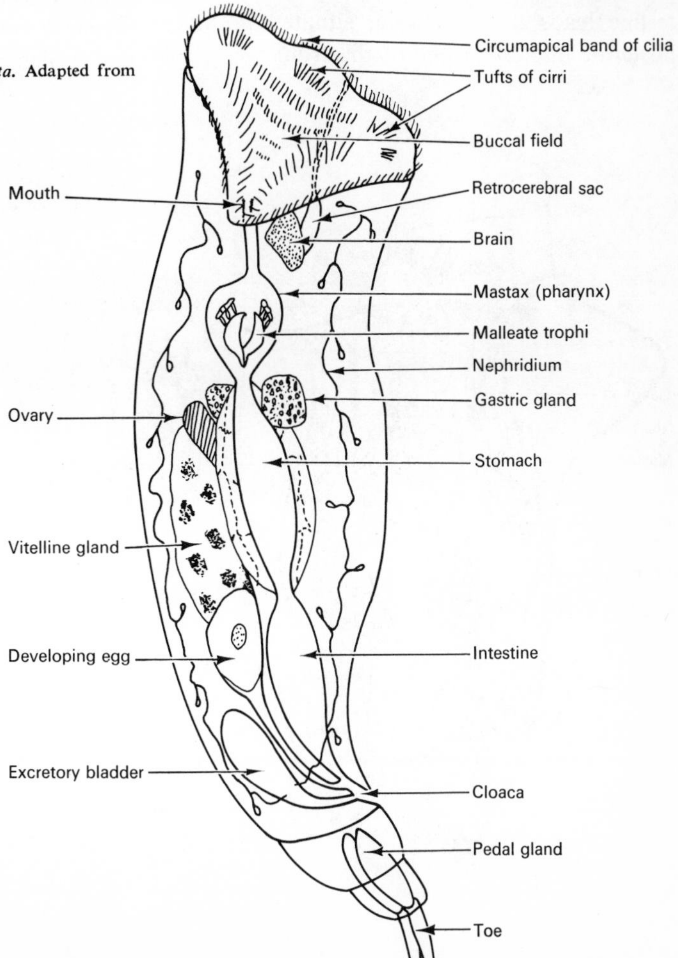

tral side variously edged by other cilia.

The mouth opens directly or by way of a short tube to the pharynx or *mastax* (Fig. 9-2). This muscular organ contains a complex jaw structure of hardened cuticle called the *trophi,* usually composed of seven parts which function in the most primitive form as two components to masticate the food. The two components are the *incus* (anvil) and *malleus* (hammer). The trophi exhibit an extensive variety of forms correlated with the great variation in feeding habits among rotifers, and of course the structure is very important taxonomically. A pair of salivary glands opens into the mastax or to the digestive tract anterior to it.

From the mastax a short esophagus leads to an enlarged stomach supplied with a pair of gastric glands. Large ciliated cells compose the stomach wall. A short ciliated intestine leads to the cloaca, situated in the posterior middorsal line of the trunk.

Rotifers are dioecious. Males are much smaller than females and differ structurally both internally and externally. Some rotifers reproduce principally, and others entirely, by parthenogenesis. Usually there is a single ovary, closely associated with a single vitellarium or yolk gland (Fig. 9-3). An oviduct leads to the cloaca. In the males a single sperm duct, supplied with a pair of accessory glands, leads to the gonopore. The terminus of the sperm duct is supplied with a cirrus, and fertilization usually occurs directly through the body wall of the female.

There is no special respiratory apparatus. Excretion is performed by a pair of protonephridia which empty through the cloaca. The brain or cerebral ganglion lies near the dorsal body wall above the mastax. Nerves from sensory elements such as the papillae within the corona and lateral eyespots (when present) run to the brain, which often carries a median eyespot embedded in its dor-

Fig. **9-3** *Brachionus,*(a) female with four eggs; (b) male; (c) protonephridium (flame-bulb) greatly enlarged. From Hertwig, *A Manual of Zoology* (translated and edited by J. S. Kingsley) 1902, Holt, Rinehart & Winston, Inc.

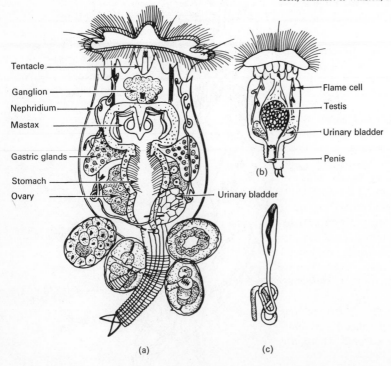

Tentacle

Ganglion

Nephridium

Mastax

Gastric glands

Stomach

Ovary

Urinary bladder

Flame cell

Testis

Urinary bladder

Penis

(a)   (b)   (c)

sal surface. Various motor nerves supply muscles, and additional ganglia may be associated with complex areas such as the mastax musculature. A pair of ventral nerves curves laterally from the brain and runs to the foot; some ganglionic enlargements may occur en route.

Cleavage initially is determinate and spiral, but later takes on a bilateral pattern, at least for *Ploesoma*. Most rotifers are oviparous and have a shell which is absent on the eggs of ovoviviparous species. A number of rotifers produce eggs that develop parthenogenetically. Such eggs are diploid and are called *amictic* eggs. The females that produce them are called amictic females. Amictic eggs are sometimes known as summer eggs and they hatch relatively soon after deposit. Usually seasonally, and hence probably influenced by hormones, a generation of parthenogenetically produced females give rise to eggs that have undergone meiosis and hence are haploid. These eggs are somewhat smaller and are called *mictic* eggs. If not fertilized, they develop into haploid males. If fertilization ocurs, they grow larger and develop thick shells. Such eggs are called dormant or winter eggs and are very resistant to a variety of adverse conditions. When these eggs hatch they produce only amictic females.

Orders of Rotifera

Order 1 Seisonidea This is a small group of primitive, marine Rotifera, parasitic on the gills of the primitive malacostracan crustacean, *Nebalia*. Paired gonads, a reduced corona, and an elongate foot terminating in an adhesive disc are characteristic. *Seison, Paraseison.*

Order 2 Bdelloidea These rotifers can creep or swim. The foot is telescopic and usually bears spurs and two to four retractile toes. In Bdelloidea, the trochal ciliary ring is divided into two stalked portions. Males are unknown in this group of fresh-water rotifers. *Philodina, Rotaria.*

Order 3 Monogononta This group includes free-swimming and attached rotifers. Locomotion is performed by the corona. There are never more than two toes. Some forms may develop a lorica. *Epiphanes (= Hydatina), Asplanchna, Proales.*

CLASS GASTROTRICHA

Gastrotrichs are minute aquatic animals. Most of them are in the lower half of a range that measures from 100 to 600 micra in length. Shortly behind the blunt or slightly lobed anterior end in fresh-water forms, the body narrows gradually in a so-called neck before enlargement into an ovoid or spindle-shaped trunk which terminates in a fork called the furca (Fig. 9-4). Marine gastrotrichs are more uniformly cylindroid.

Fresh-water gastrotrichs are placed in the order Chaetonotoidea; the other order, Macrodasyoidea, is strictly marine. Unless otherwise noted, this account will be based on fresh-water forms.

Externally, groups of long sensory cilia project on the head lobe. Cilia, primarily for

Fig. 9-4 *Chaetonotus*, a gastrotrich. After Goodchild 1950, *Selected Invertebrate Types* (F. A. Brown, Jr., ed.), courtesy of John Wiley & Sons, Inc.

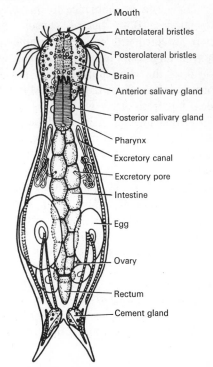

Mouth
Anterolateral bristles
Posterolateral bristles
Brain
Anterior salivary gland
Posterior salivary gland
Pharynx
Excretory canal
Excretory pore
Intestine
Egg
Ovary
Rectum
Cement gland

locomotion, occur on the usually somewhat flattened ventral surface of head, neck, and trunk. The head cilia may occur uniformly or in patches. Two parallel rows of cilia extend caudally in most Chaetonotoidea, although in some species two parallel rows of intermittent clumps of cilia develop. In at least one marine species, cilia occur in transverse rows on the ventral surface. The cuticle may be thickened as a mosaic of plates or, more frequently, it develops overlapping scales. Caudally curved spines commonly protrude from these scales. This spination may vary regionally in a given species.

In most Chaetonotoidea one or two pairs of adhesive tubes open on the furca. Small adhesive glands open through them to supply a fluid for temporary attachment. Other openings are the terminal or slightly ventral mouth; the anus, usually opening dorsally near the base of the furca; paired excretory pores opening midway on the ventral surface and a posterior gonopore.

The mouth, which may be armed with bristles, opens to a small buccal capsule. The pharynx is an elongated, thick-walled muscular organ with a triradiate lumen which bears noteworthy resemblance to this organ in nematodes. Both buccal capsule and pharynx are lined with cuticle. A simple epithelium of large cells forms the midgut, and cuticle lines the very short rectum. No excretory system is known for the Macrodasyoidea, but fresh-water gastrotrichs have a pair of protonephridia. A large bilobed brain lies lateral and dorsal to the pharynx. A pair of lateral nerve strands extend caudally from the brain.

Reproduction is by parthenogenesis in most Chaetonotoidea, testes being reduced or absent in all but one or two genera in these hermaphroditic animals. The Macrodasyoidea are monoecious also and possess one or two testes. The genital systems open by united or separate gonopores. One or two ovaries are characteristic of gastrotrichs. A condition of protandry and the presence of a vestigial copulatory bursa in a few gastrotrichs suggest cross-fertilization. Two kinds of eggs are produced by at least some fresh-water species. One of the kinds is more resistant to adverse conditions. There is no metamorphosis and no ecdysis in the development of gastrotrichs.

CLASS NEMATODA

The nematodes or roundworms are elongate, cylindrical Aschelminthes which generally are threadlike and of uniform diameter, or which taper very gradually from the mid-

Fig. 9-5 Two free-living nematodes; (a) an adult female, *Turbatrix aceti*, often found in vinegar and called the vinegar eelworm. After Goodchild 1950, *Selected Invertebrate Types* (F. A. Brown, Jr., ed.) courtesy of John Wiley & Sons, Inc. (b) *Criconomoides macrodorum*, occurring in leaf mould. (Note annulations and the long black stylet at the anterior end.) 18-19, 20-21, 23-24, 27-28, lateral views of ant. and post. ends, respectively for *Criconemoides rusticum, C. mutabile, C. demani,* and *C. sphaerocephalum,* respectively; 22, post. end of *C. mutabile* larva; 25, *C. annulatum* (ant. end, lateral view; post. end, ventral view); 29, *C. macrodorum* (lateral view). After Taylor 1936, *Trans. Amer. Microsc. Soc.,* 55:391.

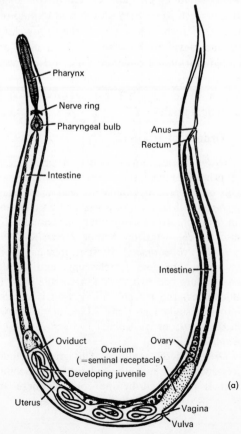

Pharynx

Nerve ring

Pharyngeal bulb

Anus

Rectum

Intestine

Intestine

Oviduct

Ovary

Ovarium (=seminal receptacle)

Developing juvenile

(a)

Uterus

Vagina

Vulva

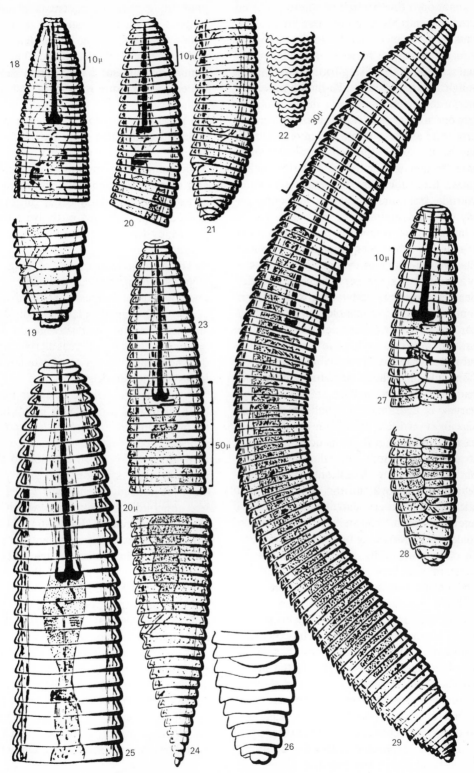

(b)

point toward the extremities where they may terminate in a sharp point. The anterior extremity may end bluntly in lips or in a rimmed concavity in some parasitic nematodes, while in free-living forms, long bristles and ornate spines mark the mouth area. The nearly complete absence of cilia in two large groups of very successful animals (nematodes and insects) in an exceptionally notable feature. While the body surface appears smooth and glistening in parasitic nematodes, the cuticle is frequently sculptured with fine transverse striations, and occasionally more pronounced grooves suggest pseudosegmentation (Fig. 9-5). Spines and bristles on the trunk are more common among free-living roundworms.

Nematodes are a very successful group. There are marine, fresh-water, and terrestrial nematodes. It is probable that only a fraction of the free-living species have been described. Parasitic species are certainly less numerous than their free-living relatives, and thousands of parasitic nematodes have been described. As a group they are better known because of their larger size and the detrimental effects of their parasitism in plants and animals. While most parasitic roundworms are less than an inch long, there are a number of astonishing exceptions. Female kidney worms in dogs and the guinea worm in man which occurs subcutaneously may reach lengths of over three feet, while females of the genus *Ascaris* may be nearly a foot long. On the other hand, free-living nematodes range in size between 200 micra and five centimeters, but most are microscopic.

There are far fewer varieties of roundworms infecting plants than occur in animals, but as indicated by Chitwood and Chitwood, there is markedly less host specificity exhibited in plants, so that the potential parasitism is less restricted and the economic loss tremendous in plant crops of commercial importance. Plant nematodes cause serious losses of which the average person is completely unaware, but because of

plant injury and consequent crop reduction, he pays higher prices on such things as potatoes, walnuts, citrus fruits, tea, tobacco, and ornamental plants. In the United States annual crop losses have been reliably estimated to be from a quarter to half a billion dollars.

Free-living nematodes, which undoubtedly greatly outnumber those parasitic in plants and animals, have a world-wide distribution. They inhabit the mud in both fresh-water and marine environments and are numerous in terrestrial soil. They occur in hot springs and have been thawed out alive from polar ice. Many live at great depths in lakes and oceans.

The nematode parasites of man and of common domesticated animals are well known. It is of interest that omnivorous or carnivorous animals such as man, dog, cat, and pig each have parasite species numbering in the thirties; whereas herbivorous cattle, sheep, and horses can harbor from fifty to seventy nematode species.

As is characteristic of Aschelminthes, the body surface is a cuticle. It is produced by the adjacent epidermis, which is commonly called hypodermis and occurs in a number of distinctive layers. In addition to the regular transverse striations and grooves previously mentioned, attention is called to fin-like longitudinal thickenings which are of frequent occurence (Fig. 9-6). These fin-like ridges occur laterally and are called *alae.* Three kinds are distinguished: longitudinal alae are continuous along the sides of the body; cervical alae, restricted to parasitic roundworms, occur at the anterior end in both sexes; and caudal alae occur at the posterior end in the males of many species and have a copulatory function. In some nematodes they have evolved into a bell-like expansion termed a *bursa,* which may or may not be supported by muscular rays. In *Enterobius vermicularis* (the pinworm, a too-common parasite in children and a form often examined in the

Fig. 9-6 Nematode morphology at the termini. From Belding, *Textbook of Clinical Parasitology* 1942 (2nd ed., 1952), by permission of Appleton-Century-Crofts.

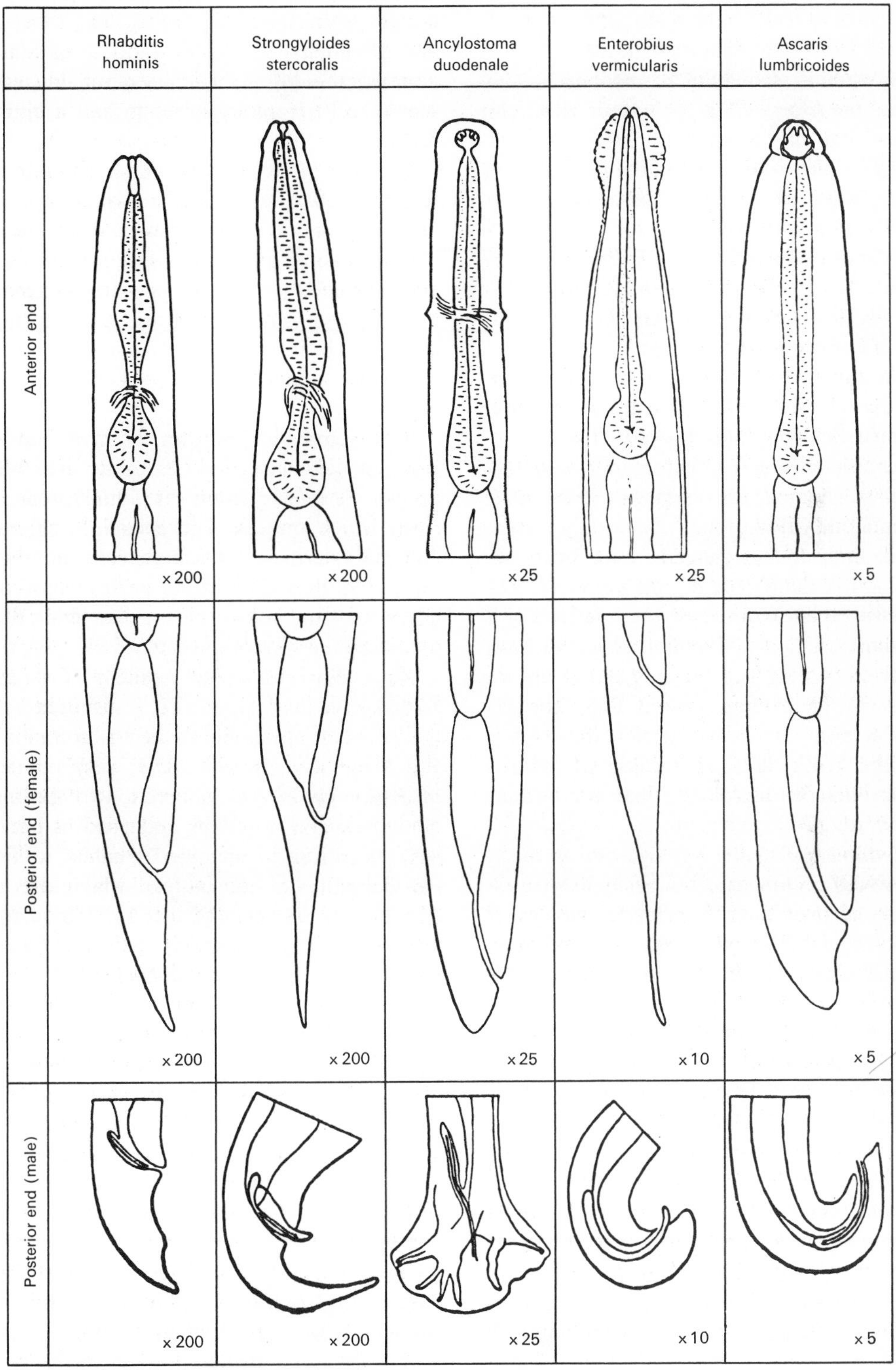

	Rhabditis hominis	Strongyloides stercoralis	Ancylostoma duodenale	Enterobius vermicularis	Ascaris lumbricoides
Anterior end	× 200	× 200	× 25	× 25	× 5
Posterior end (female)	× 200	× 200	× 25	× 10	× 5
Posterior end (male)	× 200	× 200	× 25	× 10	× 5

laboratory), cuticular blisters occur laterally which superficially resemble cervical alae. Blistering with different distribution is characteristic of some other nematodes.

The second element of the nematode body wall is the *hypodermis*. This layer is cellular or syncytial and is commonly thickened internally into four longitudinal bands or ridges called chords. The lateral chords are usually larger than the dorsal and ventral ones and frequently contain the excretory canals. The nuclei of the hypodermis are restricted to the chords, which also carry the principal longitudinal nerves.

The third element of the body wall is longitudinal muscle, which occurs in a single layer in the quadrants between the chords. A considerable nomenclature has been developed to identify the variations in the muscular organization.

The body wall is pierced by the excretory pore and in the female by the gonopore. The digestive tract terminates in a subterminal opening which also functions for the male genital system. All of these openings are located on the median ventral line. The excretory pore is anterior, and the female gonoduct, usually at the midpoint of the body, may be displaced either forward or backward.

Examination of the anterior end in many nematodes reveals external evidence of a bilateral symmetry. The primary pattern is judged to be a symmetrical distribution of six lobes or lips fringing the terminal mouth. A median sagittal section would separate the lips into two groups of three each. These may be designated as laterodorsal, lateral, and lateroventral. In some nematodes, a hexaradiate distribution of nerves is correlated with the tactile sense organs distributed on or adjacent to the six lips. On each side of the lip complex is a chemoreceptor called an *amphid,* more prominent in aquatic nematodes. This distribution is also indicative of a bilateral symmetry.

Many variations from the hexaradiate lip condition occur. One common pattern which is characteristic of *Ascaris* is a triradiate lobation to form a median dorsal and two lateroventral lips. This arrangement has received support as being primitive, since it is correlated with the triangular or triradiate lumen of the pharynx common in nematodes. It is therefore assumed that the six-lipped condition arose by subdivision of the trilobate pattern. In some nematodes, the lips occur as two lateral lobes. When the lip structure is greatly reduced, it sometimes is replaced by a circular ridge or collar among some parasitic nematodes.

Organ Systems

In the typical nematode, the mouth opens into a somewhat cylindrical cavity called the *buccal capsule* or stoma. It is lined with cuticle, which may be thickened into supportive rods and in addition may be provided with armatures such as the teeth and cutting plates of the hookworms of man and other animals. The cuticle-lined muscular pharynx (often called esophagus) has a Y-shaped lumen with the base of the Y disposed ventrally. Pharyngeal glands occur in each of the three wall sectors. The shape of the basically cylindrical pharynx is important taxonomically. It may be elongated and conical, increasing in diameter caudally. Either the cylindrical or conical form may have one or more bulblike expansions. The more common bulb at the posterior end is often set off by a constriction and encloses a valve which opens to the intestine. The intestine or mesenteron, typically with a wall of simple epithelium, may be ovoid or flattened in cross section. Adjacent to the lumen, intestinal cells have a striated border which has been interpreted as composed of degenerate, fused cilia, structures not otherwise occurring in Nematoda. The intestine pursues a direct course to the rectum or proctodaeum where a cuticular lining reappears. In male roundworms, the sperm duct joins the rectum so that caudally it functions as a cloaca.

A great many nematodes live on bacteria

or on the products resulting from bacterial action. This is particularly true of many free-living nematodes and the free-living stages of parasitic ones such as the hookworms. Many nematodes feed on the lower plants such as algae and fungi. The vinegar eel, *Turbatrix aceti*, utilizes the yeasts and bacteria in wine vinegar. Some nematodes are external predators on higher plants; they withdraw the cell contents after penetrating the cell wall with a protrusible stylet. Although a few genera of plant parasites feed on the above-ground foliage, most parasitize roots or other underground portions of the plant. Results of nematode root infection are often nonspecific. Various injuries occur, resulting in reduction in the root system, rotting, and, in some genera, characteristic gall structures and other root malformations. Oddly enough some nematode infections cause root proliferation, but usually this is production of small, limited roots at the expense of the normal root system.

A number of free-living nematodes are carnivorous and feed upon protozoa and the eggs and adults of other small invertebrates, while some nematodes are facultative and can survive as parasites or free-living. *Neoaplectana glaseri* is such a nematode which can parasitize insects and attempts have been made to use it as a biological control for the Japanese beetle. When normal food supplies are insufficient, a larval stage parasitizes immature and adult insects—such as the Japanese beetle.

Among vertebrates, nematodes parasitize a large number of different organs, tissues, or cavities, and a given species tends to be tissue or organ specific in its parasitism.

The nervous system is composed principally of a series of usually paired ganglia (Fig. 9-7), a trunk of connective fibers encircling the pharynx (nerve ring), and a series of longitudinal nerves connected by various commissures. Six nerves from the nerve ring run forward to the sensory organs on the lips. A dorsal nerve which runs caudally in the hypodermis arises directly from

the ring. Other longitudinal nerves arise from the generally paired ganglia associated with the nerve ring, of which the lateral ganglia are most prominent. Nerves to the amphids arise from these ganglia. The lateral and ventral nerve trunks join prominent ganglia at the caudal end of the animal. Numerous sensory papillae occur in this region, particularly in the male. A pair of *phasmids* open laterally near the posterior end. These are minute glands containing sensory elements and are innervated from the main posterior ganglia. The presence or absence of phasmids has been used by prominent specialists to divide the Nematoda into two subgroups.

Two types of excretory systems appear to be present in nematodes, neither of which is provided with any nephridia-like organs. In the tubular pattern, a pair of tubes occurs in the lateral chords (Fig. 9-7). A ventral branch from each tube joins to empty through the ventral excretory pore. Such an excretory system is called H-shaped. It is frequently modified to a U shape by loss of the anterior arms; or unequal loss produces an asymmetrical system. Frequently one or a pair of saclike excretory organs occurs near the excretory pore in some parasitic nematodes. These appear to be equivalent to an excretory organ in marine nematodes called a *renette*.

The reproductive system of nematodes is tubular with the gonad continuous with the genital duct, which is modified as a uterus in the female and as a seminal vesicle and ejaculatory duct in the male. In the female, the reproductive system is usually double and opens through a common gonopore called the vulva (Fig. 9-7). A short vagina joins the vulva to the two uteri which may lie parallel or are disposed in opposite directions. Only a single testis is present in most male nematodes. The sperm duct opens into the cloaca. Various copulatory structures are formed from modified cuticle in the cloacal wall. These include no more than two *spicules* (Fig. 9-6) and frequently a guide known as a *gubernaculum*. The ventrally curved tip of the body is a copulatory adaptation in male nematodes lacking a bursa.

Nematode eggs are small and nearly yolk-free. They undergo a type of bilateral determinative cleavage. Most nematodes are oviparous, and the development of the embryo begun in the uterus is completed after the egg is released but before it is hatched. Some nematodes exhibit ovoviviparity.

All nematodes undergo a series of *four*

Fig. 9-7 Nematode morphology; various organ systems, *a*, anus; *ag*, anal ganglion; *ant*, anterior nerve trunks; *c*, cloaca; *cc*, circumcloacal commissure (male); *dnt*, dorsal nerve trunk; *e*, esophagus; *ep*, excretory pore; *et*, excretory tubules; *ejd*, ejaculatory duct; *i*, intestine; *lnr*, circumesophagael ring; *lnt*, lateral nerve trunks; *m*, mouth; *ov*, ovary; *od*, oviduct; *ovj*, ovejector; *r*, rectum; *s*, spicules; *sr*, seminal receptacle; *sv*, seminal vesicle; *t*, testis; *u*, uterus; *v*, vulva, *va*, vas deferens; *vnt*, ventral nerve trunk. From Belding, *Textbook of Clinical Parasitology*, 1942 (2nd ed., 1952), by permission of Appleton-Century-Crofts.

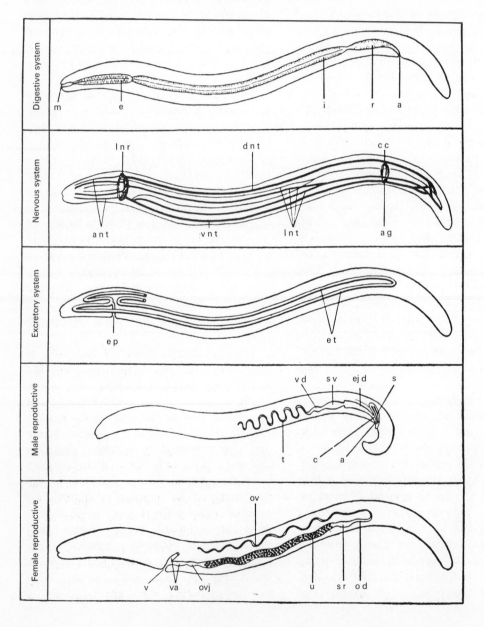

molts which divests them of the old cuticle, although it may be retained briefly as a flexible protective coat in some cases. Although ecdysis typically begins after hatching, the first molt occurs within the shell in some species. The series of molts allows for growth of the nematode, and there is a gradual development to maturity of the sex organs during this postembryonic period.

Considerable variation occurs in the life cycles of parasitic roundworms. For plant parasites, the plant may be simply an additional food source among many, or the parasite may be unable to complete its life cycle without recourse to a plant host. Nematodes may be parasitic in insect hosts only during immature stages or only as adults. In some species the parasitism involves both insect and plant hosts. Nematode parasites of man illustrate a number of life-cycle variations.

Fig. 9-8 Life cycle of *Trichinella spiralis*, cause of trichinosis. From Belding, *Textbook of Clinical Parasitology*, 1942 (2nd ed., 1952), by permission of Appleton-Century-Crofts.

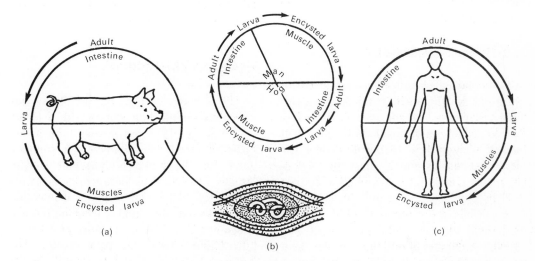

Fig. 9-9 Life cycle of the pin or seat worm, *Enterobius vermicularis*. (a) man infected with parasite; (b), (d), and (e) infective ovum; (c) hand contaminated with ovum; (f) man infected by ingesting ovum; (a) to (d) reinfection; (a) to (e) cross-infection. From Belding, *Textbook of Clinical Parasitology*, 1942 (2nd ed., 1952), by permission of Appleton-Century-Crofts.

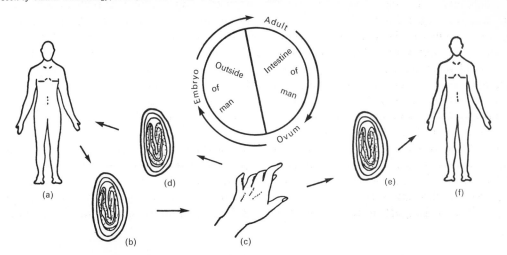

Man ingests *Ascaris* eggs with contaminated food or water; hookworm eggs hatch in the soil and the immature stage reaches the blood-stream by active penetration; man gets trichinosis (Fig. 9-8) by eating insufficiently cooked pork containing encysted immature stages; and the larval stages of some other nematodes reach man through the bites of blood-sucking insects. *Ascaris* and hookworms complicate the picture by undergoing lung migrations before settling down as adults in the intestine. Of course there are some additional variations among the 32 species of roundworms infective in man (Fig. 9-9).

Systematic Relationships

Taxonomy or classification of a group of organisms has the practical intent of providing a systematized organization or filing system to achieve a rational and convenient plan of relationships. In the ultimate sense these relationships must express the phylogeny of the group, but in the interim, conjectural patterns have to be utilized.

No definitive position has been reached concerning the taxonomic position of Nematoda. A number of authors consider them to be an independent phylum. Supporting this position, Chitwood and Chitwood divide the phylum into two classes, based primarily upon the presence or absence of phasmids plus some other commonly divergent features. The reliability of this separation was disputed by Hyman, but the classes called *Phasmidia* and *Aphasmidia* have had considerable acceptance. In the second edition of Fresh-water Biology (Ward and Whipple, 1959) class names are given as *Secernentea* and *Adenophorea* respectively in a section in which B. G. Chitwood is co-author. More recently Thorne follows this binary subdivision, while even more recently Goodey rejects it, and the two systems do not agree on all of the orders.

Indicative of the great diversity evident in nematodes is the relatively large number of high taxa (taxonomic groups). In their 1950 revision, Chitwood and Chitwood list four orders, subdivided into eleven suborders and into 24 superfamilies.

By definition higher taxa are broader in scope and in practice more subject to generalization. Of necessity, they will continue to have extended usage in a group such as nematodes until evolutionary history of these worms is less vague. If the nematodes are a monophyletic group as seems probable, it seems axiomatic to look for clues to their ancestry among free-living aquatic and probably marine roundworms.

CLASS NEMATOMORPHA

The Nematomorpha or Gordiacea are exceedingly long, thin worms with a length that may be 300 times greater than a diameter of about one millimeter. A common name for the group is horsehair snakes. Usually the cuticle of these worms lacks the smoothness of the more familiar nematodes. It is thickened into a kind of irregular mosaic, and sometimes these thickenings protrude as little knobs which may bear bristles. The mouth is terminal or slightly ventral. At the posterior end, two or three lobes extend caudally beyond the terminal or ventral cloaca in some nematomorphs; in others the posterior end is rounded. In both sexes, reproductive ducts empty through the cuticle-lined cloaca. There is no excretory pore, since this system is lacking in Nematomorpha.

Unlike nematodes, nematomorphs do not have the epidermis adjacent to the cuticle thickened into lateral chords, although all nematomorphs exhibit a ventral chord and some also have a dorsal thickening. A layer of longitudinal muscle lines the external wall of the pseudocoele (Fig. 9-10). Large parenchymatous cells occupy the pseudocoele in the developing nematomorph. The common walls of many of these cells may break down to form irregular, semipartitioned longitudinal channels, or a single continuous pseudocoele.

Digestion in most nematomorphs is poorly understood. Nutritive substances apparently enter the body by absorption through the general somatic surface, since frequently neither the mouth nor the pharynx ever develops a lumen. The midgut, composed of a single layer of cells, ends blindly in some members of the group. Caudally the intestine or remnant of it receives the genital ducts.

The principal nervous system is composed of a ring around the foregut and a longitudinal tripartite ventral cord which is either adjacent to the epidermis or continuous with

Fig. 9-10 Larva of a nematomorph, *Paragordius,* with proboscis evaginated and retracted. After Montgomery 1904, courtesy Acad. Nat. Sci., Philadelphia.

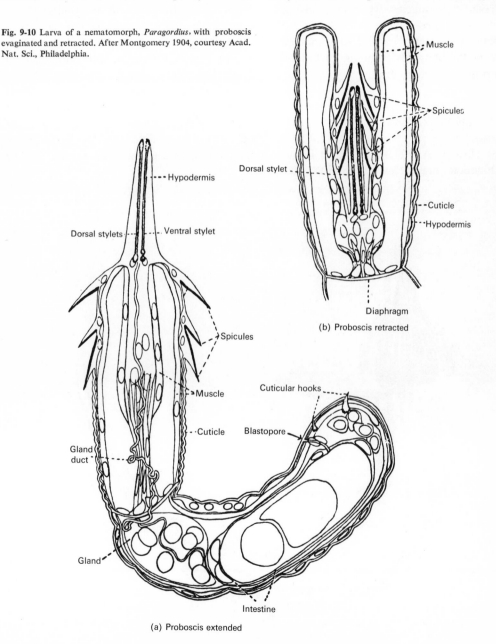

Muscle

Spicules

Dorsal stylet

Cuticle

Hypodermis

Diaphragm

(b) Proboscis retracted

Hypodermis

Dorsal stylets — Ventral stylet

Spicules

Muscle

Cuticle

Gland duct

Gland

Cuticular hooks

Blastopore

Intestine

(a) Proboscis extended

it through a median ventral membrane.

The Nematomorpha are dioecious; fertilization is internal. Most species have paired, irregularly tubular gonads. Fresh-water nematomorphs lay eggs in long strings. Upon hatching, the young enter (either by ingestion or boring) a variety of arthropod hosts. For marine forms these hosts are Crustacea, while the fresh-water species typically parasitize insects, either those living in water or frequenting the stream margin. Development occurs in the body cavity of the arthropod, and a single ecdysis occurs.

CLASS KINORHYNCHA

This class of Aschelminthes, also known as Echinodera, are exclusively marine. They average less than one millimeter in length and their most distinctive feature is a segmented body. Kinorhynchs are bottom-dwellers in shallower shore waters, where their locomotion is limited to crawling in the bottom mud or among algae. Slow forward progression is accomplished by using the extended head with its five to seven circlets of spines as an anchor. Contraction of the longitudinal musculature pulls the trunk forward. The muscular system is not unlike that in rotifers, except that both longitudinal and diagonal fibers function in sectors between the adjacent cuticular plates marking the segmentation externally. The ventral nerve cord, only slightly differentiated from the adjacent epidermis, is modified as ganglia intrasegmentally to meet the need of the muscle sectors.

Fig. 9-11 *Echinoderes* sp. After Shipley, 1896, courtesy of the original publishers of *Cambridge Natural History*, Vol. II, Macmillan & Co. Ltd.

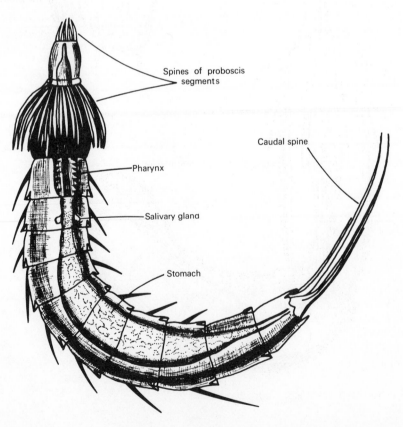

Spines of proboscis segments

Pharynx

Salivary gland

Stomach

Caudal spine

The body is divided into thirteen (rarely fourteen) regular segments of which the first somewhat rounded segment is the head (Fig. 9-11). It bears a mouth centrally, surrounded by a concentric series of spines. The head is retractile into the second segment or neck, or else head and neck are retractile into the third segment. A row of spines occurs middorsally and laterally on the segmented body, and bristles are common on the broad surfaces of the cuticle. The flattened ventral surface is grooved medially. A pair of adhesive glands open ventrally in the anterior half of the kinorhynch body.

The stomodaeal cuticle forms a heavy collar at the front end of the pharynx and extends into the buccal cavity when the head segment is retracted. The pharynx is a cylindrical muscular organ similar to that in nematodes. The remainder of the digestive tract is walled with a simple epithelium and is provided with some muscle externally. Constricted areas occur between the midgut and the stomodaeum and proctodaeum.

The principal portion of the nervous system consists of a nerve ring around the pharynx in the region of the collar and of a midventral cord provided with segmentally arranged ganglia. Some nerve elements also occur in the lateral and middorsal epidermal chords. No cilialike structure occurs in kinorhynchs, except for the flagella of the solenocytes.

Paired gonads open by paired gonopores located on the subterminal segment in these dioecious animals, and the males possess copulatory spicules. The embryology is unknown.

REFERENCES

Ackert, J. E., Some influences of the American hookworm. Amer. Midland Natural., 47:749, 1952.

Bayliss, H. A., The systematic position of the nematoda. Ann. Mag. Natur. Hist. 12(9): 165, 1924.

Belding, D. L., Textbook of clinical parasitology (2nd ed.). New York: Appleton, 1952. (A third edition is dated 1965.)

Brunson, R. B., Gastrotricha. In (W. T. Edmondson, ed.) Ward and Whipple's Freshwater biology (2nd ed.). New York: Wiley, 1959.

Chitwood, B. G., Gordiida. In (W. T. Edmondson, ed.) Ward and Whipple's Freshwater biology (2nd ed.). New York: Wiley, 1959.

———, and M. W. Allen, Nemata (pp. 368-401). In (W. T. Edmondson, ed.) Ward and Whipple's Fresh-water biology (2nd ed.). New York: Wiley, 1959.

———, and M. B. Chitwood, An introduction to nematology, 240 pp. Baltimore, 1937-1940.

———, Ibid., Section I revised, 213 pp. Baltimore, 1950.

de Beauchamp, P. M., Recherches sur les rotifers: les formations tégumentaires et l'appareil digestif. Arch. Zool. Exp. et Gen., 10:(4)1, 1909.

Edmondson, W. T., Rotifera (pp. 420-494). In (W. T. Edmondson, ed.) Ward and Whipple's Fresh-Water biology (2nd ed.). New York: Wiley, 1959.

Fewkes, J., On the development of certain worm larvae. Bull. Mus. Comp. Zool. Harvard, 11:167, 1883.

Filipjev, L. N., The classification of the free-living nematodes. Smithson. Miscel. Coll., 89(6):1, 1934.

Goodey, T., Soil and freshwater nematodes (rev. ed., ed. J. B. Goodey). London: Methuen, 1963.

Harris, J. E., and H. D. Crofton, Structure and function in the nematodes: internal pressure and cuticular structure in Ascaris. J. Exp. Biol., 34:116, 1957.

Hyman, L. H., The invertebrates: Acanthocephala, Aschelminthes, and Entoprocta, Vol. III. New York: McGraw, 1951.

Lee, D. L., The physiology of nematodes. San

Francisco: W. H. Freeman, 1965.

May, H., Contributions to the life history of *Gordius* and *Paragordius*. Ill. Biol. Monogr., 5:1, 1919.

Montgomery, T., Development and structure of the larva of *Paragordius*. Proc. Acad. Natur. Sci., Phila., 56:738, 1904.

Myers, F. J., Brackish water and marine Rotatoria. Trans. Amer. Microsc. Soc., 55:428, 1936.

Packard, C. E., Observations on the Gastrotricha, indigenous to New Hampshire. Trans. Amer. Microsc. Soc., 55:422, 1936.

Pennak, R. W., Fresh-water invertebrates of the United States. New York: Ronald, 1953.

Peters, B. G., On the anatomy of the vinegar eelworm. J. Helminth., 5:183, 1927.

Remane, A., Gastrotricha and Kinorhyncha. *In* (H. G. Bronn, ed.) Klassen und Ordnungen des Tierreichs, Bd. IV, Abt. II, Buch I, Teil 2, (pp. 1-382). Leipzig: Akad. Verlag, 1936.

Sacks, M., Observations on the embryology of an aquatic gastrotrich, *Lepidodermelia squammata* (Dujardin, 1841). J. Morphol. 96:473, 1955.

Shapeero, W. L., Phylogeny of Priapulida. Science, 133:879, 1961.

Thorne, G., Principles of nematology. New York: McGraw, 1961.

Wallace, H. R., The biology of plant parasitic nematodes. New York: St. Martins, 1964.

10

ACANTHOCEPHALA, ENTOPROCTA, AND PRIAPULIDA

The three phyla included in this chapter exhibit varying similarities to the Aschelminthes. Only the Acanthocephala are at all numerous, over 500 species having been described. The Entoprocta have about one tenth this number and Priapulida number less than a dozen. Except for the Entoprocta, the other phyla generally exhibit *eutely*. All three phyla have a body wall of cuticle and epidermis; longitudinal muscle in the body wall is a common feature also. Protonephridia occur in all three groups, although limited to a single subdivision of the Acanthocephala.

PHYLUM ACANTHOCEPHALA

This phylum is composed of obligatory parasites which lack a digestive tract. They are generally cylindrical and mostly under an inch in length, although a species parasitic in pigs may reach a length of two feet. The phylum name is derived from the feature of a protrusible proboscis embedded with recurved hooks. The fully extended proboscis exhibits a neck devoid of hooks or spines. The main body or trunk in a number of Acanthocephala is armed with spines of varying size and distribution. Some species have a marked appearance of segmentation externally. It is called pseudosegmentation since it is confined to the surface and does not affect internal organs except (rarely) the longitudinal layer of muscle in the body wall.

The longitudinal layer of body wall muscle lines the pseudocoele. A thin sheath of circular muscle lies external to the longitudinal layer. The remainder of the body wall is composed of an epidermis, histologically differentiated into three layers and covered by a thin cuticle. The inner layer of the epidermis contains huge epidermal nuclei, relatively constant in number for each species, and a network of channels usually linked with enlarged vessels running lengthwise. These channels and vessels constitute the lacunar system. Although restricted to the body wall, it is considered to facilitate the distribution of food which must be absorbed through the body wall. The giant nuclei of the epidermis occupy relatively constant positions in the main lacunar channels.

Internally, there is a muscular sac, called the proboscis receptacle, at the anterior end of the pseudocoele. Muscles attached internally to the tip of the proboscis run to the proboscis receptacle, and are continuous with bands that continue through the pseudocoele to insert on the body wall. These are designated as proboscis and receptacle retractors, respectively. In some species, additional retractors are attached between the neck and the body wall.

From the caudal end of the proboscis receptacle, or nearby on the body wall, two elongate, thin-walled ligament sacs extend caudally as part of the reproductive complex (Fig. 10-1). In the male, two testes lying one behind the other are joined by a nucleated strand. Each testis is provided with a sperm duct. The two sperm ducts run caudally in the ligament sac which joins a muscular genital sheath within which they unite. A common duct from a group of unicellular cement glands joins the sperm duct, which terminates at the cirrus or penis. The cirrus lies at the base of an eversible sac, the *bursa,* which functions as a clasping organ in copulation.

The female lacks a persistent, well-defined gonad since the ovary is subdivided into ovarian balls which occur in the fluid of the ligament sacs or the pseudocoele. The ligament sacs communicate with an elongate, bell-shaped tubule called the *uterine bell* (or sometimes, selective apparatus). The bell narrows to join the uterine tube. Here again eutely is evident in the large and relatively constant number of the nuclei of the cells forming the tube. A pair of pouches extend cephalad from the tube which subsequently joins a muscular uterus. The uterus joins a short vagina which opens to the outside.

An eversible cavity called the *bursa* functions to grasp the female at copulation. Sperm are discharged into the uterus through a penis and the female gonopore is blocked by secretions which harden to form a plug and prevent sperm escape. Eggs are fertilized about the time they escape from the ovarian balls. The fertilization membrane forms inside the original egg membrane, and it apparently thickens to form the refractive, rigid inner shell. It is separated from the developing larva *(acanthor)* by a thin elastic membrane (Moore). A thick outer shell (apparently cellular in structure in some species) is covered externally by a thin, easily lost membrane.

Developing embryos are engulfed by the uterine bell. Mature ones are moved into the uterine pouches prior to escape from the

Fig. 10-1 *Neoechinorhynchus crassus* male. Note thickness of body wall in this optical section. After Van Cleave 1919, courtesy of the Ill. Nat. His. Survey.

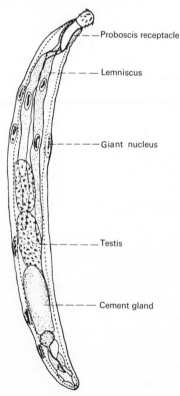

— Proboscis receptacle

— Lemniscus

— Giant nucleus

— Testis

— Cement gland

parent, while immature larvae are returned to the pseudocoele.

In more primitive Acanthocephala, a pair of excretory tubules branch to a mass of protonephridia or flame-bulbs. In both sexes these tubules join ducts of the reproductive system, so that the terminal portion of the latter are urogenital ducts. Phylogenetically, this feature is of great interest, since protonephridia occur as excretory organs in acoelomate animals.

The nervous system consists of a ganglionic mass located on a median wall of the proboscis receptacle. It is considered to be ventral, in correlation with the ventrad position of the larger proboscis hooks and with concavity of the body in species that show these features. A number of nerves, some of which are paired, arise from the ganglion. Some sense organs occur on the proboscis, and in the male around the external genitalia. In this sex, branches of nerves enter paired genital ganglia situated in the base of the penis.

Near the conjunction of the body wall and proboscis receptacle, two club-shaped structures called *lemnisci* appear to be outgrowths of the inner epidermal layer and they contain similar lacunar channels. The lemnisci lie free in the body cavity. Clark (1964) states that Hammond in a personal communication reported the hydrostatic action of the lemnisci and proboscis apparatus in *Acanthocephalus*. At the anterior end, the proboscis cavity was demarked from the trunk pseudocoele by the proboscis receptacle. On either side of the receptacle lies a saclike lemniscus. When the spiraled muscle fibers in the receptacle contract, both length and diameter of the receptacle are reduced (because of the spiral) and the proboscis is everted. Neck muscles serve to keep the hydrostatic effect on the proboscis isolated from fluid changes in the trunk pseudocoele, since the contracted neck muscles exert pressure on the lemnisci so that the fluid in their lacunae is forced into

lacunar spaces of the proboscis and neck to effect proboscis dilation and its extended use as an anchor without interfering with other body activities.

The fertilized egg goes through determinate cleavage which appears to be a spiral cleavage modified by the constriction of the enclosing membranes. Development inside the embryonic membranes continues, forming a larval stage called an *acanthor*. Differentiation of this larva includes the appearance of three pairs of hooks at the anterior end, and the formation of a bivalved shell between the embryonic membranes. Acanthors pass out of the definitive vertebrate host with the feces. To continue the life cycle, infective acanthors must be ingested by suitable intermediate hosts. The latter are usually Insecta when the definitive host is terrestrial, Crustacea when the definitive host is aquatic.

PHYLUM ENTOPROCTA

This small phylum of pseudocoelomate animals has also been called Kamptozoa and Calyssozoa. These small sedentary animals occur singly or in colonies. An individual consists of an oval or bell-shaped body called the *calyx*, provided with a ring of tentacles, and a stalk, either provided with an attachment disc or arising from a horizontal stolon in colonial forms (Fig. 10-2). Most Entoprocta are marine, but a single genus, *Urnatella*, occurs in various locations in the United States east of the Mississippi River as well as in Texas and in parts of southern Asia.

Entoprocta are frequently placed in the group *Bryozoa* or *Polyzoa* with another group of small colonial animals of similar structure. Entoprocts differ from the latter in several ways. Both ends of the recurved alimentary canal open within the circle of tentacles. The term Entoprocta was derived from this feature. In the true Bryozoa, the anus opens outside the tentacle ring and the alternate name Ectoprocta has been applied to them. The Bryozoa have a true coelom, which in some forms contains cilia, whereas the Entoprocta have a pseudocoele. Embryologically, the latter group has a spiral determinate cleavage, while the Bryozoa have a radial cleavage. Entoprocts have protonephridia, absent in all stages of ectoprocts. These and other features seem to establish at most only a very remote relationship.

The *calyx* in Entoprocta tends to be flattened laterally, and the tentacles, which vary in number, are bilaterally disposed in a pair of opposing curved rows to form a circlet or crown of tentacles. An oval concavity called the vestibule or atrium lies within the tentacle crown. Mouth and anus open at opposite ends of the vestibule. In the median line and anterior to the anus, which may be elevated on a papilla, is the gonopore. A median excretory pore jointly serving the paired flame-bulb nephridia opens between gonopore and mouth, also in the midline. The tentacles can be flexed radially into the vestibule. Entoprocts are ciliary feeders.

Fig. 10-2 *Barentsia*, an Entroproct. After Rogick 1950, *Selected Invertebrate Types* (F. A. Brown, Jr., ed·), courtesy of John Wiley & Sons, Inc.

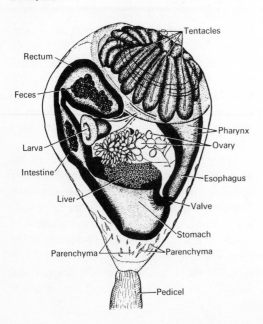

Cilia on the inner faces of the tentacles function to transport food particles to a pair of ciliated furrows disposed along the periphery of the vestibule just within the tentacles. These furrows terminate at either end of the mouth (Fig. 10-2).

The entoproct peduncle or stalk projects from the bottom of the calyx, which is the embryologically dorsal side. The stalk may be relatively uniform in diameter or it may exhibit a series of constrictions or enlargements. In some forms, transverse septa may subdivide the stalk, and septa are also common in species which produce horizontal stolons. Cuticle, which may bear spines, occurs on the outer surface of the calyx and on stalks and stolons. Muscle within the epidermis is characteristically longitudinal. It is most evident in the stalk, particularly in septate forms where it may be restricted to enlarged nodules. Other muscle encircles the calyx rim and some occurs within the tentacle pseudocoeles. Large, thin-walled cells forming a loose network occupy the pseudocoele.

Organ Systems

The digestive system is limited to the calyx and lies in the median plane. It is a recurved tube differentiated principally by changes in the size of the lumen, thickness of the simple epithelial wall, and height of cilia. The nervous system is centered in a large, somewhat bilobed ganglion which lies between stomach and vestibular wall. Paired nerves given off ventrally from this ganglion supply the tentacles; other paired nerves arise dorsally which innervate muscle of the stalk and other organs. A single pair of nephridia occur anterior to the ganglion. These open in the midline through a single nephridiopore. Some entoprocts are dioecious and some are hermaphroditic. Gonads are paired and open by a common duct. In some hermaphroditic species, protandry is thought to occur. The floor of the vestibule below the gonopore is pocketed to form a brood chamber in females and monoecious animals.

Asexual reproduction occurs by budding localized on the calyx in solitary species and restricted to stalks and stolons in colonial forms.

Fertilization is internal and the zygote undergoes spiral cleavage. Hyman emphasizes the differences between the ciliated larvae of entoprocts (particularly the primitive species) and the trochophore.

PHYLUM PRIAPULIDA

This small group of stout marine worms is very old but it is limited to two genera containing five or six species. These are small cylindrical animals with a shorter introvertible anterior end called a *presoma* or *proboscis* (Fig. 10-3). It is spined around the terminal mouth and bears longitudinal rows of papilla which sets it off sharply from the longer trunk which is externally marked by regular annulations, sometimes with warty or spinelike projections.

The relatively straight alimentary canal lies in the body cavity which, according to Shapeero (1961), is a nucleated peritoneum and hence a true coelom, but earlier reports considered the cavity to be a pseudocoele. The excretory system is composed of solenocytic protonephridia and is in close association with the gonad to form a pair of urogenital organs in these dioecious animals. The nervous system consists of an anterior ring around the alimentary canal and a midventral nerve cord similar to that in the Kinorhyncha. The entire nervous system is located in the epidermis, and the nerve ring shows no ganglionic enlargements; both features indicate a primitive condition.

Arranged radially in the body cavity are short and long bands of retractor muscles connecting the proboscis with the body wall. Locomotion is effected by the almost explosive eversion of the inverted pharynx into the soft bottom substrate in which these animals live. The hydrostatic dilation of the everted proboscis anchors it and at the same time

fluid removal reduces the trunk in size. It is then pulled forward to envelop the proboscis. In this process the proboscis loses fluid to the trunk, which swells sufficiently to act as an anchor prior to the next lunge of the proboscis.

Priapulids are found buried in the soft bottom of cold ocean waters of the continental shelf down to a depth of 500 meters. It is of interest that one species occurs in both arctic and antarctic waters separated by a huge barrier of temperate and tropical waters in which they have never been found. Fertilization occurs externally and swarming takes place in winter. The normal ecology of the group presents some difficulties in studying early embryology.

Lang (1953) studied the development of *Priapulus caudatus*. In this species cleavage was radial, a coeloblastula was formed, and

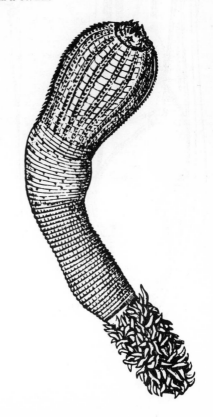

Fig. 10-3 *Priapulus* adult. After Shipley 1896, courtesy of the original publishers of *Cambridge Natural History,* Vol. II, Macmillan & Co. Ltd.

gastrulation occurred by invagination. Fertilization occurs in sea water and development is direct, with the larvae internally similar to the adult (Fig. 10-4), although externally they are covered by a series of cuticularized plates to form a protective lorica.

The phylogenetic position of the Priapulida is uncertain. If Shapeero is correct, they are coelomate animals and do not belong in any close association with the pseudocoelo-mates. Until the origin of the body cavity is determined by embryological studies, it seems best to remove them from the Phylum Aschelminthes, but to keep them associated with this phylum and with the Acanthocephala, because of their secondary radial symmetry, the type of protonephridia, the similarity of the nervous system to Kinorhyncha, and similarities of the reproductive system and of pseudosegmentation with the nematodes.

Fig. 10-4 (1) the larvae of *Priapulus caudatus* and (2) *Halicryptus spinulosus:* (a) dorsal view; (b) lateral view. After Lang 1948-49, courtesy of the Arkiv för Zoologi.

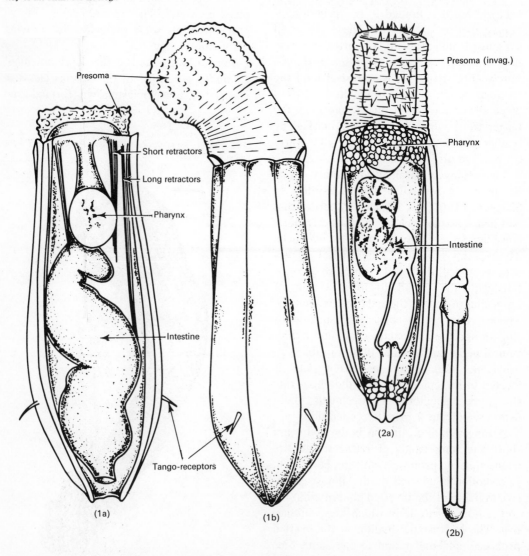

Presoma

Presoma (invag.)

Short retractors

Long retractors

Pharynx

Pharynx

Intestine

Intestine

(2a)

Tango-receptors

(1a)

(1b)

(2b)

REFERENCES

Brien, Paul, Classe des Endoproctes ou Kamptozoaires. *In* (P. Grassé, ed.) Traité de zoologie, Tome V. Paris: Masson et Cie, 1959.

Clark, R. B., Dynamics in metazoan evolution. Oxford: Clarendon, 1964.

Hyman, L. H., The invertebrata: Acanthocephala, Aschelminthes, and Entoprocta, Vol. III. New York: McGraw, 1951.

Lang, K., On the morphology of the larva of *Priapulus caudatus* Lam. Arkiv för Zoologi, 41a, No. 9 (1948), 8 pp.

———, Die Entwicklung des Eies von *Priapulus caudatus* Lam. und die systematische Stellung der Priapuliden. Arkiv för Zoologi, 5:321, 1953.

Leidy, J., *Urnatella gracilis,* a fresh-water polyzoan. J. Acad. Natur. Sci., Phila., 9:1, 1884.

Moore, D. V., The life history and development of *Moniliformis.* J. Parasitol., 32:257, 1946.

Pennak, R. W., Fresh-water invertebrates of the United States. New York: Ronald, 1953.

Shapeero, W. L., Phylogeny of Priapulida. Science, 133:879, 1961.

Van Cleave, H. J., Acanthocephala from the Illinois river. Bull. Ill. Nat. Hist. Surv., 13:225, 1919.

———, Relationships of the Acanthocephala. Amer. Natural., 75:31, 1941.

Ward, H. L., Studies on the life history of *Neoechinorhynchus cylindratus. Trans.* Amer. Microsc. Soc., 59:327, 1940.

11

PHYLA ANNELIDA, ECHIURIDA, AND SIPUNCULIDA

The Annelida constitute a phylum of some 8,600 species with a number of distinctive characteristics shared generally or reduced or lost secondarily. The elongated body is divided externally into rings or segments and this feature correlates with a metameric arrangement of internal organs in typical annelids. A spacious perivisceral cavity or coelom of bilateral origin is commonly separated into segments by apposition of the peritoneum of adjacent chambers. Most or all of these intersegmental septa may be incomplete or lost completely during ontogeny. Chitinous, rodlike, paired setae (chaetae) are rare among Archiannelida and Hirudinea, almost universally present in Polychaeta and Oligochaeta. A nonchitinous cuticle is characteristic of most annelids, as is a single preoral segment called *prostomium*.

Certain organ systems are consistent for the phylum. There is an outer circular and an inner longitudinal muscle layer in the body walls. The circulatory system is closed, mostly restricted to discrete blood vessels, but involving or replaced by a sinusoidal system in Hirudinea (leeches) and occasionally in other annelids, particularly around the intestine. Paired ectodermal nephridia, in some cases combined with mesodermal coelomoducts, are typical. Beginning with a subpharyngeal or subesophageal ganglion, which represents fusion of two or more pairs of ventral ganglia, the ventral nerve cord connects a chain of ontogenetically paired ventral ganglia. In adults, members of a pair of ganglia are often fused into a single body. Around the pharynx oblique commissures connect the subpharyngeal ganglion with the dorsal cerebral ganglion or brain.

Giant fibers occur within the nerve cord of many annelids. In *Arenicola,* one of these is median and somewhat dorsal in position relative to two giant nerve fibers lying laterally. These giant nerve fibers are syncytial and interconnected. Some smaller polychaetes, such as the sea mice (*Aphrodite* and its relatives) and *Chaetopterus,* lack giant fibers.

Nereis has an additional and smaller pair of giant fibers, which are not syncytial however. In earthworms, the giant fibers have fatty sheaths perhaps analogous to myelinated vertebrate nerves, but the fatty sheath is absent in polychaetes. Leeches do not possess giant fibers. Giant fibers provide for nearly simultaneous stimulation of longitudinal muscles, thus effecting an expeditious escape response, particularly if the withdrawal is into the safety of a tube or burrow.

Phylum Annelida is commonly divided into three major classes: the Polychaeta, Oligochaeta, and Hirudinea, and two small classes: the Archiannelida and the Myzostomida.

Development is direct in the Oligochaeta and Hirudinea, but the Polychaeta, Archiannelida, and Myzostomida produce a pelagic larva called *trochophore,* a type which occurs repeatedly among schizocoelic Bilateria.

The majority of annelids are small worms, a great deal smaller than *Lumbricus terrestris,* the familiar earthworm, which may reach a length of thirty centimeters. The group Oligochaeta, to which *Lumbricus* belongs, has representatives varying from less than one millimeter to South American and Australian giants as long as two meters. Polychaeta vary from a few millimeters to several feet in length, but most are less than a foot long. Hirudinea are mostly small, but some larger ones may be ten centimeters or more extended. The secondarily simplified Archiannelida and Myzostomida are all very small.

The three big groups of annelids—Polychaeta, Oligochaeta, and Hirudinea—have marine as well as fresh-water representatives, while the Archiannelida and Myzostomida are strictly marine. However, it is only the exceptional polychaete (some seventeen species in nine genera) that is not either marine or euryhaline, while the typical oligochaete lives in a fresh-water or terrestrial habitat, and for the most part is not equally well adapted to both. Polychaetes occur along the seashore between tide levels and in continental shelf waters, although some are benthonic. Polychaetes have a wide distribution, being found in coastal waters as far north as Norway, northern Canada, and Siberia. Except for deserts, the oligochaetes have cosmopolitan distribution in the temperate and tropical zones. The northern continents have a somewhat limited but related fauna as compared with tropical and southern hemisphere areas. Southern South America, New Zealand, and the southern tip of Africa have some genera in common.

Some Oligochaeta occur in very cold waters. Some members of Family Enchytraeidae live in pools formed in melting ice of glaciers, while worms of the family Lumbricidae have been found in regions where there is a perpetually frozen undersoil. *Eclipidrilus frigidus* inhabits cold streams high in California mountains. Beddard reports that several species of oligochaetes have been found at an altitude of 10,000 feet. The Hirudinea have a general world distribution in temperate and tropical areas where the environment has sufficient moisture. Fresh water is the most common habitat, but several continents of the southern hemisphere have land leeches, and a number of marine forms are permanent parasites on elasmobranch fishes, particularly.

Geologically, annelids are a very ancient group, but the fossil record is meager since these worms do not have extensive hard parts likely to be preserved. Sedimentary rocks beginning with the Ordovician Period have yielded *scolecodonts,* which are interpreted as jaws and denticles of polychaetes. There are also some records of acicula, setae, and scales or elytra, as well as fossilized burrows and "castings" considered to be of annelid origin.

The Echiurida with about sixty species and the Sipunculida with about 250 species show annelid relationship through spiral cleavage, trochophore larvae, and schizocoelic coelom formation producing a spacious body cavity.

Nephridia occur in both groups, and the Echiurida possess setae and show some evidence of metamerism.

SPECIAL FEATURES OF ANNELIDA

Because of the common presence of setae, many classification systems place the Polychaeta and Oligochaeta in a group called

Fig. 11-1 Setae: (a) to (f) Polychaeta; (g), (h) Archiannelida; (i) to (l) Oligochaeta; (a) pectinate (*Eunice*); (b) bordered (*Amphitrite*); (c) barbed (*Hermione*); (d) hooked (*Arenicola*); (e) jointed (*Nereis*); (f) crochet (*Amphitrite*); (g), (h) bifurcate (*Saccocirrus*); (i) bifurcate (*Nais*); (j) pectinate (*Tubifex*); (k) capilliform (*Aelosoma*); (l) sigmoid (*Lumbricus*). Adapted from various sources.

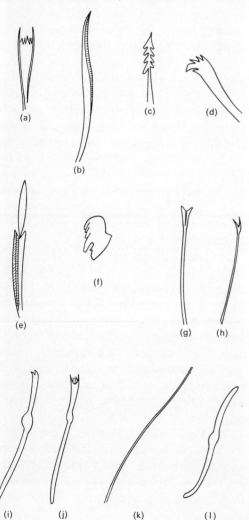

Chaetopoda, but setae occur in the leech, *Acanthobdella,* in some *Archiannelida,* e.g., *Saccocirrus* and in Echiurida. The typical seta is a bristle or rod of chitin, a nonprotein compound containing a substituted glucose with NH_2. The hollow calcareous setae of *Euphrosyne,* a polychaete, are exceptional.

The seta is secreted by a formative cell at the base of a cylindrical pocket from which it protrudes. Setae used primarily in locomotion (swimming, crawling, or burrowing as the case may be) and in maintenance of a grip on burrow walls are of several types. Among polychaetes, these bristles have been classified as: (1) simple, with the variously hairlike or spinelike form frequently modified by hooks, fringes, serrations, or forked; (2) jointed; and (3) uncinnate, which is a short, hooked form (often called crochet), with or without secondary hooks, and which does not extend below the basal plate of the epidermis into the body cavity (Fig. 11-1). Typical setae among oligochaetes are S-shaped, unjointed, and frequently possess a swelling or nodulus along the shaft.

The annelids exhibit some marked advances in the nervous system. They possess a nerve net beneath the epidermis and external to the layer of circular muscle. Fibers from the ventral ganglion connect with it segmentally. The segmental nerves arising from these ganglia not only serve the segment of which they are a part, but also have branches to immediately adjacent segments. Removal of the ventral nerve cord for not more than three segments does not prevent the passage of a peristaltic wave in *Lumbricus.* The by-pass is effected by an overlapping peripheral nerve net. Normally the peristaltic wave is accentuated by successive segmental reflex action. Polychaetes *(Arenicola)* are unable to transmit peristaltic waves via the peripheral nerve shunt. The nerve net of annelids has the function of accessory sensory relay similar to the diffuse nerve net of Cnidaria and Ctenophora, but in the segmented Bilateria it has little or no function in locomotion, which is under the control of the central nervous system. Removal of the brain in *Nereis* results in overactive but aimless activity. A similar but less pronounced effect occurs in *Lumbricus,* since slow burrowing, eating, and some other activities can occur. With removal of the subpharyngeal ganglion, all activity ceases. This ganglion functions as the motor center, while the brain serves as a sensory center regulating and inhibiting nonproductive activity in the intact worm. Inhibitory control occurs in annelids and is a significant development in the evolution of the nervous system.

Several invertebrate phyla have representatives which are able to produce light. Among the annelids, this bioluminescence occurs both among marine polychaetes and terrestrial oligochaetes. The tubiculous polychaete, *Chaetopterus,* is particularly well known for its "phosphorescence" (Fig. 11-2). Some earthworms secrete phosphorescent globules or granules which reach the surface through dorsal pores or other openings. In some oligochaetes, a wave of photogenic cell response passes caudally from the point of stimulation, which suggests influence either of the nervous system or an oxidative threshold receding toward the posterior end.

One of the characteristics of typical annelids is the segmental arrangement of internal organs. Not only are the excretory and reproductive organs metamerically arranged, but ducts of the two systems may be variously compounded so that a single duct serves a dual function. In addition to the problem of homology established by this duality, a more fundamental question involves the germ-layer relationship of the two basic units of the annelid excretory system: protonephridia and metanephridia. Neither issue has received a definitive answer.

Both types of nephridia typically open to the exterior by nephridiopores, but protonephridia internally are closed by *solenocytes,* whether found in trochophore larvae or in some polychaete and archiannelid adults, whereas metanephridia communicate with

the coelom by ciliated funnels called *nephrostomes.* The solenocyte (Fig. 7-4) may well be homologous with the protonephric flamebulb of the acoelomate phyla, which, however, is characterized by a ciliary tuft rather than a flagellum as in the solenocyte. It is the contention of Goodrich that proto- and metanephridia are homologous and that they are ectodermal or ectomesodermal in origin.

Associated with the coelom in a number

Fig. 11-2 Bioluminescence in *Chaetopterus.* From Harvey 1952 (after Panceri), courtesy of Academic Press Inc.

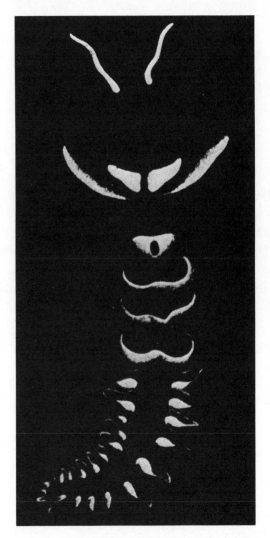

of polychaetes is another tubule which functions for the release of gonadal products to the surrounding water. This tubule is called a coelomoduct or gonoduct and is of undoubted mesodermal origin. Its funnel-shaped ciliated mouth in the coelom is called a *coelomostome*. In some annelids the coelomostome or its duct fuses with the duct of the nephridium so that a common exit occurs for excretory and gonadal products. Such a compound organ is a *nephromixium* (Fig. 11-3). If the fusion involves a protonephridium, a protonephromixium is formed. When the fusion involves a metanephridium, it is called a metanephromixium or mixonephridium. Such nephromixia have a dual germ layer origin if Goodrich is right, but anatomically a metanephromixium is often indistinguishable from a metanephridium.

There is a wide distribution of protonephridia in the animal kingdom. They occur in all acoelomate and most pseudocoelomate groups, in many polychaetes and archiannelids, in echiurids, in priapulids, in molluscs, in phoronids, and in *Amphioxus*. The protonephridium is the excretory organ of the widely occurring trochophore larva. Metanephridia occur in Brachiopoda, Polychaeta, Oligochaeta, Archiannelida, Hirudinea, Sipunculida, Pogonophora, and Phoronida.

Class Polychaeta

Polychaeta, with about 5300 species, constitutes the largest class of Annelida. Typically polychaetes are marine, dioecious annelids with external fertilization and a trochophore larva. Externally they exhibit a distinct head with prominent appendages, and well-defined trunk segmentation with paired lateral segmental outgrowths called parapodia from which arise numerous setae. As with other invertebrates, preserved laboratory and demonstration material belies the brilliant coloration and iridescence characteristic of many polychaetes.

Polychaetes have long been divided into two groups: Errantia, in which there is an active, mobile existence, and Sedentaria, in which life tends to be sedentary and restricted by adaptation to tube or burrow existence. Pelagic life and tube-dwelling originated more than once, and the separation of active and sedentary forms is not a natural one; however, the terms will be used for the convenience they offer. *Nereis* is an example of an errant polychaete and it exhibits features

Fig. 11-3 Phylogenetic stages from a separate coelomoduct and metanephridium to a mixonephridium. After Goodrich 1945, *Quart. J. Microsc. Sci.,* courtesy of the Company of Biologists Limited.

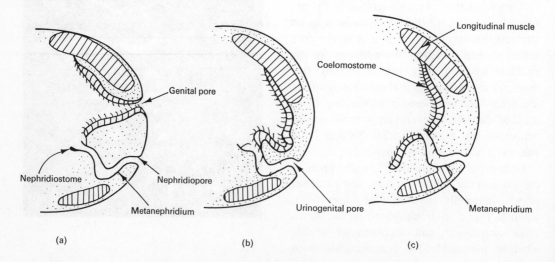

coordinated with active life. The head or prostomium is well developed and bears a pair of tentacles, two pairs of eyes, and a pair of palps. The body is somewhat flattened dorso-ventrally, and parapodia are well developed for locomotion and respiration. Associated with these sensory organs a prominent brain is developed within the prostomium. By contrast, *Arenicola* is adapted for burrowing, having the prostomium devoid of appendages, reduced parapodia, and a cylindrical body, and the brain is inconspicuous.

The prostomium is an organ of considerable interest not only for its varied development in annelids, but for its possible homology with topographically similar structures in arthropods. The prostomium and (at the posterior end of the annelid) the *pygidium* are respectively pre- and postsegmental. The prostomium reaches its greatest development in the Polychaeta. In oligochaetes and leeches it is reduced, and the brain in most species has shifted caudally from the prostomium. The first trunk segment is called the *peristomium,* and sometimes consists of two or more fused segments. In *Nereis,* two segments are incorporated in the peristomium, indicated externally by two pairs of sensory structures called cirri, and internally by two pairs of ganglia which remain distinct from the brain. The cirri are derived from the parapodial structures of their respective segments. The pygidium is usually small. Occasionally it bears sensory organs such as eyespots or cirri (one pair in *Nereis).* What mesoderm appears in either prostomium or pygidium is derived by growth from adjacent segments.

Feeding and Nutrition Considering the varied living modes of polychaetes, a diversity of feeding habits has evolved, and conversely. Digestion among annelids is extracellular. Plankton and detritus are the principal food sources for many polychaetes. For tube-dwellers, feeding has often led to the production of feeding tentacles which can be extended from the tube. Worms in

the family Terebellidae live in permanent tubes on the ocean floor and have extensible tentacles. In some species, the tentacle has an external ciliated groove. Fine detritus is caught in mucus secreted by cells on the tentacle and moved toward the mouth by ciliary action. Tentacles creep over the surface of the mud by ciliary action, and particles too large to be moved by ciliary beat are conveyed toward the mouth by retraction of the entire tentacle. Another tube-dweller, the sabellid *Eudistylia,* is aptly called a *featherduster* worm. A feathery crown of prostomial tentacles which are vascularized to function as gills are extended out the tube opening. Cilia on the gills of this filter not only create currents to bring microorganisms into contact with mucus, but convey the mucus toward the base. Various sorting mechanisms may reject particles that are too large. The tentacles in *Eudistylia* are provided with light-sensitive spots. Passing shadows, which are potential enemies, cause instant withdrawal of head and tentacles into the safety of the tube.

Chaetopterus is a tube-dweller with a very specialized feeding method (Fig. 11-4). *Chaetopterus* pumps water through the tube. The dorsal or notopodial portions of three parapodia create the propelling force by scooping the water in front and then expanding to close the tube. The arc of the notopodial beat carries them caudally so that their action propels the water somewhat like a piston-stroke. Farther forward, another pair of modified notopodia block the tube peripherally. Medially these notopodia do not meet, but secrete a mucus sheet between them. This sheet serves as a filter and eventually extends as a thimble-shaped bag with most of the caught food at the bottom. A ciliated cup rolls the food and mucus into a pellet. The worm stops mucus secretion and reverses the cilia in a groove leading forward to propel the food pellet to the mouth.

A number of polychaetes eat sand or mud to obtain food present in it. The lugworm *Arenicola* is a large annelid living in a

U-shaped burrow in intertidal beach sand. The burrow has one permanently open end up which the worm backs to deposit castings from the intestine. The other arm of the U represents the head shaft and is filled with the surface layer of organically rich sand and mud, which continues to cave in as the animal feeds. The lugworm has a proboscis or pharynx, which is everted into the mixture in the head shaft. Mucous secretion causes adherence of the sand and organic matter, which is swallowed when the proboscis is inverted. While feeding, castings are deposited at regular intervals of 30 to 40 minutes. In *Arenicola*, the mouth opens into the inverted muscular proboscis or pharynx (Fig. 11-5). Retractor muscles fan from the pharynx to the body wall passing through the first coelomic septum or diaphragm. Except for three at the anterior end and a few at the posterior end, all coelomic septa are incomplete. The tubular esophagus begins at the pharynx and continues past the three diaphragms to its junction with the stomach. This organ is a glandular tube somewhat larger than the esophagus, with the surface covered with yellowish chlorogogue tissue. Inside the posterior portion of the stomach and continuing in the intestine to the anus is a median ventral ciliated groove. The functional beat of these cilia is caudad.

Arenicola is an efficient burrower. In burrowing, the lugworm swallows very little sand, but forces its passage by vigorously poking its body into interstices in the sand. The presence of the anterior septa probably increases burrowing efficiency by preventing expansion of the corresponding segments or eversion of the pharynx due to hydrostatic action of muscle contraction in the nonseptate

Fig. 11-4 (a) Diagram of annelid feeding in its tube, and (b) dorsal view of anterior end of worm. 1, mouth; 2, wing-like projection from the edge of which mucus is secreted; 3, mucous bag; 4, food ball being rolled up in the ciliated cup; 5, "fan"; 6, ventral suckers; 7, dorsal groove lined with cilia along which the food ball is carried forward to the mouth. After MacGinitie and MacGinitie 1949, courtesy of the McGraw-Hill Book Company.

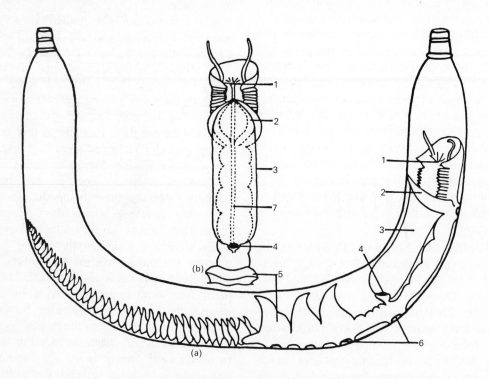

portions of the body.

A number of polychaetes are predaceous and possess variously shaped jaws and denticles. Some of these function for holding the prey and it is swallowed whole; others can tear bits of tissue. *Syllis* has a single dorsal tooth for stabbing; a poison gland is associated with it. Most predaceous annelids feed on other small animals (crustaceans, molluscs, other annelids, etc.). Some of the predaceous annelids probably eat some seaweed, but *Neanthes brandti,* which may reach a length of six feet, appears to be a vegetarian and feeds almost entirely on seaweeds along the Pacific Coast.

The clam or sandworm, *Nereis,* called ragworm in the British Isles, possesses a buccal region which is eversible and which is armed with paragnaths or denticles. When this buccal region is everted, the very muscular pharynx is brought forward and two strong chitinous jaws protrude. The pharynx opens into a narrower esophagus which is supplied with a pair of pouchlike glands. The remain-

Fig. 11-5 *Arenicola;* (a) lateral external view and (b) dorsal internal view (modified after Ashworth). After F. A. Brown, Jr. 1950, *Selected Invertebrate Types* (F. A. Brown, Jr., ed.), courtesy of John Wiley & Sons, Inc.

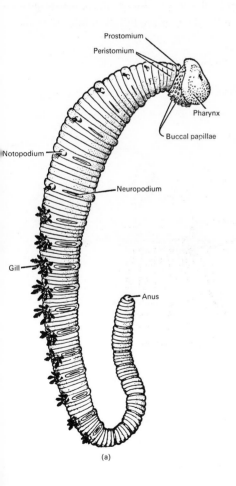

(a)

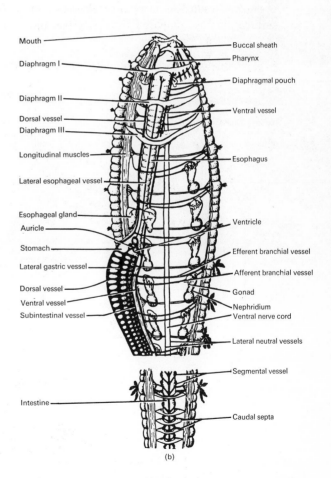

(b)

der of the alimentary canal is a rather uniform muscular intestine regularly constricted by coelomic septa (Fig. 11-6).

Respiration and Circulation   In the annelids generally, the skin is the fundamental organ of respiration, but for larger worms or those living in a confined environment such as tubes outgrowths already existing for other functions have become specialized with increased vascularization. In some cases gills have risen de novo.

Aerobic respiration involves exchange of oxygen and carbon dioxide through body surfaces. It should be remembered from general biology that growth of a spherical organism results in a relative decrease in surface area as compared with protoplasmic volume, so that the area-volume ratio is a function of optimal metabolism. Dales points out that a cylindrical organism such as an annelid can grow in length indefinitely if the body radius remains constant and that some earthworms less than an inch in diameter reach a length of over six feet.

Projections from the annelid body increase surface area, and greater vascularization within these projections as well as effective circulation of body fluids favor respiratory exchange. Structures that have taken on a respiratory function include palps, prostomial tentacles, parapodia, and either anterior or posterior cirri. Many of these structures are ciliated. In *Arenicola*, the lugworm, there are many pairs of highly branched gills containing coelomic diverti-

Fig. 11-6 Anterior end of *Nereis*; (a) dorsal and (b) ventral views, and (c) an isolated parapodium.

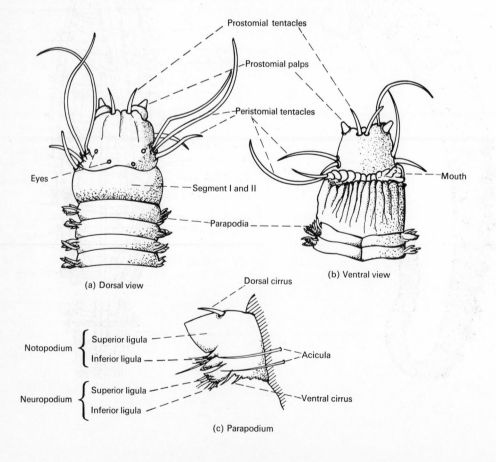

cula (Fig. 11-7). Fine blood vessels occurring between the coelomic peritoneum and the epidermis provide pathways for the blood between efferent and afferent branchial vessels. These gills are associated with the notopodium. They are red from the respiratory pigment, hemoglobin, and undergo rhythmic contractions. The gills are aerated in this tube-dweller by a current of water forced through the burrow by peristaltic body action when the burrow is immersed. When the tide is out, the lugworm may occasionally back up into the permanent tube and the gills obtain oxygen from the air present. Experimentally, lugworms have survived for several hours in an oxygen-free environment.

Arenicola has a number of longitudinal blood vessels. Above and below the intestine, respectively, there is a highly contractile dorsal vessel carrying blood cephalad, and a ventral vessel carrying blood caudad. In *Arenicola cristata* efferent branchials from the last seven pairs of gills empty into the dorsal vessel, while gills and nephridia receive blood from the ventral vessel. Branchial vessels from the four anterior pairs of gills empty into a subintestinal vessel. Around the anterior intestine or stomach there is a gastric plexus connecting the subintestinal and lateral gastric vessels with the dorsal vessel. Other longitudinal vessels include a pair lateral to the nerve cord and a pair at the

level of the nephridia. At the anterior end of the stomach, the lateral gastric vessels enlarge to form a pair of auricles. These empty into large contractile ventricles which relay blood from the gastric sinus into the ventral vessel. Caudally segmental vessels carry blood directly from the ventral to the dorsal vessel.

There are so many variations in type and site of respiratory organs and distribution of blood vessels in polychaetes that only a few features can be noted. The fanworms, such as *Sabella,* utilize the extruded feathery crown for both respiration and feeding, although some respiration is carried on by other surfaces. In this same genus, one species lives in a tube ending blindly in the mud, whereas others have a tube open at both ends. Obviously the problem of irrigating these tubes differs. Experiments in which the crown is amputated indicate that the sabellid can survive and regenerate a new crown, if the worm is able to irrigate its tube to receive oxygen. The specialized tube-dweller, *Chaetopterus,* circulates water through its tube by the beat of the three notopodial fans (Fig. 11-4). In *Nereis,* respiration occurs over the body surface, especially on the dorsal side and on the nonciliated tonguelike lobes of the notopodia called *ligula,* which are highly vascular (Fig. 11-8). It will be seen that blood to the ligula and subepidermal capillaries arises from blood vessels and sinuses lying laterally on the intestine, and returns to the dorsal vessel. Lateral segmental vessels from the ventral vessel supply the neuropodia and ventral wall and organs, and more caudally other lateral vessels carry blood directly to the dorsal vessel. In Fig. 11-8, it may be noted that a number of blood vessels end blindly, but many of these are contractile so that an ebb and flow circulation is maintained in them. *Nereis* has no hearts, and circulation is achieved by contractility in the blind ends; in the segmental vessels arising laterally from the gut; and in the main longitudinal vessels, especially the dorsal one.

Fig. 11-7 Parapodium and gill of *Arenicola.*

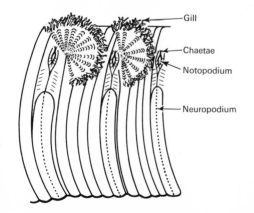

Gill

Chaetae

Notopodium

Neuropodium

Various respiratory pigments occur in the Annelida. The most common is hemoglobin (erythrocruorin). It is found in many polychaetes, oligochaetes, and in gnathobdellid leeches, in such familiar genera as *Nereis, Lumbricus,* and *Hirudo.* In most annelids hemoglobin occurs in the plasma. *Nephthys hombergii* is a polychaete reported to have two kinds of hemoglobin, one dissolved in coelomic fluid and the other dissolved in the plasma. In the polychaete *Glycera,* hemoglobin is contained within corpuscles in the coelomic fluid, since this polychaete has a degenerate vascular system. It is interesting to note that the respiratory pigments dissolved in plasma generally have a very large molecular or aggregate size as compared with such pigments contained in corpuscles, a feature apparently correlated with osmotic balances.

Other pigments include hemerythrin in the corpuscles of the polychaete, *Magelona,* and chlorocruorin in the plasma in annelids of the Order Sabellida as well as in two related orders. *Serpula,* in the same order as *Sabella,* has both hemoglobin and chlorocruorin. All of these respiratory pigments contain iron, and hemoglobin and chlorocruorin are both porphyrins, although of different kinds. Hemerythrin is a globulin.

Small annelids generally lack respiratory pigments. Their oxygen requirements are met by oxygen in solution in body fluids. In larger animals part of the oxygen continues to be supplied this way, but the presence of respiratory pigments with specific oxygen affinity is an important augmentation. Some of these pigments can accumulate oxygen at low environmental concentrations and therefore are of real significance in supplying tissues with oxygen. Carbon monoxide has a greater affinity for hemoglobin than does oxygen. The use of this poison can demonstrate the relative importance of hemoglobin in oxygen transport, although of course this varies among species since the hemoglobins differ. The acid effects often occurring under conditions of pollution and decomposition or under normal respiration in an intertidal burrow at low tide may increase the affinity of hemoglobin for oxygen. Under such times of stress, the presence of respiratory pigments may be of special importance, although a number of annelids with respiratory pigments are able to survive anaerobically for a considerable period.

Fig. 11-8 Diagram of *Nereis* vascular system indicating segmental distribution of vessels, sinuses and capillaries, as seen from posterior side of the segment. Adapted from Dales 1963 and from Ramsay 1952.

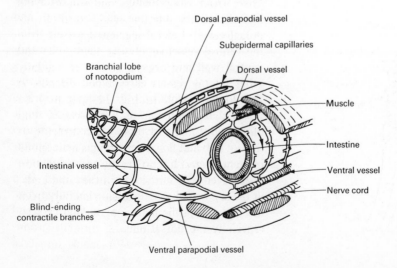

Dorsal parapodial vessel

Subepidermal capillaries

Branchial lobe of notopodium

Dorsal vessel

Muscle

Intestine

Intestinal vessel

Ventral vessel

Nerve cord

Blind-ending contractile branches

Ventral parapodial vessel

Excretion   It has already been noted that two general types of nephridia occur among polychaetes. In addition most polychaetes have vascular as well as coelomic fluid, both of which aid in the elimination of wastes. Representatives of at least three orders (phyllodocids, capitellids, and terebellids *(Polycirrus)*) do not have a blood vascular system. In addition to this variation, the size of the polychaete, the septate condition of the coelom, the adaptation to varying degrees of salinity, and confinement within a restricted area, such as with many tube-dwellers, are modifying factors related to excretory and hydrostatic needs.

Protonephridia occur in polychaete trochophore larvae and in several families of the order, Phyllodocida. Metanephridia are characteristic of other adult polychaetes. *Nereis* has a fairly typical metanephridial structure with a ciliated nephrostome opening on the anterior face of a septum. A canal proceeds caudally into the next segment, where it becomes an extensively coiled mass of ciliated tubules enclosed in a vesicle on the posterior face of the septum. From these tubules, a collecting tubule leads to an opening ventral to the neuropodium on either side. Multiplicity of nephrostomes, reduced coiling of the ciliated tubule, and location of the nephridiopore are common variations. Tubiculous forms in some cases have only a single nephridiopore (sabellids) or a paired *(Owenia)* development of epidermal tubes to reduce tube fouling.

There is great variability in the blood supply to the nephridium. One species of *Nereis* differs from other members of this genus in lacking any extensive vascularization of the nephridium. There is some evidence for a correlation between salinity of environment and blood supply in nereids. The blood supply appears to be more extensive in those animals living in brackish water and hence subject to frequent osmotic stress. This implies a hydrostatic function analogous to that of the contractile vacuole among protozoa.

Ammonia appears to be the principal nitrogenous waste in polychaetes. Various phagocytic amoebocytes not confined to the coelomic fluid pick up particulate waste. In some of the errant polychaetes, the coelomostome is modified into a crescent-shaped ciliated organ. This functions in an excretory capacity by collecting waste-laden phagocytes from coelomic fluid and transferring soluble waste products by diffusion to the adjacent nephridial canal, since these ciliophagocytal organs have no opening either to the exterior or to the nephric duct.

In *Arenicola,* excretion as well as discharge of genital products is served by a nephromixium. There are six pairs of nephromixia beginning with segment V. Since septa are lacking in *Arenicola* in this region, the principal support for the nephromixia is the ventral body wall and part of the oblique musculature (Fig. 11-9).

Nervous System and Sense Organs   The polychaetes have a dorsal cerebral ganglion or brain located in the prostomium. The bilobed structure of the brain is indicative of its origin from paired ganglia innervating the anterior end. In *Nereis,* the principal pair of circumpharyngeal commissures, paralleled by an accessory pair, pass obliquely to the first ventral ganglion in the third segment. This ganglion is the foremost of a chain of ganglionic enlargements correlated with segmentation. In polychaetes, the brain and ventral cord arise from separate primordia, and the connectives joining them are established later.

The brain of the tube-dweller, *Arenicola,* is minute (Fig. 11-9). It has two principal lobes lying just beneath the skin. A single pair of commissures pass obliquely around the pharynx and give off nerves to the prominent statocysts and to the buccal and pharyngeal region. The ventral nerve cord is a flattened rod without ganglionic enlargments. Paired lateral branches arise from it, and those innervating parapodia are quite prominent. As is typical with many annelids,

Arenicola has giant nerve fibers within the nerve cord.

Special sense organs are well developed in a number of polychaetes, especially among errant forms. Various projecting organs such as tentacles, palps, and cirri are certainly sensitive to touch. Tactile or chemosensory cells occur in the epidermis of *Nereis*. Nereids also have two pairs of eyes situated dorsally on the prostomium, as well as light-sensitive cells aggregated around cuticular pits. Such organs occur in various exposed places on the annelid body. In some polychaetes, the most prominent eyespots are located on the pygidium. *Arenicola* has eyespots located on the prostomium in the vicinity of the brain, but usually these are only visible in young specimens.

Chemoreceptors called *nuchal organs* occur on the prostomium. In *Arenicola,* the nuchal organ is in the shape of a U-shaped groove; in *Nereis,* they are paired, ciliated shallow grooves behind the eyes, and in many polychaetes the chemosensory cells are situated in shallow pits and are innervated from the brain. In some annelids, destruction of nuchal organs has been shown to reduce or to prevent food recognition.

Arenicola and some other burrowers or tube-dwellers are somewhat unique in the possession of statocysts or otocysts. Usually there is a single pair, and in the lugworm *Arenicola* the innervation of the statocysts connects with the circumpharyngeal connectives (Fig. 11-9). Three kinds of statocysts occur in the genus *Arenicola*. One of these is a ciliated cavity opening externally and provided with sand grains as statoliths. The

Fig. 11-9 Anterior portion of dissected *Arenicola* to show some of the organs. Note relationship of nephridia to oblique musculature shown on the left and to longitudinal musculature on the right.

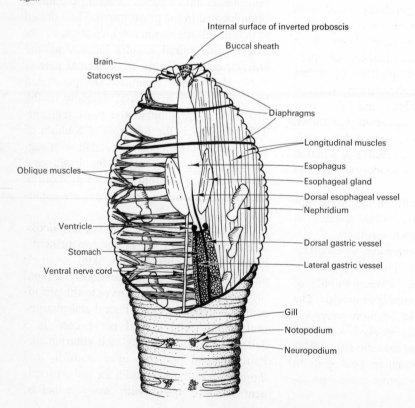

Internal surface of inverted proboscis
Buccal sheath
Brain
Statocyst
Diaphragms
Longitudinal muscles
Oblique muscles
Esophagus
Esophageal gland
Dorsal esophageal vessel
Nephridium
Ventricle
Stomach
Dorsal gastric vessel
Ventral nerve cord
Lateral gastric vessel
Gill
Notopodium
Neuropodium

other two types are spherical capsules lacking an external orifice and with a secreted statolith. These two kinds differ in the presence or absence of cilia. Statocysts function as a response to gravity; hence they are important in orientation of the worm.

Reproduction and Embryology Typical polychaetes are dioecious and oviparous, with the gonads developing during the breeding season from mesodermal derivatives of coelomic epithelium. Gametes escape through gonoducts (coelomoducts), nephridia, nephromixia, or by rupture of the body wall, and fertilization occurs in sea water.

Although most polychaetes exhibit no structural difference between individuals filled with gonadal products and those which are not, there are several instances in which extensive anatomical modifications appear. Many species of *Nereis* exhibit dimorphic or polymorphic stages. A typical dimorphic pattern results in the following changes. An extensive posterior portion of the body produces remodeled parapodia which have finlike expansions and paddle-shaped setae. This modification produces a more efficient swimming organ as well as an increased respiratory surface. Another common change is a marked increase in eye size. This modified stage of *Nereis* was at one time given the separate generic name of *Heteronereis,* since it was thought to be a new genus. This actively swimming stage, heteronereis, allows for species dispersion, as well as providing for swarming to insure maximal utilization of gametes. The heteronereis has been considered to have a non-sexual anterior portion, the *atoke,* and a posterior portion, the *epitoke,* containing sexual products. In some nereid species the heteronereis phase never occurs and gametic products are produced in the anatomically unmodified body. An extreme instance of the development of an atoke and epitoke division occurs with the palolo worms of the polychaete family, Eunicidae. The best-known species of the Pacific Ocean is the Samoan palolo, *Eunice viridis. E. schemacephala*

occurs in the Atlantic in waters around the West Indies. In these life cycles, the atoke portion remains in the coral burrow, while the epitoke breaks free to swarm at the surface. With *Eunice viridis,* this process happens with an exact periodicity at the beginning of the last quarter of the October-November moon. Tropical island natives collect large numbers for food at this time. The asexual atoke will regenerate a new posterior end. In some polychaetes, the epitoke produced develops a head before separating from the nonsexual portion, and some species produce chains of such individuals. One species, *Syllis ramosa,* produces side-branch budding of either sterile or reproductive individuals.

Typical polychaete eggs undergo segmentation in a pattern parallel to that in polyclad tubellarians, nemertines, molluscs, and archiannelids. This process is called spiral cleavage, and cell-lineage studies have traced the fate of the individual blastomeres in the embryology of each of these groups. The uniformity of development is striking.

Cleavage is holoblastic, rhythmic, and unequal almost from the start. In polychaetes, the first two cleavages are meridional and result in four blastomeres, one of which is markedly larger than the others (Fig. 11-10 (a)). This cell is labeled D and the others A, B, and C, respectively. The third cleavage is unequal and oblique and results in the production of a quartet of small cells called micromeres, whose vertical axes are not coincident with those of the respective macromeres mutually derived at the third cleavage, but instead lie vertical to the grooves separating the macromeres. This position would be equivalent to a 45-degree rotation of one quartet of cells at the eight-cell stage in radial cleavage (Fig. 11-10(c)). This shift from the vertical, occasioned by the oblique spindles axes (see Fig. 11-10(b)) at the third cleavage, together with some subsequent cleavages, inspired the term *spiral cleavage*. If the first shift or rotation in spiral cleavage was clockwise it is called dextrotropic; if counterclockwise, laevotropic. During spiral cleavage these two rotations alternate.

At the eight-cell stage in spiral cleavage the four larger cells or macromeres are designated by the coefficient 1, i.e., 1A, 1B, 1C, and 1D, while the respective micromeres are 1a, 1b, 1c, and 1d (Fig. 11-10(c)). With the fourth cleavage, the macromeres

Fig. 11-10 Spiral cleavage in Polychaetes. Drawings (a) and (b) represent the 4-cell stage, lateral and animal pole views respectively. Drawings (c) and (d) are animal pole views at later stages. At the right is a scheme to indicate quartette orientation and labelling system. The 2a-2d and 1a′-1d′ quartettes have both divided. Cell 4d forms coelomic mesoderm; 4a, 4b, 4c, and the macromere quartette form endoderm; the remainder, ectoderm and ectomesoderm.

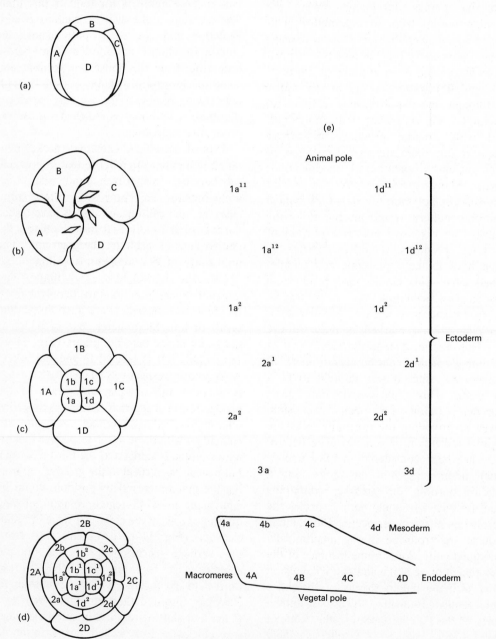

divide again to produce a new quartet of micromeres designated 2a, 2b, 2c, and 2d, and the macromeres are now named 2A, 2B, 2C, and 2D, respectively.

When the first quartet of micromeres divides, daughter cells are distinguished by the use of exponents. Cell 1a gives rise to cell $1a^1$ and cell $1a^2$, with exponent 1 used for the cell nearer the animal pole. When these cells eventually divide, the daughter cells are called respectively $1a^{11}$ and $1a^{12}$, and $1a^{21}$ and $1a^{22}$, with the second exponent appended to the first. The terminal exponent 1 again indicates the daughter cell nearer the animal pole. All cells bearing the same letter (e.g., a) are in the same quadrant and all cells headed by coefficient 1 are descendants of the first quartet of micromeres (Fig. 11-10(d)).

The earlier formed quartets undergo division before the macromeres complete their series of cleavages. These micromeres overgrow the larger cells, a process known as epiboly. The origin of the descendants of any primary quartet of micromeres can be traced; but to avoid confusion attention should be focused on the four primary quartets produced by cleavage of the macromeres. At the eight- cell stage the first quartet of micromeres has been produced and lies at the animal pole. The macromeres divide again at right angles to the third cleavage; this second quartet, labeled 2a, 2b, 2c, and 2d, lies between the first quartet and the macromeres now designated 2A, 2B, 2C, and 2D, respectively. At the next macromere division, the third primary quartet of micromeres is produced and interposed between the second quartet and the macromeres which now are designated by coefficient 3 (i.e., 3A, 3B, 3C, and 3D). The fourth division of the macromeres produces the fourth primary quartet of micromeres (Fig. 11-10(e)). Because of unequal division, the 4d cell is actually larger than the 4D macromere in polychaetes. The 4d cell has special significance and is commonly called the *mesentoblast* or M cell. It is the ancestral cell of the endomesoderm, and in polychaetes it divides into two *teloblast* cells which in turn are the progenitors of the two mesodermal bands and of all the endomesoderm. The first three micromere quartets and their daughter cells are destined to produce ectoderm and some larval mesodermal derivatives of it (mesectoderm). The first quartet and its descendants produce the anterior ectoderm of the trochophore including the brain. The second quartet will give rise to circumoral and stomodaeal ectoderm, the ventral nerve cord, and as a result of epiboly, the pygidium. The third quartet produces additional ectoderm in these regions, contributes to the stomodaeum, and gives rise to larval solenocytes. Endoderm is derived from 4a, 4b, and 4c micromeres plus the now much-reduced macromeres.

The trochophore is a biovate or biconical larva which bluntly tapers or is rounded toward either end (Fig. 11-11). At the dorsal apex is the ciliated apical organ. Various latitudinal bands of cilia encircle the larva, the most constant or typical being the preoral prototroch and the postoral metatroch. Rarely the entire surface is covered with a uniform ciliary layer. A ciliated digestive tube passes from a lateral mouth to an anus at the lower apex. Immediately beneath the apical

Fig. 11-11 Trochophore of *Polygordius*. After Richards 1931, courtesy of John Wiley & Sons, Inc.

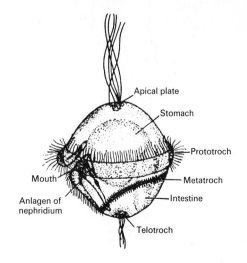

Apical plate

Stomach

Prototroch

Mouth

Metatroch

Intestine

Anlagen of nephridium

Telotroch

organ is a ganglion connected by longitudinal nerves with various nerve rings, the most prominent of which lies just below the prototroch. A pair of solenocytic nephridia derived from the third quartet lie latero-ventrally in the blastocoele near the paired mesodermal bands. Eventually the planktonic trochophore metamorphoses with reduction or loss of larval features between the apical plate and the pygidial region which bears the anus. The definitive prostomium arises from the apical plate region and the growing mesodermal bands develop a metamerism soon followed by transverse grooves in the ectoderm (Fig. 11-12). The zone of growth is immediately anterior to the pygidium, so that the oldest segments are most distal from it and structurally most advanced. This growth encroaches on and eventually obliterates the trochophoral blastocoele. In some polychaetes, the growth of mesodermal bands will penetrate the prostomium and pygidium, but these are secondary developments and do not change the fundamental presegmental and postsegmental nature of these termini. Duration of planktonic life varies for trochophoral and post-trochophoral stages.

Systematic Resume Polychaetes can be arranged into a large number of distinctive families. Fauvel lists 37 families, which are not grouped into orders. Dales includes 51 families grouped into 14 orders and points out that division into subclasses Errantia and Sedentaria does not mirror the evolution of polychaetes. Only brief mention can be made here of some of the characteristics identifying Dales' orders.

Order 1 Phyllodocida Parapodia are expanded dorsally into leafy or scalelike projections (elytra in family Aphroditidae) which involve the notopodium or dorsal cirrus. The Phyllodocida are mostly active worms which are predaceous or scavengers. There is an elongate, uniformly muscular pharynx, or an eversible muscular tube leading to a bulbous muscular pharynx (nereids), or a tubular muscular pharynx separated by a thin-walled esophagus from a muscular proventriculus (syllids). Dales includes 15 families in this order, nine of which have protonephridia or protonephromixia. *Aphrodite, Glycera, Hesione, Nephthys, Nereis, Syllis.*

Order 2 Capitellida Five families are included in this order, which vary from small, threadlike forms to large robust types (arenicolids). Some have elongate segments as indicated by the name of bamboo worms (maldanids). There is a relatively thin-walled proboscis which functions to dig in sand and mud, and which by alternate eversion and inversion ingests the sand or mud for the contained organic matter. *Capitella, Arenicola, Scalibregma, Clymenella, Ophelia.*

Order 3 Sternaspida The single family includes small, grayish, pear-shaped worms with a crown of arched setae on each of the first three segments and a sclerotized posterior shield provided with many snakelike gills. There is a simple, rounded proboscis, and the intestine is greatly coiled. The posterior gills protrude above the mud in which the animal lives. *Sternaspis.*

Fig. 11-12 An older trochophore of *Polygordius*, showing beginning of definitive segmentation. The embryonic body between the apical plate and the definitive segments will be largely resorbed in the metamorphosis. After Richards (after Woltereck) 1931, courtesy of John Wiley & Sons, Inc.

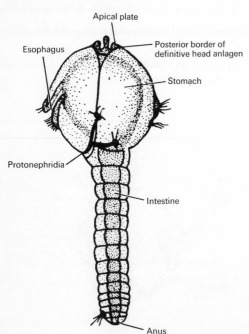

Apical plate

Esophagus

Posterior border of definitive head anlagen

Stomach

Protonephridia

Intestine

Anus

Order 4 Spionida   This group has evolved tentacle-feeding. Usually there is a pair of simple tentacles derived from palps on the prostomium. The proboscis is simple or reduced and used in digging. Tentacles in some forms sweep the mud and wipe caught debris on the proboscis. A few have a fleshy lobe on the prostomium. Eight families are included in this order. *Polydora, Scolelepis, Chaetopterus, Sabellaria.*

Order 5 Eunicida   These elongate worms have a ventral proboscis usually armed with replaceable teeth and provided with apposable jaws. A number are tube-dwellers. Many are herbivorous on algae and others are robust predators. *Histriobdella* has a single pair of parapodia and is an ectoparasite of lobsters. *Ichthyotomus* is parasitic on the gills of eels. Notopodial gills and prostomial tentacles tend to be elaborate in tubiculous forms, but such appendages are lacking in most others. *Eunice, Onuphis, Halla, Histriobdella, Ichthyotomus.*

Order 6 Amphinomida   These are elongate worms with an unarmed, ventral proboscis, calcareous setae, a fleshy lobe on the prostomium, and with biramous highly branched parapodia. They are included in a single family. *Amphinome, Euphrosyne.*

Order 7 Magelonida   The worms in the single family in this order are sand-dwellers with an oval, flattened prostomium lacking antennae but with papillose palps and with an enormous balloonlike proboscis. *Magelona.*

Order 8 Ariciida   These worms grouped in a single family have an unarmed proboscis which contains an extrusible secondary dendritic proboscis with which sand is licked up. The prostomium is without appendages, and a somewhat flattened thoracic region is differentiated from a more cylindrical abdomen. *Aricia, Scoloplos.*

Order 9 Cirratulida   Three families are included in this order, named from the usual presence of long respiratory cirri which arise latero-dorsally on many segments. The prostomium is small and lacks appendages. The long, feeding tentacles arise from the dorsal side of an anterior segment. Body segments are short and compact. Both cirri and tentacles are thrust up to the surface of the mud in which these animals live. *Cirratulus, Ctenodrilus, Dodecaceria.*

Order 10 Oweniida   The single family included in this order is composed of worms which build a flexible tube of shell fragments. The prostomium is fused with the peristomium, lacks the usual appendages, but has a more or less fringed, ciliated encircling membrane. These animals are suspension feeders, but can also use the ciliated crown to sweep the mud near the tube. The cylindrical body has elongate anterior segments and short posterior segments. *Owenia, Myriochele.*

Order 11 Terebellida   Three families are included in this order. They are deposit feeders with extremely extensile prostomial tentacles usually grooved and ciliated on one side. The tentacles are controlled principally by a complicated set of muscles within the hollow interior. In some forms the tentacles can be retracted into the mouth. There is a protrusible ventral buccal organ which is bulblike and sometimes folded on itself when retracted. These tentacles explore the surface near the tube or burrow; mucus aids in capturing food. Most species in this order live in permanent burrows or tubes. *Amphitrite, Amphicteis, Pectinaria, Polycirrus.*

Order 12 Flabelligerida   The annelids in the single family are mud-dwellers with a body tapering caudally and composed of short, papillose segments. A buccal organ is lacking and feeding is accomplished by prostomial tentacles. The prostomium and peristomium with eyes, palps, and tentacles can be inverted as a tube into the anterior end. The gut in these annelids is highly coiled. *Flabelligera, Stylarioides.*

Order 13 Psammodrilida   The single species, *Psammodrilus balanoglossoides,* is a small worm living in sand. Segmentation is indistinct, but the body is divided into three regions. The first is composed of a large bulbous prostomium and a papillose peristomium. The second region is designated pharyngeal and externally shows three pairs of parapodia reduced to dorsal cirri. The trunk region has two pairs of ventral cirri and belts of cilia. *Psammodrilus.*

Order 14 Sabellida   This order is composed of two prominent families. Commonly called fanworms or featherduster worms, these annelids have a bilateral, prostomial crown of tentacles which are branched or pinnate. One tentacle is distally enlarged to form an operculum when the crown is retracted into the tube. Each half of the crown may be spiraled, and individual tentacles are often grooved and ciliated. In *Sabella,* larger cilia produce an ascending current axially through the crown. Tubes are composed of sand or shell fragments (sabellids) or are calcareous (serpulids). *Branchiomma, Eudistylia, Pomatocerus, Sabella, Serpula.*

Class Clitellata

Two prominent groups of annelids often considered as separate classes are here joined in the Clitellata. One of these groups, containing some 3,000 species, is the Oligochaeta composed of earthworms and their fresh-water and estuarine allies. The second group contains some 300 leeches, collectively termed Hirudinea. Clitellata are typically fresh-water or terrestrial worms. They lack a distinct head and parapodia and possess few or no setae. These annelids are commonly hermaphroditic, possess a permanent or transitory clitellum, and have a reproductive system provided with special ducts. The characteristic internal fertilization is an adaptation to terrestrial existence.

Subclass Oligochaeta Typically, oligochaetes are distinctly annulated, cylindrical worms living in terrestrial burrows or in the bottom silt of fresh-water streams, ponds, and lakes, often around submerged vegetation. While most fresh-water annelids occur in easily wadable waters, some members of the family Tubificidae occur at the bottom of deep lakes, often in tremendous numbers. Many tubificids occur in streams heavy with pollution. In general most fresh-water oligochaetes are well-adapted to conditions of reduced oxygen, which frequently accompany the presence of considerable organic debris.

Two families of oligochaetes have representatives which exhibit graduations from aqueous to terrestrial environment. In the family Enchytraeidae some species live in a habitat of constant immersion in sea water, some occur on the shore under stones, and some are completely terrestrial. Worms in the family Haplotaxidae live in fresh-water swamps, some species being semiterrestrial in adjacent soil of high water content. The presence of a gizzard in these worms is unusual among aquatic annelids. Terrestrial oligochaetes have a widespread distribution where moisture conditions are adequate. In addition to Lumbricidae, which includes such familiar genera as *Lumbricus, Allolobophora,* and *Eisenia,* earthworms occur in at least three other oligochaete families, which are Glossoscolecidae, Megascolecidae, and Eudrilidae. Most oligochaetes subsist primarily on organic detritus; predators, parasites, or commensals are rare. *Branchiobdella* is an oligochaete that has a leechlike appearance derived convergently. This small worm is unique among oligochaetes in having a constant number of segments of which four form the head and eleven compose the trunk, although the last three or four are less distinct and show fusion with the large caudal sucker. The prostomium is apparently lost, and the mouth with dorsal and ventral lips is armed with a pair of jaws. Another leechlike characteristic is the absence of setae. *Branchiobdella* is ectocommensal and perhaps occasionally ectoparasitic on crayfish.

Although *Branchiobdella* is the only oligochaete with a constant number of segments, some other fresh-water genera have fewer. In the families Aeolosomatidae and Naididae, the number of segments varies from eight to forty while the long, threadlike Haplotaxidae may have nearly 500 and Alma (Glossoscolecidae) may have somewhat more than 500.

Feeding and Nutrition Among the Oligochaeta, the alimentary canal is typically a straight tube, beginning beneath the prostomium with the mouth which opens to a small buccal cavity. Behind this lies the muscular pharynx, followed by a somewhat constricted esophageal region (commonly ciliated in aquatic oligochaetes) which in turn opens into the intestine. *Pontodrilus,* an oligochaete living in seaweed just above high-tide level along the Mediterranean shore, has an alimentary canal of this sort. *Aeolosoma,* a small aquatic oligochaete, employs a ciliary feeding method, sweeping detritus-containing microorganisms into the mouth by the cilia-directed current of the prostomium (Fig. 11-13).

The familiar earthworms possess some additional adaptations, primarily of the esophagus. *Lumbricus terrestris* has a paired pouch and gland complex associated with it. These have been collectively termed calciferous glands and they function to excrete excess calcium. The material produced by these glands is chemically inactive and does

Fig. 11-13 *Aeolosoma,* ventral and lateral views. Note cilia on ventral surface of prostomium.

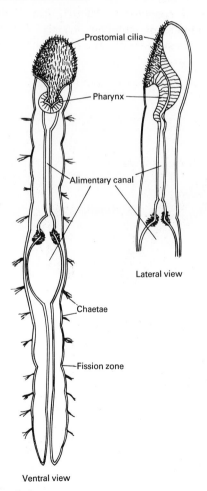

Prostomial cilia

Pharynx

Alimentary canal

Lateral view

Chaetae

Fission zone

Ventral view

not contribute appreciably to modification of the *p*H of intestinal contents, which remains fairly constant. Increased acid produced during feeding in *Lumbricus* is neutralized by a shift in the excretory end-products: less urea and more ammonia is produced.

Another esophageal modification is the frequent presence of a thin-walled crop followed by a muscular gizzard lined with chitin. This latter organ functions to masticate food. Posterior to the gizzard, the intestine is somewhat constricted intersegmentally by the septa, and possesses a covering of yellow chloragogue cells containing yellowish-brown granules called chloragosomes. Metabolism and storage of oil and glycogen occurs in the chloragosomes. They also produce some of the end-products of nitrogen metabolism, namely, ammonia and urea. Internally, the intestine has a median, dorsal infolding called the *typhlosole* which increases the absorptive area (Fig. 11-14). The typhlosole is large in Lumbricidae, smaller in earthworms in the families Megascolecidae and Glossoscolescidae, and some of these have additional glands communicating with the intestine.

Lumbricus tears off softened bits of organic matter from decaying leaves and other materials. This is largely accomplished by a kind of sucking action combined with a pincer effect between pharynx and prostomium. In feeding as well as in burrowing considerable quantities of earth are swallowed. These are deposited as castings within the burrow in some earthworms. *(L. terrestris)* and at the opening of the burrow in other forms, similar to the practice of *Arenicola*. In *Lumbricus,* the esophagus is innervated from the circumesophageal ring, and posterior to the esophagus segmentally derived antagonistic nerve fibers enter the gut ventrally or dorsally through the septa for augmentatory or inhibitory action respectively. These provide impulses for a variety of gut movements.

Respiration and Circulation   Among the aquatic families of oligochaetes, the body wall is thin and well supplied vascularly and it serves as the principal respiratory organ.

A number of oligochaetes, as well as some polychaetes, regularly take water into the intestine through the anus, and this water serves a respiratory function. *Tubifex* has no gills, but the smaller posterior portion (commonly bright red from hemoglobin) extends from the tube within which the animal lives, the degree of extension bearing some inverse correlation to the amount of oxygen available. *Tubifex* hemoglobin has a strong affinity for oxygen, which apparently is an advantage to this worm which thrives in polluted waters often low in oxygen. Undoubtedly the undulating action of the extruded body in *Tubifex* serves a respiratory function.

There are also some gilled oligochaetes. *Branchiura,* in the same family as *Tubifex,* has both a dorsal and a ventral row of gills at the posterior end, and some of the Naididae *(Dero)* possess a number of ciliated,

branchial caudal processes. Most terrestrial oligochaetes utilized a highly vascular body wall for respiration, but the large glossoscolecid, *Alma,* from Africa, has gills vascularized by loops between the ventral and dorsal vessels.

The Oligochaeta have a closed circulatory system also, but owing to the frequent presence of valves and more direct segmental connectives, circulation is often more vigorous than in polychaetes. Blood is propelled principally by the main longitudinal vessels and in some forms by contractile connectives between the dorsal and ventral vessels. In *Lumbricus,* segmental vessels supply the intestine, nephridia, and body wall (Fig. 11-15). Valves occur in the hearts and at the segmental junctions with the dorsal vessel. *Lumbricus terrestris* has additional prominent longitudinal vessels. There is a median subneural and a pair of latero-neural

Fig. 11-14 Cross-section of *Lumbricus*. After Goodrich 1945, *Quart. J. Microsc. Sci.,* 86: 113, courtesy of the Company of Biologists Limited.

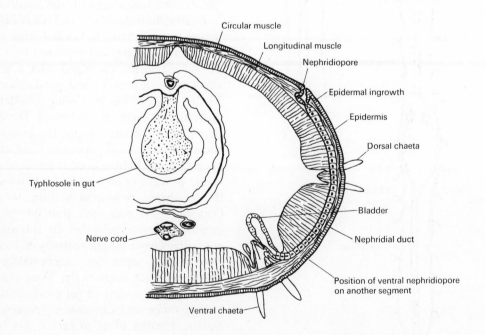

tubes (Fig. 11-15).

Excretion In *Lumbricus,* a pair of metanephridia occur in all but the first few and the last segments. As with the polychaete, *Nereis,* the nephrostome is on the anterior face of the septum, while the main body of the nephridium lies in the segment behind this mesentery. The nephridial body is composed of three well-vascularized loops, the first of which is traversed three times by the excretory tubule, while the second is traversed twice. The third loop is composed principally of the muscular duct or bladder which opens through the nephridiopore either dorsolaterally or ventrolaterally.

Laverack points out that about half of the nitrogen lost per day by earthworms occurs as mucoid-proteins in the mucus. For excretion in a more strict sense, the end-products of nitrogen metabolism for the most part are ammonia and urea. Both of these substances

are produced in many tissues. The gut wall has been found to have more of both substances than either body wall or muscle. It appears that most of the ammonia and urea are formed in the chloragogen cells. Both blood and coelomic fluid have less urea and ammonia than does the urine in earthworms examined. Probably nephridia obtain these substances from both coelom and blood, and the chloragogen cells release these wastes either by diffusion or by disintegration. Needham reported that *Lumbricus terrestris* has increased acid production occurring at feeding that is offset by an increase in ammonia excretion. It would be interesting to know if this relationship holds for those megascolescids in which nephridia empty into the intestine.

Another earthworm structure is associated with excretion. The calciferous glands function to get rid of excess calcium, which is

Fig. 11-15 Circulation in *Lumbricus.* Segments XI and XII are shown. Adapted from various sources.

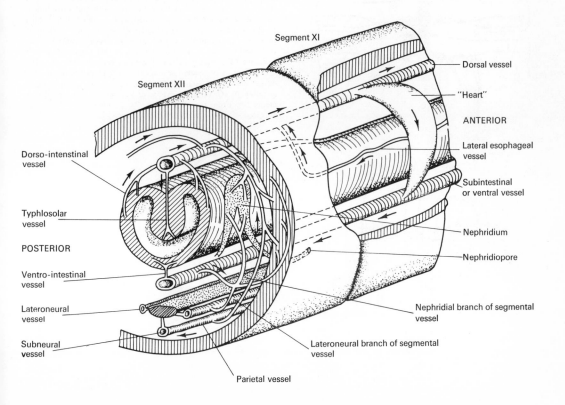

Segment XI

Segment XII

Dorso-intenstinal vessel

Typhlosolar vessel

POSTERIOR

Ventro-intestinal vessel

Lateroneural vessel

Subneural vessel

Parietal vessel

Dorsal vessel

"Heart"

ANTERIOR

Lateral esophageal vessel

Subintestinal or ventral vessel

Nephridium

Nephridiopore

Nephridial branch of segmental vessel

Lateroneural branch of segmental vessel

voided through the anus as calcium carbonate concretions. Carbon dioxide is an excretory product. Carbonic anhydrase, which functions in a reversible reaction combining carbon dioxide and water to form H_2CO_3 (carbonic acid), is present in the calciferous glands and nearby tissues of the digestive tract. Carbonic acid, which would ionize to increase acidity (lower pH), combines with calcium ions as calcium carbonate. It appears that the calciferous glands function in excretion concomitant in part with a buffering effect on body fluids.

Nervous System and Sense Organs In polychaetes, it has been pointed out, the brain and ventral nerve cord arise from separate primordia. In the Clitellata these two portions of the central nervous system are in continuity from the beginning, and in oligochaetes a new brain can be regenerated from nerve-cord tissue. Regenerative ability

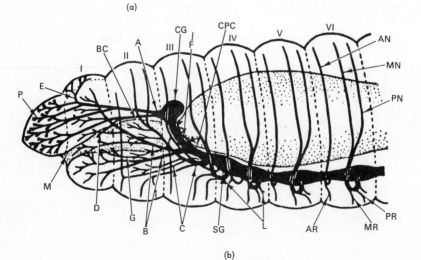

Fig. 11-16 (a) Dorsal and (b) sagittal views of the anterior end of the earthworm nervous system. (a) Dorsal view of the arrangement of the larger nerves in the anterior segments. To avoid confusion, the terminal branches of some of the paired nerves have been omitted from one side of segments 1 and 2. (b) Lateral view of the arrangement of the larger nerve trunks in the left half of the anterior segments of the earthworm *Lumbricus terrestris.* A, nerve from lateral region of cerebral ganglion which passes to the prostomium; AN, dorsal ramus of anterior segmental nerve; AR, ventral ramus of anterior segmental nerve; B, nerve from near middle region of circumpharyngeal connective which passes to segment 1; BC, buccal cavity; C, nerves from ventral region of circumpharyngeal connective which pass to segment 2; CG, cerebral ganglion; CPC, circumpharyngeal connective; D, branch of nerve to prostomium that supplies tissues of dorsal region of buccal cavity; E, nerve that supplies the portion of prostomium in the dorsomedian region of segment 1; F, gangliated thickening of enteric nerve plexus that supplies tissues of ventral region of buccal cavity; G, median ventral nerve; H, nerve to ventral region of buccal cavity; L, septal nerve; LS, lateral actae; M, mouth opening; MN, dorsal ramus of median segmental nerve; MR, ventral ramus of median segmental nerve; P, prostomium; PN, dorsal ramus of posterior segmental nerve; SG, subpharyngeal ganglion; VNC, ventral nerve cord; VS, ventral setae; I-VI, segments 1-6. From figures 1 and 2, W. H. Hess 1925, *J. Morph.* 40:235.

varies among polychaetes, and there are many unanswered questions about regeneration among the annelids. Paired peripheral nerves occur in each segment throughout the annelids. In *Lumbricus,* the prostomium is innervated from the brain which (as in most oligochaetes) lies in the third segment. Nerves to the peristomium and the second body segment arise from the circumesophageal connectives. The subesophageal ganglion in *Lumbricus* is the fused ganglia of segments three and four and it supplies innervation for these segments. Typical body segments have three pairs of nerves to tissues of the respective somites with the two posterior pairs arising in close proximity (Fig. 11-16). Commonly the ventral nerve cord is separated from epidermis by the layer of circular muscle, but in the Archiannelida, some Polychaeta, and the fresh-water oligochaete, *Aeolosoma,* the ventral nerve cord is adjacent to or continuous with the epidermis (Fig. 11-17). *Aeolosoma* differs from other oligochaetes in having the brain located in the prostomium (Fig. 11-17).

Special sense organs are not well developed in the oligochaetes. Some of the small aquatic

forms possess epidermal eye-spots, and there are sensory hairs or papillae probably tactile in function. The earthworm, *Lumbricus,* has special spindle-shaped epidermal cells which have an olfactory function of limited range.

Reproduction and Embryology Among hermaphroditic Clitellata copulation and cross-fertilization are typical and the gonads are always provided with special ducts. As

Fig. 11-17 *Aeolosoma* nervous system, (a) frontal section of the anterior portion and (b) a cross-section show epidermal relationship of the nervous system. From figures 1 and 12, E. M. Brace 1901, *J. Morph.,* 17: 185.

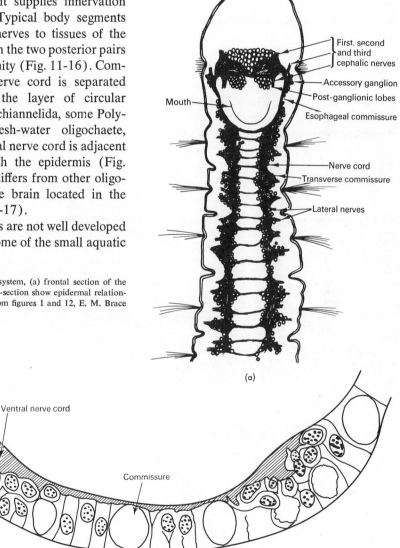

First, second and third cephalic nerves

Accessory ganglion

Post-ganglionic lobes

Esophageal commissure

Mouth

Nerve cord

Transverse commissure

Lateral nerves

(a)

Ventral nerve cord

Commissure

(b)

in *Lumbricus,* the young develop inside a cocoon secreted by the clitellar glands. In addition to this function, the clitellum produces mucus enveloping the apposing but reversed ventral surfaces at copulation. Genital setae aid in securing the copulating partners (Fig. 11-18). Since with *Lumbricus,* worms of disparate size may copulate, the mucus assists in isolating channels for transfer of sperm from the male gonopore of each partner to the spermatheca or seminal receptacles of the other partner. The clitellum also secretes albumin in which the eggs will be deposited.

There is great variation in extent of the clitellum. In those species of *Aeolosoma* in which it has been seen, it is restricted to the ventral side of two segments. In other freshwater forms, two or occasionally three segments are involved, in *Lumbricus* it includes some six or seven somites beginning with segment 31 or 32, and in *Alma* 48 to 60 segments are incorporated.

In *Lumbricus terrestris,* sperm leave the vasa deferentia in segment 15 and accumulate in the partner's seminal receptacles in segments nine and ten. After copulation, the cocoon formed by the clitellum slides forward to receive eggs from the oviduct in segment 14 and subsequently to receive the temporarily stored sperm from the seminal receptacles. Fertilization occurs within the cocoon. The elasticity of the cocoon closes it terminally as the earthworm retracts from it.

The embryology of the earthworm was studied by Wilson in the genus *Allolobophora,* but there is close agreement with *Lumbricus.* At the first cleavage, two unequal blastomeres result, the larger of which again divides unevenly. Additional segmentation results in an embryo with two large cells, two middle-sized cells, and three or four smaller cells. A one-layered, spherical blastula is formed later. The two large cells are the primary mesoblasts and are the progenitors of all the mesoblastic cells (Fig. 11-19). The

Fig. 11-18 Transverse section through pairing earthworms to show penetration of genital setae and secretion of diverticular glands into the partner worm. *nc,* nerve cord; *ct,* connective tissue; *lm,* longitudinal muscle; *cm,* circular muscle; *fg,* finely-granular gland cells of clitellum; *cg,* coarsely-granular gland cells of clitellum; *e,* epidermis. From Roots (after Feldkamp), "The Earthworm," 1956, *New Biology,* No. 21, Penguin Books Ltd.

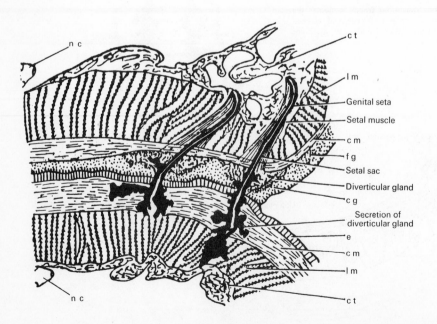

Fig. 11-19 Earthworm embryology. (a) Early blastula with mesoblast cells still at the surface; (b) lateral view of the later blastula with the ventral endoderm cells flattened prior to invagination; (c) right lateral view of embryo with germ-bands established; (d) older embryo showing developing nephridia and coelomic cavities. (*Continued on page 176.*)

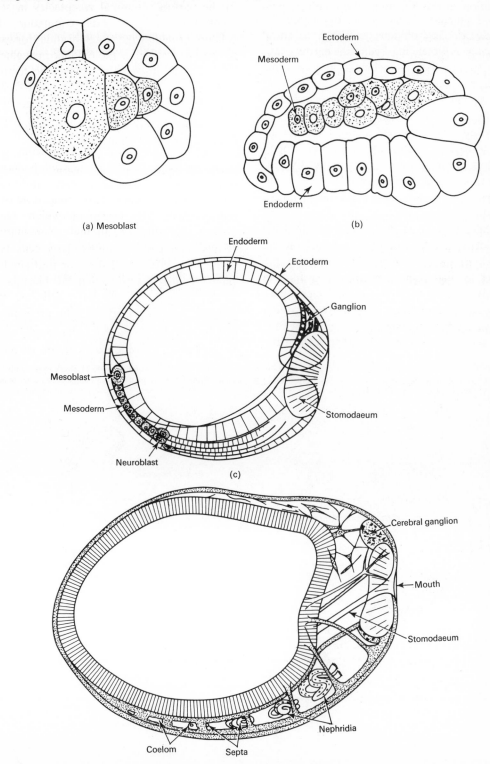

embryo subsequently flattens and elongates, and there is a prominent blastocoele into which the mesoblastic cells proliferate. Development is direct and no trochophore is produced. Any obvious similarity to spiral cleavage is largely masked in the earthworms, less so in other oligochaetes and in some leeches.

Systematic Resume The Oligochaeta include those Clitellata which have pronounced segmentation, a prostomium anterior to the mouth, and a well-developed coelom commonly intersegmentally divided. There is a small number of relatively simple setae in rows, pairs, or bundles on each segment.

Dales follows Michaelsen in dividing the Oligochaeta into four orders, based on the relationship of the segments containing the testes to their respective gonopores and the relative proximity of the seminal receptacles or spermathecae. Those oligochaetes in which the vasa deferentia open on the adjacent caudad segment are termed Plesiopora from the classical roots meaning near and pore. Plesiopora fall into two groups, depending upon whether the spermatheca open nearby or far forward.

Order 1 Plesiopora Plesiothecata These plesiopores have the seminal receptacles opening on the same or on a nearby segment or occasionally are absent. These annelids are aquatic in fresh-water mainly, but a few live in brackish or marine waters. Five families are included in the order. *Aeolosoma, Bothrioneurium, Dero, Nais, Tubifex.*

Order 2 Plesiopora Prosothecata The single family, Enchytraeidae, has spermathecae far forward of the male gonopore site. Most species are terrestrial or live in brackish water. *Aspidodrilus, Enchytraeus, Lumbricillus.*

Order 3 Prosopora In these oligochaetes, the male gonopores open on the testicular segment when there is only one pair of testes; otherwise they open on the segment that houses the most caudal pair of testes. These fresh-water worms occur in two families: Lumbriculidae, which resemble earthworms, and the Branchiobdellidae, which are leechlike and commensal or parasitic externally on crayfish.

Fig. 11-19 (*cont*): (e) Older embryo showing lateral blood vessel and metamerism evident externally. From figures 24, 32, 48, 50, and 51, E. B. Wilson 1889, *J. Morph.*, 3: 387.

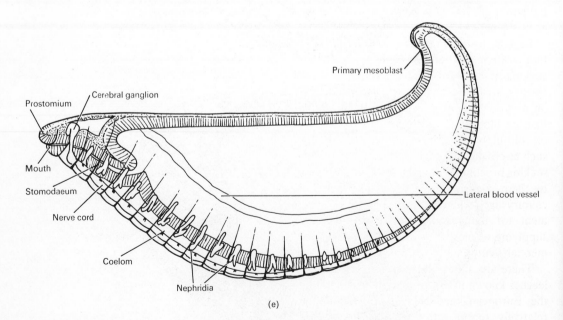

(e)

Agriodrilus, Lumbriculus, Branchiobdella.

Order 4 Opisthopora In these annelids, the male gonopores open on a segment usually some distance caudad to the posterior pair of testes. Most of these worms are terrestrial. Most of the earthworms occur in four of the eight families. The Haplotaxidae are plesioporous but show other features relating them to the Opisthopora. Haplotaxids live in fresh water and very marshy soil. *Alma, Pontoscolex, Lumbricus, Eisenia, Allolobophora, Pheretima, Megascolex, Haplotaxis.*

Subclass Hirudinea Hirudinea or leeches are the least numerous of the three major groups of annelids, having about 300 described species. These fresh-water, terrestrial, and marine worms possess several features indicating their relationship to the oligochaetes. The typical lack of setae, presence of suckers, and constancy of segment number are distinctive external features of leeches (Fig. 11-20). There are 33 segments, a condition masked by marked secondary annulations and by modifications due to the development of suckers. Leeches stand apart from other annelids in the possession of a double diagonal layer of muscle in the body wall between the circular and the longitudinal strata as well as dorso-ventral strands in each segment.

Leeches have an unsavory reputation since they are commonly considered to be blood-sucking parasites of man. Actually many leeches are scavengers or predators feeding on a variety of invertebrate animals. Others that are bloodsucking are primarily parasites of cold-blooded vertebrates or invertebrates such as crustaceans and molluscs. The blood-sucking proclivities of leeches was emphasized by their extensive use in medical practice a century ago, when bloodletting was a treatment for many human disorders and the supplying of leeches was an important commercial venture, particularly in Europe.

There are about 50 species of fresh-water leeches known in the United States, including the European medicinal leech, *Hirudo,* a relatively recent introduction. *Macrobdella*

decora is the most common North American blood-sucking leech on man and other mammals. Fresh-water leeches particularly are often distinctly colored sometimes with stripes and spots, and many can undergo color change due to the presence of chromatophores. A number of species are warty, especially among fish parasites. Few leeches are less than one or more than five centi-

Fig. 11-20 *Helobdella* (leech) showing segmentation, annulation and internal anatomy. I-XXVII, somites; 2-70, annuli. After Moore (modified from Castle) in Ward and Whipple, *Fresh-water Biology* (W. T. Edmondson, ed.) 2nd ed., 1959, courtesy of John Wiley & Sons, Inc.

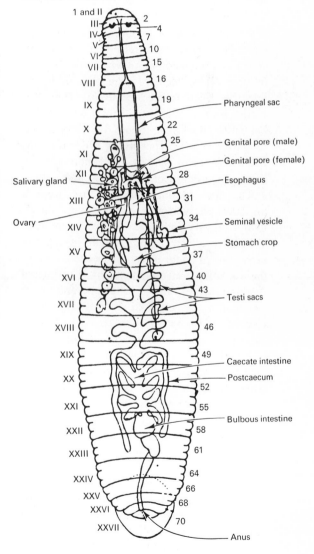

meters long. *Hirudo medicinalis* may be as long as twelve centimeters, and some tropical leeches are reported as considerably longer.

Feeding and Nutrition As already indicated, the Hirudinea utilize a variety of food materials. A number of leeches are jawless (Order Rhynchobdellida) and penetrate host tissues with a protrusible proboscis probably aided by digestive enzymes. Another group of leeches are jawed (Order Gnathobdellida) and have no proboscis. The anterior sucker contains a shelf-like fold, the velum, behind which are three muscular jaws: one dorsal and two latero-ventral. In *Hirudo,* each of these jaws has a serrate cutting blade which converges toward a common axis with the other jaws when activated. A Y-shaped incision is produced. In other leeches in this order, such as *Haemopis,* the jaws are blunt, and this leech is predaceous on slugs and earthworms, swallowing them whole, but is known to attack man. Some food is obtained by scavenging. Leeches in the order Pharyngobdellida have similar food habits since there is no armament on the muscular ridges.

The true bloodsucking leeches have a muscular pharynx well supplied with unicellular salivary glands. Three significant chemicals appear to be present in salivary secretions in some if not all leeches. One of these is *hirudin,* an anticoagulant. Its principal function seems to be the prevention of coagulation of ingested blood, but some leeches inject it to increase blood flow. Perhaps a more important factor is the injection of a chemical causing capillary dilatation to provide a copious supply of blood. In addition there is some evidence for a local anesthetic effect on the host tissues for some leeches.

Many bloodsucking leeches feed with great infrequency. The amount of blood taken may increase the weight of the leech three- or fourfold, and digestion of these large meals may take several months. Experimental work on *Hirudo* indicates the general absence of protein-splitting enzymes. Additional work shows that a symbiotic bacterium, *Pseudomonas hirudinis,* is able to break down red blood cells and fats, apparently has a bacteriostatic or bactericidal effect on other bacteria which would cause putrefaction notoriously absent in the leech alimentary canal, and is transmitted to the cocoon so that the developing young are provided with this essential agent in nutrition.

Behind the pharynx, a more or less short esophagus or gullet leads to the midgut or crop (Fig. 11-20). Typically the crop is not a tubular organ, but is supplied with a varying number of paired gastric caeca. In the bloodsucking forms, the blood is stored and condensed in these caeca. Whether digestion occurs here or in the thin-walled intestine is not clear. The intestine may have one or more pairs of intestinal caeca and eventually joins a short ectodermal rectum which opens externally, usually dorsal to the posterior sucker.

Respiration and Circulation Most Hirudinea respire through the integument, which is well supplied with capillaries, but there is a number of species with gills. *Branchellion,* a parasite of elasmobranchs, is provided with lateral leaflike gills; and *Ozobranchus,* parasitic within the mouths of crocodiles and pelicans and on turtles, has paired gills with many fingerlike branches.

In the setigerous annelids, it should be remembered, there is a contractile dorsal vessel transporting blood cephalad and a generally noncontractile ventral vessel carrying blood in the reverse direction. Segmentally arranged branches supply body-wall, nephridia, and other organs, and often form a plexus around the intestine. The coelom is spacious. Leeches vary widely from this pattern. The coelom becomes reduced to a series of channels usually called sinuses. Among some of the proboscid leeches (rhynchobdellids) segmental vessels are absent, and reduced dorsal and ventral vessels are contained within coelomic sinuses. Even here, the coelomic fluid circulates to transport respiratory, excretory, and nutritional materials. Propulsion of coelomic fluid is largely accomplished by the development of contractile tissue in the lateral coelomic sinuses. In a gnathobdellid like *Hirudo,* even embryonic traces of blood vessels have disappeared. A dorsal, a ventral, and paired lateral coelomic tubular sinuses are responsible for circulation with the lateral channels contractile. The respiratory pigment, hemoglobin, is present in solution in the coelomic fluid.

Excretion   The leech organ of excretion is a metanephridium of which there are 10 to 17 pairs. It is composed of a ciliated nephrostome forming a liplike funnel which communicates through a narrow channel with an enlarged, bulblike capsule containing phagocytic amoebocytes or specialized coelomocytes. In some primitive leeches the capsule communicates with the exterior through a nonciliated intracellular channel in a cord of nephridial cells. Among higher leeches there is no direct communication between capsule and nephridial canal, so that diffusion, probably into coelomic fluid, serves as an indirect communication. In *Hirudo* and its allies, ciliated organs probably homologous with nephrostomes of other leeches occur in communicating branches of the coelom (Fig. 11-21). These also have no direct communication with the nephridial tissue.

In oligochaetes, the excretory function of chloragogen cells included formation of ammonia and urea. Another function is storage of glycogen and fat. In leeches no single tissue combines these functions. In proboscid leeches coelomic epithelial cells and so-called pigment cells derived from adipose cells accumulate pigmented granules. In the jawed leeches such as *Hirudo,* fine channels of the coelomic system are associated with masses of spheroidal cells. These masses are called *botryoidal tissue.* In addition there are fine channeled strands called vaso-fibrous tissue. Both these and the botryoidal tissue accumulate brownish granules. It is believed that these tissues bear a correspondence to the excretory functions of oligochaete chloragogue cells.

Nervous System and Sense Organs   The basis of determination of leech segmentation is the presence of nerve ganglia. There are 34 such ganglia, but the first ganglion is considered to be the equivalent to the presegmental prostomial ganglion in other annelids. The nerve cell bodies in the ganglia are grouped in structures called capsules or follicles; six typically occur for each ganglion. The prostomial ganglion constitutes the brain and lies at the level of the fifth to seventh segment, depending on the genus. It innervates the prostomium and the first pair of eyes. The ganglion of the first segment separated into its component halves lies on the circumpharyngeal connectives. The subpharyngeal ganglion is a composite of ganglia from the next three or four segments, depending upon the genus. The typical

Fig. 11-21 Diagram of nephridium indicating relationships to sinus system and testis sac in *Hirudo.* Modified from various sources.

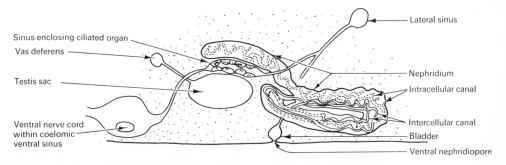

Sinus enclosing ciliated organ
Vas deferens
Testis sac
Ventral nerve cord within coelomic ventral sinus
Lateral sinus
Nephridium
Intracellular canal
Intercellular canal
Bladder
Ventral nephridiopore

segments have two pairs of nerves in each somite with the anterior pair primarily innervating the dorsal and the posterior pair the ventral moiety. The ventral nerve cord may be fused or separated into paired strands. Ganglia of the seven or more segments condensed in association with the posterior sucker form a single mass. A sympathetic or stomatogastric system is composed of a circumpharyngeal ring and a nerve reticulum over much of the alimentary canal.

Leeches possess a number of special sense organs. Sensory nerve endings often localized on papillae occur in the epidermis and are in communication with a subepidermal nerve net. These are principally touch and temperature receptors. Groups of tall fusiform cells called *sensillae* are most numerous on the anterior end and on the middle annulus of most segments. They appear to be tacto- and chemoreceptors. Light-sensitive cells characterized by a fluid-filled refractile vacuole occur in sensillae. In addition there are a number of pairs of eyes (five in *Hirudo),* in which numerous photoreceptor cells occur in a pigment cup.

Reproduction and Embryology Leeches are hermaphroditic; cross-fertilization is characteristic. At least some of the gnathobdellids are protandrous and an extended period exists between copulation and union of gametes.

Sperm encased in spermatophores produced by the prostate gland in gnathobdellids are introduced into the vagina by means of an eversible penis (Fig. 11-22). While mutual exchange of spermatophores in this group is possible, it appears to be infrequent.

In other leeches, an intromittent organ or penis is usually lacking. In these annelids copulation results in the mutual exchange of spermatophores produced by glandular secretion of the male duct near the gonopore. These bicornuate spermatophores adhere to the body surface of the copulating partner, in some forms in a region specialized for spermatophore reception. It is believed that the adhering neck of the spermatophore

contains digestive enzymes to facilitate penetration, aided by contraction of the extruding spermatophore. Fertilization occurs in the coelomic chambers containing the ovaries. Sperm reach the ovaries by traveling through connective tissue to the ovarian sac.

In Hirudinea, a cocoon is produced by secretory activity of the clitellum, a structure in many species only evident during the breeding season. It should be recalled that in the earthworms union of gametes occurs after the eggs reach the cocoon. In the leeches the eggs are fertilized before deposit in the cocoon. Usually the cocoon is an elastic belt formed around the annelid. As the worm backs out of this belt, the ends close due to elasticity or are plugged by secretion of glands on the anterior sucker. In some glossiphonids, clitellar glands are limited to the ventral surface, and the cocoon forms like an expanding bubble as eggs are discharged into it from the female gonopore. Cocoons in this family tend to be thin-walled, a vulnerable feature offset by parental care. Developing embryos are soon freed from the cocoon, but remain attached to the parent by a transitory holdfast at first and later by the

Fig. 11-22 Reproductive system in *Hirudo.* Annuli in segments X, XI, and XII are shown. Modified after various sources, but principally after Mann 1962.

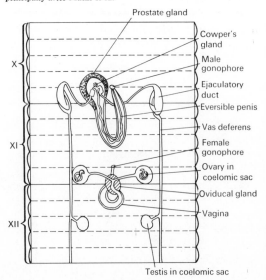

Prostate gland

Cowper's gland

Male gonophore

Ejaculatory duct

Eversible penis

Vas deferens

Female gonophore

Ovary in coelomic sac

Oviducal gland

Vagina

Testis in coelomic sac

posterior sucker. Other leeches, depending on the species, deposit cocoons in the bottom mud, attached to submerged objects, in damp places terrestrially, and in some fish parasites attached to the host.

Development in leeches is derived from the spiral cleavage seen in polychaetes. In some of the glossiphonids the early cleavages reveal a close parallel with that in polychaetes. Later embryology approximates the development seen in oligochaetes.

Systematic Resume   The Hirudinea includes those Clitellata having 33 segments externally grooved to form annuli, terminal suckers, and typically no setae. Internally there is a double layer of diagonal muscles in the body wall lying between the typical annelid muscle layers. The coelom is usually limited to narrow channels; blood vessels are reduced or absent. Leeches are usually grouped into four orders.

Order 1 Acanthobdellida   The single genus, *Acanthobdella,* parasitic on salmon in Russian and Finnish rivers and from Lake Baikal in Siberia, depicts a link with the oligochaetes. The body is limited to 30 segments and has setae on the first five. There is a slightly reduced but still septate coelom and intact dorsal and ventral blood vessels, but the anterior sucker is missing. *Acanthobdella.*

Order 2 Rhynchobdellida   These jawless leeches are strictly aquatic and are characterized by a protrusible proboscis. Blood vessels are retained and lie within coelomic channels. Proboscid leeches are divided into two families. The Glossiphonidae are somewhat flattened and limited to fresh water. The Piscicolidae are more cylindrical and are common parasites of fresh-water and marine fish. *Glossiphonia, Helobdella, Placobdella, Theromyzon, Branchellion, Ozobranchus, Piscicola, Pontobdella.*

Order 3 Gnathobdellida   Two prominent and one minor family comprise the Gnathobdellida. These aquatic and terrestrial leeches lack an eversible proboscis but have three jaws usually armed with serrate teeth or blades. The Hirudidae have five pairs of eyes with a single annulus between the third and fourth pair and with at least two annuli in segments XXIII, XXIV, and XXV. The Haemadipsidae have four pairs of eyes with the third and fourth pair separated by two annuli. Segments XXIV, XXV, and XXVI have a single annulus each. This family is tropical and subtropical and well adapted for terrestrial life. *Haemopis, Hirudo, Macrobdella, Haemadipsa.*

Order 4 Pharyngobdellida   Four or five families are included in this order, but only Erpobdellidae is common. These aquatic and terrestrial leeches are carnivorous on various invertebrates, including earthworms for some terrestrial species. The pharynx is similar to that of the Gnathobdellida but jaws and teeth are absent. Sometimes there are one or two stylets present in the mouth. Six to eight pairs of eyes are separated into two groups. The male reproductive system lacks a penis. *Dina, Erpobdella, Trocheta.*

Class Archiannelida

The Archiannelida is an obscure group of diverse animals, most of which possess some annelid characteristics. All of them show segmentation, although in *Polygordius* only a faint annulation suggests it externally. In *Protodrilus,* segmentation is emphasized by girdles of cilia, while *Saccocirrus* and *Nerilla* have well-marked segments. *Dinophilus* possesses six to seven segments, each of which bears one or more bands of cilia dorsally, or may be uniformly ciliated. The coelom is reduced in some species, which have a pair of small cavities lateral to the intestine separated by gonads from a small median ventral cavity in the posterior body, but communicating with the lateral chambers through narrow channels in the midregion of the body. *Dinophilus* has five pairs of segmentally arranged protonephridia. Gonads occur caudally in the body. The ovary produces two sizes of eggs, of which the smaller become males and the larger females.

Polygordius develops through a trochophore larva (Fig. 11-11). In metamorphosis to the adult, most of this trochophore is telescoped between the apical region which will form the adult prostomium and the developing segments (Fig. 11-12). Sexes are separate in all the Archiannelida except *Protodrilus*.

Class Myzostomida

The Myzostomida constitute a small class of highly specialized commensal and parasitic annelids. The adult body is usually disclike, circular, or elliptical in outline and generally well under a centimeter in length. Ten or more pairs of cirri commonly project from the disc margin. The mouth is usually anterior on the ventral surface and lies within a pouch from which the muscular pharynx can be protruded. Also on the ventral surface are five pairs of parapodia dispersed in a circular arrangement. Each parapodium is provided with an aciculum and a hooked seta.

Internally the coelom is greatly reduced and replaced by parenchymatous tissue. The intestine gives off highly branched caeca which extend nearly to the periphery of the disc. There is a single pair of metanephridia. Myzostomids are mostly hermaphroditic and protandrous. The gonads are extensive. Fertilization is internal with the aid of a spermatophore. Development is through a trochophore stage.

Myzostomids are mostly ectoparasitic or ectocommensal on crinoid echinoderms, but a few are internal parasites of brittlestars and some starfish.

Phylogenetic Considerations

In general, annelids are a well-delineated phylum of great antiquity. Yonge has pointed out that they are a part of that group of animals whose nutritional mechanisms can be adapted to a variety of food types, a versatility favoring radiation.

The Polychaeta represents the only class with a real geologic history substantiated by fossils. This was probably favored by a marine habitat and by the development of hard parts subject to fossilization. Jaws and denticles, often described under the term scolecodonts, have been found from the Ordovician to Recent, and many of these show a close similarity to contemporary species. Such fossils are particularly abundant near the bioherms or ancient reefs of the Silurian Period. In addition, setae, acicula, and elytra have appeared in the geologic record. Aciculae are represented in situ in the fossil polychaete *Eunicites avitus* from the Jurassic. Additional evidence is supplied by the finding of tubes or burrows as well as castings such as are characteristic of present-day forms like *Arenicola*. Some annelids build up burrow walls of secreted material, often embedded with gravel and debris. Such a construction would provide an efficient mold for fossil preservation. In the middle Cambrian a number of annelid genera have been found. Shrock and Twenhofel speak of these as belonging "to widely separated and only distantly related extinct families of annelids." It is evident that annelids were well established in ancient times.

Fossils interpreted as marine Oligochaeta have been found as early as the Silurian Period (one of these from New York limestone) and there are a few vestiges from the upper Ordovician, but the total record is sparse. There appears to be no fossil record of Hirudinea.

Geographical distribution of contemporary forms also indicates the success of this phylum. One genus of land leeches, *Haemodipsa*, occurs in most tropical areas south of the equator. In colder parts of the southern hemisphere, *Arenicola assimilis* occurs not only on the major continents, but in New Zealand, South Georgia, and Kerguelin, an isolated island in the southern Indian Ocean. The oligochaete family, Lumbricidae, although introduced elsewhere, is indigenous to North America, Europe, and northern Asia, where it ranges far north.

No really close link ties the Oligochaeta to the Polychaeta. The oligochaete *Aeolosoma* shows the most primitive characters, including a ventrally ciliated prostomium, a cerebral ganglion within the prostomium, the nervous system continuous with the epidermis, ciliated nuchal pits, and asexual reproduction by budding. Such features as an indistinct clitellum, a reduced coelom, and ciliary feeding may be secondarily derived rather than primitive. Marcus (1958) considers the aeolosomatids as a small side branch of the unknown link between the two setigerous groups. The other aquatic oligochaetes probably represent two divergent groups, the tubificids being ancestral to one and the Lumbriculidae to the other. Stephenson (1930) considers the general absence of a gizzard and the location of the male gonopore on the same segment as the testes as primitive characters. He regards the Lumbriculidae as the most primitive of extant oligochaetes. They may have given rise to some aquatic forms on one hand and to the terrestrial groups by way of the Haplotaxidae on the other.

Michaelsen and Stephenson agree that the Hirudinea and the Oligochaeta are closely related. Leeches bear some resemblance to the Haplotaxidae, and this oligochaete family is near the ancestral path to the leeches. The Acanthobdellida show a number of features suggesting an intermediate position between oligochaetes and leeches. This group can be placed on a side branch of the main stem leading to the leeches. The Glossiphonidae and the Piscicolidae would appear next but on divergent branches, the latter group leading to the jawed Gnathobdellidae from which the Pharyngobdellidae diverged. The Archiannelida probably evolved from early polychaete ancestors with the loss of setae and parapodia and the retention of ciliary bands and a nervous system continuous with the epidermis. They represent a heterogeneous group indicative of relatively unsuccessful radiations from the polychaete stem.

PHYLUM ECHIURIDA

The Echiurida constitute a small group of something over 60 species. They are wormlike, protostomatous coelomates with bilateral symmetry. Their length ranges from a few millimeters to several feet. The far eastern echiurid *Ikedo taenioides* may reach a trunk length of forty centimeters with a nonretractile proboscis nearly five feet long. Most echiurids are less than a foot in length. They are benthonic animals ranging from shallow into very deep water, a number having been found as deep as 30,000 feet in the Pacific Ocean. *Thalassema melitta* occurs in the tests of sand dollars (Echinodermata), entering in younger, smaller stages and eventually being imprisoned by its own growth. Echiurids generally live in permanent burrows, which are often U-shaped, or they inhabit crevices in corals and rocks. Some of the smaller ones occur in silt and bottom mud.

In these worms, the body is divided into a cephalic lobe commonly called a proboscis and a somewhat larger sausage-shaped or fusiform trunk with the posterior half frequently attenuated. There is no external evidence of segmentation in the adult. The proboscis is extensile, but not retractable into the trunk, and at the distal end it bears a forked or trumpet-shaped terminus. The proboscis has a deeply grooved, ciliated undersurface which functions in the ciliary feeding characteristic of the group.

Except in the genus *Saccosoma,* there is a ventral pair of large chitinous setae on the anterior part of the trunk, while some genera possess one or two rings of setae more caudally.

Organ Systems

At the anterior end of the trunk, ventral to the base of the proboscis, the mouth opens to a muscular pharynx. There is an elongated stomodaeal portion of the digestive tract which includes the pharynx, an elongated sinuous muscular esophagus, an internally papillate crop or gizzard, and sometimes a short section called a stomach. The stomodaeal portion leads to an intestine which may be as much as four times the trunk length, and which is thrown into a number of coils. It joins the bulbous, probably proctodaeal rectum which opens caudally by a terminal anus. A pair of sometimes branched caeca called anal sacs are contractile, usually embossed externally with ciliated funnels, and open to the rectum. They form the principal excretory system. Internally in the intestine, there is a well-defined ciliated trough along the medio-ventral line, opening at either end to a tube called the *siphon* which lies within the gut peritoneum adjacent to the intestine. The alimentary canal is supported dorsally by a mesentery in some species and by a series of connective-tissue strands in others. In addition to the anal sacs, there are one to many pairs of metanephridia, usually more numerous in males. *Bonellia* is an exception with an unpaired nephridium. In *Echiurus,* the single pair of nephridia open just posterior to the anterior setae. Echiurid metanephridia probably have some excretory function but they also serve as gonoducts.

In most Echiurida, there is a closed circulatory system similar to that in annelids. The ventral blood vessel lies near the nerve cord and communicates with the dorsal vessel by branches encircling the intestine. In some echiurids, these peri-intestinal vessels are in the nature of a sinus, and in others they are strongly contractile. In the proboscis, the dorsal vessel continues along the median line to the anterior end. Here it forks, and the two branches run laterally back to the trunk where they join below the pharynx to form the ventral vessel of the trunk. *Urechis,* lacking blood vessels, facilitates respiratory exchange through periodic intake of water into a thin-walled posterior section of the intestine which is bathed by coelomic fluid containing hemoglobin.

The nervous system is composed of a ventral, nonmetameric nerve cord with irregular lateral branches arising from it. At the anterior end circumpharyngeal connec-

Fig. 11-23 An Echiurid: *Bonellia viridis* (a) female (after Huxley); (b) male much enlarged (after Spengel). From Hertwig, *A Manual of Zoology* (translated and edited by J. S. Kingsley) 1902, Holt, Rinehart & Winston, Inc.

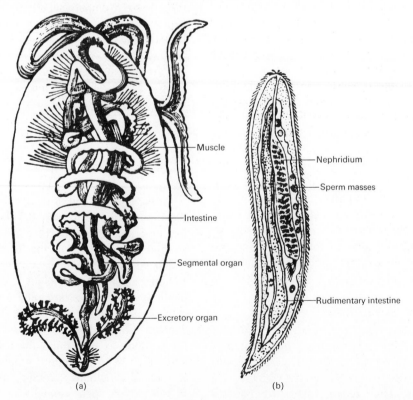

Muscle

Intestine

Segmental organ

Excretory organ

Nephridium

Sperm masses

Rudimentary intestine

(a)   (b)

tives enter the proboscis and run laterally to join at the anterior end. This unganglionated loop, a feature correlated with a lack of development of special sense organs, is homologous to the annelid brain; it supports the conclusion that the proboscis or cephalic lobe is equivalent to the annelid prostomium.

These animals are dioecious; the gonads are poorly differentiated areas of the ventral mesentery and coelomic wall in the posterior trunk. Typically, gametes are released through the anterior nephridiopores and fertilization occurs in sea water. However, in *Bonellia*, fertilization is internal. The minute males live as parasites in the female nephridial sac which functions as an egg-storage organ. In a related genus males are found in the female foregut. Young larvae of *Bonellia* (modified by the presence of much yolk from the more typical trochophores of other echiurids) are sexually undifferentiated but with potentialities for either sex. If they develop in contact with an adult female, they become males, but otherwise they develop into females. In some *Bonellia* females the trunk may reach a length of eight centimeters and carry a proboscis that can be extended to a meter's length (Fig. 11-23). Males are usually less than three millimeters long. They are small, cigar-shaped animals uniformly ciliated and without a proboscis. They lack a circulatory system and have a greatly reduced coelom and digestive tract (Fig. 11-23).

Affinities

The Echiurida exhibit a number of features indicating annelid affinity. They have spiral cleavage and typically develop into trochophores. Some forms show a transitory metamerism in the development of the nervous system and coelom origin. They possess chitinous setae and metanephridia. Finally the loop of the nervous system in the proboscis is considered equivalent to the circumenteric connectives and dorsal "brain" in polychaetes as is the ventral nerve cord in the two groups.

PHYLUM SIPUNCULIDA

This phylum of marine worms has species which vary from a few millimeters to the nearly two feet in length characteristic of *Sipunculus nudus*, but most sipunculoids are under a foot long. The group contains about 250 species united in a dozen genera commonly not grouped into families. Well-known genera include *Golfingia*, *Phascolosoma*, and *Sipunculus*. Sipunculoids are benthonic organisms occurring from the littoral zone into deep water. They burrow in the ocean floor or retreat into crevices in rocks for protection. They are wormlike animals whose body is usually sharply divided into two areas (Fig. 11-24). There is an enlarged posterior section called the trunk, at the anterior end of which a slender introvert of varying length can be rapidly extruded. The body shape in different genera may vary from cylindroid to

Fig. 11-24 *Golfingia* (*Phascolosoma*), (Sipunculida). After F. A. Brown, Jr., 1950, *Selected Invertebrate Types* (F. A. Brown, Jr., ed.), courtesy of John Wiley & Sons, Inc.

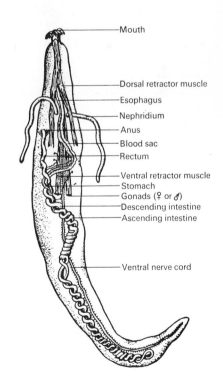

- Mouth
- Dorsal retractor muscle
- Esophagus
- Nephridium
- Anus
- Blood sac
- Rectum
- Ventral retractor muscle
- Stomach
- Gonads (♀ or ♂)
- Descending intestine
- Ascending intestine
- Ventral nerve cord

saccate or pear-shaped. Because some species can contract to an oval body similar in shape to a peanut, the name of peanut worm has been applied. The introvert represents the anterior portion of the body and includes the head, so it is not a proboscis.

When the introvert is fully extended it terminates in an oral disc, at the center of which is the mouth. At its periphery the oral disc is festooned with tentacles or lobes, each having a ciliated groove leading to the peristomial area. The number of tentacles varies, but in some species apparently increases with age. Fluid-filled channels, usually one to three, occur in the tentacles or tentacular lobes, and these are in contact with a ring or plexus around the esophagus and with one or two tubular contractile sacs which lie on the dorsal, or dorsal and ventral, sides of the esophagus. These sacs serve as reservoirs when the tentacles are contracted. Although these channels are not connected with the coelom, similar cellular elements occur in both.

Immediately behind the oral disc the surface of the introvert is smooth, an area sometimes delimited by ridges. The remaining body surface may be variously marked with papillae, spines, and thornlike hooks.

Sipunculoids have neither parapodia nor setae. Internally they have a spacious non-septate coelom with only traces of mesentery. They lack a discrete circulatory system, but contractile tubular sacs occur on the dorsal, and in several genera also on the ventral, side of the esophagus. These communicate with one or more channels within each tentacle. The inner surface of this system is studded with scattered tufts of cilia, and the fluid present appears to be similar to that in the coelom including hemerythrin in corpuscles.

Organ Systems

The digestive tract is an elongate, highly coiled tube. The mouth opens terminally on the introvert. The intestine is recurved, with descending and ascending limbs commonly coiled in a tight spiral. The prominent anus opens middorsally near the anterior end of the trunk in all species except one, in which the anus is on the introvert. Depending upon the genus, one, two, or four retractor muscles extend from the esophagus to insertions on the trunk wall. Extrusion of the introvert is effected by hydrostatic pressure exerted through the coelomic fluid. The intestine is more or less uniform throughout its length. Its lining may be generally ciliated, but there always is a ciliated groove or trough which begins near the mouth and which ends at the terminal rectum near where the rectal caecum arises. The digestive tract is supplied with a number of glands, but its lack of marked muscular areas, together with the ciliated grooves on the tentacles, indicate that sipunculoids are ciliary feeders. Like annelids they ingest considerable amounts of soil and debris. Organic material suitable for food would doubtlessly be present in this material.

The nervous system is similar to that of annelids; there is a brain dorsal to the anterior digestive tract, and circumenteric commissures lead to a single, nonganglionated ventral nerve cord. Nerves, often irregularly dispersed, lead to muscles and to various sensory end-organs in the body wall. Some genera possess a nuchal organ which is a lobed projection of ciliated cells on the edge of the oral disc. These cells are probably chemoreceptors. Various groups of sensory cells occur in pits and on papillae as well as on the general epidermis. Externally eyes are absent but pigment spots occur on the brain of some sipunculoids and, although recessed, are similar to pigment-cup ocelli.

Sipunculoids possess a metanephridial excretory system which fundamentally is paired. Nephridiopores open ventrally near the anterior end of the trunk. Some accumulation of wastes is performed by certain coelomic elements. Modified cells of coelomic peritoneum around the gut and on both surfaces of the tentacular sacs accumulate yellow granules and are similar to the chloragogue cells of annelids. In some species, chloragogue cells are associated in the formation of peculiar excretory structures called *fixed urns*. These arise as tube- or vaselike projections of the peritoneum enclosing a vacuolated interior and capped by a ciliated cell bearing groups of cilia. In some species, chloragogue cells are numerous around the base of the urn. In some but not all sipunculoids the urns may break off to swim in the coelomic fluid, and they may carry a rim of chloragogue cells opposite the ciliated end. The urns accumulate wastes and foreign materials, which may be retained as excretory masses in the coelom or removed by nephridia. A somewhat similar excretory function is performed by coelomic amoebocytes.

There is no circulatory system as such, but a respiratory pigment, hemerythrin, occurs within cells in the coelomic fluid, and they are sufficiently numerous in some species to produce a pinkish color. This pigment occurs

also in the polychaete genus *Magelona*.

Sipunculida are dioecious animals with relatively primitive gonads modified from the peritoneal wall. Gametes are liberated to the outside through nephridiopores. Spiral cleavage and the development of trochophore larvae are characteristic.

Affinities

The Sipunculida are protostomatous, schizocoelic animals whose early embryology tends to parallel that of annelids, and whose central nervous system (dorsal lobes, circumenteric connectives, and ventral cord) is similar. However, the ventral cord in annelids shows a bilateral origin, absent in Sipunculida. Of most significance is the absence of any indication of metamerism either in development or in the mature organism. The group is probably as old as the annelids and diverged from the preannelid stock.

REFERENCES

Bahl, K. N., Excretion in the Oligochaeta. Biol. Rev., 22:109, 1947.

de Beauchamp, P. (and P. Fauvel, M. Avel, H. Harant, P. Grassé, C. Dawydoff, and J. Roger), Annélides (pp. 3-713). *In* (P. Grassé, ed.) Traité de zoologie, Tome V, Fasc. I. Paris: Masson et Cie, 1959.

Beddard, F. E., Oligochaeta and Hirudinea (pp. 345-408). *In* (S. F. Harmer and A. E. Shipley, eds.) The Cambridge natural history (reprint edition), Vol. II. Codicote, England: Wheldon & Wesley, 1959.

Benham, W. B., Archiannelida, Polychaeta, and Myzostomaria (pp. 239-344). *In* (S. F. Harmer and A. E. Shipley, eds.) The Cambridge natural history (reprint edition), Vol. II. Codicote, England: Wheldon & Wesley, 1959.

Chapman, G., and G. E. Newell, The role of the body fluid in relation to movement in soft-bodied invertebrates, I, The burrowing

of *Arenicola*. Proc. Roy. Soc. London, 1348:431, 1947.

Dales, R. P., Annelids. London: Hutchinson University Library, 1963.

Dawydoff, C., Classe des Echiuriens (pp. 855-907). *In* (P. Grassé, ed.) Traité de zoologie, Tome V, Fasc. I. Paris: Masson et Cie, 1959.

Goodrich, E. S., The study of the nephridial and genital ducts since 1895. Quart. J. Microsc. Sci., 86:113, 1945.

Hess, W. N., The nervous system of the earthworm, *Lumbricus terrestris*. J. Morphol., 40:235, 1925.

Hyman, L. H., Sipunculida (pp. 610-696). *In* The invertebrates: smaller coelomate groups. New York: McGraw, 1959.

Lavarack, M. S., The physiology of earthworms. New York: Macmillan, 1963.

Mann, K. H., Leeches (Hirudinea). London:

Pergamon Press Ltd., 1962.

Michaelsen, W., Oligochaetan. *In* (W. Kükenthal and T. Krumbach, eds.) Handbuch der Zoologie—eine Naturgeschichte des Tierreichs. Berlin: Walter De Gruyter, 1928.

Prosser, C. L., The nervous system of the earthworm. Quart. Rev. Biol., 9:181, 1934.

Ramsay, J. A., The osmotic relations of the earthworm. J. Exp. Biol., 26:46, 1949.

———, A physiological approach to the lower animals. Cambridge: Cambridge U.P., 1952.

Shrock, R. R., and W. H. Twenhofel, Principles of invertebrate paleontology (2nd ed.). New York: McGraw, 1953.

Stephenson, J., The Oligochaeta. London: Oxford U. P., 1930.

Tétry, A., Classe des Sipunculiens (pp. 785-854). *In* (P. Grassé, ed.) Traité de zoologie, Tome V, Fasc. I. Paris: Masson et Cie, 1959.

Wells, G. P., The mode of life of *Arenicola marina* L., J. Marine Biol. Assoc., 26:170, 1945.

Wilson, E. B., The embryology of the earthworm. J. Morphol., 3:387, 1889.

Wolf, A. V., Paths of water exchange in the earthworm. Physiol. Zool., 13:294, 1940.

Yonge, C. M., Evolution and adaptation in the digestive system of the Metazoa. Biol. Rev., 12:87, 1937.

12

PHYLUM
MOLLUSCA

Nearly everyone claims some acquaintance-ship with members of this large phylum, whether it be through clam chowder, pearl fishing, aquarium snails, garden slugs, cuttle-bone for the canary, or the press-agented villain of marine pictures, the octopus. These few examples are inadequate to picture the great diversity that exists in this group. It is a very large phylum, containing over 80,000 contemporary species. In addition, thousands of fossil species are known. Since the rich-ness of the fossil record is roughly propor-tional to the existence of hard parts favorable for geologic preservation, it is apparent that some skeletal structure is a common feature of the group. This feature is a shell which is typically external and which furnishes housing for the soft body parts. Simpson (1949, p. 27) speaks of the Mollusca as "the most varied, dominant, successful of the primary aquatic phyla, both at the present time and throughout the fossil record." Mol-lusca are abundant both in the ocean and in fresh-water habitats, and have developed a number of successful terrestrial forms.

This phylum, characterized by animals possessing such general features as a soft body, usually some sort of shell (Fig. 12-1), and a primarily aquatic habitat, has diversi-fied with remarkable variety and marked success, from some hypothetical archetype. Mollusca range in size from microscopic snails to clams with shells four feet long, or squid whose total length may reach fifty feet. Some Mollusca tunnel in wood or stone, some burrow in sand or mud, a number are active swimmers, many are active crawlers. Some are adapted to deep salt-water habitat, some to the shore, some to the fluctuating condi-tions of the estuary; some are strictly aquatic in fresh water, and terrestrial species include some adapted to arid habitat.

Since an aquatic habitat is almost universal for the members of this phylum, studies of nutritional adaptation, respiration, excretion, and reproductive modification, which are phenomena particularly responsive to such

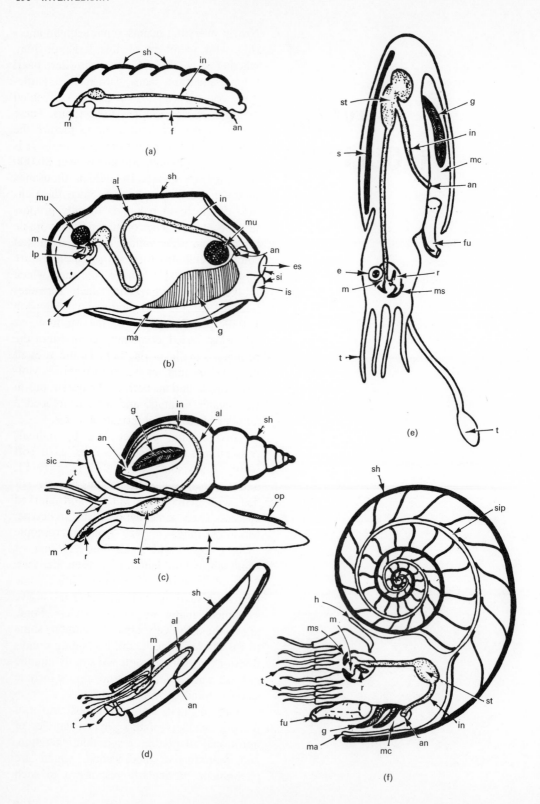

Fig. 12-1 (See page 190.) Shell relationships in five classes of Mollusca. (a) Amphineura; (b) Pelecypoda; (c) Gastropoda; (d) Scaphopoda; (e), (f) Cephalopoda. *al*, alimentary canal or digestive tube; *an*, anus; *e*, eye; *es*, exhalant or excurrent siphon; *f*, foot; *fu*, hyponomic funnel; *h*, hood; *in*, intestine; *is*, inhalant or incurrent siphon; *lp*, labial palp; *m*, mouth; *ma*, mantle; *mc*, mantle cavity; *ms*, horny mandibles or jaws; *mu*, muscle; *r*, buccal cavity containing odontophore and radula; *s*, sepion, or internal shell; *sh*, shell; *si*, siphon; *sic*, siphonal canal; *sip*, siphuncle; *st*, stomach; *t*, tentacle. (Drawings by Turner adapted from numerous authors.) After Shrock and Twenhofel 1953, courtesy of McGraw-Hill Book Company.

environment, have yielded much evidence for the phylogenetic orientation of the larger subdivisions of the phylum.

The generalized molluscan body (Fig. 12-2) is composed of a flattened muscular foot enlarged at the front into a head containing a mouth, special sense organs, and some internal concentration of nerve tissue. Permanently retained within the shell is a median dorsal hump called the *visceral mass.* Surrounding the visceral mass is a membrane called the *mantle,* which secreted the shell and continues to line it. Between the periphery of the shell and the visceral mass the mantle is infolded, and at the posterior border it is enlarged into a chamber called the mantle cavity, containing the respiratory complex and apertures for the digestive, excretory, and reproductive systems. Cilia cover much of the body surface and line the mantle or pallial cavity. The cilia are responsible for the essential water currents within the mantle

cavity. A true coelom exists in the small cavities around the gonad and heart (pericardium). Spongy sinusoidal areas in the body are filled with blood and constitute a *hemocoele.* Morton speaks of these blood-filled spaces as constituting a "hemoskeleton" (or hydrostatic skeleton) which allows advantageous changes in body shape associated with burrowing, anchorage, and functional shape of body parts expanded from the shell. Such a "skeleton" is seen repeatedly in soft-bodied animals.

Fundamental Characteristics Typically, Mollusca are unsegmented, coelomate animals which are bilaterally symmetrical, but a recently discovered primitive genus (*Neopilina*) possesses metamerically arranged gills, renal organs, and muscles. A shell-gland is present in the typical molluscan embryo. Later, a fold, called the mantle, takes over the function of shell production and also contributes to the formation of respiratory

Fig. 12-2 Diagram of a hypothetical or archetypal Mollusc. (Adapted by Turner.) After Shrock and Twenhofel 1953, courtesy of McGraw-Hill Book Company.

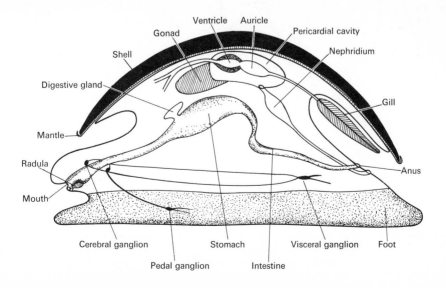

organs. Typically, the shell contains soft body parts collectively termed the visceral mass. A muscular portion of the body called the *foot* is primarily locomotor in function. Normally outside the shell, it can be retracted into it. A marine habitat was characteristic of the ancestral mollusca, and a trochophore larva continues to be common among marine species. The phylum can be divided into the following six classes: Monoplacophora, Amphineura, Gastropoda, Scaphopoda, Bivalvia, and Cephalopoda.

CLASS MONOPLACOPHORA

This primitive group prior to 1957 was known only from Cambrian to Devonian fossil remains, and possessed a shallow saucer- or cone-shaped shell. The living monoplacophoran, *Neopilina galatheae,* was dredged from deep Pacific water off the coast of Central America. This mollusc has a flat cone-shaped shell which measures three to four centimeters in diameter. The mouth has two pairs of appendages and a radula with one median and five lateral teeth in each transverse row. A crystalline style is present. Five pairs of gills occur in a circumferential mantle groove around the disc-shaped foot. (A second species with six pairs of gills has since been found.) Other evidences of segmentation occur for the kidneys, auricles, shell muscles, and possibly the gonads (Fig. 12-3). The nervous system is a very simple type with ten commissures connecting the

Fig. 12-3 *Neopilina* (*Vema*) *ewingi* (Monoplacophora). After Clarke and Menzies 1959, *Science*, 129: 1026.

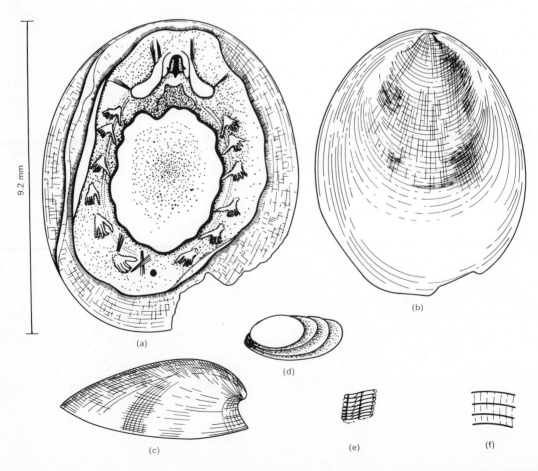

9.2 mm

(a)

(b)

(c)

(d)

(e)

(f)

longitudinal cords. The coelom appears to be divided into paired dorsal sacs into which the renal organs open, a pericardium around the heart, and possibly a ventral gonocoele. The extent of the coelom and the metameric condition of several organs renews interest in the origin of Mollusca.

Class I Monoplacophora These molluscs are characterized by a small, depressed cone-shaped shell and a broad foot. The under surface is reminiscent of that in the chitons. The sexes are separate, and (unique among living molluscs) there is a metameric distribution of five or six pairs of gills and also a segmental arrangement of renal organs, auricles, and possibly gonads (Fig. 12-3). *Neopilina.*

CLASS AMPHINEURA

As suggested by the name, this group generally possesses double longitudinal nerve cords without nerve-cell bodies concentrated into localized ganglia, characteristic of the more advanced classes (Fig. 12-4). At the anterior end is a ring commissure. The more ventral pair of nerve cords are called *pedal* and are united at intervals by commissures beneath the digestive tract. The intestine, however, is innervated by nerves from the stomatogastric system arising from cerebral commissures and by branches of the *pallial* (palliovisceral) nerves, which are a pair of large lateral cords supplying the rest of the posterior body. The pallial nerves unite dorsal to the rectum.

Besides having taste and touch receptors, the exposed upper surface of chiton-shell valves is sensitive to light. Discrete light-sensitive structures are called *megalaesthetes*. In some chitons, these megalaesthetes have the lens, retina, and pigment of simple eyes. On the valves, they are surrounded by papillate receptors (*micraesthetes*) presumed to be touch receptors and are very numerous. Morton reports upward of 3,000 on the anterior valve of one species with additional thousands scattered over the remaining valves.

More degenerate members of this class (Aplacophora) lack a discrete shell but possess calcareous spicules embedded in the cuticle. Among the well-known chitons, typically eight bilaterally symmetrical plates articulate with each other to form a flexible dorsal shell. These shell valves are secreted by and are sometimes partly covered by the mantle. A browsing food habit is accomplished by a movable rasplike organ called a *radula*. The chitons are well represented in antiquity, with fossils 400 million years old. Amphineurans are marine and commonly have a trochophore larva.

The chiton mantle is a rugged rim usually called a girdle, and it usually extends beyond the shell periphery. Frequently the mantle is ornamented with various spines and scales. Although the flat foot is responsible for ordinary surface adherence, the girdle can be forced against the smooth surface substrate to produce a suction-cup effect.

Between the girdle and the foot there is a channel containing a single row of gills (fewer in number and more caudal in primitive chitons). The row of ciliated ctenidia or gills

Fig. 12-4 *Chiton,* dorsal view of animal with shell removed to show the nervous system and gills. From Hertwig (after Haller), *A Manual of Zoology* (translated and edited by J. S. Kingsley) 1902, Holt, Rinehart & Winston, Inc.

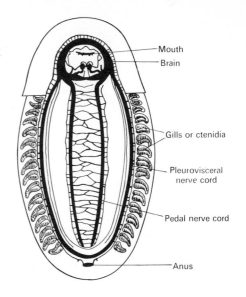

Mouth
Brain
Gills or ctenidia
Pleurovisceral nerve cord
Pedal nerve cord
Anus

divides the channel into an outer inhalant and an inner exhalant trough. Water enters the inhalant trough wherever the girdle is relaxed, and it escapes from the exhalant trough behind the anus.

The circulatory system contains the respiratory pigment hemocyanin, and consists of a heart located in the pericardial cavity and arterial and venous vessels communicating through hemocoelic sinuses. Blood is circulated through the paired kidneys and the gills before return to the symmetrical heart, which is composed of two auricles and a single ventricle. The cavities that enclose the kidneys and the gonads, together with the pericardium, constitute the coelom. The kidneys communicate with the pericardium as well as directly with the mantle cavity.

In some species, the embryological continuity of the divisions of the coelom is evidenced by utilization of the pericardium and/or kidney lumen for discharge of genital products. Other species have separate genital ducts opening to the cloaca. Most of the Amphineura are dioecious, but one of the groups composed of more wormlike forms is hermaphroditic. Development of the fertilized eggs is by spiral cleavage (see the account in Chapter 11). A trochophore embryo is typical.

The evolutionary position of the Amphineura is difficult to assess. Some representatives lack both foot and shell. Chitons appear among Cambrian rocks, but the late Cambrian already shows diversity into the three big classes of Mollusca. Certainly none of these classes seems ancestral to the Amphineura or to the other definitive class, Scaphopoda, and these in turn did not directly give rise to the big classes. Probably a common ancestor emerged far back in the Precambrian which gave rise to the various classes of Mollusca. Certainly living Amphineura have evolved from some more primitive form, so that any hypothetical archetype (depending upon Amphineuran morphology) must be approached with an open mind (Fig. 12-5).

Class II Amphineura This group is characterized by bilateral symmetry. Such special sense organs as tentacles are absent, and otocysts are rudimentary. The mantle is large.

Fig. 12-5 Generalized Mollusc (compare with Fig. 12-2). 1, jaws; 2, radula on odontophore; 3, nerve ring; 4, salivary glands; 5, esophageal glands; 6, stomach; 7, protostyle with food string; 8, digestive diverticula; 9, gonad; 11, ventricle and intestine; 12, left auricle; 13, pericardium; 14, left kidney; 15, hypobranchial gland; 16, osphradium; 17 ctenidium (showing currents); 18, epipodial tentacles; 19, pedal nerve cords; 20, pallial nerve chords. After Morton, *Molluscs*, 1958, Hutchinson and Co. Ltd. Courtesy of the author.

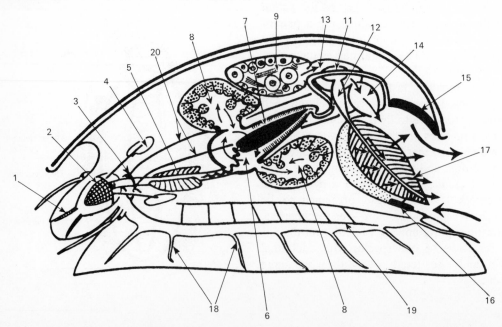

Order 1 Polyplacophora These molluscs have a large, ventral flattened foot and a shell of eight transverse plates. The long radula has many rows of variously shaped teeth. *Chiton, Mopalia, Nuttalina, Stenoplax.*

Order 2 Aplacophora These aberrant, wormlike forms (Fig. 12-6), whose shell is reduced to calcareous spicules embedded in the mantle, have a reduced foot and a simple radula. *Neomenia, Chaetoderma.*

CLASS GASTROPODA

This class, which includes slugs, snails, whelks, and limpets, no longer possesses a gonocoele communicating directly with the pericardium. This feature is shared by the Scaphopoda and Bivalvia. In addition, the Gastropoda possess a prominent head, asymmetry with common reduction or loss of organs on the morphological left, a one-piece shell which is typically coiled, and a flattened foot.

The Gastropoda is a very ancient group with about 15,000 fossil species described and a larger number contemporary. Possibly their ancestors lived in shallow marine water, which is still the habitat of the majority of species today. Such an environment is subject to environmental stresses, and this successful group of molluscs is represented in marine, brackish-water, fresh-water, and terrestrial forms.

The typical gastropod has a distinct head with mouth, eyes, and tentacles; a visceral mass nonextrusible from the shell, and a broad ventral foot which has an undulating action to produce locomotion (Fig. 12-7). A pedal gland, opening ventrally just behind the mouth, provides the foot with a mucoid

Fig. 12-6 An aplacophoran mollusc, *Chaetoderma*. From Schechter (adapted from Simroth) 1959, courtesy of Prentice-Hall, Inc.

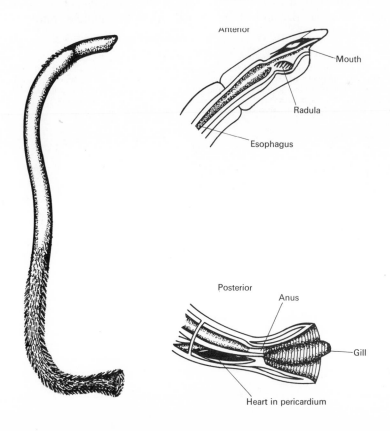

Anterior

Mouth

Radula

Esophagus

Posterior

Anus

Gill

Heart in pericardium

slime lubricant. The foot and head can be retracted into the shell by action of the columellar muscle. In gilled forms, a horny plate called an operculum situated on the posterior dorsal aspect of the foot serves to close the shell aperture when the foot is retracted into the shell.

The visceral hump originates by proliferation of the larval midgut which is forced into an inverted U shape, a process known also as flexure, and continues to grow dorsally. The principal volume of the visceral hump is composed of a digestive gland often called the liver. Its right and left digestive lobes develop asymmetrically, the right being larger. This asymmetry may be due to an earlier asymmetry of the mesodermal bands in the larva in which the right is larger. The anterior portion of the right mesodermal band gives rise to larval muscle cells, some of which curve around the foregut to terminate in the left side of the head and foot area, but maintain a posterior attachment to the right side of the developing shell. Because of its

early asymmetrical growth, the visceral mass enclosed by the mantle folds upon itself to initiate the process of *coiling*. Since the mantle is responsible for shell formation, the shell develops spirally. The coiling normally occurs around a solid or hollow axis, termed the *columella*, although in some forms (cowries) the columella is resorbed. In most Gastropods the spiral is dextral, that is, in following the coils from apex to opening, in a specimen held with the apex up, a clockwise pathway is traced. In a few species the situation is reversed, and a sinistral (counterclockwise) form occurs, e.g., *Physa*. Spiral cleavage is reversed in these forms also.

It was noted that asymmetrical growth initiated coiling. The flexure that preceded coiling was not the cause, since a similar flexure occurs in the Scaphopoda, Bivalvia, and Cephalopoda. A phenomenon peculiarly unique to the Gastropoda is called *torsion*. Torsion can be described roughly by picturing an elongated, bilaterally symmetrical animal with the middle third of the body

Fig. 12-7 Morphological variations in three orders of Gastropoda. 1, mouth; 2, foot; 3, tentacle; 4, eye; 5, penis; 6, cerebral ganglion; 7, pleural ganglion; 8, pedal ganglion; 9, statocyst; 10, siphon; 11, supraintestinal connective; 12, subintestinal connective; 13, sperm channel; 14, mantle cavity; 15, osphradium; 16, ctenidium; 17, parietal ganglion; 18, anus; 19, hypobranchial gland; 20, rectum; 21, auricle; 22, visceral ganglion; 23, heart cavity; 24, outlet of nephridium; 25, foot; 26, operculum; 27, vascular network of the lung; 28, breathing aperture; 29, kidney; 30, parapodial lobe; 31, genital ganglion; 32, shell. (Drawings by Turner, modified after Lang, 1900; numbered as in Wenz, 1938.) After Shrock and Twenhofel 1953, courtesy of McGraw-Hill Book Company.

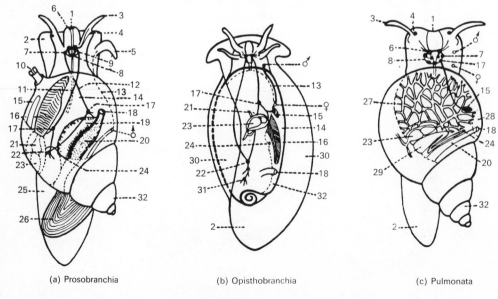

(a) Prosobranchia   (b) Opisthobranchia   (c) Pulmonata

Fig. 12-8 *Patella vulgata*, (a) prior to torsion and (b) with a 90° torsion. *A* to *F*, larval retractor cells. After Crofts 1955, *Proc. Zool. Soc.*, London, 125: 711, courtesy of the author and the Society.

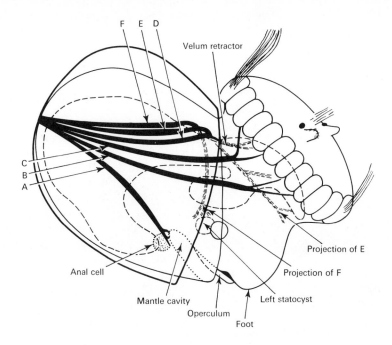

(a)

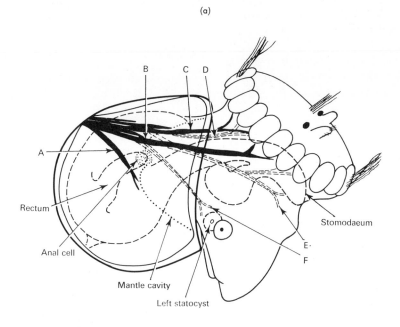

(b)

carrying a dorsal, shell-covered visceral hump and imagining that this middle third is rotated 180 degrees counterclockwise about a vertical axis and through a frontal plane. It is obvious that the orientation of many organs will be altered. Torsion evidently was an evolutionary success, since one-third of molluscan genera are Gastropoda. Garstang has suggested that torsion was of value primarily to the larva, since head and velum could be withdrawn into the protection of the shell before rather than after the less vulnerable foot, which was the case in the pretorsion animal. Morton considers torsion is of value to the adult also, converting the mantle cavity "from primarily a cloaca with gills into an organ in sensitive touch with the environment of the head."

Some Gastropoda do not exhibit coiling, but all have undergone torsion. It is obvious that flexure did not initiate torsion, because the latter does not occur among the other classes of Mollusca. Torsion and coiling are independent processes, but asymmetry of development contributes to both.

Torsion appears to develop in two phases. In veliger larvae, which are pelagic, the first phase occurs while the animals are planktonic. It is due to the contraction of asymmetrical muscle derived from the right mesodermal band and extending over the foregut between the right shell interior and the left side of the foot and head (Fig. 12-8). This first phase of torsion causes a rotation of about 90 degrees, the site of torque being the necklike region between the head-foot complex and the visceral mass within the shell. Garstang in 1928 had already suggested retractor muscle asymmetry, but proof of its occurrence did not appear for several years. The first phase of torsion occurs rapidly as the muscle fibers develop retractile power. The second 90-degree phase of torsion occurs more slowly. Its cause seems to be differential, asymmetric growth, and primarily with the development of the columellar muscle and the pedal musculature of the right side. In some gastropods, torsion is entirely a growth process.

Many Gastropoda are shell-less or have reduced shells. In the Opisthobranchia, detorsion has occurred with restoration of bilateral symmetry. The most primitive of this group are burrowing forms which have developed a broad head shield. This development has pushed the mantle cavity further back, and Morton has suggested that this may be the initiation of detorsion.

Food-Getting and Digestive Processes

Except for the Bivalvia, all molluscan classes utilize a radula associated with food intake. The radula (Fig. 12-9) is a somewhat flexible ribbon containing teeth, the arrangement and shape of which are of taxonomic value, particularly among Gastropoda. The immediately functional portion of the radula lies above and is partly controlled by a cartilaginous elevation in the floor of the buccal cavity termed an *odontophore*. The radula functions in many snails as a movable rasp (Fig. 12-10), and the microscopic particles freed are captured by mucus. Grasp is obtained upon the food mass by two jaws. Enzymes reported from snails have included cellulases, but the evidence seems to favor

Fig. 12-9 Radular teeth in some Amphineura and Gastropoda. (a) Teeth in an Aplacophoran and (b) in a Polyplacophoran. The others represent various patterns among Gastropoda. (b) to (h) and (m) show the central teeth and the row to the left of center. After Morton, *Molluscs*, 1958, Hutchinson and Co., Ltd. Courtesy of the author.

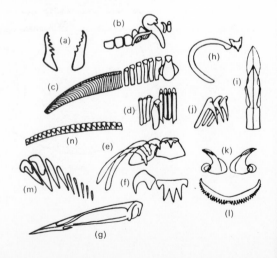

their origin from microorganisms. Among carnivorous gastropods, proteolytic enzymes have been reported.

The buccal cavity narrows to an esopha-gus. Ducts, emptying into the buccal cavity, run on either side of the esophagus and arise from salivary glands which lies parallel with the crop into which the esophagus empties.

Fig. 12-10 Sagittal section through jaws and radula of a gastropod. (Adapted from Lang 1900, by Turner.) After Shrock and Twenhofel 1953, courtesy of the McGraw-Hill Book Company.

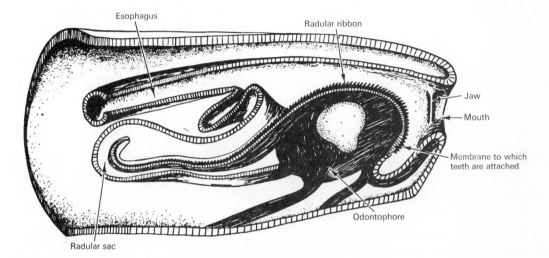

Fig. 12-11 Anatomy of a dissected *Helix*. From Hertwig, *A Manual of Zoology* (translated and edited by J. S. Kingsley) 1902, Holt, Rinehart & Winston, Inc.

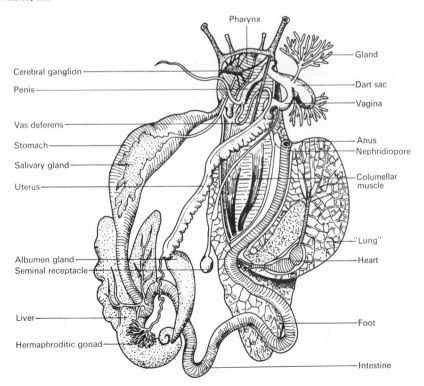

Behind a posterior constriction of the crop, the lumen enlarges to form the stomach. This organ is embedded in the large "liver" from which it receives secretions. The tubular intestine runs from the stomach, and after looping through the kidney, opens into the mantle cavity generally toward the right (Fig. 12-11). Herbivorous species generally have a longer, carnivorous a shorter intestine.

Respiratory Adaptations

The Gastropoda have a respiration based on their aquatic history. Primarily this function is accomplished through paired ctenidia derived from the mantle. In many Gastropoda the paired condition of the gills has disappeared so that only a single ctenidium persists. The reduction of paired auricles to one is correlated with the gill reduction. In the

Fig. 12-12 Diagrams illustrating the relationship between ctenidia (gills), osphradia, and hypobranchial glands in various gastropods. Note relationship of effective respiratory current to those organs. After Yonge 1947, courtesy of the author and of the Royal Society of London.

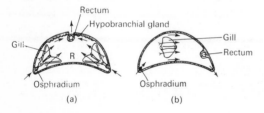

(a) (b)

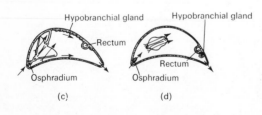

(c) (d)

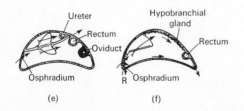

(e) (f)

snails with ctenidia, a large mantle opening favors respiration, but with the terrestrial (Pulmonate) snails, gills have disappeared and the mantle roof has become the respiratory membrane, although it may have carried some of the respiratory load even in gill-bearing snails. The opening to this mantle "lung" is reduced to avoid excessive evaporation. Muscular movements of the mantle floor provide a breathing mechanism. Not only do many intermediate stages between ctenidial respiration and mantle lungs persist, but among the pulmonates a return to an aquatic habitat has produced a gill-like modification of the mantle wall, which is not homologous, however, to the ancestral ctenidium.

Many gastropods possess an organ in the mantle cavity called an *osphradium* (Fig. 12-12). It is described as having a water-testing function. Yonge and others have shown that the osphradium development is correlated with the amount of sediment in the environment, at least in many Mollusca. The osphradium may be paired or unpaired, and in some species appears only during larval stages. It is absent in adult terrestrial snails and in nudibranchs, the latter lacking a respiratory cavity.

In the snails, blood is pumped from the ventricle into the aorta, which bifurcates to supply the visceral hump and the head. From the latter, a pedal artery may loop to supply the foot. Blood passes from these arteries to lacunar spaces not defined by epithelial walls. From these hemocoelic sinuses, blood arrives at a circular vein associated with "lung" or gill as the case may be. In some of the more primitive snails a "renal-portal" system exists, whereby blood is transported through the kidney before going to the respiratory organ. After passage through respiratory organs, the blood reaches the auricle through ctenidial (branchial) and/or pallial veins. Blood never enters the pericardium, which represents part of the true coelom. Some respiratory pigments have been reported from snails. These include hemoglobin

(*Planorbis*) and the much more common hemocyanin of *Helix* and other snails.

Excretion

Excretion is accomplished primarily by the kidney. This organ originated as one of a pair, but in the typical dextral snail the kidney, which arose embryologically on the left, and owing to torsion appeared topographically on the right, atrophies. The kidney lies near the pericardium with which it typically communicates. The kidney is a tubular, rather compact organ, variously infolded. It discharges through the mantle cavity. Variously modified pericardial glands with excretory function exist among the gastropods. These discharge through the coelomic pericardium and the reno-pericardial connectives. Aquatic snails excrete ammonia and urea, but insoluble uric acid occurs in land snails where water conservation is essential.

Nervous System and Sense Organs

The nervous system is represented by a series of paired ganglia and connectives. A pair of cerebral ganglia, connected by commissures, lies above the esophagus near the crop. From each cerebral ganglion, on either side of the esophagus there are connectives to a pedal and to a pleural ganglion. The two pedal ganglia are closely united. Basically there is a paired, triangulate complex of the three ganglia on either side of the esophagus, with the cerebral pair united above and the pedal pair united below it. Commissures run back from the respective pleural ganglia and pass to paired parietal ganglia, then continue to a visceral ganglion which in some forms still reveals its paired origin (Fig. 12-7). Owing to torsion, the parietal ganglia are often displaced, with the right coming to lie above, and the left below, the intestine. Detorsion resulting in secondary symmetry confuses the picture. Among Pulmonates, the chiasma of the longitudinal commissures is lost as the parietal ganglia are pulled forward by shortening of the connectives, until the original symmetry of the nervous system is restored.

The head and associated sense organs are supplied from the cerebral ganglia, in part via a pair of buccal ganglia which are connected by a commissure beneath the esophagus. The pedal ganglia innervate the foot, while the mantle receives its nerve supply primitively from the pleural and later by additions from visceral and parietal ganglia. In the higher Gastropoda, there is an increasing centralization of the nervous system with the ganglia concentrated in a ring around the gullet.

Specialized sense organs include eyes, statocysts, and osphradium. A pair of cephalic eyes are commonly on or near the tentacles. Some species possess pallial eyes. The statocyst (Fig. 12-13) are spherical organs lined with cilia whose inner ends support a secreted concretion. The osphradium is a specialized epithelial sense organ of the mantle cavity associated with respiratory function. Its chief action is to test the amount of sediment in the water on its way to the gill. Various specialized olfactory areas occur, most commonly on the tentacles.

Fig. 12-13 A generalized statocyst. From Hertwig, *A Manual of Zoology* (translated and edited by J. S. Kingsley) 1902, Holt, Rinehart & Winston, Inc.

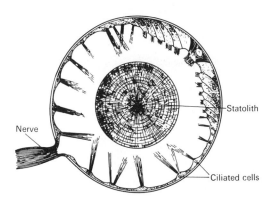

Nerve

Statolith

Ciliated cells

Reproduction and Embryology

Only the lowest order of snails is predominantly dioecious. Among them sexual dimorphism is slight. The gonad is never paired. In monoecious species, the gonad has some ova-producing areas and some which give rise to sperm. A condition of protandry tends to prevent self-fertilization, which is further blocked by the path taken by introduced spermatophores. A number of variations exist for conveying gametes to point of discharge. In some cases there is only a single duct, in others a partly divided duct, and in a third group the sperm duct and oviduct are separate throughout. Commonly the sperm duct terminates in a copulatory organ. In most gastropods, fertilization is internal and copulation must occur. Various conditions of oviparity and ovoviviparity exist. In the former, eggs are laid in large masses, usually embedded in a gelatinous secretion. In some marine forms, where fertilization is external, eggs are laid singly.

The fundamental embryology of gastropods involves spiral cleavage. Reference should be made to Chapter 11 for an account of spiral cleavage. In the Gastropoda, it should be mentioned that one of the macromeres (3D) divides to produce daughter cells, one of which (4d) is destined to produce the mesoderm. Spiral cleavage leads to a larval stage called a trochophore (Fig. 12-14). *Patella* produces a typical trochophore, variously modified in more advanced species. The fate of the blastopore, which is often considered to have evolutionary significance, in most of the group is directly or indirectly related to the future anterior end of the alimentary canal, but in *Paludina,* a form which has little yolk, it remains as the anus.

Characteristic of the trochophore is a band of cilia around the somewhat ovoid embryo. This ciliary band, which is just dorsal to the mouth, is called the prototroch. It represents the primordium of the future *velum*. In most Gastropoda, it becomes extended as a bilobed or multilobed, sinuous, ciliated ridge or flap providing efficiently for locomotion in the more generalized marine forms. Among terrestrial and fresh-water forms, this larval stage with velum is called a *veliger* (Fig. 12-15), and is passed within the eggshell in these telescoped life cycles.

Fig. 12-14 The molluscan trochophore (by Turner). After Shrock and Twenhofel 1953, courtesy of the McGraw-Hill Book Company.

Fig. 12-15 The molluscan veliger larva (by Turner). After Shrock and Twenhofel 1953, courtesy of the McGraw-Hill Book Company.

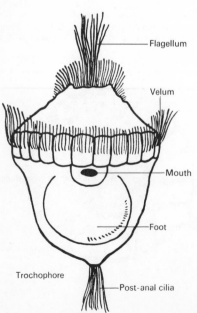

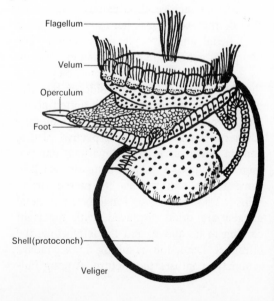

During the trochophore and veliger stages, the bilateral symmetry characteristic of younger embryos is lost. Among pelagic veligers, it is during the pelagic stage that the first phase of torsion occurs. During differential growth associated with the second phase of torsion the velum is resorbed, the size of the foot increases, the operculum which developed on the dorsal foot surface is lost in many forms, and the shell takes on its adult character, except in those naked forms in which it is lost.

Class III Gastropoda Typically this group possesses a single, coiled shell, an enlarged flattened foot, and a distinct head with tentacles. A unique phenomenon called torsion occurs in the development of all gastropods.

Order 1 Prosobranchia In these gastropods, torsion is retained and the mantle cavity is anterior. The visceral nerve cords are twisted into a figure eight. Shells generally vary between two types: a conical spiraled type with operculum and an uncoiled conical or dish-shaped shell with large aperture. Most species are dioecious. The group is divided into three suborders showing increased specialization. *Haliotis, Patella, Paludina, Littorina, Nassarius.*

Order 2 Opisthobranchia Molluscs in this group are monoecious. Detorsion has largely obliterated the effects of larval torsion. The mantle cavity is more posterior and, when not lost completely, opens widely. The shell is reduced, internal, or missing. The single ctenidium is lost in some species and respiration assumed by other body surfaces. This order is divided into many subgroups and includes those opisthobranchs known as nudibranchs or sea slugs. *Akera, Clio, Pneumonoderma, Actaeonia, Acochlidium, Tritonia, Jorunna.*

Order 3 Pulmonata This group of gastropods is monoecious. They have not undergone detorsion, but exhibit a secondary symmetry of the nervous system (Euthyneura) by shortening of the visceral connectives and concentration of the ganglia. An operculum is absent except in the marine genus *Amphibola.* Typically there are two pairs of tentacles. Gills are lacking, with the wall of the mantle cavity (lung) adapted to respiratory function. One

of the two suborders is aquatic, the other terrestrial. *Limnaea, Planorbis, Helix, Agriolimax.*

CLASS SCAPHOPODA

The Scaphopoda, of which *Dentalium* is the best-known representative, are marine molluscs living below low-tide level. (Fig. 1-2). West Coast Indians used these shells for wampum. These rather uniform shells are slightly curved cones open at both ends. The smaller end of the shell is older and thicker. It represents the posterior end of the animal, while the outside of the curve is the ventral surface. The mantle cavity is a continuous chamber of varying diameters opening at both ends. Since the animal is normally buried in the sand with only the posterior end protruding, the posterior opening to the mantle cavity functions in both an incurrent and an excurrent capacity (Fig. 12-16). Because of shape, common names for *Dentalium* are "tooth" or "elephant tusk" shells. About two hundred living and three hundred fossil species have been described. The latter go back to the Ordovician.

Fig. 12-16 Diagrammatic organization of *Dentalium,* Scaphopoda. Adapted from various sources.

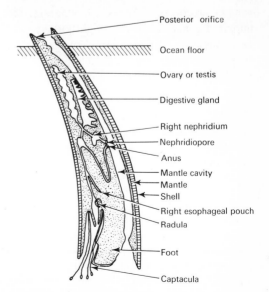

- Posterior orifice
- Ocean floor
- Ovary or testis
- Digestive gland
- Right nephridium
- Nephridiopore
- Anus
- Mantle cavity
- Mantle
- Shell
- Right esophageal pouch
- Radula
- Foot
- Captacula

The Scaphopoda exhibit molluscan characters in the possession of a foot, shell, mantle, and trochophore and veliger larval stages. Similarities to primitive bivalves include symmetry of the visceral nerve commissures, and a mantle which arises as a bilobed structure, later fusing. They resemble the gastropods in possessing a well-developed radula. Also, the gonad discharges into the right kidney as it does with *Haliotis,* the abalone, and some of its relatives. The Scaphopoda lack ctenidia, and have a reduced vascular system without a distinct heart. Respiration occurs through the mantle.

These bilaterally symmetrical animals have a proboscis-like head situated at the larger or anterior end of the shell, into which it can be retracted. The head lacks eyes, but in *Dentalium* possesses tentacle-like contractile filaments called *captacula,* which are both sensory and prehensile and are used for obtaining the microorganisms used for food. The foot is broadly conical and can be extended from the anterior end of the shell to serve efficiently as a burrowing organ. The paired statocysts on the foot are adjacent to the pedal ganglia, but are innervated from the cerebral ganglia. As with gastropods and bivalves, paired pleural and visceral ganglia are present. Sexes are separate; the unpaired gonad utilizes the right kidney duct as a passage. An irregular cleavage of the singly laid ovum results in a modified trochophore and an even more modified veliger larva. The blastopore shifts forward until it serves as a primordium for the mouth.

Class IV Scaphopoda The shell of these molluscs is an elongated, slightly recurved cone, open at either end. The mantle also is tubular, communicating with both ends of the shell. With the large (anterior) end of the shell typically buried in sand, circulation of water through the mantle cavity is accomplished through the posterior opening by ciliary currents. The Scaphopoda lack gills, and the mantle wall serves as a respiratory organ. There is a well-developed radula. The sexes

are separate and the larva develops through a trochophore stage. *Dentalium, Siphonodentalium, Pulsellum.*

CLASS BIVALVIA

The various names applied to this class of Mollusca are indicative of anatomical features. These include layered gills (Lamellibranchia), hatchet foot (Pelecypoda), symmetry associated with right and left shell valves (Bivalvia), and the absence of a head (Acephala). The Bivalvia are bilaterally symmetrical animals, with reduced cephalization, a ventral wedge-shaped foot, gills, and a bilobed mantle which produces a two-valved shell arranged in parallel plates. Marine forms metamorphose through trochophore and veliger larval stages.

The shell valves, held from separating at the dorsal edge by the hinge ligament, exhibit concentric lines of growth. These radiate out from a dorsal swelling called the *umbo,* whose terminus, the beak, points anteriorly in common forms. The beak marks the beginning of shell growth. The interior of an empty valve shows markings which represent the attachment of organs, primarily muscular and pallial, to the shell. Dorsally in the shell at either end are rounded scars of the *adductor* muscles. Only one adductor (the posterior) is retained in the scallop (*Pecten*) and the oyster (*Ostrea*). In those bivalves with two adductors a smaller, generally more triangular scar of foot *retractor* muscles occurs near each adductor scar. Paralleling the free shell margin and running from one adductor scar to the other is the *pallial line,* which marks the shell attachment of the pallium or mantle. In some forms a posterior triangular indentation of the pallial line represents the pallial sinus. It marks the position of the foot retractor muscle. The length of this scar provides information about the size of the siphons. Since siphon size is indicative of habits, the pallial sinus scar is particularly useful in fossil study. The shell valves are closed by adductor contraction and opened by elasticity of the hinge ligament, which may be internal or external.

Both prismatic and nacreous layers of the shell are calcareous. The prismatic layer is secreted by the rim of the more lateral mantle layer. Just within this peripheral lobe of the mantle is a groove which produces the *periostracum*. The inner calcareous (nacreous) portion of the shell is secreted by the surface of the external epithelium of the mantle. When iridescent, the nacreous layer is called mother-of-pearl; but in some bivalves it has a dull, chalky appearance. The hinge ligament is a new development with the lamellibranchs. It is an elastic, uncalcified connective between the valves and is composed principally of the same organic material that occurs in the shell.

Next to Gastropoda, the Bivalvia is the largest group of Mollusca for both fossil and contemporary species. Naturally, fossil classification has been based primarily on shells, and an extensive terminology utilizing shell shape, tooth pattern at the hinge line, and muscle scar patterns has grown up. The first fossils date from the lower Ordovician. All Lamellibranchia are aquatic, and primarily marine. The accompanying drawing (Fig. 12-17) provides some understanding of common adaptive variations in recent species. In general, the bivalves are burrowing forms, lying variously buried at the bottom of the bodies of water in which they make their home.

The mantle lies as a thin membrane between soft body parts and each valve. Although firmly attached to the respective shell valve at the pallial line, each lobe has a free margin which extends beyond the pallial line, at least to the shell rim. In some of the more archaic species these extended mantle borders never fuse, but in many common forms discontinuous fusion occurs at the posterior end to provide two openings, which are variously modified into tubes (Fig. 12-18). The two openings or tubes are called *siphons* and represent the apertures for water circulation; the dorsal one is excurrent or

Fig. 12-17 Class Lamellibranchia. Diagrams (not all to the same scale) showing habitat adaptations among pelecypods. *A, Pholas,* the rock borer; *B, Ostrea,* the oyster; *C,* an extinct form in which one valve served as an operculum to the other modified as a cone; *D, Mytilus,* the black sea mussel attached to a wooden pier by a byssus; *E, Teredo,* the shipworm, a destructive wood borer; *F, Mya,* the mud clam with a long siphon; *G,* a burrowing form with a long double siphon; *H, Ensis,* the razor clam, with a short double siphon *I, Venus,* almost completely buried in bottom sediment; *J, Crassatellites,* in a depression in sand; *K, Nucula,* a primitive form which moves along the surface of the sand; *L, Pecten,* shown swimming at left and lying on the bottom at right. After Shrock and Twenhofel (adapted from Berry) 1953, courtesy of the McGraw-Hill Book Company.

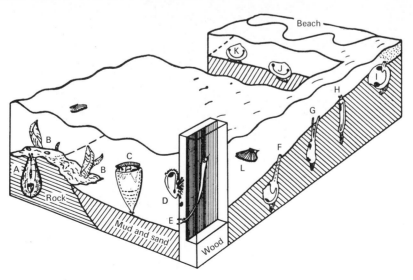

Fig. 12-18 Anatomy of *Nucula*, a primitive lamellibranch. From Hertwig (after Drew), *A Manual of Zoology* (translated and edited by J. S. Kingsley) 1902, Holt, Rinehart & Winston, Inc.

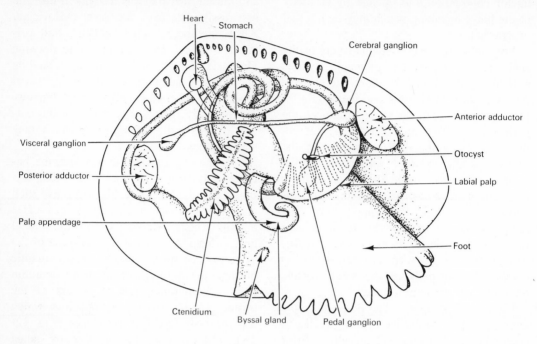

Fig. 12-19 The scallop, *Pecten*, showing internal organs. After Pierce 1950, *Selected Invertebrate Types* (F. A. Brown, Jr., ed.), courtesy of John Wiley & Sons, Inc.

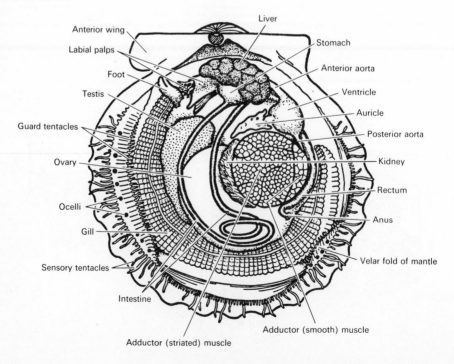

exhalant, while the ventral (which in some forms is not in anatomical fusion ventrally) provides the incurrent or inhalant path. The mantle margin is sometimes provided with pigmented areas, glands, sensory spots, and in the Arcidae and Pectinidae (Fig. 12-19), eyes (ocelli).

Food-Getting and Digestive Processes

Cilia on the gill surfaces activate a flow of water carrying microscopic food material as well as oxygen into the mantle cavity. Some of the water in this cephalad flow filters through the gills to function in respiration while part is carried forward to the labial palps, where the microorganisms caught in a mucous ribbon enter the digestive tract. Ultimately this water also reaches the gills. In some species, a ciliated ridge causing a current to move caudally occurs along the inner edge of the mantle. This current serves to reject unsuitable food material.

The mouth is median and usually opens between paired labial palps just ventral to the anterior adductor muscle, in those species retaining this muscle. The mouth leads through a short gullet to a large stomach which is often provided with caeca and in addition receives ducts from the adjacent digestive gland or "liver." Near the entrance to the intestines, and sometimes communicating with it, is a caecum containing a peculiar translucent, gelatinous rod called crystalline style, which projects into the stomach. Owing to ciliary action, this rod rotates and its end is eroded against a thickened stomach roof. The rotation causes the *crystalline style* (Fig. 12-20) to act as a capstan as the mucous ribbon containing food becomes wrapped around it. The rod is secreted by the caecum within which it lies. It appears to be an extracellular amylolytic enzyme associated primarily with a herbivorous diet. The intestine leaves the stomach ventrally and loops through the viscero-pedal complex before returning dorsally to pass through pericardium and, in most forms, the heart ventricle. The posterior end of the intestine (rectum) passes dorsal to the adjacent adductor muscle before ending in the excurrent stream. Generally, the intestinal lumen is ciliated and portions contain a ridge, the *typhlosole.*

Respiratory Adaptations

The lamellibranchs are commonly separated into orders on the basis of ctenidial structure but this does not appear to be a natural grouping, except for the Protobranchia. A ctenidium is a respiratory organ with leaflike branches extending from a common axis, and in the Protobranchia the ctenidia occur in double rows of short, broad leaves lying nearly horizontal in the mantle cavity. In the filibranchiate and eulamellibranchiate types, the gills or ctenidia are thin V-shaped plates in cross section (Fig. 12-21). Yonge (1947) suggests that such elongated filaments evolved "by ventral extension of the *middle* of the original horizontal filament." Each of these V-shaped gill plates (laminae or demibranchs) therefore has an inner and an outer lamella which in the filibranchiates are infirmly held together by apposing and interlocking discs of cilia. In the pseudolamellibranch bivalves of Order Anisomyaria, cilia still occur to interlock the lamellae, but the reflected end of each filament is fused with the mantle laterally or with the foot-

Fig. 12-20 Diagram of a crystalline style of a lamellibranch. From J. A. Ramsay, *Physiological Approach to the Lower Animals,* 1952, courtesy of the Cambridge University Press.

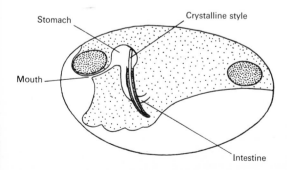

Stomach

Crystalline style

Mouth

Intestine

Fig. 12-21 Cross-section of a clam. From Hertwig, *A Manual of Zoology* (translated and edited by J. S. Kingsley) 1902, Holt, Rinehart & Winston, Inc.

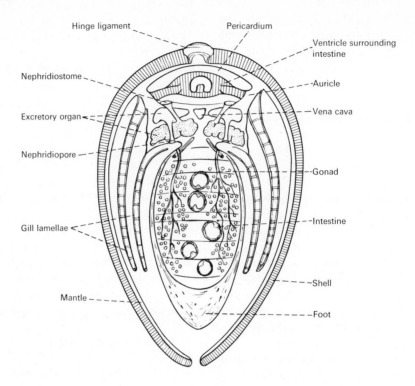

Fig. 12-22 Lamellibranchia. Diagrammatic sagittal view of a fresh-water mussel such as *Anodonta*, with left gill bank partly dissected. The arrows indicate water circulation.

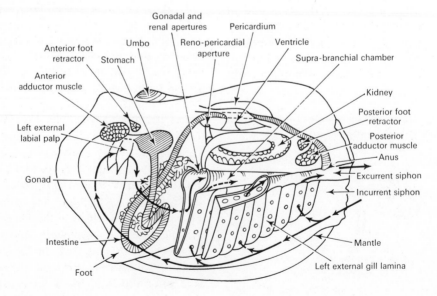

base medially to produce a sturdier gill. In the eulamellibranch gill, vascular connectives may join adjacent filaments as well as forming a supportive framework between the two lamellae of each V-shaped plate. In the filibranchiate gill the interlamellar junctions are nonvascular, while in the eulamellibranchiate type regular vascular junctions occur. Cilia on gill surfaces create the functional water currents.

In the eulamellibranch gill the flat sides of each filament are provided with *lateral* cilia whose beat propels the water between the filaments through ostia into the interlamellar spaces, where it eventually reaches the suprabranchial chamber and is expelled through the excurrent siphon. At the distal end of the filament, *frontal* cilia which face the mantle cavity have a functional beat toward the tip or ventral aspect of the gill laminae, along which occurs a food groove. Between the lateral and frontal cila, the long *laterofrontal* cilia, often fused into paired membranelles, form a filter between adjacent filaments, and the beat of these cilia is toward the distal end of the filament. Microscopic food caught by laterofrontal cilia is carried in a network of mucus to the food groove where other ciliary currents transport it so that it eventually reaches the labial palps. Other cilia beating in the reverse direction discard unusable particles.

In Protobranchia, however, gill cilia do not function in food-getting. Water, after passing through the gills (Fig. 12-22), reaches the excurrent siphon via the suprabranchial chamber. In suborder Septibranchinacea, gills have modified into transverse muscular septa. Muscular contraction of the septa forces water through variously paired ostia into the supraseptal chamber, whose walls function as respiratory surfaces.

The circulatory system is an open type, since in many organs the blood flows through lacunar spaces or sinuses unlined by typical vascular epithelium. From these lacunae, a venous system conveys most of the blood through the kidneys to the gills from whence it goes to the auricles. A small amount of blood aerated in the mantle may reach the auricles without going through the kidney. The function of the mantle as a respiratory organ tends to vary inversely with efficient gill respiration.

The heart (Fig. 12-22) lies within a generally dorsal pericardium and is composed of a muscular ventricle and paired, generally symmetrical auricles which open to the ventricle by paired slits. The pericardium itself contains no blood, as is apparent in species with hemoglobin as a respiratory pigment. Blood leaves the ventricle through an anterior and a posterior aorta, but the latter is reduced or missing in protobranchs and some anisomyarians (*Mytilus*).

Excretion

Paired kidneys are the principal organs of excretion. Each of them consists essentially of a U-tube (Fig. 12-22) lying posterior and ventral to the pericardium. The typically more glandular ventral arm of the kidney communicates with the pericardium. The dorsal arm is thin-walled and bladderlike and empties into the mantle cavity or the suprabranchial chamber through ciliary action. Additional excretory function is performed by pericardial glands. When these exist as diverticula of the pericardium they are known as *Keber's organs*. They usually occur at the anterior end of the pericardium.

Nervous System and Sense Organs

Four pairs of ganglia are apparent in some of the more primitive Lamellibranchia. These ganglia are the cerebral, pleural, pedal, and visceral pairs. In most bivalves, the cerebral and pleural ganglia are fused on either side of the gullet above which they connect by a commissure. From the cerebropleural ganglia, paired connectives run ventrally into the foot to connect with the fused pedal ganglia. Another pair of connectives pass through kidney tissue to paired visceral ganglia lying near the posterior adductor muscle. Often these visceral ganglia are fused into a single body.

In addition to tactile sensibility, a number of specialized sense organs occur. One of these is the *osphradium* situated near the posterior end of the gill. It serves to sample respiratory fluid primarily for sediment. Although it is associated with an accessory ganglion near the right visceral ganglion, its innervation arises from the cerebro-pleural complex. Statocysts (otocysts) occur in the foot near the pedal ganglia, but their innervation also arises from the cerebro-pleural ganglia. Eyes occur on the mantle rim in a number of forms. In the scallop, *Pecten,* they are of various sizes and each occurs on a short stalk or tentacle along the mantle edge of both valves, but not necessarily in symmetry.

Reproduction and Embryology

Most of the Bivalvia are dioecious, but there are a number of forms including the genera *Ostrea,* (oysters) *Pecten* (scallops), and some *Anodonta* (fresh-water clams) in which hermaphroditism is characteristic or common. Genital products are discharged through a common aperture with the kidney, or through a separate, nearby genital duct. Commonly such apertures open to the suprabranchial chamber, where the gametes are carried out the excurrent channel and fertilization is external. In marine forms, free-living trochophore and veliger larvae are characteristic. Some fresh-water species exhibit this pattern, but most incubate the embryo in characteristic locations, usually in the gills. In these latter forms, e.g. *Anodonta,* the ova do not leave the parent, since the ovary has a separate aperture into the pallial cavity. Fertilization occurs with the entry of sperm via the inhalant siphon. Usually the outer gill lamellae are utilized as *marsupia.* The characteristic shell-gland of the larva initially produces an unpaired shell, which

later is replaced by paired valves (Fig. 12-23), each of which is triangular in shape. In many species, each valve bears hooks and a median thread called a *byssus,* secreted in front of the mouth. This provisional byssus is not homologous with the threads secreted from the ventral foot surface, and which serve for temporary or permanent attachment in the sessile or sedentary orders of lamellibranchs. These larvae, called *glochidia,* may over-winter in the marsupium, but eventually are released to the surrounding water, where as free-swimming larvae they make contact with a suitable fresh-water fish host and remain as ectoparasites for several weeks. Metamorphosis occurs with loss of larval features, and formation of a mouth, and just before the sexually immature larvae leave the fish host, the intestine breaks through to form an anus.

Class V Bivalvia These are typically bilaterally symmetrical Mollusca in which the rudimentary cephalic region has lost tentacles, radula, salivary glands, and eyes. The compressed body is enclosed in a two-lobed mantle which produces a bivalved shell that is hinged dorsally and is closed ventrally by the action of two adductor muscles. Within the mantle are two pairs of ctenidia which lie lateral to the median wedge-shaped foot. Gill cilia create a current in the pallial cavity of these sedentary animals to introduce microscopic

Fig. 12-23 Glochidium of *Anodonta.* From Hertwig (after Balfour), *A Manual of Zoology* (translated and edited by J. S. Kingsley) 1902, Holt, Rinehart & Winston, Inc.

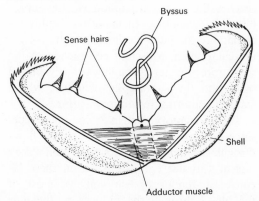

Byssus

Sense hairs

Shell

Adductor muscle

food as well as oxygen with the water. Food particles are sorted by ciliary action and transported to the mouth in mucous strands. The lamellibranchs are typically dioecious, and marine species produce trochophore and veliger larvae.

Order 1 Protobranchia This group of bivalves is unquestionably a natural one, retaining a number of primitive features. The relatively few living genera are specialized, but show an evolutionary progression in the process of food-getting as this role passes from head to gill. The gills are composed of flattened, leaflike, nonreflected pairs of filaments arranged in rows lateral to the anterior-posterior axis. The gill rows are restricted to the posterior portion of the mantle cavity. A hypobranchial gland lateral to each gill is homologous to that in prosobranch gastropods. The foot has a flattened plantar surface. Animals in this order are dioecious. The gonad has retained a primitive connection with the kidney. Two adductor muscles are characteristic. *Nucula, Yoldia, Malletia.*

Order 2 Taxodonta This order, together with the next order (Anisomyaria), constitutes the sessile or sedentary branch of Douvillé. These are oldest after the protobranchs. The Taxodonta lack siphons. The mantle is widely open. The byssus develops from the whole edge of the foot. The two adductor muscles are approximately equal in size. The long uniform teeth of the hinge tend to diverge ventrally. The usual resting position leaves the dorsal side up, and the valves are symmetrical. Two aortae arise from the heart. *Arca, Limopsis.*

Order 3 Anisomyaria Siphons are not formed, and the mantle is widely open. The foot and byssus have moved forward with reduction in the anterior adductor muscle, resulting in the anisomyarian condition. In some species the anterior adductor is lost, and the animal is then monomyarian. There is a tendency for the two valves to become unequal, and the resting position is usually on the right valve. The foot decreases in size. The hinge is without teeth and has an external ligament. Usually a single aorta arises from the heart. *Mytilus, Pinna, Pecten, Ostrea.*

(The next two orders, Schizodonta and Heterodonta, constitute the so-called "normal"

branch of Douvillé. They generally appeared later in geologic history than the "sessile" branch. Animals in these orders tend to live at or near the surface, or burrow actively and generally are not attached. This involves reduction in importance of the byssus. Adductor muscles are isomyarian or dimyarian.)

Order 4 Schizodonta This group is generally dimyarian. One family is mainly fossil. The other families live in fresh water, and many of these produce a parasitic larval stage called a glochidium. Adults possess a schizodont dentition which is variable, but commonly shows two-limbed, inverted-V-shaped teeth arranged in a fan shape. *Unio, Anodonta, Lampsillis.*

Order 5 Heterodonta This is a typically dimyarian group. The heterodont dentition is characterized by a few well-developed cardinal teeth lying under the ligament and usually some less well-defined teeth lying beyond the ligament and called lateral teeth. The valves are of approximately equal size and the ligament is external. *Cardium, Cyprina, Tridacna, Venus.*

(The last group of Bivalvia, Douvillé placed in a so-called deep-burrowing group. Most of them show extensive shell modification involving specialization for a burrowing function; in others the shell has become weak and fragile. Along with the burrowing habit, there is extensive fusion of the mantle, the hinge is weak, and the valves tend to gape. Most species are hermaphroditic.)

Order 6 Adapedonta In this group, the hinge teeth are degenerate or lost. The gills are folded or the external gill may be directed dorsally and is without folds. The siphons are mostly elongate. When shell ligament is retained, it is usually external. The mantle edges are almost entirely fused in members of this order. *Pholas, Ensis, Teredo.*

Order 7 Anomalodesmata This order contains two subgroups of marked diversity.

Suborder 1 Anatinacea These are hermaphroditic Anomalodesmata, but the ovary is distinct from the testis. They possess a eulamellibranchiate gill characterized by regularly spaced vascular junctions. The external demibranch or lamina is directed dorsally and not reflected. The foot is usually small and hinge teeth are missing. *Cochlodesma, Peri-*

ploma, Pandora.

   Suborder 2 Septibranchinacea In this group the gills are transformed into perforate, paired muscular septa. The group is dimyarian and two siphons are present. The foot is elongate. The septibranchs are marine and carnivorous. *Cuspidaria, Cetoconcha, Poromya.*

CLASS CEPHALOPODA

   This class of Mollusca are complex, bilaterally symmetrical, marine animals. The prominent head bears paired eyes and is surrounded by one or two rings of retractile,

sucker-bearing tentacles developed from the anterior portion of the foot. The head bears a pair of beaklike jaws and a radula. In such dibranchiate cephalopods as the cuttlefishes, squid, and octopuses, the shell if retained is internal, having been enveloped by the mantle which functions in respiration and locomotion. The head protrudes from a collar formed by the free edge of the mantle (Fig. 12-24). Water enters the mantle cavity between this mantle edge and the visceral mass. Locomotion is accomplished by the expulsion of water through the funnel, which represents the fusion of paired foot elements.

   The use of the terms anterior and posterior and dorsal and ventral in the morphological sense does not agree with their physiological usage in such an animal as the squid. The internal shell is on the functionally dorsal side since it is uppermost as the animal swims, although anatomically this is the anterior aspect. Similarly, the siphon is ventral, although morphologically it is posterior. Likewise, mouth and tentacles are functionally anterior and the pointed, fin-bearing end of the squid is posterior, al-

Fig. 12-24 Diagrammatic representation of some of the internal organs of a male squid, *Loligo.*

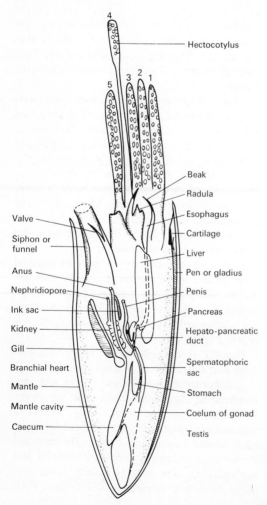

Fig. 12-25 *Argonauta* (the paper nautilus) female. From Hertwig (after Rymer Jones), *A Manual of Zoology* (translated and edited by J. S. Kingsley) 1902, Holt, Rinehart & Winston, Inc.

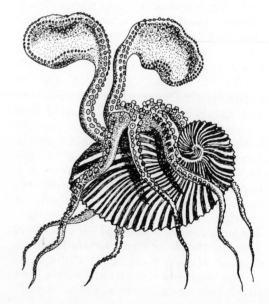

though morphologically these are ventral and dorsal, respectively. Thus we see that the physiological application of these terms represents a shift of roughly 90° from the morphological application.

Some forms, which bear fins variously extended back from the morphologically dorsal end, utilize these fins in swimming. The living dibranchiate cephalopods are subdivided on the basis of arm or tentacle number into the Decapoda (Sepiida) and the Octopoda. Both of these groups are characterized by the absence of a typical external shell (the shell (Fig. 12-25) in *Argonauta* females is a nonhomologous exception), by the presence of one pair (the posterior) of gills or ctenidia, a siphon fused from paired primordia, an ink-sac opening into the mantle cavity, and complex eyes containing a lens. *Nautilus* (Fig. 12-26) is the only living non-coleoid cephalopod. It is characterized by the presence of two pairs of gills, a funnel of unfused paired primordia, and an external, chambered shell, and it lacks an ink-sac and lenses.

The Cephalopoda represent a very ancient group. Over 10,000 species of fossil cephalopods have been described, but only about 400 living species are known. The fossil record indicates two periods of geologic prominence, first in the early Paleozoic and again in the middle Mesozoic. Gill structure leaves no geologic impression, so that it is not clear whether the ancestors possessed one or two pairs of gills. The heavily yolked egg with correlative embryology and absence of a distinctive motile larva separates Cephalopoda from other Mollusca. Nautilus has a rich geologic ancestry, some representatives of which possessed a straight-coned shell (Fig. 12-27), whereas others had a plano-spiraled shell (coil in a single plane). About one-fourth of the shell constituted the living chamber and the remainder of the partitioned cone is called *phragmocone,* the various septa being perforate. From the visceral hump of the animal in the living chamber there is a rodlike or tubular fleshy prolongation of the body called the *siphuncle* enclosed in a calcareous tube. The sipuncle apparently functions to secrete gas for buoyancy into the unoccupied chambers of the *Nautilus* shell.

Fig. 12-26 *Nautilus* female with part of shell removed. From Hertwig (after Ludwig-Leunis), *A Manual of Zoology* (translated and edited by J. S. Kingsley) 1902, Holt, Rinehart & Winston, Inc.

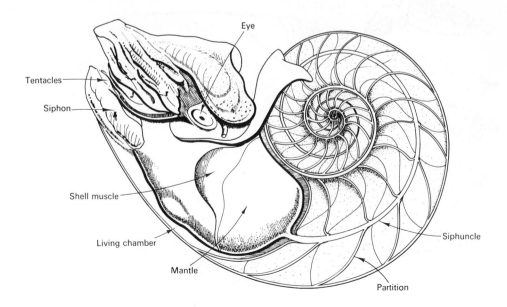

The septal junctions with the shell wall are visible as lines called *sutures,* which may be simple or extremely tortuous. In the Belemnoidea, extinct cephalopods with ten arms and an internal shell, the shell has three portions, one of which is a hollow septate structure corresponding to the nautiloid phragmocone. In addition, a flat or shield-shaped structure extending toward the arms is called the *proostracum,* and at the apex of the phragmocone there is a solid calcareous *rostrum* or *guard.* Modification of the proostracum as a horny plume or *gladius* occurs in *Loligo.* The cuttlefish, *Sepia,* has a calcareous skeleton composed of the rostrum and the upper side of the phragmocone.

The Ammonoidea constitute the largest subdivision of Cephalopoda. They appeared in the early Devonian, are thought to have evolved from nautiloids, and became extinct by the end of the Cretaceous, during which they were not only the largest but also the most numerous invertebrates. Morton reports some 600 genera representing over 160

families. The group is of paramount importance as stratigraphic zonal markers in paleontology. Some evidence indicates that the ammonoids arose from coiled nautiloid ancestors while straight-shelled nautiloids gave rise to coleoid cephalopods.

Food-Getting and Digestion

The alimentary canal begins centrally from the base of the tentacle ring as a rounded muscular mass called the buccal bulb, which is marked by two interlocking beaklike mandibles (Fig. 12-24). Within the buccal cavity is a fleshy elevation and a caecum from which the radula protrudes. Paired salivary glands open into the buccal cavity. Some of the secreted material acts as an anesthetic or poison on the animals used for food. Running aborally into the visceral mass is the cylindrical esophagus, which in some forms (octopods and nautiloids) has an enlargement called the crop. The esophagus passes through the liver before it empties into a

Fig. 12-27 Evolution of the cephalopod shell. (a) a primitive orthocone; (b) *Piloceras* (L. Ordovician); (c) a belemnoid; (d) a primitive sepioid *Belosepia*; (e) *Sepia*; (f) *Spirulirostra*; (g) *Spirula*; (h) *Conoteuthis*; (i) *Loligo*; (j) *Sepia* (entire animal); (k) *Spirula* (entire animal). 1, guard; 2, phragmocone; 3, pro-ostracum. After Morton 1958, *Molluscs,* Hutchinson and Co. Ltd., courtesy of the author.

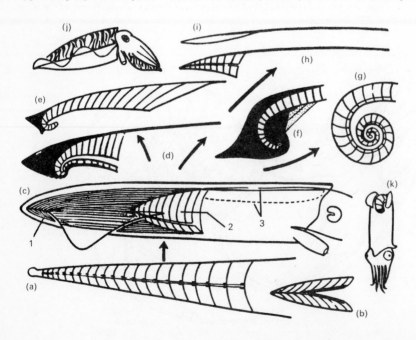

muscular pouch, the stomach. An elongated caecum extends through the aboral portion of the visceral mass and joins the stomach. Adjacent to the stomach is another digestive gland termed the pancreas. Ducts of pancreas and liver empty into the caecum through a joint hepato-pancreatic duct. The stomach empties to the tubular intestine near the esophageal orifice, and the anus opens from the rectum into the mantle cavity near the internal end of the funnel. Cephalopods are carnivorous, feeding on fish and on other invertebrates.

Many cephalopods have a rectal diverticulum termed an ink-sac. The "ink" is discharged through the siphon and serves as a "smoke-screen," but MacGinitie and Mac-Ginitie point out that it has a paralyzing effect on the olfactory organs of the enemy predator. Some squids turn much darker momentarily when a potential predator approaches. The emission of a compact ink cloud may allow the now paler cephalopod to escape, with the ink forming a pseudo-target.

Respiratory Adaptations

Among the dibranchiate cephalopods the characteristic high activity makes a real demand on the respiratory system. Water has a definite circulatory path through the mantle cavity; it enters between mantle collar and the visceral mass and is expelled through the funnel. This system provides continued renewal of oxygenated sea water but also serves for locomotion. The gill filaments are robust to withstand the water current and they no longer have cilia (Fig. 12-28). In the living coleoid forms, gill efficiency is increased by the development of fine capillaries. *Nautilus* differs by the presence of more blood lacunae and by osphradia. There are no capillaries in the ctenidia, but the presence of two pairs of gills (tetrabranchiate) offsets the lesser efficiency of the gills and of funnel pumping action.

In the squid, nonaerated blood returns from tentacles and oral region through the anterior vena cava, which divides and passes through the kidney as precaval vessels. Together with blood from paired postcaval vessels and tributaries, blood is carried to the branchial hearts. These are contractile chambers, one of which exists at the base of each gill. From them blood is forced through branchial arteries and gill capillaries. Another branch from each branchial heart services the mantle. Aerated blood from the gills is carried to the paired systemic auricles through branchial veins possessing valves. It then moves to the asymmetrical ventricle for distribution through anterior and posterior aortae. It is interesting to note that the squid heart and probably most molluscan hearts are myogenic like the vertebrate heart; that

Fig. 12-28 Transverse section through the pallial region of the cuttlefish, *Sepia*. Redrawn from Morton 1958, *Molluscs*, Hutchinson and Co. Ltd., courtesy of the author.

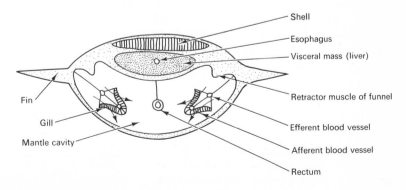

is, the beat is still initiated within heart muscle after all nerves are anesthetized or destroyed.

Molluscan blood commonly possesses the respiratory pigment hemocyanin, which is blue when oxygenated and otherwise colorless. Hemocyanin in the squid, *Loligo,* can carry 7 to 9 times more oxygen than sea water, and in general is a more efficient oxygen carrier than that of Gastropoda. Among the factors changing the affinity of the blood for oxygen is blood acidity, which is directly related to carbon dioxide content. Increase in acidity reduces the ability of the respiratory pigment to combine with oxygen. In *Loligo,* hemocyanin functions well at a CO_2 partial pressure well below that in the alveolar mixture in man's lungs. This is important for the squid, which lives in an environment in which the amount of oxygen is relatively constant although small. A given volume of air contains more than 40 times more oxygen than an equal volume of sea water in equilibrium with air. Carbon dioxide is much more soluble in sea water than is oxygen, and readily diffuses from the gills into sea water. With the loss of CO_2 the affinity of hemocyanin for oxygen is increased, while in the squid tissues the CO_2 content increases and oxygen is released. It is significant that a single circulation of the squid blood normally will remove over 90 per cent of the contained oxygen. Therefore while there is little reserve, the environment normal for the squid is probably sufficiently uniform that oxygen can be readily replaced.

The squid as a representative of the Cephalopoda has a valved, closed circulatory system with blood propelled by heart contraction. It possesses an efficient blood pigment, extensive respiratory surfaces, and a mechanism for renewing the oxygen-containing sea water.

Excretion

In living coleoid Cephalopoda, the kidneys are paired sacs containing some glandular epithelium. They open near the anal opening.

Each renal sac is traversed by the corresponding precava arising from bifurcation of the vena cava. A renopericardial canal connects each renal sac with the pericardium. In the tetrabranchiate *Nautilus,* four renal sacs occur and each opens separately to the mantle cavity. In this form the pericardium does not communicate with the kidneys, but has paired apertures leading directly to the pallial cavity.

Nervous System and Sense Organs

The nervous system is centralized about the esophagus as paired ganglia. Four pairs are associated, but variant amounts of fusion obliterate their identities somewhat. On the dorsal side of the esophagus in the squid, the cerebral ganglia are fused into a supraesophageal body. This ganglion gives off optic stalks laterally, which via optic ganglia connect with the eyes. On the other side of the gullet, the partly fused pedal and visceral ganglia occur. The paired pedal ganglia supply nerve tracts to the tentacles and to the funnel. Laterally placed pleural ganglia are in close fusion with the respective visceral ganglion. Paired pallial and visceral nerve trunks arise from the pleuro-visceral complex.

Cephalopoda are complex animals, well supplied with special sense organs. In addition to a well-developed tactile sense, there are optic, olfactory, and balance specializations. The eyes (Fig. 12-29) are remarkably well developed and are analogous to the eyes of vertebrates, possessing anterior and posterior chambers, cornea, lens, iris, and retina. The retina is "direct" rather than inverted as with the vertebrate eye. The lens arises from two primordia, and focusing is accomplished by pressure in the posterior chamber, which modifies the distance between lens and retina.

The olfactory organ is represented by a depressed area below either eye which is innervated from the cerebral ganglia. The osphradia of Gastropoda and Lamellibranchia are similarly supplied from the cerebral ganglia. Ospharadia occur only in Nautilus among living Cephalopoda, but the olfactory areas of other forms may have assumed part of their function.

The organs of balance are the statocysts. These are embedded in cartilage near the pleuro-visceral ganglion on either side. Essentially they are ciliated chambers containing a specialized concretion, the statolith. As with snails and bivalves, the cephalopod statocysts receive their nerve supply from the cerebral ganglia.

Chromatophores are not special sense organs, but they are remarkably developed in Cephalopoda. They are microscopic pigment sacs expanded by muscles under nervous control. Contraction is due to their own elasticity. Among sepioids, chromatophores containing different pigments occur in three layers, and color change is accomplished with great rapidity.

Normal octopuses in a laboratory tank will attack food, and since they are voracious they will do this repeatedly. This behavior was utilized to investigate memory and to associate response and memory with anatomical portions of the nervous system. If attractive food such as crab was suspended in the laboratory tank with an octopus, it was recognized, approached, captured, and taken to the cephalopod's shelter for devouring. When a second crab was offered adjacent to a suitable visible electrode, the attacking octopus was shocked, literally turned pale by chromatophore change, and retreated to its shelter. After a few trials, the octopus learned to discriminate between a crab with and without the electrode. Young reviews the factors of learning and discrimination in the octopus and in other cephalopods. Boycott and Young studied the octopus brain from serial sections and mapped out many of the complex connections in it. The brain is a lobate structure with the vertical lobes lying dorsal and long axes parallel to the main axis of the brain; behind them successively are the superior frontal, inferior frontal, and superior buccal lobes with their axes at right

Fig. 12-29 Diagrammatic section of cephalopod eye. From Hertwig (after Gegenbaur), *A Manual of Zoology* (translated and edited by J. S. Kingsley) 1902, Holt, Rinehart & Winston, Inc.

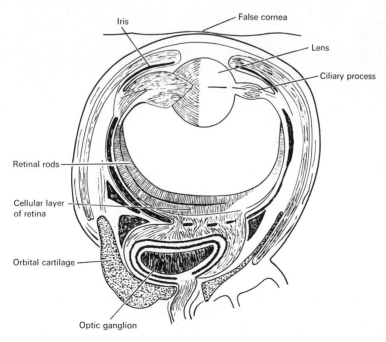

Iris

False cornea

Lens

Ciliary process

Retinal rods

Cellular layer of retina

Orbital cartilage

Optic ganglion

angles to the brain axis. Below the position of the vertical lobes, paired optic tracts extend laterally to the huge optic lobes situated behind either eye.

If the intact cuttlefish, *Sepia,* is separated by a glass plate from suitable food such as a prawn, it will attack at first with great vigor, then with lesser vigor until cessation. This form of learning will occur in experimental animals in which the vertical lobe has been removed. In a number of other tests, it was shown that cephalopods (especially octopuses) could discriminate between variously shaped figures. In some of these experiments, memory was retained two and four days although the accuracy was somewhat less. If optic nerves are severed, the blind octopus, after recovery, can locate and catch food. Removal of the optic lobes instead of sectioning optic nerves showed no effect on discrimination based on chemo-tactile reactions. Removal of the vertical lobes disturbed memory capacity, so that an intact animal which had learned not to attack food (electrical deterrent) did not recognize the electrode and attacked the food at once. In another experiment normal animals were trained unilaterally for visual response. When the opposite eye was tested, the response was likewise normal, but this transfer capacity was lost with removal of the vertical lobes. It is apparent that the learning responses in the cephalopod are complex and interlocking systems, with optical and chemo-tactile stimuli both contributing to the response in the intact animal.

Reproduction and Embryology

Cephalopods are dioecious. Some sexual dimorphism exists. Among the decapods, the fourth pair of arms (numbered from the dorsal aspect) in the male is elongated and carries suckers reduced in extent and size (Fig. 12-24). The function of these modified arms is the placement of sperm sacs (spermatophores) within the body of the female. The special arm is called a hectocotylus. In some species in which this arm normally becomes detached within the body of the female, it has been described as a trematode or as a reduced parasitic male cephalopod. In the octopods, usually hectocotylization is not bilateral, the second or third arm being modified for this purpose. Another dimorphic feature in the Octopoda occurs in the genus *Argonauta.* Not only is the female much larger than the male, but she produces a paper-thin, delicately spiraled shell which is not chambered and whose chief function is as an eggcase. In *Nautilus,* a modification of four tentacles is persistent and forms the spadix, an organ comparable to the hecto-cotylus. Sexual dimorphism is also marked in this group by the presence of some 60 tentacles in the male and 90 in the female.

The gonad in Decapoda lies in the aboral (functionally posterior) end of the coelom, this portion of which might logically be termed a gonocoele. The single gonoduct arises from the capsule surrounding the gonad and terminates in the pallial cavity with various accessory organs developed en route. Some cephalopods have retained bilateral gonoducts. In the male, the sperm duct enlarges to form the seminal vesicle, which bundles the sperm into transparent-walled sacs having a complex ejaculatory apparatus. These sacs, called spermatophores (Fig. 12-30), are ultimately transferred to a thick-walled spermatophoral sac (Needham's sac) for storage. The gonoduct continues orally to open into the pallial cavity just left of the middle.

In the female, the enlarged oviduct arises from the coelomic capsule around the ovary, and runs orally to open to the left of the median line. Shortly behind the aperture, there is an enlargement called the oviducal gland which forms the egg capsule. A pair of long, ovoid nidamental glands, decreasing in size orally, lie on either side of the ink-sac. These glands, which extend over much of the anterior viscera, empty into the mantle cavity near the oviducal aperture. They secrete the enveloping matrix for the egg masses. In *Nautilus,* a similar function is performed by the mantle wall for the singly laid eggs. Fertilization occurs in the mantle cavity, after which the egg masses are de-posited and adhere to solid objects.

The embryology of the dibranchiate cephalopods differs from that of other Mollusca because of the large amount of yolk in the eggs. As is characteristic of such eggs, cleavage is discoidal and meroblastic, occurring as incomplete grooves in the embryonic protoplasm or germinal disc (Fig. 12-31). Proliferation of these cells leads to a layer of cells forming a rounded disc. Later, a second cell layer appears between the first layer and the yolk. Thickening of the original cell mass produces the slightly elevated primordium of the mantle, while a concavity in this early mantle represents the shell gland primordium. On either side of the mantle and below it, a pit appears which represents the eye rudiment. Still nearer the embryo-yolk margin, a ring of buds develops. Ultimately these will form the arms or tentacles (Fig. 12-32). By respective arm growth and decrease of the yolk sac as yolk is utilized, the morphologically ventral (topographically anterior) aspect of the adult squid becomes apparent. If an elongated, cone-shaped embryo is visualized, the ventral end is composed of tentacles encompassing the yolk sac. Immediately dorsal, the cone would be modified by the developing primordia of eyes, funnel, and gills, and at the dorsal extremity the mantle would be grow-

Fig. 12-30 Spermatophore of *Loligo.* After Pierce 1950, *Selected Invertebrate Types* (F. A. Brown, Jr., ed.),courtesy of John Wiley & Sons, Inc.

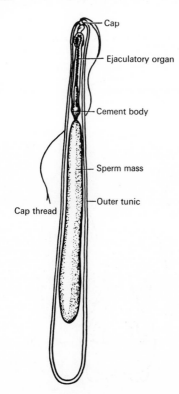

Fig. 12-31 Two stages in the development of the germinal area of *Sepia.* Adapted from Hertwig (from Balfour, after Kölliker), *A Manual of Zoology* (translated and edited by J. S. Kingsley) 1902, Holt, Rinehart & Winston, Inc.

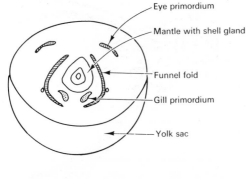

(a)

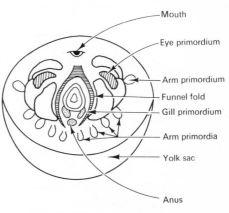

(b)

ing as a skullcap which eventually will envelop the gills and the dorsal end of the funnel (Fig. 12-33).

Finally, it should be noted that this class alone among Mollusca fails to produce a larva even remotely like a trochophore. The relationship of Cephalopoda to the other Mollusca is retained through similar body organization, including shell, mantle, ganglia of the nervous system, and the odontophore and radula of the digestive system.

Class VI Cephalopoda These are typically pelagic Mollusca with bilateral symmetry. The foot has modified in two directions—on the one hand forming a crown of tentacles around the mouth, and on the other giving rise to a

Fig. 12-32 Development of *Loligo*. From Hertwig, *A Manual of Zoology* (translated and edited by J. S. Kingsley) 1902, Holt, Rinehart & Winston, Inc.

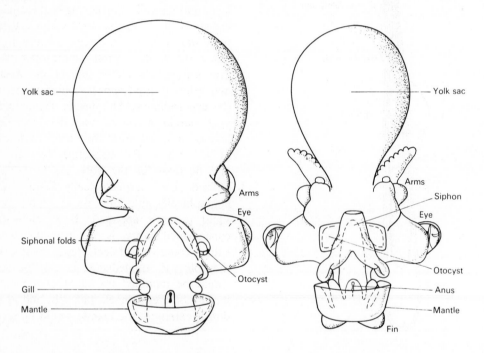

Fig. 12-33 An older embryo of *Loligo*, seen from the right side. From Brooks 1880, *Anniv. Mem. Boston Soc. Nat. His.*, Vol. 2.

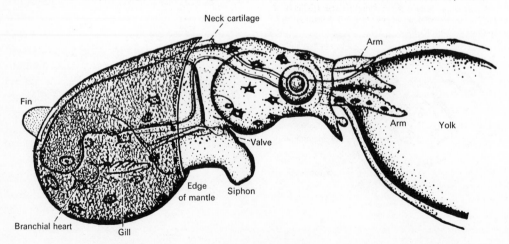

funnel used for expulsion of water from the pallial cavity. The shell is either chambered, or internal and reduced, or absent. The head is well developed and bears complex eyes. The mouth, opening in the center of the ring of tentacles, is armed with beaklike jaws. A radula is present in the buccal mass. One or two pairs of ctenidia are present in the mantle cavity. Development is direct from large-yolked eggs characterized by discoidal cleavage.

SUBCLASS 1 NAUTILOIDEA This group produces straight or coiled chambered shells with simple sutures at the junction of the internal septa with the outer shell. The septa, themselves, are concave, with their concavities on the side nearer the living chamber. The siphuncle is central. The group has been subdivided into 14 orders containing 75 families and at least 300 genera, but the genus *Nautilus* is the only survivor. It lacks an ink-sac but has four ctenidia and four kidneys, and it may be that these features are in general characteristic of this subclass. *Nautilus.*

SUBCLASS 2 AMMONOIDEA This group produced coiled, chambered shells with the septa wrinkled and the sutures exceedingly tortuous. The concavities of the septa are on the opposite side from those in *Nautilus*. The siphuncle tends to be marginal. A tetrabranchiate structure and absence of an ink-sac may have been typical. This group apparently arose from coiled Nautiloids. It has been subdivided into two orders containing 163 families; all are extinct. *Hamites, Baculites, Bactrites.*

SUBCLASS 3 COLEOIDEA In this group, the shell is internal and reduced or missing entirely. Two gills and two kidneys are characteristic. The presence of an ink-sac attached to the lower intestine is common. The group probably arose from straight nautiloid ancestors. Thiele subdivides the Coleoidea into three orders, but following paleontology, the name Sepiida is substituted for Decapoda.

Order 1 Sepiida This group is characterized by ten arms, of which two (in living species at least) tend to be retractile. Pedunculated suckers occur on the arms, although in the retractile pair the suckers are generally restricted to the extremities. The shell is internal and may be reduced to a vestige. The heart lies in the coelomic cavity. A pair of lateral fins is a common feature in the group, which is divided into three suborders. One of these, the Belemnoidea, deserves special mention. It is an extinct group whose ancestors were straight nautiloids and who in turn are ancestral to all living Cephalopoda, except *Nautilus. Belemnoteuthis, Spirula, Sepia, Loligo, Onchoteuthis.*

Order 2 Vampyromorpha This small group is known as vampire squids. They are deepwater inhabitants and are less than a foot long. In addition to eight equal arms, they possess a pair of retractile tentacles, which Morton suggests are not homologous with the retractile tentacles of the Decapods. The arms are connected by a web used in swimming. An uncalcified gladius is present. A radula is absent. *Vampyroteuthis.*

Order 3 Octopoda This group has eight arms, each of which bears sessile suckers. True fins are missing. Except in the fossil genus, *Palaeoctopus,* where a vestige remains, no internal shell is retained. However, the female *Argonauta* produces an external shell which serves as an egg case, and is secreted by specialized arms and not by the mantle. *Argonauta, Octopus, Eledone, Palaeoctopus.*

PHYLOGENETIC CONSIDERATIONS

The magnitude, diversity, and age of the Phylum Mollusca contribute to the difficulty of interpreting its evolution. All of its major subdivisions are themselves ancient, and since fossils, although generally numerous, are typically limited to hard structures, interpretation of origins must be limited to hypotheses. Within the major classes evidence of evolution has a firmer basis, with contemporary but still relatively primitive genera available for study. Examination of features held in common by each of the classes will suggest a possible archetypical mollusc, albeit based on study of already specialized forms.

One of the features indicative of less specialized Mollusca is the presence of a broad creeping surface. Yonge (1947) has suggested that the "Loricata (Amphineura)

. . . must have diverged from the common stock before the Gastropods, have never lost their dependence on life on a hard stratum, and have, indeed, become more highly specialized for it." The Archeogastropoda is a subgroup of Prosobranchia which has retained bilaterality of gills, auricles, and kidneys and which includes the limpets with a secondarily flattened shell. The Archeogastropoda show similarity to Amphineura in the retention of a broad creeping surface, but there is also a parallel in methods of food handling. Both groups are intertidal microphagous herbivores feeding primarily during the immersed phase. The radula is long and in need of rather constant replacement. Similar esophageal glands produce amylolytic enzymes. Owing to the rasping process of the radula, variously sized particles are ingested, usually enveloped in a mucous string. In both groups there is development of a sorting mechanism to separate fine and coarse particles. A similar structure occurs in bivalves. The digestive glands of primitive gastropods and Amphineura produce enzymes to split celluloses.

The Polyplacophora are the least modified Amphineura, and the search for an archetype might well begin with them. They possess bilateral symmetry with mouth and anus at opposite ends. There is a dorsal shell of eight overlapping plates. This interlocking condition is probably a specialization: a flat cone-shaped shell or the presence of calcareous spicules embedded in the mantle is probably more primitive. The mantle forms a fleshy rim or girdle around the shell and serves for close apposition to the substrate. Such a mantle is probably also a specialization, adapted to the mode of existence.

For the primitive archetype, in a bilaterally symmetrical animal, paired ctenidia would be expected. A radula, present in most molluscan classes, would be evident. The nervous system would likely be at least as primitive as that in the Amphineura, and special sense organs such as eyes or tentacles might well be undeveloped. Morton's concept includes not only such sense organs as tentacles, but also an osphradium and hypobranchial gland in the pallial complex (Fig. 12-5).

Finally, the archetype would include the presence of a coelom and a hemocoele, while a projection of its life cycle suggests a trochophore larva and spiral cleavage.

Acceptance of a suitable archetype still does not explain its ancestral path. The Mollusca hold a number of features in common with the Turbellaria. Particularly, external cilia, intracellular digestion, elementary nervous system, spiral cleavage, and possibly hermaphroditism suggest relationships. On the other hand, the similarity of spiral cleavage, trochophore larvae, and the metamerism in the newly found *Neopilina* support the earlier annelid theory. The concepts of neoteny and paedomorphosis in the annelid ancestor had been advanced to bridge this gap earlier. Of course, both annelids and molluscs could have arisen independently from turbellarians.

The archetype bears considerable resemblance to the Polyplacophora. Whether the Aplacophora are primitively simpler or secondarily degenerate is difficult to assess. Certainly some of them lack separate genital ducts, which is an archaic feature. The two groups descended from a common ancestor, possibly Monoplacophora.

The gastropods constitute the largest class of Mollusca. While spiral coiling is a common feature, the independent process of torsion occurred in all gastropods. Knight has supplied evidence that the upper Cambrian fossil genus, *Bellerophon,* had undergone torsion, even though the single pair of retractor muscle scars are symmetrical. He suggests that the asymmetry was due to a lag in the development of one muscle of the pair. Knight believes that torsion and asymmetry can be independent processes and that the marginal slit or sinus in the symmetrical shell of *Bellerophon* was an adaptation after torsion had caused a need for change in the sanitary disposal of waste products. Geologic history supplies no evidence of torsion before

Bellerophon (Fig. 12-34).

Torsion and coiling have both contributed to asymmetry among Gastropoda. The archeogastropod prosobranchs are the least specialized, and with the exception of the Neritacea, are all marine. The left (post-torsional) gonad disappears, and for most there is a similar fate for the left kidney, but in the Neritacea the right kidney rather than the left is lost. The development of a terrestrial mollusc from a marine ancestor involves solution of the problems of water balance, respiration, internal fertilization, and resistant egg capsules. The Neritacea appear to have solved part of the problem. They have moved into fresh water, they have internal fertilization, and structurally they show resemblance to higher prosobranchs.

Without question, the prosobranchs are ancestral to the Opisthobranchia by way of so-called monotocardiate prosobranchs, i.e., those with a single auricle and pectinibranch gill. In turn, the Pulmonata arose either from a closely related prosobranch group or from an early offshoot of the Opisthobranchs themselves.

The Scaphopoda can be traced back to the Ordovician. The gonad utilizes the right kidney for discharge, which is reminiscent of some Archeogastropoda. Paired kidneys, a mantle originating as two lobes, and the structure of the nervous system suggest relationship to the Lamellibranchia.

The lowest group of Bivalvia is the order

Fig. 12-34 Diagrams showing probable arrangement of the pallial organs in the pre-torsional ancestors of the Gastropoda. After Yonge 1947, courtesy of the author and the Royal Society of London.

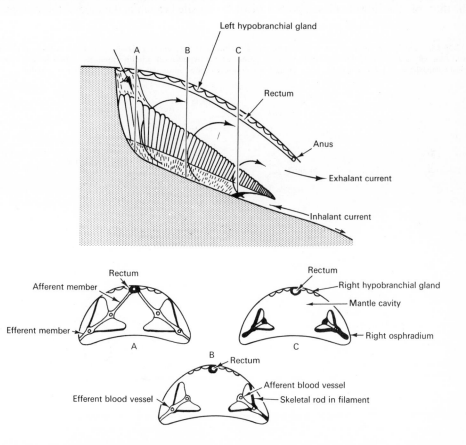

Protobranchia (Fig. 12-35). Yonge (1939) concludes that it "represents the one unquestionably natural group within the class." Only a few genera occur in this order. The Nuculidae (Fig. 12-18) were already established in the Silurian period. The gills are bipectinate and resemble those of early gastropods. The nearly horizontal gills divide the mantle cavity to separate the exhalant from the inhalant chamber. Lateral cilia on the filaments carry water to the exhalant chamber. Cilia edging the filaments serve to catch and conduct particles in the water to the midline where they are discarded into the inhalant chamber. Yonge (1947) has traced the evolution of the food-collecting cilia of filibranch and eulamellibranch bivalves from the cilia (called frontals) on the ventral edge of the protobranch filaments. *Nucula* possesses an osphradium that is homologous with that of the lower Gastropoda. Most

Bivalvia are ciliary feeders. None possesses a radula, and the mouth has lost contact with the substratum. The intermediate mechanism for food collection is illustrated by the lip prolongation (palp proboscides) in *Yoldia,* another Protobranchia. Naturally, these brief examples are insufficient to establish evolutionary sequence. Correlative evidence has been produced for structure and function of other body parts.

The classification used for the Bivalvia follows the Douvillé ecological scheme which attempts to avoid the limitations of classification restricted to soft parts such as the gill structure on the one hand, and hinge characteristics useful to the paleontologist on the other. Since shell and gill are both modified by habitat, such a classification tends to harmonize the older systems. The Douvillé scheme proposes three major lineages. The sessile branch is the oldest. Its representatives

Fig. 12-35 Diagrams illustrating stages in the evolution of the Lamellibranchia, showing significant changes in body orientation, form of shell, foot, gills and heart, alimentary canal and labial palps. (a) is a hypothetical primitive molluscan; (b) a protobranch stage; (c) a typical eulamellibranch lacking siphons. After Yonge 1939, courtesy of the author and of the Royal Society of London.

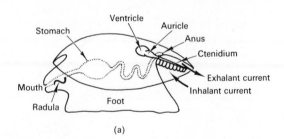

(a)

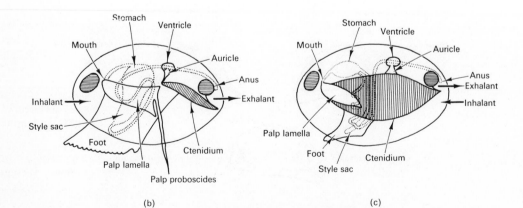

(b)   (c)

are generally characterized by lack of siphons, and by the development of a byssus in the adult for attachment. The normal branch occurs as actively mobile on the sea bottom. The deep-burrowing branch are those living in a more or less permanent burrow. They have long siphons and poorly developed hinges. Probably all three groups arose from separate protobranch stocks, and convergence introduces some hazards in delimiting the groups. The Septibranchinacea is a suborder in which a muscular septum has replaced the gills. They appear to belong in the deep-burrowing branch, although derived from more immediate ancestors which have lost the deep-burrowing habit.

The Cephalopoda constitute a very ancient group of which more are extinct than contemporary. Marcus (1958) suggests that such features as the posterior position of the mantle, the communication between gonadal and pericardial sections of the coelom, separate excretory and genital ducts, and bilateral symmetry indicate the establishment of the cephalopods before the gastropods, scaphopods, and lamellibranchs. Within the class, the path of evolution is clearer. The Nautiloidea are oldest and gave rise to the others. They were dominant in the early Paleozoic, and only the "living fossil" *Nautilus* is not extinct. It has a chambered, external shell. At first this shell was slightly curved or straight. Later coiled shells gained the ascendency.

The subclass Ammonoidea are all extinct, but were more numerous than the Nautiloidea. They first appeared in the late Silurian period and arose from coiled nautiloids. The extinct suborder Belemnoidea, of the Order Coleoidea, arose in the Triassic. They were derived from straight-shelled Nautiloids, but the shell was internal and was composed of three parts: rostrum, phragmocone, and pro-ostracum. Among living decapods, *Spirula* retains a coiled phragmocone; the "shell" of *Sepia* (cuttlefish) represents the upper side of the phragmocone plus a small rostrum; and the "pen" of *Loligo* (squid) is the pro-ostracum (Fig. 12-27). Finally, among the living Coleoids, there appear to be two branches of specialization. One of these is the highly active, pelagic group of which the squids *Loligo* and *Onycoteuthis* are representative. The other group is less adept at swimming, is semisedentary, and is better adapted for crawling. *Octopus* is such a cephalopod.

REFERENCES

Barnes, H. F., and J. W. Weil, Slugs in gardens: their numbers, activities, and distribution, Part 1. J. Animal Ecol., 13:140, 1944.

Bidder, A. M., The digestive mechanisms of European squids. Quart. J. Microsc. Sci., 91:1, 1950.

Cox, L. R., and Rees, W. J., A bivalve gastropod. Nature, 185:749, 1960.

Douvillé, H., Classification des Lamellibranches. Bull. Soc. géol. France, 4th Ser., 12:419, 1912.

Drew, G. A., The anatomy, habits, and embryology of *Yoldia limatula*. Mem. Johns Hopkins Univ. Biol. Lab., No. 4 (1900), 39 pp.

Duncan, C. J., The evolution of the pulmonate genital system. Proc. Zool. Soc. London, 134:601, 1960.

Crofts, Doris R., Muscle morphogenesis in primitive gastropods and its relation to torsion. Proc. Zool. Soc. London, 125:711, 1956.

Fretter, V., The genital ducts of *Theodoxus, Lamellaria,* and *Trivia,* and a discussion of their evolution in Prosobranchs. J. Marine Biol. Assoc., 26:312, 1946.

Garstang, W., The origin and evolution of larval forms. Presidential Address, Section D, Zoology Report of Brit. Assoc. Adv. Sci., 1928.

Knight, J. B., Primitive fossil gastropods and their bearing on gastropod classification. Smithson. Misc. Coll., 117(13):1, 1952.

Lemche, H., A new living deep-sea mollusc of the Cambro-Devonian class Monoplacophora. Nature, 179:413, 1957

———, and K. G. Wingstrand, The anatomy of *Neopilina galatheae*. Galathea Exped. Rep., 3:7, 1959.

MacGinitie, G. E., and N. MacGinitie, Natural history of marine animals. New York: McGraw, 1949.

Marcus, E., On the evolution of the animal phyla. Quart. Rev. Biol., 33:24, 1958.

Morton, J. E., Molluscs. London: Hutchinson, 1958.

Pelseneer, P., Mollusca. *In* (E. R. Lankester, ed.) A treatise on zoology. Part V. London: A. & C. Black, 1906.

Portmann, A., and others, Embranchement des Mollusques (pp. 1521-2164). *In* (P. Grassé, ed.) Traité de Zoologie, Tome V, Fasc. II, 1960.

Ramsay, J. A., A physiological approach to the lower animals. Cambridge: Cambridge U. P., 1952.

Raven, C. P., Morphogenesis: the analysis of molluscan development. New York: Pergamon, 1958.

Richards, A., Outline of comparative embryology. New York: Wiley, 1931.

Schindewolf, O., Concerning the evolution of the Cephalopoda. Biol. Rev., 9:458, 1934.

Shrock, R. R., and Twenhofel, W. H. Principles of invertebrate paleontology (2nd ed.). New York: McGraw, 1953.

Smith, F. G. W., The development of *Patella vulgata*. Philos. Trans. Roy. Soc. London, (B) 225:95, 1935.

Yonge, C. M., The protobranchiate Mollusca: a functional interpretation of their structure and evolution. Philos. Trans. Roy. Soc. London, (B) 230:79, 1939.

———, The pallial organs in the aspidobranch Gastropoda and their evolution throughout the Mollusca. Philos. Trans. Roy. Soc. London, (B) 232:443, 1947.

———, The sea shore. London: Collins, 1949.

Young, J. Z., The evolution of the nervous system and the relationship of organisms and environment (pp. 179-204). *In* Evolution, essays presented to Goodrich. London: Oxford U. P., 1938.

———, Learning and discrimination in the octopus. Biol. Rev., 36:32, 1961.

13

ARTHROPODA
AND
PARARTHROPODA

Over 82 per cent of living animal species are arthropods. Many of these species are represented by untold numbers of individuals. Philosophically and economically (since arthropods are man's most important competitors) we are interested in determining the reasons for this success. Examination of morphological features provides the first clues.

ARTHROPOD FEATURES

In common with the annelids, arthropods possess a segmented body. Varied degrees of specialization in successive somites of arthropods commonly resulted in an unlike (heteronomous) segmentation, in contrast with the homonomous metamerism characteristic of the earthworm and its allies. Arthropods vary from the nearly homonomous metamerism seen in some primitive species and frequently in immature stages to the nearly complete absence of body segments in adult Acarina (mites and ticks). In both annelids and arthropods, the first evidences of segmentation appear in the mesoderm during ontogeny. In addition to the parallels exhibited in the development of metamerism in the two phyla, their close relationship is evident in the similarity of nervous systems, with a dorsal brain connected around the foregut to a metamerically disposed chain of ventral ganglia.

While it is accepted that the arthropods were derived from primitive annelids or that both groups came from a common ancestor, it is the distinctive features that set the arthropods apart, and which account for their remarkable success.

The most obvious of these, and the one from which the phylum name was derived, is the presence of paired, jointed appendages.

The jointed limb of arthropods is unique among invertebrates, but within the Arthropoda it shows great variation in number of segments, in size of corresponding segments,

227

and in junction with the body. Some species even have a different number of segments on one pair of legs than are typical of other pairs. In addition, while most of the paired appendages primitively were locomotor, they have been adapted to a multitude of functions with pronounced structural modification. Search for a prototype ancestral to the arthropod limb requires decision as to whether the primitive appendage was biramous or uniramous.

Many aquatic arthropods have a biramous limb which is represented by a basal axis composed usually of two segments. The distal segment bears two branches, one of which (called endopodite) is mediad and the other (called exopodite) laterad. Biramous limbs are characteristic of Crustacea and also of extinct Trilobita.

A uniramous limb is characteristic of such tracheate groups as Arachnida, Insecta, and Myriapoda. Neither the oldest fossils nor the embryologies of these arthropods indicate the presence of an early biramous appendage which conceivably could have become uniramous by reduction. If the Arthropoda are indeed monophyletic, the limb divergence must have occurred in an ancestor predating the oldest fossils, or consideration must be given to the hypothesis that limb variation shows no phylogenetic significance for the major groups, but only within these groups.

Jointed appendages, to be effective, must operate from a relatively rigid base. This takes the form of a chitinous exoskeleton in arthropods and probably preceded evolution of the jointed appendage. The arthropod exoskeleton is a cuticle composed of two primary layers secreted by the underlying layer of epidermal cells. The thin outer layer, called epicuticle, is refractile and waxy and provides a generally impervious surface. The thin cuticle covering many respiratory surfaces in this group is less waxy to allow permeability to water and to gases.

The inner layer, called procuticle, is a relatively thick stratum distinctively characterized by the presence of a cellulose-related polysaccharide called chitin, which provides elasticity and flexibility to the skeleton. Chitin is absent from annelid cuticle, but is a component of their setae. The arthropod procuticle is penetrated by minute pore-canals containing cytoplasmic filaments extending peripherally from the epidermal cells. In limited areas increased rigidity in the outer portion of the procuticle is the result of infiltration of calcium salts and a hardening of protein components to a horny consistency, accompanied by a reduction in chitin content. The hardened layer of the procuticle is called exocuticle; the more flexible inner lamina is the endocuticle. Since the epicuticle is not extensible, mobility in the arthropod is retained at the body and appendage joints by the formation of folds, and by the absence of a hardened exocuticle.

Cuticle not only covers the external surface of the arthropod but lines such surface invaginations as the foregut and hindgut, tracheal systems where present, and the external portions of some reproductive ducts. In addition, where the secreting epidermal cells are infolded, various knobs and ridges develop on the inner surface of the skeleton. These serve as a base for muscle attachment and are called *apodemes* (Fig. 13-1).

In Arthropoda, specialization has resulted in sectional organization of the segments into groups called *tagmata* (singular, *tagma*). The foremost tagma is the head. It is composed of a maximum of six segments, some of which are commonly not apparent in a study of the adult structure. In the mandibulate arthropods (those possessing a pair of jaw appendages known as mandibles), the head by definition never carries appendages whose primary function is locomotor. Among Trilobita and Arachnomorpha locomotor appendages do form an integral part of the anterior tagma, which in these groups is designated as a prosoma.

Among annelids, the combination of prostomium and peristomium is considered to represent the head. In the Onychophora, the head is marked off from the trunk and

Fig. 13-1 Composite diagram of arthropod cuticle. Adapted from various sources.

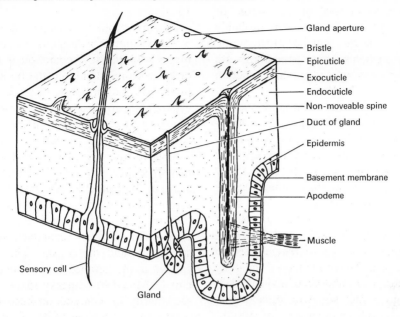

- Gland aperture
- Bristle
- Epicuticle
- Exocuticle
- Endocuticle
- Non-moveable spine
- Duct of gland
- Epidermis
- Basement membrane
- Apodeme
- Muscle
- Gland
- Sensory cell

Fig. 13-2 Theoretical evolutionary stages of arthropods. (a) A primitive lobopod, common ancestral form of the Onychophora and Arthropoda; (b) a derived form with longer and slenderer legs; (c) a primitive arthropod with sclerotized integument, jointed legs, and gill lobes on the coxae; (d) a fairly generalized modern crustacean, *Anaspides tasmaniae*. 1 *ant*, first antenna; 2 *ant*, second antenna; *Mxpd*, maxilliped; *Plpds*, pleopods; *Prpds*, pereiopods; *Tel*, telson; *Urpd*, uropod II-XVIII, body segments. After Snodgrass 1956, courtesy of the Smithsonian Institution.

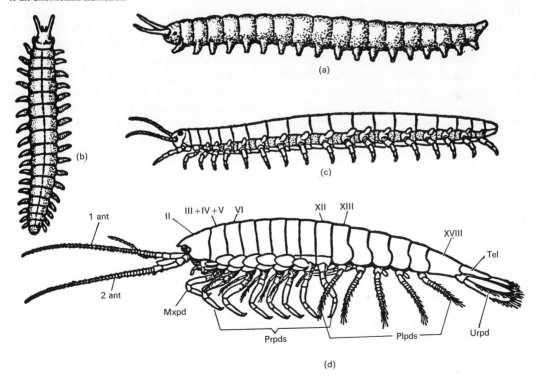

(a)

(b)

(c)

1 ant   II   III + IV + V   VI   XII   XIII   XVIII   Tel

2 ant   Mxpd   Prpds   Plpds   Urpd

(d)

is composed of three segments. The arthropod head is composed of an *acron* or embryonic cephalic lobe which probably corresponds with the annelid prostomium, followed by segments whose appendages are modified for sensory or gnathic function (Fig. 13-2).

Behind the head, the arthropod body is composed of the trunk, which is often differentiated into an anterior thorax and a posterior abdomen. In cases where some or all of the thoracic segments are closely associated with the head, the combined tagma is called a cephalothorax. This modified body division is characteristic of the crayfish or lobster. Among the Trilobita and Arachnomorpha, cephalothorax is sometimes used in place of prosoma. The remainder of the body is the opisthosoma or abdomen, divided when apparent into a mesosoma or preabdomen and a more posterior metasoma or postabdomen. In the Myriapoda (centipedes and millipedes) the body is divided into head and trunk, and in Insecta three well-defined body regions, namely, head, thorax, and abdomen, are characteristic and diagnostic.

With the development of the relatively rigid exoskeleton in arthropods, the hydrostatic, fundamentally segmental skeleton characteristic of annelids has been replaced as a locomotor method by the presence of

Fig. 13-3 Diagrammatic cross-section of an arthropod segment showing the relation of the legs and the basal leg muscles to the areas of the body wall. *a,b,* axis of movement of leg base; *Cxpd,* coxopodite; *DMcl,* dorsal longitudinal muscles; *DV,* dorsal blood vessel; *I,J,* dorsal promotor and remotor muscles of leg; *K,L,* ventral promotor and remotor muscles of leg; *O,* levator muscle of telopodite; *P,* podial, or pleural, area of body wall; *Q,* depressor of telopodite; *Stn,* sternum, *Tlpd,* telopodite; *VMcl,* ventral longitudinal muscles; *VNC,* ventral nerve cord. After Snodgrass 1935, courtesy of the McGraw-Hill Book Company.

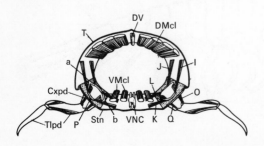

joints activated by internal muscles (Fig. 13-3).

Another profound change is the reduction of the coelom in arthropods. In annelids, the turgor essential to locomotion is a function of the coelomic fluid and the body musculature. With the formation of a relatively nonexpandable exoskeleton this coelomic function has been largely replaced, and the coelom has been reduced to components associated with reproductive and some excretory structures. The closed circulatory system seen in the annelids has become an open system with the blood propelled by a contractile dorsal vessel and frequently with distribution through secondary vessels into sinuses around the organs. This system of sinuses is the hemocoele. It is derived principally from two sources: spaces appearing secondarily in a mesoderm-filled embryonic blastocoele, and remnants of the coelom which have lost their peritoneal character. Unlike the coelom, the hemocoele has no external communication. It has hydrostatic functions such as wing expansion in insect metamorphosis.

Cephalization is a remarkable feature in Arthropoda. Varying numbers of primitively locomotor trunk appendages have diversified for sensory and feeding function and have been incorporated into the head. Correlated with the external manifestations of cephalization is increased centralization of the nervous system. In more primitive arthropods and some larval stages the dorsal brain connected around the foregut to a segmentally disposed chain of paired ventral ganglia mirrors the annelid pattern. In such major groups as the Crustacea and Arachnomorpha fusion of thoracic and abdominal ganglia into a single large unit has occurred, not only among forms in which the abdomen is reduced (as would be expected) but also among genera with a prominent abdomen. Among higher insects (such as some beetles and flies) a similar fusion of the thoracic and abdominal ganglia has occurred. Functional development of instinctive behavior reaches a high level, particularly among social insects.

Arthropods are typically oviparous and the eggs have determinate cleavage with little or no regulatory power. Frequently the eggs undergo development within protective brood-chambers as in some crustacea or attached to body appendages as in the common crayfish and in the strange-appearing marine Pycnogonida. In the latter case, it is the male to whom the egg masses are attached. Female spiders protect their eggs by enclosing them in an egg sac constructed of silk from special glands, and in some species the female keeps active watch over the egg sac and over the young spiders which emerge from it. Some insects are ovoviviparous, with the eggs hatching internally so that living young are produced. In a few forms a placentalike structure associated with the reproductive system is developed. Such arthropods are actually viviparous.

Since normal development of most arthropod eggs is dependent upon the food stored within the egg shell, a large amount of yolk is typical. The distribution of yolk in such eggs is usually centrolecithal. The term is somewhat misleading, since the early nuclear divisions of the developing egg may occur deep in the yolk and only later do these nuclei migrate and join with surface cytoplasm at the yolk periphery. Only secondarily is the yolk truly centrolecithal. Internally the surface layer of cells at first may not be walled off from the underlying yolk, which in some cases is segregated into cones or pyramids. The segmentation pattern associated with centrolecithal eggs is termed superficial cleavage. A few arthropods have small-yolked eggs exhibiting holoblastic or total cleavage. Somewhat intermediate between these extremes are some eggs which at first undergo total cleavage. Later, when the yolk is aggregated centrally, these eggs change to superficial cleavage.

The development of scorpion eggs forms a notable exception. Here the peripheral segmentation is reduced to a discoidal area. The early cleavage restricted to this area is similar to that occurring in birds and other large-yolked vertebrates. Among scorpions this discoidal cleavage arose as a specialization of superficial cleavage. A type of cleavage in crustaceans which resembles the spiral pattern of annelids and molluscs has been reported for *Lepas* (goose barnacle) and for *Polyphemus* (a water flea). If annelids are ancestral to arthropods, a spiral cleavage pattern might well be expected to persist in the latter phylum. The little evidence for spiral cleavage in arthropods is indeed tenuous.

Similarities in embryology exist between some Arthropoda, Annelida, and Onychophora. The blastopore tends to elongate and to close medially in all of these groups, and mesoderm forms from proliferation of posterior teloblastic cells. The developing mesoderm becomes sectioned into somites, each of which may produce a transitory coelomic cavity.

At hatching or viviparously, arthropod young are larvae which commonly must undergo considerable *metamorphosis* before reaching the adult condition. Since the external skeleton is limiting, it must be shed, a process called molting or *ecdysis*. Included in material cast off at molting is the chitinous lining of the ectodermally derived foregut and hindgut, respectively the stomodaeum and proctodaeum. So-called discontinuous growth occurs rapidly in the interval between shedding the old exoskeleton and the hardening of the new one. Successive larval stages may differ only slightly from preceding ones, or may involve complete internal reorganization for a different habitat and changed food requirement. Within the arthropod subdivisions, metamorphosis provides a number of clues to phylogenetic relationship. In more primitive metamorphosis the number of segments in the hatched larva is less than the number characteristic of the mature adult, and the additional segments are added in successive molts. This pattern is called *anamorphic*. In *epimorphic* development the larva emerging from the egg possesses the definitive number of segments. The additional segments occurring in anamorphic development arise from a proliferation zone immediately anterior to the posterior terminal section. Such a growth zone is also characteristic of annelids and Onychophora.

MAJOR SUBDIVISIONS OF ARTHROPODA

The arthropods are bilaterally symmetrical animals typically with a jointed exoskeleton containing chitin. A pair of jointed appendages occurs on some or all segments. Internally a pair of preoral ganglia are connected to a ventral chain of ganglia joined in segmental series by a pair of longitudinal nerves. With the coelom reduced, the principal body cavity is a hemocoele. The phylum is characterized further by striated muscle and the general absence of cilia, although cilia or cilialike structures are reported from gametes and sensory organs of insects.

Subphylum Trilobita

These are extinct, marine arthropods whose fossils exhibit dorsally a median and two lateral lobes and one pair of uniramous antennae. Ventrally the successive segments bear legs which have been interpreted as biramous. The many species are placed in one class with four or five orders.

Subphylum Arachnomorpha

The members of this group lack antennae, and typically possess a pincer or chela terminally on the first appendage. Included in the group are the horseshoe crabs (*Limulus*), scorpions, spiders, ticks, mites, and a number of less familiar representatives.

Subphylum Crustacea

The group is characterized by the presence of two pairs of antennae. Beginning with the second pair of antennae, the appendages are biramous. Presence of gills is correlated with the typical aquatic habitat. A larva, called *nauplius,* is common. Crustacea include such

forms as copepods, barnacles, crayfish, lobsters, shrimps, and sow bugs.

Subphylum Labiata

These arthropods have only one pair of antennae, equivalent to the first antennae of the Crustacea. A pair of fused appendages form the *labium,* from which the subphylum name is derived. These appendages are equivalent to the second maxillae in Crustacea. Centipedes, millipedes, and insects are the larger groups included in the Labiata.

PARARTHROPODA

The Pararthropoda is utilized as a convenient group in which to place those animals which show arthropod affinities and yet are sufficiently divergent to warrant separation. The Onychophora, Tardigrada, and Pentastomida will be considered here.

Onychophora

The origin of Arthropoda repeatedly has been related to a group of animals which appear to be intermediate between annelids and arthropods. This group, the Onychophora, contains over sixty extant species, all of which live in tropical or south temperate zones, where they are restricted to habitats of high humidity. *Peripatus,* the best-known genus, is a wormlike animal with a somewhat blunt anterior end and a more tapered posterior (Fig. 13-4). The cephalic end bears a pair of *preantennae,* which are to be distinguished from the antennae of arthropods, since they originate from an embryonic segment that persists in Onychophora, but is lost in arthropod development. Externally, segmentation is evidenced only by the metameric series of short conical legs and by the cephalic lobe, which is not distinctly marked off from the body, but which apparently is composed of three segments bearing, respectively, the preantennae, the jaws composed of two pairs of thin chitinous plates, and opening of the slime glands on the paired oral papillae. A pair of eyes, structurally similar to those of annelids, occurs at the base of the antennae.

The integument is a thin, nonmoist cuticle which is so pliant that the animal can squeeze through exceedingly narrow apertures. The cuticle is transversely marked by irregular annular striations and by numerous papillae, each capped with a chitinous spine.

The alimentary canal begins with a lobed-lip area opening to a buccal cavity containing the jaws and a median dorsal tongue. Immediately behind the buccal cavity is a muscular pharynx into which paired salivary glands empty through a median canal. The posterior limit of the ectodermal foregut joins the short narrow esophagus. The endodermal midgut is a straight tube and it leads

to a short hindgut, which like the foregut is lined with cuticle continuous with that of the outer body surface. Onychophora are carnivorous. Digestion occurs in the gut lumen, or externally on food too large to swallow. A number of digestive enzymes have been identified.

The nervous system in general is similar to the annelid-arthropod pattern, with a dorsal brain and a pair of ventrally situated nerve cords connected by numerous commissures. However, in Onychophora these nerve cords shift laterally and never fuse, being separated by a paired series of latero-ventral muscle strands.

Respiration is accomplished through two systems. One of these is composed of thin-walled invaginated coxal vesicles which open ventrally on the legs. The cavities of these vesicles can be increased by contraction of muscular strands, and decreased by pressure of body fluid. The second system is composed of numerous, typically unbranched *tracheal* tubes which serve all parts of the body and which open in groups into tracheal pits. The external openings of the tracheal pits are called stigmata. These are irregularly distributed over the body surface and bear no correlation with metamerism. Neither stigmata nor trachea possess control mechanisms to prevent water loss, and this is the chief factor limiting distribution of Onychophora to an environment of high humidity.

The excretory organs of Onychophora have been described as nephridia. This is incorrect. They might better be defined as coelomoducts in which the paired segmental structures open in each segment at the leg bases. There is no question that most of this excretory unit represents a mesodermal coelomic remnant, but the distal, ectodermal enlargement designated as a bladder suggests the protonephromixium occurring in some polychaetes (Fig. 13-5). Ciliated epithelium occurs near the inner end of the coelomoduct and also appears in the reproductive ducts of Onychophora, another structure of coelomic

Fig. 13-4 Diagrammatic lateral view of the internal structure of *Peripatus.* After Cuénot 1949, in *Traité de Zoologie,* Tome VI (P. Grassé, ed.), courtesy of Masson et Cie.

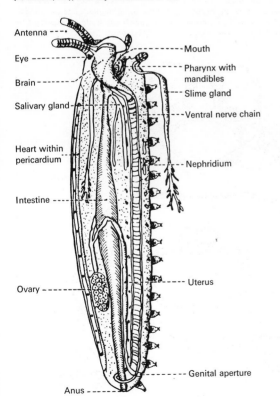

Antenna

Eye

Brain

Salivary gland

Heart within pericardium

Intestine

Ovary

Mouth

Pharynx with mandibles

Slime gland

Ventral nerve chain

Nephridium

Uterus

Genital aperture

Anus

origin. The excretory system does not provide an additional hurdle to success in a terrestrial environment, since the nitrogenous waste is a semisolid concentrate apparently thrown off through the intestine.

The onychophoran reproductive systems are of coelomic origin, and bear great similarity to those of Arthropoda. The sexes are separate and the paired gonads are tubular. In the male, the testes empty into a bulbous chamber, the seminal vesicle. These in turn open to irregularly coiled vasa deferentia which join to form a median, elongated ejaculatory duct. Here masses of sperm are encased in a covering to form a spermatophore, with some of the material forming the spermatophoric case derived from the vasa deferentia.

In the female, the paired ovaries lie dorsal to the alimentary canal and are often united at the rear end. From the other end, the oviducts lead forward, pass ventrad on either side of the intestine and turn caudally to unite beneath the rectum to form the vagina which opens to the exterior. In some forms, the posterior halves of the oviducts are modified as uteri. In the few oviparous species, the median tube is modified to form an ovipositor.

Most Onychophora are viviparous, but in some of these the egg carries enough yolk that the developing embryo is only partly dependent upon uterine secretions. In eggs without yolk, the eggs become attached to the uterine wall and nourishment is obtained directly from the parent through a *placenta*.

Cleavage patterns vary. Some species with much yolk have a superficial cleavage, while some with little or no yolk show total cleavage. Eventually a stereogastrula is formed,

Fig. 13-5 Diagrams of an Onychophoran, illustrating development of the coelom and origin of the lateral nerve cords. In (a) the coelom is a pair of lobed cavities; in (b) and (c) the dorsal lobes have become the gonadal cavities, the lateral lobe is lost and the ventral lobe elongates and joins an ectodermal invagination to form nephridia; (d) illustrates the hypothesis that the posterior gonoducts are modified nephridia. The ventral ectodermal lobes (called "ventral organs") give rise to the lateral nerve cords which ultimately are separated by lateroventral muscle. After Cuénot 1949, in *Traité de Zoologie*, Tome VI (P. Grassé, ed.), courtesy of Masson et Cie.

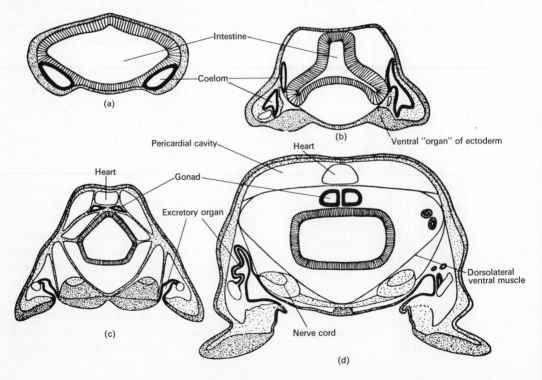

in some cases by overgrowth or epiboly of presumptive ectodermal cells to leave a small, ventrally located blastopore. With elongation of the embryo, and with it the blastopore, the latter is narrowed and assumes a dumbbell shape. Ultimate fusion of the lateral lips of the blastopore leaves the two ends to form mouth and anus, respectively. These ultimately connect with a lumen in the endoderm, formed by increased vacuolization of endodermal cells or by ingrowth of an endodermal cell layer to encompass the yolk. Meanwhile mesoderm has appeared by proliferation of cells near the posterior end of the blastopore. Two lateral masses of cells grow forward as mesodermal bands on either side of the elongating blastopore. These mesodermal bands subsequently will break up into a metameric series of coelomic units, and the cavities that appear in them are the primorida of reproductive ducts and the mesodermal portion of the excretory system.

The Onychophora are economically unimportant, but phylogenetically they evoke great interest. They possess a number of characteristics in common with the Arthropoda, a number of lesser significance showing similarity to annelids, and some unique features justifying their placement in a separate phylum. The thin body wall, unstriated muscle, cilia in reproductive and excretory ducts, the series of paired coelomoducts, and the eye structure show annelid similarity, although some or all of these features may be due to convergent or parallel evolution.

The arthropod features are more significant. These include a prominent hemocoele, a heart with ostia, tracheae, jaws apparently derived from locomotor appendages, a re-

duced coelom, the pattern of development of the reproductive system, and an increasingly chitinous integument reducing water loss and necessitating ecdysis.

The Onychophora differ from both annelids and arthropods in the total lack of external segmentation, except for the serially repeated legs. These show no history of evolving from the annelid parapodium, and they lack the jointed character of the true arthropod appendage. The paired nerve cords in the onychophoran are separated by dorsoventral muscle strands. The head is limited to three segments, which bears some similarity to the anterior portion of the myriapodan head.

The Onychophora is an ancient terrestrial group which may have arisen from a presumably marine, fossil form named *Aysheaia* (Fig. 13-6). The head is even more primitive than in *Peripatus,* having a terminal mouth followed by a pair of branched appendages. Other appendages are the six-clawed legs. Surviving Onychophora show terrestrial adaptations by internal fertilization, by the common condition of viviparity, by utilization of semisolid nitrogenous waste to reduce water loss, and by decreased permeability of the integument, but their open tracheal system with its attendant loss of water vapor is a factor limiting their terrestrial existence to an environment of high humidity. Features held in common with annelids are probably convergent. The closer relationship to the Arthropoda suggests a Precambrian ancestor which gave rise to Onychophora on one hand and to arthropods on the other.

Tardigrada

Another group of animals of somewhat uncertain phylogenetic position show resemblance to Onychophora and like them possess features also characteristic of Arthropoda. A common name for Tardigrada is "water bear." The Tardigrada have a broad distribution. A large number of species is included in some 15 genera and has been reported

Fig. 13-6 *Aysheaia*, a restoration of a supposed early onychophoran fossil. After Hutchinson 1930, courtesy of the United States National Museum.

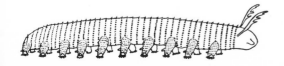

from the northern hemisphere, particularly from Europe. There are eight nonmarine genera described; five of these have been found in the United States.

Active Tardigrada are minute aquatic animals commonly found in droplets and films of water adhering to lower terrestrial plants and in water in the interstices between sand grains on beaches. Occasionally water bears may occur in bottom debris or on aquatic plants in relatively shallow water. The largest water bears are about 1.2 millimeters long, but most species are less than half this length.

The wide distribution is related to the minute size of these animals; to the ability to become anabiotic, a kind of suspended animation; and for aqueous species, to encystment. *Anabiosis* is most common among semiterrestrial species. When the habitat becomes desiccated, these animals lose water and assume a somewhat barrel shape called a *tun*. They can survive for a number of years in this condition, dependent upon reserve food supply. Upon restoration to the proper aquatic environment, the animal is restored to an active stage usually within a few hours.

The body of a water bear (Fig. 13-7) is divided indistinctly into a head and four trunk segments, the latter indicated by four pairs of stumpy, unjointed, four-clawed legs. The posterior pair of legs is terminal. The body is covered with a cuticle which is not chitinized, but which contains a substance related to chitin. Cilia are absent in the group. The head contains a dorsal brain with paired commissures leading to a subesophageal ganglion. Paired ventral nerves join a chain of four ganglia. Eyes are common in many species.

Most Tardigrada are herbivorous. Minute plant cells are pierced by a pair of mouth stylets, and juices are sucked into the digestive system by the action of the muscular bulb of the pharynx. A few species utilize body fluids from small metazoans.

Some Tardigrada possess three small glands which are excretory in function. These communicate with the gut lumen and are found near the posterior end of the midgut. Additional excretory waste is discarded at ecdysis.

All Tardigrada are oviparous and some produce two kinds of eggs, which differ in shell thickness. Fertilization sometimes occurs

Fig. 13-7 Tardigrada—anatomy of a female *Macrobiotus* (water bear). After Marcus, in Ward and Whipple, *Fresh-Water Biology* 1959 (W. T. Edmondson, ed.), 2nd ed., courtesy of John Wiley & Sons, Inc.

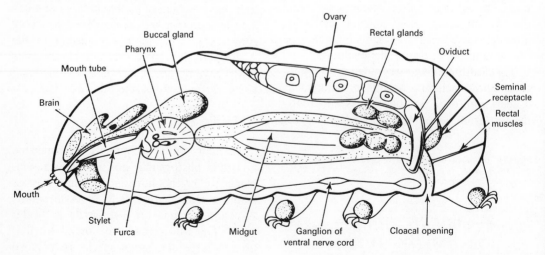

within the old but not yet discarded cuticle of the female at ecdysis. In other species fertilization is truly internal. After hatching, the young develop through a series of six molts, which differs from the number in mites (Acarina) with which Tardigrada have sometimes been classified. Eutely or cell constancy is characteristic, so that size increase is due to enlargment of already existing cells.

The Tardigrada can be considered as a phylum, and their characteristics generally place them parallel with the Onychophora. The terminal mouth, multiple claws, and marine habitat (for some) are suggestive of the extinct *Aysheaia,* and perhaps they arose as another offshoot of this possible onychophoran ancestor. In addition to morphological differences from Onychophora and Arthropoda, they also have enterocoelous mesoderm.

Pentastomida (Linguatulida)

The third group to be placed in Pararthropoda is the Pentastomida (Linguatulida). A common name applied to some members of this group is tongue-worm. The pentastomids are highly modified by parasitism with reduction or loss of many tructures. One stage of larval metamorphosis possesses two or three pairs of unjointed legs reminiscent of the tardigrade limb (Fig. 13-8). The nervous system, although reduced, reveals segmentation. The cuticle is chitinous, and pentastomids undergo ecdysis. Adults show annulations in the cuticle but no other external suggestion of segmentation. As is the case with the Tardigrada, cilia are absent, but unlike that group the pentastomids have striated muscle.

Fig. 13-8 Pentastomida: (a) larva of *Porocephalus clavatus* and (b) Tardigrada, *Macrobiotus.* From Hertwig (after Stiles), A Manual of Zoology (translated and edited by J. S. Kingsley) 1902, Holt, Rinehart & Winston, Inc.

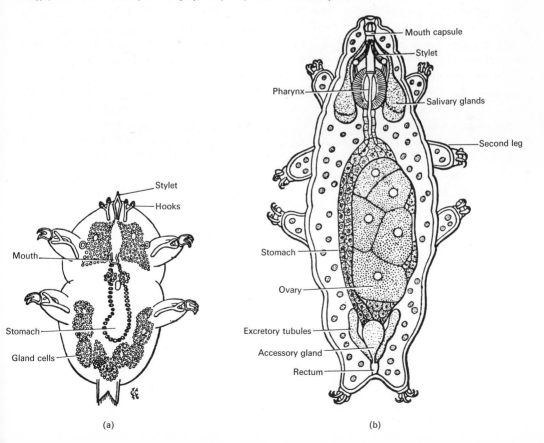

(a)

(b)

The life cycle of the tongue-worm, *Linguatula serrata,* is well known. The adult stage occurs in nasal passages and sinuses, usually in dogs, although other mammals including man may be infected. The female parasite may reach a length of four inches. These somewhat flattened worms taper bluntly at the anterior end (which bears two pairs of hooks) and gradually toward the posterior end. Mucus from the nasal passages carries resistant embryonated eggs. These hatch when swallowed by a suitable intermediate host, such as man and other mammals. The larvae migrate to suitable visceral organs. After metamorphosis, which includes several molts, the young stage can migrate to the nasal passages of the host or be taken into the mouth of a suitable final host, where they attach until able to migrate to the nasal passages. Other species of pentastomids are parasitic in reptiles (especially crocodiles and tropical snakes) and in gulls and terns.

It is apparent that the Pentastomida show arthropod affinities, but the unjointed larval leg structure, particularly, indicates relationship to Tardigrada and justifies their removal from Arachnida, with which they are often associated. Osche studied larval stages of more primitive pentastomids which had three pairs of appendages in addition to antennal primorida. He found the first pair of these appendages to be distinctly postoral. Osche recognizes a similarity in development of these pentastomids to mandibulate arthropods.

REFERENCES

Bursell, E., and D. W. Ewer, On the reactions to humidity of *Peripatopsis moseleyi* (Wood-Mason). J. Exp. Biol., 26:335, 1950.

Cuénot, L., Onychophores, Tardigrades, Pentastomides (pp. 3-75). *In* (P. Grassé, ed.) Traité de zoologie, Tome VI, 1949.

Handlirsch, A., Arthropoda. *In* (W. Kükenthal and T. Krumbach, eds.) Handbuch der Zoologie, 3(1):211, 1926-1927.

Heatley, N. G., The digestive enzymes of the Onychophora (*Peripatopsis spp.*). J. Exp. Biol., 13:329, 1936.

Hutchinson, G. E., Restudy of some Burgess Shale fossils. Proc. U.S. Nat. Mus., 78(Art. 11):1-24, 1930. (*Aysheaia.*)

Imms, A. D., The ancestry of insects. Trans. Soc. Brit. Ent., 3:1, 1936.

Manton, S. M., Habits of life and evolution of body design in Arthropoda. J. Linn. Soc. Zool. London, 44:58, 1958.

Osche, Günther, Arthropodencharaktere bei einem Pentastomiden Embryo (*Reighardia sternae*). Zool. Anzeiger, 163(5/6):169, 1959.

Snodgrass, R. E., Evolution of the Annelida, Onychophora, and Arthropoda. Smithson. Miscel. Coll., 97(6):1, 1938.

———, Comparative study of the head of mandibulate arthropods. Ithaca: Comstock, 1951, 118 pp.

Tiegs, O. W., and S. M. Manton, The evolution of the Arthropoda. Biol. Rev., 33:255, 1958.

Vandel, A., Généralités: composition de l'embranchement des Arthropodes (pp. 79-158). *In* (P. Grassé, ed.) Traité de zoologie, Tome VI, 1949.

14

TRILOBITA
AND
ARACHNOMORPHA

These two subphyla appeared to be related primarily by the similarity of the embryological stages of *Limulus* (the horseshoe or king crab) with immature stages of trilobites. The trilobed structure is particularly indicative. However, some authorities suggest a close relationship between Trilobita and Crustacea. Certainly all three subphyla were well established in the Lower Cambrian, and the known Trilobita, which are all extinct, were too specialized to be considered as ancestral directly to either the Crustacea or the Arachnomorpha. All three probably emerged from a common ancestor in the Precambrian.

SUBPHYLUM TRILOBITA

At the beginning of the Palaeozoic era a dominant group of arthropods occurred in the sea. These somewhat ovoid animals exhibited two longitudinal furrows which divided the dorsal aspect into a somewhat arched median lobe and two lateral, more flattened lobes. It is from this tripartite feature that the name Trilobita is derived. These arthropods ranged in size from less than a half inch to more than two feet; the majority averaged two to three inches. Trilobites became extinct in the Permian Period, leaving a fossil record that extended over 300 million years. Thousands of species, many from incomplete remains, have been recorded, and these are variously classified into three to five orders. Trilobites are strictly marine and are commonly found associated with fossils of other sea-dwelling animals.

Trilobites exhibit the feature common to arthropods of having the body divided into regions or tagmata. There are three general body divisions, identified as the head, thorax, and pygidium (Fig. 14-1). The latter two are commonly grouped as the *opisthosoma,* and the head section is called the *prosoma* or cephalon.

The prosomal skeleton is a partly rounded plate continued as a pair of lateral spines projected caudally. In many species the prosoma exhibits the three-lobed topography characteristic of trilobites. The median lobe is designated as the *glabella,* and the pair of lateral lobes are the *genae* or cheeks. The latter are often subdivided by longitudinal grooves interrupted by a pair of lateral eyes into a medial fixed cheek and lateral free cheeks. Sometimes the glabella or the longitudinal furrows delimiting it suggest transverse glabellar division into five parts, correlated with the primitive segmentation of this region indicated in the shield-shaped larval stage called the *protaspis* (Fig. 14-2).

In both prosoma and opisthosoma the edges of the shell are ventrally reflected. This reflected portion of the skeleton is called the *doublure,* and in the opisthosoma it extends almost to the edge of the median lobe along which the appendages are attached (Fig. 14-3). In the prosoma the doublure extends under the anterior end and the paired antennae and median labrum arise from it. The labrum apparently covers the mouth and may correspond with the organ of the same name in other arthropods, but in none of these does it show an embryonic derivation from limbs. The antennae represent preoral appendages and are associated with the fate of the first or frontal lobe in the larva. The hypothesis has been advanced that the trilobite antennae are homologous to the antennules of the crustacea and to the antennae of myriapods and insects. In general, preoral appendages have no history of origin from ambulatory appendages, while postoral ones seem certain to have had such ancestry.

Trilobites have a unique characteristic

Fig. 14-1 Trilobita: Generalized dorsal and ventral views. After Snodgrass 1952, courtesy of the Comstock Publishing Associates.

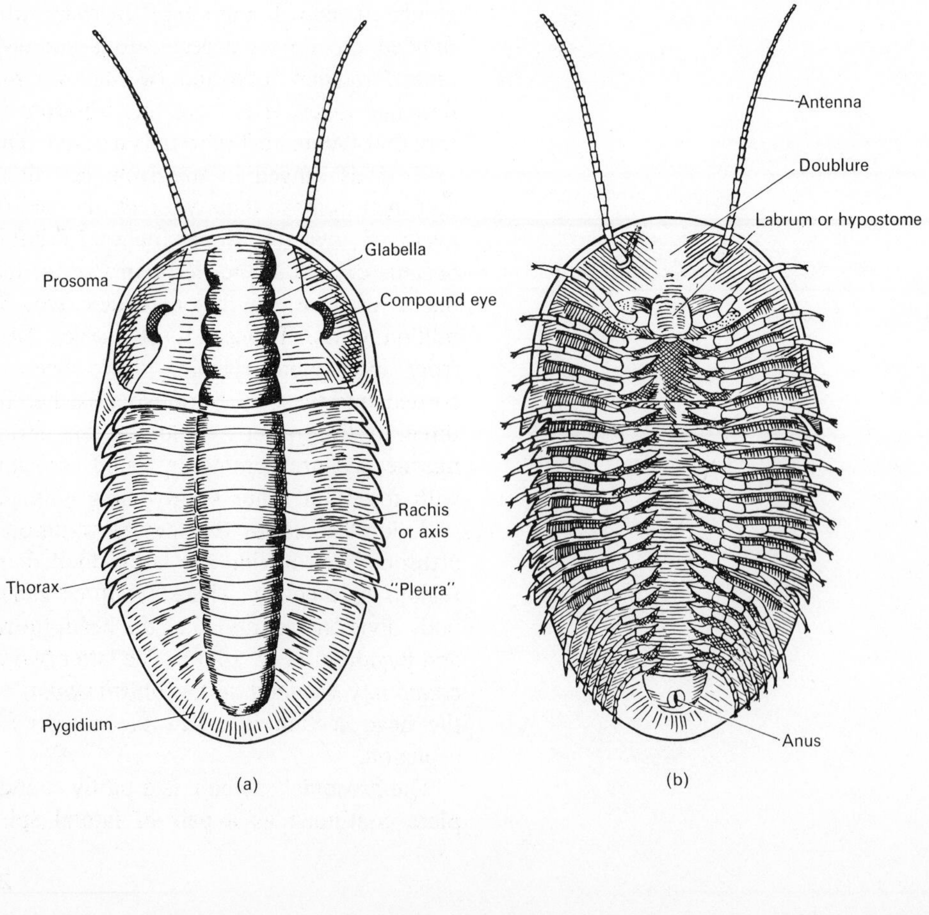

among the Arthropoda in the uniformity and lack of specialization of their appendages. The similarity of a succession of appendages suggests metachronal action. Since the outer ramus of the trilobite appendage is fringed on the caudal or ventral edge, currents produced against the doublure may have carried fine food particles. This suggests that trilobites were suspension or filter feeders, but the fringes themselves may well represent gills. In *Limulus,* the horseshoe crab, the coxal segments of paired appendages are sufficiently close to each other to provide a coarse crushing mechanism, but the appendages of trilobites are not in sufficient apposition to substantiate a parallel function. Most trilobites were chiefly benthonic and crawled over the mud or sand substrate principally by use of the sturdy inner rami. It is possible

that most of their food came from organic matter present in ingested mud. A number of trilobites apparently could make brief swimming excursions in the water; some may have been good swimmers as is suggested by their more elongate shape. The inner rami used for surface locomotion may have been somewhat flatter in swimming forms, and the outer rami which extend beyond the doublure may have been useful in swimming as well as probable producers of feeding and respiratory currents.

Interpretation of the number of leg segments suggests affinity with the Arachnomorpha. In arthropods with three claws it has been shown that the middle claw represents a reduced segment with its own musculature. If the three-clawed condition in Trilobita can be similarly interpreted, the Trilobite leg

Fig. 14-2 Protaspis: First larval stage of a Trilobite. After Whittington 1957, courtesy of the Cambridge Philosophical Society and of the author.

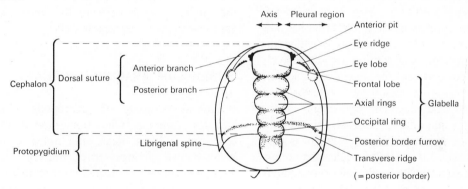

Fig. 14-3 Trilobita: Diagrammatic cross-section. After Snodgrass 1952, courtesy of the Comstock Publishing Associates.

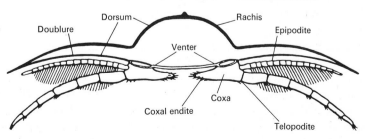

has eight rather than the apparent seven segments. This is the maximum number of leg segments in any arthropod and is retained in some living Arachnomorpha and in Class Pycnogonida, but not in Crustacea, Myriapoda, or Insecta.

The first larval stage for many Trilobites is a limbless, oval, flattened, or subspherical stage averaging a millimeter in length (Fig. 14-2). It has been designated protaspis, and from the dorsal aspect it presents a shieldlike appearance as its name suggests. Most of this surface is representative of the adult prosoma and is typically raised medially in a segmented glabellar lobe. The lateral genal areas are marked by sutures and eye lobes. The subdivision of the glabella is thought to represent an anterior frontal lobe followed by four lobes which are the precursors of somites producing the four pairs of prosomal legs. Some authorities suggest the presence of a subdivision of the frontal lobe indicating six primitive segments in all, but no appendage characteristic of it appears in the adult Trilobite. The posterior area of the protaspis is called the protopygidium. New somites are successively developed between the pygidium and the prosoma from a region just anterior to a presumed anal segment equivalent to the telson in some other arthropods. Neither the telson nor the Trilobite anal segment is considered to be a true somite, so that the youngest true somite will be the one immediately anterior to these structures. When the first transverse suture separating protopygidium from the prosoma has been delineated, the larva is called a *meraspis*. It is so designated until the definitive number of thoracic segments is produced. For those Trilobites in which meraspid but not protaspid larvae have been found, the supposition has been advanced that these species had delayed skeletal formation or that their protaspid larval stages were less suitable for fossilization. After the definitive thoracic segments have been set down, the developing trilobite is in the *holaspid* stage. The adult condition has been reached but additional molts account for size increase.

Despite the long existence of the Trilobites in the Palaeozoic their structure showed little diversity. They developed no specialized appendages for feeding unless the setiferous fringe of the epipodites so functioned. Recent evidence refutes the theory that endites on the coxal leg segments were sufficiently robust to function as efficient gnathobases for food manipulation. Trilobites may well have been bottom-feeding scavengers.

It is surmised that the Trilobita became extinct because they lost out in the competition for food to swifter and more adaptive cephalopods and crustacea. When Trilobites first appeared on the geologic scene in the early Cambrian they already possessed trilobite and arthropod characteristics and there is nothing to suggest a pre-annelid relationship. It has been suggested that a prototrilobite stem early gave rise to both the Trilobita and the Arachnomorpha. The evidence seems insufficient to rule out the possibility that an early offshoot from the same stem gave rise to the Crustacea as well.

SUBPHYLUM ARACHNOMORPHA

This is a group of arthropods which includes *Limulus* (the horseshoe crab), scorpions, spiders, ticks, and mites as the better-known living representatives. The Arachnomorpha are distinctly set apart from other members of the phylum by the absence of antennae. Currently the most commonly used name for the group is Chelicerata or Arachnomorpha, although the Trilobita have sometimes been included in the latter designation. The present work will utilize the term Arachnomorpha at subphylum rank.

The Arachnomorpha are generally less homogeneous than are other subphyla but nevertheless possess a number of common features. The preoral antennules (first antennae) do not occur, as has already been indicated. The first pair of appendages develops on the first postoral segment, is typically two- or three-jointed, and usually bears a pincer or *chela* terminally. These appendages are called *chelicerae*. Subsequent shifting of the mouth gives them a preoral orientation. On the following segment appendages called *pedipalps* occur. These are typically six-jointed and locomotor but may be chelate or pointed and used for food-getting. A generalized arachnomorph is shown in Fig. 14-4.

The body is characteristically divided into tagmata, the first of which is the cephalothorax or prosoma. The precheliceral area plus the first six segments are coalesced to form the prosoma. The four pairs of cephalothoracic appendages behind the pedipalps are walking legs, the number characteristic for this subphylum. The basal joints of pedipalps as well as those of the walking legs are commonly enlarged as gnathobases. The apposition of the gnathobases of these appendages serves a masticatory function. The posterior tagma is the abdomen or opisthosoma and appears to have a maximum of 12 primary

segments. The genital operculum is found on the second opisthosomal (eighth postoral) somite. Considerable abdominal modification occurs. The first abdominal segment (seventh postoral) frequently is reduced, or retained as a narrow isthmus, or disappears. The abdomen may be divided into an anterior mesosoma (preabdomen) and a posterior metasoma (postabdomen). In some forms the metasoma is variously attenuated or reduced to form a pygidium terminally. In some Arachnomorpha there is a postsegmental extension of the abdomen, called telson, which articulates with the terminal abdominal segment. External segmentation may not be evident, and the body may be incorporated into a single unit.

Several respiratory patterns occur among the Arachnomorpha. *Limulus* has five ventral paired platelike opisthosomal appendages posterior to the genital operculum. One hundred or more branchial lamellae occur on the protected dorsal aspect of these appendages. Because of the apposition of the lamellae, these gills have been referred to as *gill-books*. In other Arachnomorpha such as scorpions, leaflike gill lamellae occur in recessed chambers which open through ventral spiracles on segments 9 to 12. Such organs are called *book lungs*. Respiration occurs via *trachea* in some forms; others have book lungs as well as trachea. In the Palpigradida there are three pairs of eversible respiratory sacs on the ventral surface, and in some mites special respiratory organs are absent and gaseous exchange occurs through the body surface. Some Arachnomorpha possess hemocyanin, the only respiratory pigment occurring in this subphylum.

In the Arachnomorpha the sexes are separate, and larval development is oviparous or ovoviviparous. Usually there is little metamorphosis, the form that is hatched or born closely resembling the adult. In *Limulus,* however, the first larval stage bears a superficial resemblance to trilobites and has been called a trilobite stage.

The Arachnomorpha have been subdivided into three classes. The Merostomata and

Fig. 14-4 Generalized arachnomorph (chelicerate) showing main morphological features of ventral side. After Størmer 1955, from *"Treatise on Invertebrate Paleontology,"* courtesy Geological Society of America and University of Kansas Press.

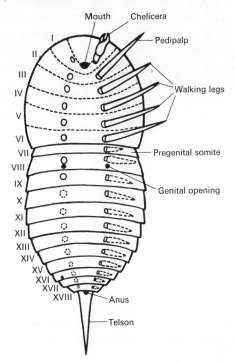

Pycnogonida are marine, and Arachnida is primarily terrestrial, although some spiders are secondarily aquatic, and mites are represented by marine and fresh-water species.

The Merostomata were ancient mostly marine arachnids that were especially prominent in the early and middle Paleozoic. Many of them were of large size, and some eurypterids reached over two meters in length. All of the eurypterids are extinct, but three genera of Xiphosura including the well-known horseshoe crab, *Limulus,* are extant. The Eurypterida, also known as the Gigantostraca, are the so-called water scorpions. While early ones were of marine origin, some later eurypterids occurred in brackish and in fresh water. The chelate condition of appendages is limited to the first pair in eurypterids, whereas Xiphosura may have multiple chelate appendages. Trunk segments, fused in the horseshoe crab, are free in the water scorpions. Eurypterids with more elongate bodies were swimming types whereas broad-bodied Xiphosura were crawling types; probably both arose from a bottom-dwelling aglaspid ancestor. The Eurypterida ancestors were probably forerunners to the terrestrial scorpions which first appeared in the Silurian. Eurypterids became extinct near the end of the Paleozoic.

Classification of Arachnomorpha

Class I Merostomata These aquatic Arachnomorpha probably originated in the Precambrian. Fossil remains of the oldest forms have been found in the lower Cambrian. Adults were crawling or groveling forms, but young larvae could swim. A brackish- or fresh-water habitat is indicated for some Merostomes.

SUBCLASS 1 XIPHOSURA These are characterized by a trilobed shield composed of the prosoma and, in some forms, part of the opisthosoma. The posterior end carried a pointed telson. Book gills occurred on biramous abdominal appendages and compound eyes were present on the prosoma. It seems likely that solid food was ingested and ground in a gizzard.

Order 1 Aglaspida These had a phosphatic exoskeleton and an indistinct trilobed condition of the dorsal shield. Only the first pair of appendages was chelate. There are 11 or 12 opisthosomal segments and a telson with a broad basal section. Fossils are restricted to the latter half of the Cambrian. Although appendages appear to be uniramous, the Aglaspida are considered to be ancestral to other Merostomes. *Aglaspis, Aglaspella.*

Order 2 Xiphosurida These bottom dwellers had a body divided into three rather rigid units hinged between the semicircular prosomal tagma and the opisthosoma in *Limulus.* A styloid telson is articulated with the opisthosomal shield. The abdomen has ten or less segments.

The king or horseshoe crabs (Fig. 14-5) derive the latter common name from the prosoma or head section, which bears laterally, caudally projected extensions. Although the horseshoe crabs bear a superficial resemblance to the Trilobites, they differ in lacking antenna and in the presence of a large caudal spine. The absence of antennae and the presence of genital apertures on the eighth body (first opisthosomal) segment are features they share with other Arachnomorpha. Dorsal segmentation of the opisthosoma can be seen in *Limulus,* in the location of pits (representative of apodemal processes) corresponding with segmental muscle; and by heart ostia.

Limulus differs from Trilobites in its structural adaptation of gnathobases, food being crushed and subdivided externally, but mechanical grinding of food particles occurs in an enlarged posterior chamber of the proventriculus (Fig. 14-6). Digestive glands open into the straight elongated tubular mesenteron, which leads to a short proctodaeum opening just ventral to the attachment of the terminal spine. Excretion in *Limulus* is accomplished by a pair of four-lobed coxal glands homologous to those in Arachnida. These glands open to the exterior near the bases of the last pair of legs. The four lobes indicate the primitively segmental arrangement of these excretory organs.

When king crabs mate, the smaller male grasps the carapace of the female and is present to deposit sperm over the eggs which the female places in successive pits in the sand between tide levels. Early larval stages reveal a pattern of four somites, indicated initially by pigment distribution. These larvae are reminiscent of the protaspis larva of Trilo-

Fig. 14-5 *Limulus polyphemus*, (a) dorsal and (b) ventral views. After Snodgrass 1952, courtesy of the Comstock Publishing Associates.

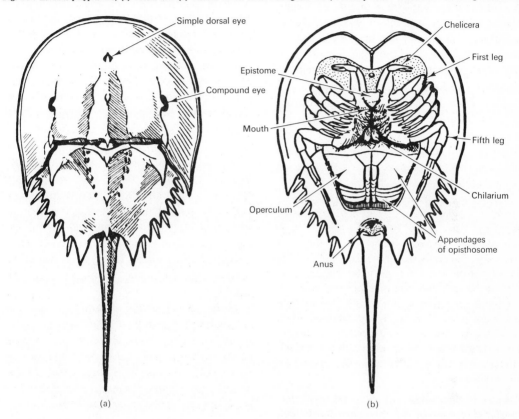

(a)   (b)

Fig. 14-6 *Limulus*, sagittal diagram. From Schechter 1959, courtesy of Prentice-Hall, Inc.

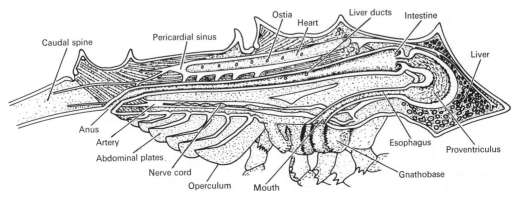

bites in which four postoral segments will give rise to the adult cephalon. Additional somites in *Limulus* arise from a generative area behind these first four somites. A later larva of *Limulus* has a rounded headshield and an opisthosoma demarked in segments. A blunt telson completes a picture of a stage which resembles (albeit only superficially) a Trilobite larva, and has been so called. In a series of successive molts the larva reaches the adult proportions, and thereafter will increase in size by less frequent ecdysis.

The Xiphosurida has a geologic history from the Silurian to the Recent. *Limulus* occurs in coastal waters along eastern North America and *Carcinoscorpius* and *Tachypleus* are extant genera in eastern Asian coastal waters.

SUBCLASS 2 EURYPTERIDA These fossil forms are found from the Ordovician to the Permian. Particularly in the Devonian, large Eurypterids occurred—some more than six feet long. Generally the prosoma is not as wide as the opisthosoma and the latter has 12 movable segments. The last pair of prosomal appendages are often spatulate and larger than the more anterior ones. Early representatives were marine, but later ones occurred in brackish or fresh water. Some were able swimmers; others were crawlers. *Stylonurus, Pterygotus, Hughmilleria.*

Class II Arachnida In these primarily terrestrial Arachnomorpha there are more than 5,400 recognized genera and more than 40,000 living species. The body is divided into prosoma and opisthosoma broadly joined, or by extreme constriction of the first abdominal segment. Maximally there are 12 abdominal segments, but the first is lost prior to the first larval stage in some forms. Only liquid food is ingested. Prey may be subdued in some groups with the aid of poison glands. Body fluids of the prey are sucked, or predigestion supplies liquefaction of solid foods. Respiration occurs through book lungs, trachea, evertible sacs, or simply through the body surface. The only respiratory pigment present in Arachnida is hemocyanin. Excretion is accomplished by coxal glands or *Malpighian tubules,* the latter being derivatives of the *endodermal* midgut.

Guanine is the nitrogenous waste product in the Arachnida, differing from the uric acid salts produced by insects. Compound eyes are not present in the Arachnida but simple eyes occur in several orders. The earliest fossils are from the Silurian.

Savory (1964) follows the classification of Petrunkevitch in dividing the Arachnida into four subclasses. These are the Latigastra, Caulogastra, Stethostomata, and Soluta. The latter two contain only fossil representatives and are not discussed here. The subclass Latigastra is characterized by a prosoma and opisthosoma broadly joined, while in the Caulogastra the first opisthosomatic somite is constricted to form a pedicel joining the prosoma. The Latigastra is subdivided into five orders, the following four with extant species: Scorpionida, Pseudoscorpionida, Opilines, and Acarina. The Caulogastra also includes one extinct order and the following seven orders which have living representatives: Palpigradida, Uropygi, Schizomida, Amblypygi, Araneida, Solifugae, and Ricinulei.

Order Scorpionida Scorpions, an ancient primitive group of arachnids, are relatively large arthropods; some exceed a length of six centimeters. In these Arachnida a carapace covers the cephalothorax (Fig. 14-7). Three to five pairs of simple eyes occur laterally on the scorpion carapace. Both chelicera and pedipalps are chelate, with the latter dwarfing the former. There are 12 abdominal segments, some Paleozoic scorpions retaining and Recent scorpions losing the first abdominal (pregenital) segment. In the latter case, *subsegmentation* of the second abdominal (eighth embryonic) segment apparently has restored the original number. The opisthosoma or abdomen in the scorpions is characteristically divided into a broader anterior mesosoma or pre-abdomen of seven segments and a narrower metasoma or postabdomen of five segments. The metasoma is often reflected dorsally over the body.

Encased terminally in the telson are paired

poison glands emptying through a caudal sting. Ventrally on the mesosoma the genital ducts open on the apparent first (eighth embryonic) segment. The next segment has a pair of comblike appendages called *pectines* found in no other orders of Arachnida. The pectines have a sensory, probably tactile, function. The next four mesosomal segments bear paired stigmata which open to the book lungs.

Scorpions are usually found in hot tropical and semitropical countries. They occur in Asia, Australia, Africa, and southern Europe. In the western hemisphere they occur throughout South and Central America and range into southern United States. Scorpions are largely nocturnal and they exhibit some negative phototropism. They are very hardy creatures that can endure freezing, extended periods without food, habitats of reduced

oxygen content, and immersion in water of many hours duration. Food of scorpions consists mostly of other arthropods including other scorpions, but they may attack small vertebrates such as lizards and mice.

Mating habits and reproduction are of considerable biological interest. There is relatively little sexual dimorphism. A courtship dance precedes mating. The male faces the female and grasps her pedipalps and commonly their recurved abdomens are entwined. Depending upon the species the courtship dance may be brief or last several hours. Afterwards the male takes the female to a suitable retreat. A hooked spermatophore may be deposited on the ground and the female is maneuvered over it until it adheres to her genital opening. Development is ovoviviparous or viviparous. In the former case large-yolked eggs undergo a dis-

Fig. 14-7 Scorpions, (a) dorsal and (b) ventral views. After Snodgrass 1952, courtesy of the Comstock Publishing Associates.

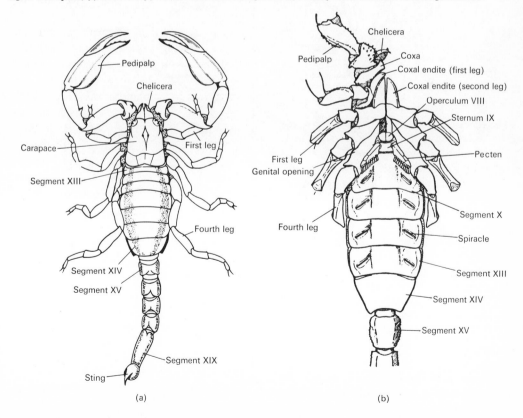

coidal cleavage not unlike that of birds, whereas viviparous eggs have little yolk. The embryos develop in caeca which receive nu- trients from the wall of the maternal intestine. After birth the young scorpions, apparently with considerable difficulty, climb

Fig. 14-8 *Hesperolpium slevini*, a Recent pseudoscorpion. After Petrunkevitch 1955, from *"Treatise on Invertebrate Paleontology,"* courtesy of Geological Society of America and the University of Kansas Press.

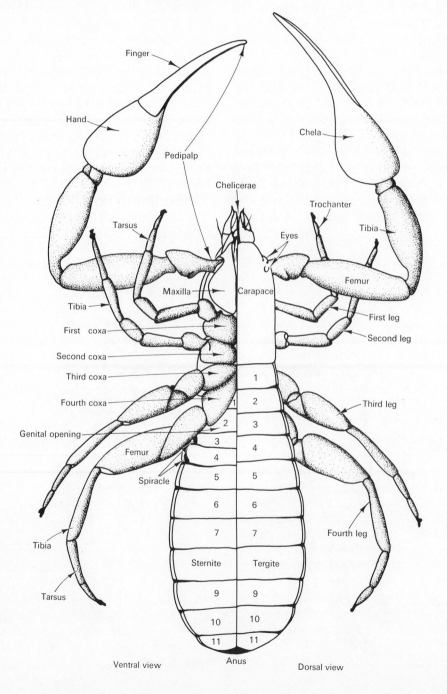

upon the back of the mother where they remain through the first molt, which usually occurs one to two weeks after birth. With the occurrence of this molt the young exhibit a rather typical scorpion structure. Five or six additional molts are typical in the life history of most scorpions.

Scorpions have developed two kinds of poisons. The less virulent kind produce a painful sting, followed by numbness and usually some swelling. The effects are usually not prolonged beyond an hour or two, but other species inject a neurotoxin which can end fatally for man or other animals. Some animals appear to be relatively immune to the poison; others, such as dogs, unusually susceptible. Some scorpion poisons have a hemolytic effect. In camping out in areas where scorpions are known to occur, it is a good precaution to shake out one's boots in the morning, since a scorpion may have utilized one of them as a retreat.

Centruroides, Hadrurus, and *Vejovis* are genera occurring in the United States. The genus *Buthus* is common in the Mediterranean region.

Order Pseudoscorpionida While this group superficially resembles true scorpions, chiefly because of the similarity of large pedipalps, they are much smaller (under half an inch in length), the abdomen does not narrow to form a metasoma, and they do not possess a caudal sting (Fig. 14-8). There are at least 1,700 described species of false scorpions, most of which are colored yellowish-brown. One or both pedipalps contain a poison gland which empties terminally on the immovable finger of the chela. Pseudoscorpions are predators on insects and other small arthropods, although the poison gland does not always seem to be utilized. Pseudoscorpions differ from all other Arachnida in having cheliceral silk glands. These open at the tip of the movable finger, and the silk is used to prepare nests for molting or as a brood-sac. In many spiders the venom glands are similarly located on the chelicera. The chelicera of false scorpions are two-

rather than three-jointed as in true scorpions.

False scorpions have nearly a cosmopolitan distribution except for the very frigid areas of the earth. Savory provides a table showing distribution of some 18 families, some of which have world-wide distribution. These arachnids are negatively phototropic and because of their small size are overlooked in their habitat among rotting leaves and under tree bark. Cloudsley-Thompson points out an interesting characteristic that serves to identify false scorpions. If leaf debris containing them is spread on white paper, they run backward very rapidly when disturbed. False scorpions also utilize many different kinds of insects, some other arthropods, and birds for transport. This practice seems restricted to female pseudoscorpions and doubtlessly has served for dissemination of the species that practice it.

During mating paired genital sacs in the male are capable of being extruded, and in the family Cheliferidae they are called "ram's-horn organs." There is a courtship dance analogous to that of true scorpions, and in those species with ram's-horn organs, these are displayed just prior to the deposit of a stalked spermatophore in front of the female. She ultimately moves forward to receive the spermatophore into her genital opening with or without the assistance of the male.

Pseudoscorpions respire by means of trachea, lack Malpighian tubules, and are oviparous. The group is much younger than true scorpions geologically, being traced back to the Oligocene. *Chelifer, Hesperolpium,* and *Neobisium* are common species.

Order Opiliones This group, sometimes called Phalangiida, carries the common names of harvestmen or "daddy longlegs." Farm children used to question these arachnids as to the location of the cows and a waving leg was usually interpreted as pointing in the general direction of the pasture. Opiliones, a name which classically means shepherd, is a group divided into three suborders. The first, short-legged, mitelike group is very primitive and exhibits an erratic distribution, such as in Florida, Oregon, central France, the East Indies, Ceylon, and parts of tropical Africa. Some members of this suborder are blind, but most have a simple eye situated on either side of an ocular tubercle on the cepholothorax. The second suborder has species that occur in Mammoth Cave in Kentucky as well as in South America, Australia, and in Old World tropics. The most important suborder includes four families, one of which is the Phalangiidae. The familiar long-legged harvestmen of North America, Europe, and North Africa occur in this group (Fig. 14-9). Whereas regeneration of lost limbs is characteristic of many invertebrates, it does not occur with the "daddy longlegs." Less than four legs is too great a handicap; and if the second pair are the only ones lost, the animals do not long survive. The second pair of legs apparently has special sensory function.

Harvestmen or harvest-spiders are typically carnivorous and capture various small invertebrates, but they are to some degree scavengers and will feed on a variety of organic matter. Some are cannibalistic and at least two families feed on snails. Cloudsley-Thompson describes mating as very casual and certainly not monogamous. Most species do not show any prenuptial courtship. There is little sexual dimorphism, although the male has a smaller body and copulation is effected by insertion of the long male penis as the participants face each other. The sexual apparatus of the female includes long ovipositors so that eggs (usually a few at a time) can be deposited deep in crevices. In some genera the female may remain to guard the eggs, which hatch in about three weeks.

Some additional features include a carapace which covers the prosoma and an opisthosoma of ten segments. These two tagmata are broadly joined, reducing the superficial similarity to spiders. The pedipalpi are not chelate and are often leglike. The legs are seven-segmented. Respiration is by trachea. Some common species include *Phalangium, Phalangodes,* and *Caddo.*

Order Acarina   This group includes the mites (Fig. 14-10) and ticks, the former commonly being minute. The group is of great economic importance to man. Several species are parasitic on man and serve also as vectors for such diseases as Rocky Mountain and Eastern Spotted Fever, Tularemia,

Fig. 14-9 *Caddo*, Opiliones (Phalangiida). After Petrunkevitch 1955, from *"Treatise on Invertebrate Paleontology,"* courtesy Geological Society of America and University of Kansas Press.

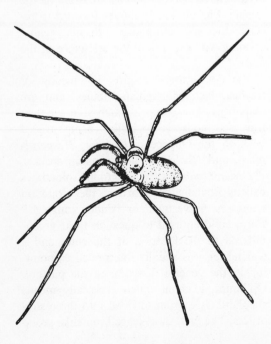

Fig. 14-10 *Sarcoptes scabiei* female, the scabies mite, ventral aspect.

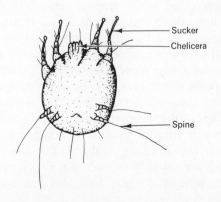

Sucker

Chelicera

Spine

and Relapsing Fever. One group of mites serve as intermediate hosts for some important tapeworm parasites of herbivorous animals, and man through his omnivorous habits is subject to one tapeworm from this group. Scabies and follicular mites occur in man. Mites infest and make unusable such stored foods as flour, and other mites destroy cheese. Mites also are serious pests on many plants. One of the most economically important mites is the so-called "red-spider" mite (*Tetranychus*), a serious and common pest on evergreens and other shrubbery. Other species attack citrus trees.

The distribution of mites is cosmopolitan. Some of this distribution is due to the small size of many members of the group; they are readily transmitted by other animals either as parasites, commensals, or "stowaways." Mites have been found on the north coast of Greenland and on the periphery of the Antarctic. Savory reports their occurrence in the fleece of mountain sheep at an altitude of 15,000 feet as well as their presence in aerial plankton at much higher altitudes. As indicated, some are parasitic and many are free-living. They are found in marine, fresh-water, and terrestrial environments and in transit in the air.

In the mites and ticks which make up the group Acarina, externally segmentation is reduced or absent and the acarid body is not clearly subdivided into the usual tagmata, but a false head called a *gnathosoma* or *capitulum* carries the chelicera and the pedipalps. Typically the legs end in claws. Among some mites, a suckerlike structure called a *caruncle* accompanies the claws. Respiration is usually by trachea, but in some forms these are absent and respiration is cutaneous. When spiracles are present, their location is important taxonomically. The acarids possess Malpighian tubules for excretion. Particularly among the mites, a very ancient group, great diversity in food habits has been achieved. Some are herbivorous, which is unusual among Arachnida. Temporary or permanent parasitism is common.

Considerable metamorphosis occurs in the life cycle of acarids. The larva hatching from the egg has three pairs of legs, and during the subsequent molt to the nymph stage another pair of legs is added. In the next and final molt, the sexual apparatus of the adult appears.

The family of mites, Trombiculidae, many of which are commonly called redbugs, have a wide distribution, although India and Africa appear to have escaped infestation. In the southern half of the United States from Nebraska eastward to Maryland *Eutrombicula alfreddugèsi* (formerly *Trombicula irritans*) attacks turtles, ground birds including baby chicks, rabbits, domesticated animals, and man. The common name of this mite is "chigger." The larval stage gains access to the host from grass or weeds. The attack in man is apt to be especially noticeable just below belt or garters which serve as an impediment to the climbing mite. These mites firmly attach to the skin, usually near a hair follicle, and inject a specialized mouthpart. Introduced saliva hardens to form a capillary tube through which the mite engorges, a process which may take several days. Subsequently, the mites drop off and the two subsequent molts occur off the host.

Poison elements in the saliva of "chiggers" cause a dermatitis which takes the form of red blotches. These may not develop for several hours after the attack. Newcomers to infected regions are especially subject to discomfort, but an immunity is developed eventually except in the more tender-skinned. The immunity may be lost after prolonged absence from an infested region.

Ticks belong to a suborder which also includes some mites, but ticks are much larger; even the newly hatched "seed tick" with but three pairs of legs is visible without a microscope. Ticks belong to a superfamily called Ixodidoidea which is subdivided into two families. In the Ixodidae or hard ticks the capitulum with its mouthparts is recessed in the anterior camerostome. In soft ticks the mouthparts are ventral. A dorsal plate called *scutum* occurs in the hard ticks, covering males completely, the unengorged females partly. Soft ticks lack a scutum. Ticks feed until engorgement, a process that involves insertion of the robust mouthparts, and which may take several days. An engorged adult female may reach the size of a small marble. The bite of some ticks injects a toxin that may cause a temporary paralysis, and rarely has caused death.

The transmitter of Rocky Mountain spotted fever, *Dermacentor andersoni,* is known as a three-host tick. The three-legged larva engorges on blood of a small mammal, and leaves this host to molt to the nymphal stage, which in turn attaches to a new host for engorgement. It leaves this host to undergo the next molt. The sexually mature adult usually feeds on larger mammals including man. Mating occurs on the host, after which the female drops off to deposit eggs. Other ticks have reduced the hazards of survival by completing the life cycle on one or two hosts. *Boophilus annulatus,* which transmits Texas cattle fever, is a one-host tick. Eastern spotted fever occurs in most states and appears to be a less virulent strain of Rocky Mountain spotted fever.

Among the Arachnida, only the scorpions have an older fossil history than the Acarina and only the spiders have more recognized genera. *Argas, Dermacentor, Ixodes, Boophilus,* and *Ornithodorus* are important tick genera and *Demodex, Eutrombicula, Psoroptes,* and *Sarcoptes* are important parasitic mites.

Order Palpigradida These animals, sometimes called miniature whip-scorpions, include a single family having about twenty species divided among four genera. An additional genus is extinct. Negatively phototropic, they occur in moist and sheltered habitats where humidity is high; they are distributed along the western side of the western hemisphere, Africa, Australia, southern Europe, and Thailand. Some species have paired eversible sacs on the ventral surface of some abdominal somites, and these sacs are thought to be respiratory. Palpigradida are carnivorous, feeding on minute invertebrates, their eggs, or possibly dead organic material. Little is known of their mating habits.

All are minute and some are less than a millimeter in length. The carapace (*peltidium*) is subdivided into three units—the anterior and posterior ones single, the middle one represented by a pair of small triangular plates. The twelfth opisthosomal segment is missing and the terminal ones are attenuated to form a pygidium. The telson extends from this as a multijointed flagellum (Fig. 14-11). The simple leglike form of the pedipalps suggests a primitive state. *Eukoenenia, Prokoenenia.*

Order Uropygi The Uropygi, sometimes known as Thelyphonida, comprise the

Fig. **14-11** *Koenenia*, Palpigradida. From Hertwig (after Wheeler) *A Manual of Zoology* (translated and edited by J. S. Kingsley) 1902, Holt, Rinehart & Winston, Inc.

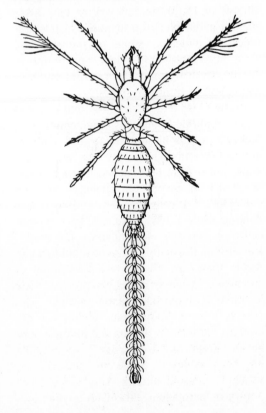

whip-scorpions (Fig. 14-12), so-named because of the telson, an elongated whiplike terminal flagellum. The Uropygi bear some similarity to scorpions, but pedipalps and particularly the abdomen are obviously different. These arachnids are mostly large, varying from one to three inches in length. They feed at night, mostly on immature or adult stages of insects and on earthworms and slugs; the large American species has been known to eat small amphibia. Uropygi produce burrows and hide in these or under stones during the day. They occur in southern United States (genus, *Mastigoproctus*), northeastern South America, southeastern Asia and Japan. *Mastigoproctus* retreats to its burrow with its prey, which has been detected by the protruding, primarily sensory front pair of legs. These legs have seven seg-

Fig. 14-12 *Mastigoproctus*, Uropygi (Thelyphonida). After Snodgrass 1952, courtesy of the Comstock Publishing Associates.

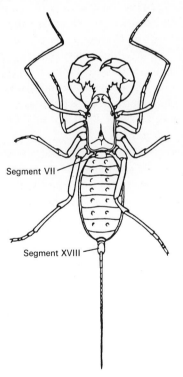

Segment VII

Segment XVIII

ments and possess a subdivided terminal tarsus. Uropygi have no poison glands but as a protective device a repugnant spray possessing formic and acetic acid components is released from the anal region.

There is little sexual dimorphism, but a courtship promenade somewhat like that of scorpions occurs. Egg-laying usually occurs in a burrow, and the approximately 25 eggs are retained in a transparent brood-sac attached to the mother. Although the young leave the brood-sac, they remain on the mother until after the first molt. It has been reported that three subsequent molts extend over as many years.

Uropygi have a special mouth adaptation, somewhat analogous to a ball-and-socket joint, in which the mouth opens at the inner end of a socket formed between the fused bases of the pedipalps. The upper lip of the rostrum fits into this depression to leave a slitlike mouth which serves as a kind of filtering apparatus. The unsegmented carapace folds under at the anterior edge. An opisthosoma of twelve segments has the terminal end attenuated to form a pygidium from which the elongated telson extends. Eyes are usually present. Both fossil and recent species belong to a single family. *Mastigoproctus* and *Prothelyphonus* are familiar genera.

Order Schizomida These arachnids are frequently grouped with the Uropygi but are much smaller (less than a half-inch long), the carapace is segmented into three adequal units, and eyes are absent (Fig. 14-13). Although actually a tropical group of wide distribution, some have survived introduction into hothouses in northern climes.

Schizomids constitute another nocturnal group. They are found in moist habitats under rocks, in leaf mold or other debris, or in the earth. These animals can leap backward and also can run forward with great speed. They are predators on small arthropods. Like Uropygi, they have repugnatorial glands. Males have not been seen. The females may construct an exitless chamber in the soil, and the eggs initially are attached to her.

Fig. 14-13 *Schizonotus*, Schizomida. After J. Millot 1949, *Traité de Zoologie*, Tome VI (P. Grassé, ed.), courtesy of Masson et Cie.

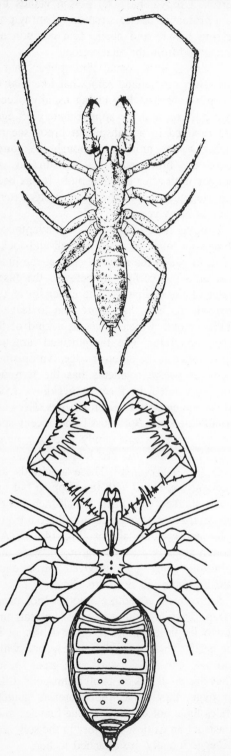

The four terminal abdominal segments form a pygidium, and there is a short telson of not more than seven segments. The mouth opens from a recess similar to that in Uropygi. *Calcitro, Schizomus.*

Order Amblypygi This group, also known as Phrynichida, lack a telson and a segmented carapace. The first pair of legs are very slender and have elongated, many-segmented tarsi which are tactile in function (Fig. 14-14). In addition to book lungs, some species have eversible sacs reminiscent of those in the Palpigradida.

These animals, commonly called scorpion-spiders, have stout, raptorial pedipalps terminating in a large movable claw. They live among rocks, in caves, or in other natural crevices where the humidity is high. A number of species occur in houses. They are common in South America, South Africa, the East Indies, and India. Some are found in southern United States. Amblypygi are predators feeding on a variety of insects and terrestrial crustaceans. There is little sexual dimorphism and mating habits are little known, but females carry an egg-sac attached to the abdomen during the reproductive period. The eggs are relatively large (2–3 millimeters in diameter) since adults only measure from 8 to 45 millimeters in length. *Tarantula.*

Order Araneida These are the spiders. A narrow pedicel joins the abdomen (opisthosoma) with the cephalothorax (Fig. 14-15). Segmentation of the abdomen is evident externally only in primitive species and in some very young stages of other spiders. Twelve opisthosomal segments are present in some primitive groups, but reduction to five or six segments is characteristic of recent forms. The carapace is not subdivided. As many as four pairs of eyes are

Fig. 14-14 *Tarantula*, Amblypygi (Phyrnichida), ventral view of body and raptorial pedipalps. After Petrunkevitch 1955, from "*Treatise on Invertebrate Paleontology*," courtesy Geological Society of America and University of Kansas Press.

common, arranged in two rows, often curved. Loss of one or more pairs of eyes is characteristic of some families of spiders. The chelicerae have two segments, with the terminal one modified as a fang and communicating with a poison gland in the cephalothorax. Respiratory structures are book lungs or trachea which open on the second and third abdominal segments in various paired combinations. Only liquid food is ingested in the Araneida. The stomodaeal foregut is composed of pharynx, esophagus, and sucking stomach and is histologically similar to the body wall from which it is derived. The sucking stomach has a somewhat tricornuate lumen which can be constricted by sphincter muscles. Muscles of opposing action attach to the internal face of the skeleton, and the combined action of these muscles provides an efficient sucking mechanism. The sucking stomach connects with the mesenteron or midgut. Before it passes by simple tube into the abdomen, a pair of large lateral tubes arise from the stomach (Fig. 14-16). These run forward, separated at first by muscles dorsal to the

sucking stomach, and often unite in front of these muscles. Each of these tubes or diverticula gives rise to four caeca which end in the proximity of leg coxae. In the abdomen the midgut enlarges and gives rise to many branched diverticula massed in the dorsal area of the abdomen. Posteriorly the midgut narrows and then enlarges caudally into a dorsal expansion called the cloaca, into which a pair of branching Malpighian tubules open. These and one or two pairs of nephridial coxal glands constitute the main excretory system. The hindgut is a short proctodaeum with chitinous lining.

Spiders capture food in several ways. All spiders are carnivorous, feeding commonly on insects, although a few large species capture small vertebrates, including birds occasionally, and cannibalism may occur when young are crowded together. Prey is captured by outrunning it, or by lying in ambush until it comes within reach, or by strategically placed webs (Fig. 14-17). Poison glands opening on the chelicerae provide a means of subduing the prey.

Ventral abdominal appendages on the

Fig. 14-15 *Latrodectus mactans*, the black-widow spider in its snare. After Kaston 1953, courtesy of H. E. Jaques and Wm. C. Brown Company, Publishers.

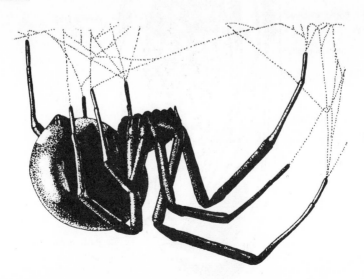

fourth and fifth opisthosomal segments form *spinnerets*. There is a maximum of two pairs of spinnerets per appendage, but most spiders retain only three pairs of the spin-

ning organs. A large number of spinning tubes commonly occur in each spinneret. These tubes may be modified into a number of types, each providing a characteristic kind

Fig. 14-16 *Argiope*, sagittal section of a spider to show internal anatomy. After Buck and Keister 1950, *Selected Invertebrate Types* (F. A. Brown, Jr., ed.), courtesy of John Wiley & Sons, Inc.

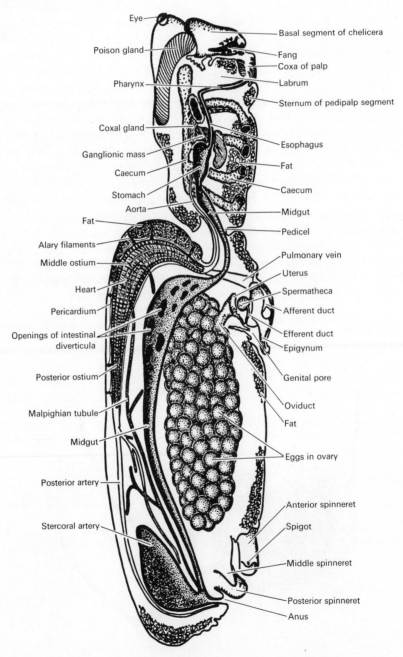

of silk strand. In some spiders with three pairs of spinnerets a perforated transverse plate called a *cribellum,* probably homologous with the first pair of spinnerets in spiders having four pairs, is correlated with a comblike bristle arrangement called a *calamistrum* on the metatarsi of the posterior legs.

Fig. 14-17 Various spider webs and snares. (a) Colony of *Uloborus*; (b) web of *Theridiosoma*; (c) *Zygiella* snare; (d) web of *Hyptiotes.* (a), (b), and (c) after J. Millot 1949, *Traité de Zoologie,* Tome VI (P. Grassé, ed.), courtesy of Masson et Cie. (d) After Kaston 1953, courtesy of H. E. Jaques and Wm. C. Brown Company, Publishers.

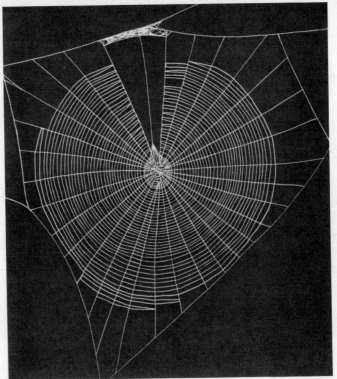

Silk is used by spiders in a variety of ways. It serves as a cover for the egg-sacs. It may be used in aerial transport, especially by young spiders. A strand is emitted by the spider which has climbed to some convenient height. This strand is wafted by a breeze, and when sufficiently long it can support the young spider, which may be carried great distances. Silk is used in the construction of webs or snares. These webs may be irregular networks or beautifully symmetrical (Fig. 14-17), and some may have a funnel-shaped retreat for the owner. Some webs are flat; others are variously domed. Tunnels of

spiders in the ground are silk-lined and even may be provided with trapdoors (Fig. 14-18). Some of the silk in webs may be adhesive, elastic, or both, and is efficient in capturing prey, which may be wrapped in a silken shroud by the spider. Another type of strand emitted by spiders is called the dragline. Dragline silk, sometimes used in the production of webs, also serves as a line of retreat to familiar territory when produced by a spider venturing from the web.

Cloudsley-Thompson discusses the forma-

Fig. 14-18 *Bothriocyrtum,* trapdoor spider in its nest. After Kaston 1953, courtesy of H. E. Jaques and Wm. C. Brown Company, Publishers.

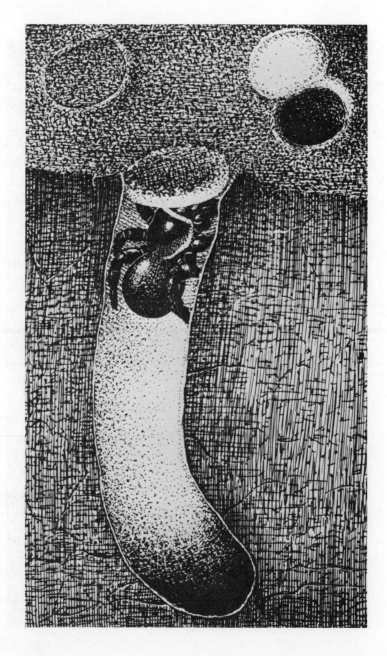

tion of an orb web. The outer frame is produced first, then a series of radii. These radii are stabilized by several closely placed spirals at their point of confluence. Next, working from the center out, the spider adds a wider-spaced spiral which serves as a temporary framework. When the spider reaches the periphery, it begins spinning the viscid or adhesive silk, working once more toward the center. As the old nonviscid framework is reached, it is destroyed. Spiders vary in renewing the web: some perform this work daily, others only when the weather is satisfactory, or when the reduced efficiency of the web necessitates repair.

Typically, the female spider is much larger than the male, and mating is a hazardous undertaking for him. If the female is not receptive, he may be killed. In some spiders, the male's intentions are indicated by a courtship promenade. In preparation for mating, the male spins a small web upon which a drop of sperm is deposited. The male spider then applies the copulatory organs on the enlarged terminal segment of the pedipalps to the sperm droplet and the sperm is transferred to these structures, which in the simpler forms are spiral tubes ending in bulbs. At copulation these spiral tubes enter the sperm receptacles of the female. Rarely the male is killed after pairing.

There are several items of special interest concerning spiders. One of these is the presence of poison glands. It has already been noted that scorpions inject poison by means of a caudal sting. False scorpions have poison glands which open on the pedipalps, while the chelicerae are the poison fangs of spiders. Although the bite of several species of spiders may cause from mild to very painful symptoms, the only spider in the United States that has a really dangerous venom is the hourglass or shoe-button spider, *Latrodectus mactans*. The name of "hourglass" comes from the shape of the red or orange markings characteristic of the under abdomen; the name "shoe-button" from the

characteristic size and shape of this relatively small black spider. *Latrodectus* spp. occur from southern Canada to Chile. *Latrodectus mactans* is particularly abundant in southern and western states but absent from Canada. Its irregular, coarse web may occur around old lumber piles, outbuildings, rock piles, and the underside of privy seats. The neurotoxin produces severe abdominal rigidity, high blood pressure and temperature, labored breathing, and other serious symptoms. Mortality rate is estimated to be about four per cent. Related spiders of this genus are dangerous arachnids in other parts of the world.

One spider, *Argyroneta aquatica,* is of special ecological interest. This spider swims under water as well as spinning a web in that environment. It utilizes a balloon or diving bell of silk to carry air bubbles down from the surface.

There are over 20,000 species of spiders in some 2,800 recognized genera. The group has a geologic history from the Carboniferous to Recent. *Agelena, Agelenopsis, Eurypelma, Lycosa, Latrodectus, Araneus.*

Order Solifugae The Solifugae is a group of about 800 species which bear such common names as "false spiders" or "wind scorpions." They differ from true spiders in that the abdomen shows a distinct segmentation, and special structures called "racquet organs" occur on the fourth pair of legs. As in Uropygi, the whip scorpions, the first pair of legs has more of a tactile than a locomotor function (Fig. 14-19).

Solifugae tend to be tropical and nocturnal and usually inhabit arid regions; some that do occur in more temperate climates hibernate or become inactive in winter. This order is well represented in north Africa, in the warmer southern areas of Europe, in Asia Minor, and India. Two families are represented in the United States, primarily in the far west, but some have been found near hot springs in the north central states. Related species occur on the western coast of South America.

These arachnids are ferocious, carnivorous predators. Mostly they utilize insects for foods, but scorpions, centipedes, spiders, and vertebrates including mice, birds, and lizards are sometimes caught and eaten. Solifugids are swift runners and capture the prey by running it down or springing upon it. They possess enormous chelicerae and pedipalps. Poison glands appear to be lacking. Surface spines and setae are common in this group. Respiration is solely by trachea which open by seven spiracles, three sets of which are paired. The geological history goes back to the Carboniferous. *Eremobates, Galeodes.*

Order Ricinulei These small arachnids, mostly less than 10 millimeters long, have a short, compact body and bear a superficial

resemblance to ticks. Only a few hundred specimens are known and these belong in two Carboniferous and two Recent genera. Eyes are absent and other sense organs show little structural identity. The cephalothorax is not segmented but bears an attached movable plate, the *cucullus,* along its anterior edge. Both chelicerae and pedipalps are chelate. The abdomen is composed of nine segments, only four of which are readily visible dorsally. The three caudal segments form a pygidium.

Most of the specimens found have been from the western coast of tropical Africa, Central America and adjacent areas of South America, and the Rio Grande and Amazon River basins. Most specimens have been found among moist fallen leaves, but some occur in caves, and some found after a rain in sandy soil of the Rio Grande may have been washed from caverns. *Cryptocellus* occurs in the New World, and *Ricinoides (Cryptostemma)* is found in Africa.

Class III Pycnogonida This class is represented by about 500 species and is divided into two orders. The Palaeopantopoda is known only from the Devonian; the Pantopoda from Devonian to Recent. The extinct order

Fig. 14-19 *Eremobates*, Solifugae. After Petrunkevitch 1955, from "*Treatise on Invertebrate Paleontology*," courtesy of Geological Society of America and University of Kansas Press.

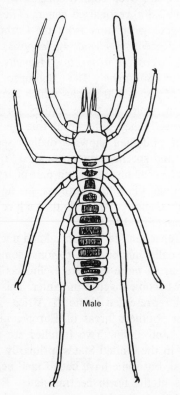

Male

Fig. 14-20 *Nymphon*, Pycnogonida. After Snodgrass 1952, courtesy of the Comstock Publishing Associates.

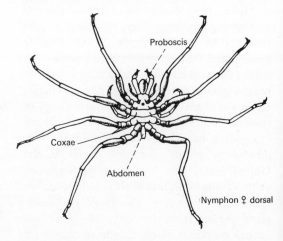

Proboscis

Coxae

Abdomen

Nymphon ♀ dorsal

lacked a proboscis and retained an abdomen of two or three reduced segments. The Pantopoda retain a proboscis and have an abdomen that is a nonsegmented nodule. The following description applies to the Pantopoda (Fig. 14-20). They are semisedentary on the ocean floor, existing from the intertidal zone (Fig. 1-2) into deep water where the adults feed on various soft-bodied animals. Pantopoda seems especially well adapted to the cold waters of Arctic and Antarctic oceans. The young are generally parasitic in or on coelenterates and molluscs. The gonopores are located on near-proximal leg segments rather than on the abdomen as in most Arachnomorpha. Three pairs of appendages occur in front of four pairs of greatly elongated walking legs, although an additional pair of walking legs occur in some species. The most anterior appendages are the chelicerae, followed closely by segmented palpiform structures. The third pair of appendages are leglike. They are always present in the male and usually in the female. These appendages are called *ovigers,* since the male carries the eggs in a spherical mass attached to them. *Nymphon.*

PHYLOGENETIC CONSIDERATIONS

The Trilobita appeared in the lower Cambrian and became extinct in the Permian, but their decline began at least 145 million years earlier during the Silurian, and all of their fossil remains have been found in conjunction with those of forms of known marine habitat. General similarity of structure indicates a comparatively conservative group, with relatively slight adaptive modifications. Except for the antennae, all trilobite appendages show close uniformity. Such an interpretation supports an affinity between the trilobite and the crustacean appendage. In the typical biramous appendage of Crustacea, the exopodite articulates with the second segment (basipodite). A lateral projection of the appendage from the first segment (coxopodite) can be considered

an epipodite. Some authorities (esp. Størmer) have equated the outer ramus of the trilobite appendage with an epipodite from its supposed origin on the proximal segment. This interpretation brings the trilobite appendage into closer similarity with the legs of some Arachnomorpha. It receives additional support from correlation in the number of segments in legs of the two groups. Perhaps the most that can be said is that Trilobita and Arachnomorpha arose from a common Prototrilobite ancestor in the Precambrian, with perhaps an even more remote linkage to the Crustacea. Størmer (1955) (Fig. 14-21) gives the known stratigraphic distribution and possible phylogenetic relationships of the Chelicerata (Arachnomorpha).

The Arachnomorpha can be divided logically into two classes: Merostomata and Arachnida. The former are aquatic and predominantly marine, the latter primarily terrestrial, although a few have returned to an aquatic habitat.

Early larval stages in *Limulus* have indications of a four-segment stage reminiscent of trilobites. The horseshoe crab differs further from Trilobita by the inclusion of seven segments in the prosoma, whereas the Trilobite prosoma or cephalon has four. In addition, Arachnomorpha lack appendages that originate preorally, as is the case for trilobite antennae. The arachnomorph chelicerae are secondarily preoral as shown by their brain innervation.

The Eurypterida were Palaeozoic Merostomata that in some cases reached a length of eight feet. Many of them were in a freshwater habitat. In addition, some bear remarkable but superficial structural similarity to present-day scorpions; both are highly specialized and much of their similarity may be a convergence.

The Aglaspida are Merostomata which have been found in the early Palaeozoic from lower Cambrian to upper Ordovician. Although some of them superficially bear close resemblance to the trilobites, they have arachnomorph features, the prosomal region

Chelicerata

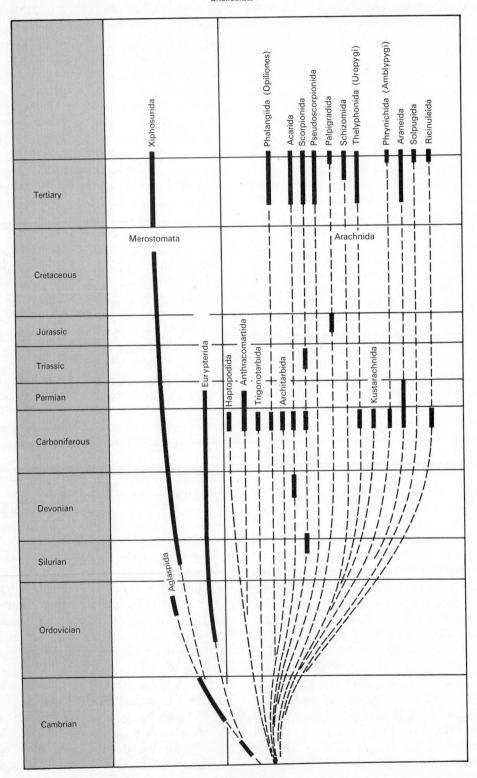

retaining six pairs of appendages including a pair of chelicerae but lacking antennae. The Aglaspida may have given rise on the one hand to Eurypterida, retaining an elongated body with considerable flexibility, and on the other to Xiphosurida with increased fusion and development of relative rigid tagmata and with adaptation to crawling or groveling. Eurypterids were probably better adapted to locomotion by swimming.

The Arachnida are air-breathing terrestrial animals with the body divided into two major tagmata: the cephalothorax or prosoma, with six pairs of appendages indicating at least six segments, and the abdomen or opisthosoma, primitively of twelve segments. None of the prosomal appendages are primitively preoral. Reduction in apparent segmentation is a common trend. In only one order does the carapace fold under to form a doublure, a structural feature present in trilobites and in Xiphosura and Eurypterida. There is some tendency for the mouth to shift backward, but this condition is already seen in *Limulus*. The horseshoe crab has coxal protuberances called gnathobases which function analogous to jaws, but even in this animal the food is ground in a gizzard. The Arachnida all ingest liquid food, and this is correlated with a considerable development of intestinal diverticula.

The Arachnida seem to have appeared in geologic history suddenly. The oldest fossils are those of some scorpions which were contemporaries of Eurypterida in the Silurian, and the lineage of Recent scorpions can be traced to a single family in the Carboniferous, while Acarina (the next oldest group) can be traced back to the Devonian. This group

has lost all trace of abdominal segmentation. Among arachnids they show the greatest variation in habitat. It has been suggested that the relatively conservative geologic history of such diverse arachnids as scorpions and mites since the Carboniferous support the hypothesis that many other arachnid orders were well established by then.

In the evolutionary consideration of internal structures, several features are particularly significant. Excretory coxal glands of coelomoduct origin show reduction in the number of segmental orifices. There is increased concentration of the nervous system ganglia into the prosoma. In these terrestrial animals there is a decreasing number of book lungs and a substitution or survival of trachea as respiratory organs. Trachea appear in various arthropod classes, which suggests two alternatives: either common ancestry or separate origin with convergence.

It seems obvious that study of the ancestry of the Arachnomorpha has not yet reached a definitive answer. Probably the Eurypterida already were too specialized to serve as the ancestral line. The Silurian scorpion, *Palaeophonus,* apparently shows subsegmentation of the second abdominal segment with retention of the first abdominal somite to produce apparently thirteen abdominal segments. Lack of subsegmentation in other Arachnida thus debars Silurian scorpions as ancestral. Some doubt has been expressed that the unknown ancestor of Trilobita and Arachnomorpha can be traced to the same proto-onychophoral line presumably progenitor of the myriapods and insects; but Crustacea apparently could have arisen from a prototrilobite ancestor.

Fig. 14-21 Diagram illustrating stratigraphic distribution and inferred phylogenetic relationships of Arachnomorpha (Chelicerata). The oldest known representatives of the Arachnida are Silurian scorpionids. The merostomes and arachnids probably diverged before the earliest Cambrian. Størmer suggests that the abrupt appearance of many arachnid orders in the Late Carboniferous reflects improved conditions of fossil preservation rather than origin in the Late Paleozoic era. After Størmer 1955, from "*Treatise on Invertebrate Pale- ontology,*" courtesy of Geological Society of America and University of Kansas Press.

REFERENCES

Cloudsley-Thompson, J. L. Spiders, scorpions, centipedes, and mites. New York: Pergamon, 1958.

Comstock, J. H., The spider book (rev. ed. by W. J. Gertsch). Ithaca: Comstock, 1948.

Hedgpeth, J. W., The Pycnogonida of the Western North Atlantic and the Carribean. Proc. U. S. Nat. Mus., 97:157, 1948.

———, On the phylogeny of the Pycnogonida. Acta Zoologica, 35:193, 1954.

Kaston, B. J., Spiders of Connecticut. Conn. Geol. Nat. Hist. Surv. Bull., 70:874, 1948.

———, and E. Kaston, How to know the spiders. Dubuque, Iowa: W. C. Brown, 1953.

Millot, J., M. Vachon and others, Classe des Arachnides. In (P. Grassé, ed.) Traité de zoologie, Tome VI. Paris: Masson et Cie, 1949.

Patten, W., and W. A. Redenbaugh, Studies on Limulus, II, The nervous system of Limulus polyphemus, with observations on the general anatomy. J. Morphol. 16:91, 1900.

Petrunkevitch, A., A study of Palaeozoic Arachnida. Trans. Conn. Acad. Arts and Sci., 37:60, 1949.

Raasch, G. O., Cambrian Merostomata. Special papers, Geol. Soc. Amer., No. 19, 146 pp., 1939.

Savory, Theodore, Arachnida. New York: Academic, 1964.

Shrock, R. R., and W. H. Twenhofel, Principles of invertebrate paleontology (2nd ed.). New York: McGraw, 1953.

Størmer, Leif, A. Petrunkevitch, and J. W. Hedgpeth, Arthropoda, 2: Chelicerata, Pycnogonida, and Palaeoisopus. In (R. D. Moore, ed.) Treatise on invertebrate paleontology. Lawrence: U. of Kansas and Geol. Soc. Amer., 1955.

———, Classes des Trilobites et Merostomoidea. In (P. Grassé, ed.) Traité de Zoologie, Tome VI. Paris: Masson et Cie, 1949.

———, Phylogeny and taxonomy of fossil horseshoe crabs. J. Paleon., 26:630, 1952.

Tiegs, O. W., and S. M. Manton, The evolution of the Arthropoda. Biol. Rev., 33:255, 1958.

Vachon, M., The biology of scorpions. Endeavour, 12:80, 1953.

Whittington, H. B., The ontogeny of Trilobites. Biol. Rev., 32:421, 1957.

15

CRUSTACEA

Crustacea for the most part are free-living marine and fresh-water arthropods. The subphylum is large, containing more than 26,000 species, and includes such familiar animals as crabs, lobsters, shrimp, barnacles, and wood lice. These few examples in no sense encompass the morphological diversity present in the Crustacea. The considerable frequency of pelagic habit and adaptive response to the consequent environmental changes might well account for many structural modifications.

The fundamentally aquatic habitat of Crustacea appears to be less restrictive to adaptive response than is the case for arthropods in other environments. Crustacea vary in length from the microscopic to the giant Japanese spider crab which may have legs more than five feet long. The crustacean body varies in form and there is great diversity in the regionation of body segments and in the structural adaptation of accompanying appendages. A number of Crustacea have bizarre shapes, including asymmetrical development correlated with unusual habitat or with a sexual dimorphism. There is conspicuous variation in color which includes reds, browns, yellows, greens, blues, and black. Many of these colors exist as granules in chromatophores in the integument or as retinal pigments of the compound eye. Changes of color, at least in the integument, have been demonstrated in the larger crustaceans to be commonly under hormone control, and it is a fertile field for further endocrine investigation.

The jointed appendages characteristic of all arthropods are of particular interest in the Crustacea. Many of these appendages are specialized for multiple functions. The appendages in a single species may be modified for the functions of sensory perception, feeding, respiration, swimming, copulation, reproduction, and protection. The appendages of bottom dwellers may be modified for walking, digging, and burrowing, and at least one marine isopod, the gribble, bores into timber immersed in water. In some Crustacea the appendages have lost all locomotory function; these animals are stalked or sessile. In this group are the familiar barnacles, frequently seen on piers exposed by low tide.

The characteristic environment of Crustacea is aquatic. In keeping with such a medium, respiration usually is accomplished through the body surface directly or through flattened or plumose projections of that surface called gills or branchiae. Usually the gills are lateral projections of proximal segments of thoracic appendages or of nearby body wall. The inner surface of the skeletal gill-cover often functions as a respiratory membrane. In the isopods (wood lice or pill bugs) and in stomatopods (mantis shrimp) flattened projections of abdominal appendages replace thoracic structures for respiration. In some isopods and other semiterrestrial or terrestrial crustaceans, chambers or pouches shelter respiratory surfaces utilized in aerial respiration. Among isopods, these may take the form of branching tubular structures called *pseudotracheae*.

The name Crustacea refers to the hardness of the chitinous exoskeleton, which in restricted areas commonly is impregnated with minerals, principally calcium carbonate. The skeleton across the joints of the body and of the appendages is not calcified and provides a flexible, water-impermeable collar joining the more heavily sclerotized regions.

One group of Crustacea (branchiopods) are almost totally restricted to fresh water, although one representative, the brine shrimp *(Artemia)*, has world-wide distribution in salt lakes; experimentally it has survived in salt concentrations from that in 10 per cent sea water to mixtures in which sodium chloride is precipitating. Other crustacean groups are entirely marine, and still others, although predominantly marine, are represented by brackish- and fresh-water and frequently even terrestrial forms.

GENERAL AND SPECIAL FEATURES

Crustacea are serially segmented animals with a pair of jointed appendages typically on each segment. The segments or somites exist between retained terminal regions which do not participate in the ontogenetic metamerism. The anterior region, called the *acron,* appears to be homologus to the prostomium in annelids, which contains a preoral ganglion associated with sense organs. In crustaceans, the labrum, eyes, and the antennules (first antennae) arise on the acron. The naupliar larva of crustaceans has uniramous antennules. The posterior unsegmented region is called the *telson.* It lacks the pair of appendages typical of true segments, but often bears two projecting rami, called styles, cercopods, or caudal furca.

Behind the acron the first definitive segment appears. In Crustacea, the antennae (second antennae of some authors) develop on it. True segmentation is evidenced internally as well as externally, and the correlation of a nerve ganglion for each segment is particularly basic. The embryonic ganglion of this second antennal segment arises postorally, but its definitive position is preoral, where it unites with the nervous tissue of the acron or cephalic lobe to form the "brain." Because of its reorientation, the fate of this somite in arthropods has received considerable attention, and it has been variously designated as the *tritocerebral, premandibular,* or *cheliceral* segment among others. The somite bearing the chelicerae in the Arachnomorpha corresponds to the crustacean antennal segment.

The simplest head structure among Crustacea is called the *protocephalon* and exists in the most primitive order (Anostraca) of the subclass Branchiopoda. A similar head is present in *Anaspides,* a primitive member of the Malacostraca, the large subclass that includes crayfish, crabs, and lobsters. The protocephalon, consisting of the acron and the tritocerebral segment, bears the labrum (an unpaired medial lobe that is the morphological anterior extremity), the eyes, the antennules, and the antennae. Although the protocephalon represents the first true head in Crustacea, in most crustaceans three additional postoral segments are incorporated with it. These three segments respectively bear the mandibles, and the first and second maxillae. Because these three pairs of appendages are associated with feeding, the somites are called *gnathal* segments.

Behind the segment bearing the second maxillae, the trunk of the crustacean shows a varied disposition to be separated into two regions, respectively the thorax and the abdomen. In the more primitive Crustacea the appendages of these segments are very similar in structure; in others the thoracic segments are limb-bearing, while the abdominal appendages are variously reduced or absent.

Carapace

An organ of remarkable diversity has a widespread distribution among Crustacea. This structure, called the carapace, develops as a fold which grows from the posterior margin of the second maxillary segment. The carapace fuses with a varying number of the dorsal plates (*terga*) of the thoracic skeleton. A relatively simple form of carapace occurs in *Triops (Apus)* of the branchiopod order, Notostraca. In *Triops*, it provides a flattened shield superficially reminiscent of the arachnomorph *Limulus*, the horseshoe crab. In the lobster and the crayfish, the carapace covers all of the thorax dorsally and grows ventrally over the paired series of gills to provide lateral shields called *branchiostegites*. In the malacostracan crustacean orders, Anaspidacea, Isopoda, and Amphipoda, a carapace is absent, but in the latter two the absence of a carapace is considered to be secondary, and in *Anaspides* a dorsal fusion of the second maxillary segment with

the segment behind it, bearing the maxillipeds, might be indicative of an early carapace primordium. A carapace is lacking in the branchiopodan order Anostraca, as indicated by the name. In several groups of crustaceans the carapace is divided into paired lateral plates or bivalves. These are closed by adductor muscles, not homologous in the various groups. This bivalve type of carapace is found in Conchostraca, Cladocera, and Ostracoda, as well as in the primitive malacostracan, *Nebalia*. In barnacles (subclass Cirripedia) the carapace forms fleshy folds (the mantle) which often are incompletely supported by hard, shelly plates.

Limb Specialization

Crustacean appendages (Fig. 15-1) structurally have undergone many adaptive modifications. Associated with a benthonic life, the primary function of crustacean appendages was locomotor. When the crustacean became a planktonic animal, various appendages became adapted for a new type of progression to facilitate food procurement, escape from enemies, and to provide for sexual reproduction. The planktonic life provided opportunity for the tremendous adaptive radiation seen in Crustacea. The primitive function unquestionably has great bearing on any hypothesis postulating the structure of the ancestral appendage. Besides having locomotor function, appendages are variously sensory, respiratory, food-getting, copulatory, and reproductive. In parasitic forms, appendages may be modified for attachment. Most appendages, especially in more primitive crustaceans, are adapted to two or more functions. Perhaps the high degree of plasticity seen in the adaptation of higher malacostracans to efficient locomotor progress following experimental amputation of various legs and combinations of legs is evidence of the fundamental labile potential of the Crustacea.

Fig. 15-1 Various crustacean appendages. After G. Smith 1904, courtesy of the original publishers of *Cambridge Natural History*, Vol. IV, Macmillan & Co., Ltd.

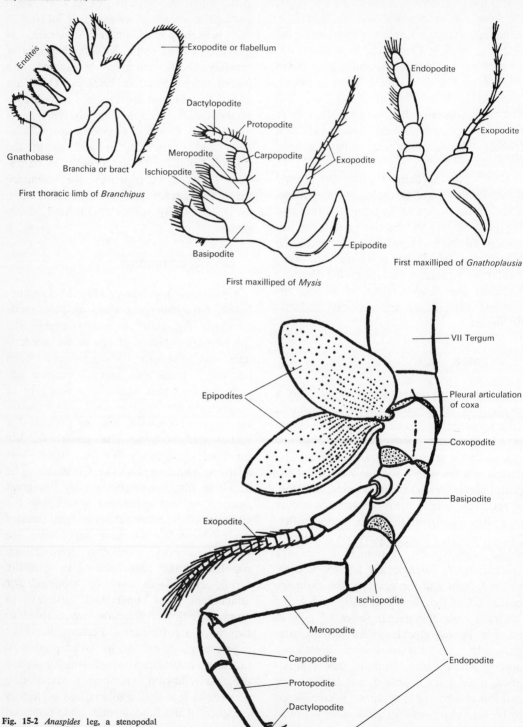

Endites

Exopodite or flabellum

Gnathobase

Branchia or bract

First thoracic limb of *Branchipus*

Dactylopodite

Protopodite

Meropodite

Carpopodite

Ischiopodite

Exopodite

Basipodite

Epipodite

First maxilliped of *Mysis*

Endopodite

Exopodite

First maxilliped of *Gnathoplausia*

VII Tergum

Pleural articulation of coxa

Coxopodite

Basipodite

Epipodites

Exopodite

Ischiopodite

Meropodite

Endopodite

Carpopodite

Protopodite

Dactylopodite

Fig. 15-2 *Anaspides* leg, a stenopodal type. After Snodgrass 1952, courtesy of the Comstock Publishing Associates.

At first glance the various crustacean appendages appear to have little in common, but more extensive study indicates that they fall into two main categories: (1) the *stenopodia,* which are cylindrical or rodlike and typically segmented, and (2) the *phyllopodia,* which are flattened, leaflike, or foliaceous, and unsegmented. The general flexibility of the latter appendage makes joints unnecessary; its effectiveness is due to turgor maintained hydrostatically. Both structural types occur in the same appendage of some crustaceans, such as the primitive malacostracan, *Nebalia.* This fact suggests that one or both types are modified from some primitive archetype (Fig. 15-1).

The stenopodium is probably closer to the archetypal walking limb (Fig. 15-2). Typically it is developed with a base *(protopodite)* of two segments, the proximal one called *coxopodite,* and the distal one, *basipodite.* In *Anaspides* (a malacostracan retaining a number of primitive features) a large ramus, the *endopodite,* appears to continue as an axis of the protopodite. The endopodite lies mediad to a smaller lateral ramus called the *exopodite.* In many crustaceans one or the other ramus is reduced or missing in one or more pairs of appendages. From the lateral aspect of the coxopodite, one (and rarely two) additional processes may develop. These are *epipodites,* which most commonly function as gills and which develop in a variety of shapes.

The malacostracan thoracic limb carries a natatory exopodite, an ambulatory endopodite, and two branchial epipodites. In these crustaceans one to three of the first thoracic appendages may be modified for gnathal function and are called *maxillipeds;* the others, typically for ambulation, are called *pereiopods.* The endopodite bears a constant number of segments (Fig. 15-2). Beginning proximal to the basipodite, these are designated consecutively as ischiopodite, meropodite, carpopodite, propodite, and dactylopodite. These divisions, plus the basipodite and coxopodite, suggest a basic limb of

seven segments. This is disputed by those investigators who derive the crustaceans from trilobites, in which the terminal median claw is identified as an additional segment *(pretarsus).* The identification of still another segment *(precoxa)* interposed between the coxa (coxopodite) and body wall of a trilobite would bring the total to nine segments. The recently discovered benthonic crustacean *Hutchinsoniella,* reported to have an eight-segmented leg, lends support to derivation of crustaceans from trilobites.

In the phyllopodium, in which turgidity is maintained by the blood, there is an axial portion bearing on its inner or median margin a series of six projections called *endites.* These may be provided with special muscles for limited movement (Fig. 15-3). One or more of the proximal endites are medially expanded and, in conjunction with those from the opposite side of the animal, perform food-manipulative functions. Such structures are called *gnathobases.* On its lateral or outer edge the phyllopodium commonly bears two projections called *exites.* The distal exite is homologous with the exopodite of the stenopodium and is provided with special muscles for swimming. The proximal exite, called a *bract,* has no muscle and performs a respiratory function. Ontogenetically it is an epipodite.

Beginning with the second antennae crustacean paired appendages have all been

Fig. 15-3 *Branchipus* (*Eubranchipus*) trunk appendage—a phyllopodal type. From Hertwig (after Gerstäcker), *A Manual of Zoology* (translated and edited by J. S. Kingsley) 1902, Holt, Rinehart & Winston, Inc.

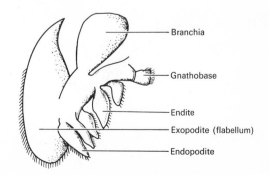

Branchia

Gnathobase

Endite

Exopodite (flabellum)

Endopodite

Fig. 15-4 The appendages of the lobster. From Schechter 1959, courtesy of Prentice-Hall, Inc.

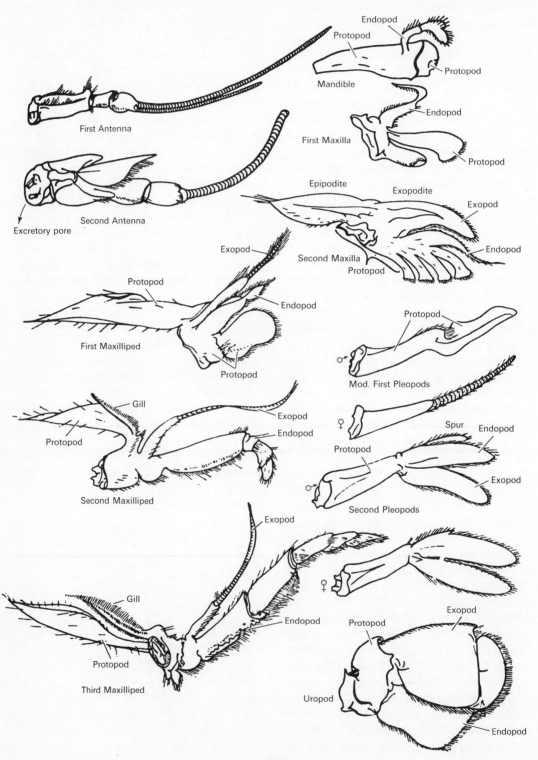

(a)

derived from a biramous prototype of the body limb. Reversion to an apparent uniramous condition is due to loss of one of the two rami, most commonly the exopodite. In many instances the total appendage has been suppressed.

The first limb-derived appendages are the antennae, which were originally postoral.

General familiarity with some larger crustaceans, such as the lobster or crayfish, clearly suggests a sensory function for antennae, and such a function is common for most Malacostraca (Fig. 15-4), but in other Crustacea the principal function of the antennae is natatory. In some males, antennae serve as claspers during copulation. Some parasitic

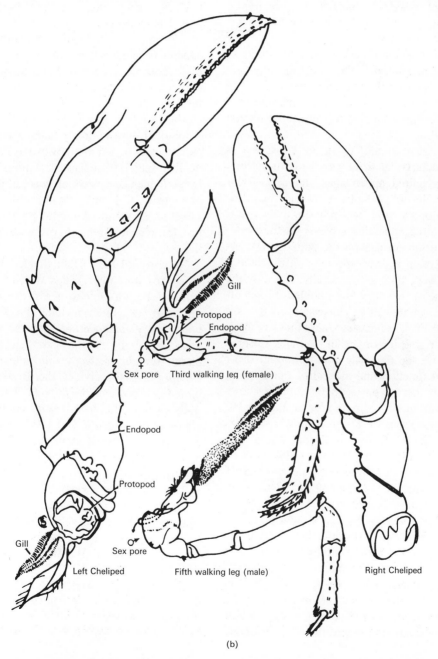

Gill

Protopod

Endopod

♀
Sex pore   Third walking leg (female)

Endopod

Protopod

Gill

♂
Sex pore

Left Cheliped   Fifth walking leg (male)   Right Cheliped

(b)

crustaceans have holdfast organs developed from antennae.

The next appendages are the mandibles, which are primarily for gnathal function and normally are closely associated with the mouth. The mandible is present not only in Crustacea (in which it frequently bears a palp), but also in myriapods and insects. Whether this fact indicates a close monophyletic grouping or is the result of convergence is disputed.

The mandibles never function alone as gnathal appendages. The two following segments, carrying the first and second maxillae respectively, are commonly incorporated with the protocephalon to form the cephalon or head.

The postcephalic trunk in Crustacea is often differentiated into an anterior portion bearing paired appendages and a posterior section devoid of limbs. However, in a few branchiopods and typically in malacostracans paired appendages occur on the posterior portion. In general the paired trunk appendages in a given species of Branchiopoda are very similar structurally, and only the first one or two pairs are modified. Frequently this modification illustrates sexual dimorphism, as is the case where they are modified for grasping organs in the male. In some copepods the first pair may be modified for gnathal function and are called maxillipeds. The number of postcephalic somites shows great variation. There may be as many as 42 in some species of *Triops* (*Apus*), whereas in the Ostracoda only indistinct traces of a few segments occur at most. Malacostraca are characterized by a constant number of trunk segments and appendages. The trunk can be divided into an anterior *thorax* and a posterior *abdomen* by the structural differences of the respective appendages and by the presence of the male genital pore on the last thoracic segment. The malacostracan abdominal appendages are typically biramous. The first five pairs, called *pleopods,* may be modified from a primitive swimming function for reproduction or respiration. The last pair,

called *uropods,* are flattened and with the telson form a powerful tail fan.

MAJOR SUBDIVISIONS OF SUBPHYLUM CRUSTACEA

Classification of the Crustacea, particularly in the higher categories, is far from definitive. The evidence supporting the phylogenetic position of these higher ranks often is not conclusive. New genera are continually being discovered, and some of these possess combinations of characteristics that argue against their placement in existing orders and subclasses, so that new ones must be erected. Additional information is being accumulated on species assigned to many orders, and some of this material suggests relationships between higher groups which was not indicated previously. Calman's classification (1909) serves as the standard and the point of departure for later revisions of crustacean systematics.

Recently (1963) Dahl divided the class Crustacea into five groups which he called cohorts. In addition to the *Ostracoda* and *Malacostraca,* these include the *Branchiopoda,* the *Cephalocarida,* and the *Maxillopoda* containing *Mystacocarida, Archicopepoda, Branchiura, Copepoda,* and probably *Cirripedia.* Dahl divides the Branchiopoda into *Anostraca* and *Phyllopoda.* The Phyllopoda include the *Notostraca* and the *Onychura* (*Conchostraca* and *Cladocera*), both with clawlike furcal rami. The Archicopepoda is represented by the Triassic genus, *Euthycarcinus.*

The subphylum Crustacea contains a single class (Crustacea) which has all of the characteristics of the subphylum. The division of the class into eight subclasses follows the scheme from Waterman and Chace (1960).

SUBCLASS 1 CEPHALOCARIDA This subclass has been erected for a primitive genus, *Hutchinsoniella,* dicovered in 1955 in Long Island Sound. This crustacean is a small, benthonic hermaphroditic animal characterized by a broad carapace and a prominent caudal furca. A second genus, *Lightiella,* has been added.

SUBCLASS 2 BRANCHIOPODA These small, free-living crustaceans have a variable number of body segments bearing relatively uniform leaflike appendages. Terminally, the abdomen carries a terminal pair of processes called a *caudal furca.* The geological history goes back to the Silurian or Devonian Period.

SUBCLASS 3 OSTRACODA These minute crustaceans occur usually in fresh and in salt water, but one species is terrestrial. The indistinctly segmented body is contained within a bivalved carapace. There are never more than four pairs of postmandibular trunk appendages. The mandibles have large, sometimes biramous palps. The abdomen is represented by the caudal furca with slender or platelike, often spined, processes. Ostracod geologic history goes back to the Ordovician Period.

SUBCLASS 4 MYSTACOCARIDA The single genus (*Derocheilocaris*) for which this subclass was erected is based on specimens found in Long Island Sound in 1943. The genus has been found more recently on the coasts of southern Africa, the Mediterranean, and South America. These minute crustaceans are more primitive than those of the next subclass, Copepoda, to which they are related, and Dahl (1956) thinks they help to bridge the gap between the copepods and the anostracan branchiopods.

SUBCLASS 5 COPEPODA These mostly microscopic crustaceans typically occur in fresh and in salt water and are free-living, commensal, or parasitic, but some Harpacticoida are semiterrestrial. These crustaceans typically have thirteen segments between the labrum and the telson which bears the caudal furca. Copepods have no geologic history, but the Triassic genus, *Euthycarcinus,* has been placed in a closely related group, *Archicopepoda.*

SUBCLASS 6 BRANCHIURA These ectoparasites of fish and amphibians are occasionally grouped with the copepods, but they differ in having compound eyes and gonopores on the fifth instead of the seventh trunk segment. The branchiuran body is dorso-ventrally flattened and possesses a laterally expanded head-fold or carapace. *Argulus* is the best known genus.

SUBCLASS 7 CIRRIPEDIA These exclusively marine crustaceans, whose best-known representatives are barnacles, as adults are attached or parasitic. The parasitic forms are highly modified, but go through distinctive nauplius and cypris larval stages similar to nonparasitic species. The cypris larva possesses all the appendages of the adult. Largely because of the bivalved shell, this larva shows a resemblance to the Ostracoda. The geologic record goes back to the Silurian or possibly the Ordovician period.

SUBCLASS 8 MALACOSTRACA This very large and very diverse group contains about 18,000 Recent species, which is approximately 70 per cent of the total number of living species described for all Crustacea. Malacostracans are mostly large crustaceans with compound, stalked eyes and typically a prominent carapace. The head is composed of five or six segments, depending upon whether the primitively preoral region is interpreted as representing one or two somites. In the more common view two somites are present in this region, but only the posterior one bears appendages and these are the antennules. Behind the antennules there are four cephalic segments, eight thoracic segments, and typically six abdominal segments all of which bear paired appendages. One primitive group (Leptostraca) have a seventh abdominal segment which lacks paired appendages. The male genital aperture opens on the last thoracic segment.

CARIDOID FACIES

The Malacostraca include such large crustaceans as lobsters, crayfish, crabs, and shrimp. In spite of the dissimilarity of mature specimens of these and other malacostracans, there is a uniformity of organization that suggests a template or archetype for the group (Fig. 15-5). The combination of structural features for this archetype is called the *caridoid facies.* This generalized malacostracan shows uniformity in the number of segments composing each body region or tagma, although embryonic Mysidacea and adult Leptostraca have seven instead of six abdominal segments. Some other common features include location of genital apertures, compound eyes on movable stalks, mandibles bearing palps, biflagellate antennules, antennae with scalelike exopodite, biramous abdominal appendages with the terminal pair flattened and with the telson forming a tail fan, and a carapace enclosing the thorax laterally. Considering the diversity within this subclass, it is evident that reduction, loss, or readaptation of one or more of these features has resulted in many departures from the archetype. Sanders (1963) has pointed out that the precaridoid morphology of Malacostraca is markedly similar to that of the Cephalocarida and concludes that the caridoid features appeared late in phylogeny.

ENTOMOSTRACA AND MALACOSTRACA

At one time the Crustacea were divided into two major groups. One of these was the taxonomic group (Malacostraca) which is still valid. The members of this group commonly possessed such features as large size, uniformity of body segments, appendages on all abdominal segments, a gastric mill, a caudally directed hepatopancreas, and a naupliar stage usually passed in the egg. All other Crustacea were grouped under the term Entomostraca. They were generally small with variable number of body segments, posterior abdominal segments often apodous, no gastric mill, the hepatopancreas directed forward, and usually a free-swimming nauplius. As a taxonomic category, Entomostraca is no longer valid, since some of the defining characters are only negative, and since their subgroups differ as much from each other as any of them do from the Malacostraca. The term Entomostraca has continued in use purely as a convenience for a composite designation of nonmalacostracan crustaceans.

FEEDING AND NUTRITION

Feeding patterns among Crustacea vary, but can be grouped into four categories. First,

Fig. 15-5 Generalized Shrimp. Most of the features parallel the caridoid facies. After Chace, Mackin, Hubricht, Banner, and Hobbs in (Ward and Whipple) *Fresh-Water Biology* (W. T. Edmondson, ed.) 2nd edition 1959, courtesy of John Wiley & Sons, Inc.

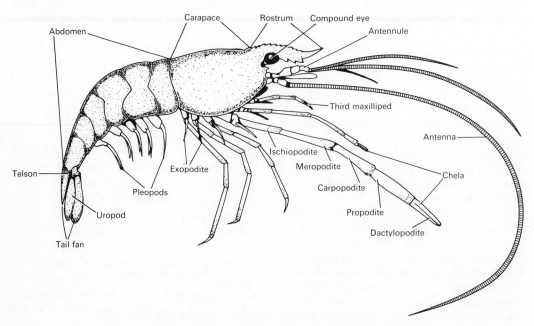

a number of Crustacea capture live animals. Some of the larger crustaceans, such as crabs and lobsters, are able to capture small fish as well as such invertebrates as worms, molluscs, and other crustaceans. Food is captured with the chela of the legs, manipulated by the third maxillipeds, and reduced to ingestible size by the mandibles. These crustaceans display considerable versatility, so that the functions of mandibles and maxillipeds may be reversed in the mechanical processes reducing the food to edible portions. Some crustaceans have specializations that serve to obtain food as well as in defense. In the pistol shrimp, *Alpheus (Crangon) californiensis,* one of the pincer-legs (*chelipeds*) is greatly enlarged and the movable "thumb" (dactylopodite) can be locked in an open position. When released, it snaps shut to stun the prey (Fig. 15-6).

In the stomatopod crustaceans (mantis shrimps) the second pair of thoracic appendages has been referred to as *jackknife claw,* with the distal segment flexed into a groove in the adjacent segment analogous to the jackknife handle. Mantis shrimps can slice in two such prey as shrimp. Since some larger ones reach almost a foot in length, they must be handled carefully to avoid injury.

Although most crustaceans do not have such specialized armaments as those just described, a great many of even the smaller ones are active predators.

A second and very common food source consists of nonliving animal matter. Scavenging, however, is usually a secondary food source, since many of the crustaceans which practice it are predators or omnivorous in feeding habits and may feed on seaweed and other algae.

A third category overlaps on the two just discussed. This feeding habit is called filter feeding. Since a great variety of adaptations to this method occur among Crustacea, its study is most important for the additional evidence it can offer on crustacean phylogeny. For instance, Dahl points out that the feeding current essential to efficient filter feeding in Branchiopoda (Phyllopoda and Anostraca) is produced by thoracic feet, and food is transported forward along the ventral food groove in part by action of the gnathobases of the appendages; but the feeding current of copepods and probably of the Mysta-

Fig. 15-7 Filtering apparatus in *Calanus*; (a) left maxilla from the right side showing caught planktonic organisms (*A,B,* and *C*); (b) filtering setae in transverse section (after Dennell) with arrows indicating direction of food-bearing current. After Marshall and Orr 1960, in the *Physiology of Crustacea*, Vol. I (T. H. Waterman, ed.), courtesy of Academic Press, Inc.

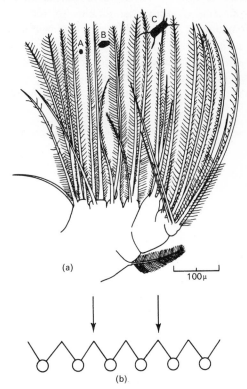

(a)

100µ

(b)

Fig. 15-6 A pistol shrimp, *Crangon californiensis.* (a) Lateral view; (b) the pistol hand "cocked." After MacGinitie and MacGinitie 1949, courtesy of the McGraw-Hill Book Company.

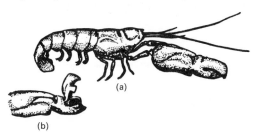

(a)

(b)

cocarida is a rotating current produced by the maxillae, and a series of gnathobases is not needed.

In addition to the need for a water current, whether induced or natural, it is essential to have some sort of filtering device (Fig. 15-7). This may occur on a variety of head and trunk appendages. The filtering mechanism commonly takes the form of pectinate or plumose setae, whose secondary fibrils overlap with those from nearby setae to produce an effective screen. Since varying appendages from antennules back to the trunk may function as filters, it is obvious that methods must have evolved to transfer food to the mouth. In the fairy shrimp, *Chirocephalus*, swimming produces a caudally directed current, and food is captured on trunk-limb filters (Fig. 15-8). Some setae on the next most caudal limb serve to comb caught particles toward the food groove. In this food groove a forward-directed current moves particles toward the mouth. The second maxillae are used as filters by many crustaceans. In the copepod, *Calanus*, the endites of the first maxillae lie against the filter. Their beat pulls water forward through the filter. Setae of nearby appendages comb the filter toward the mouth. Among the Ostracoda, the filters are developed on first maxillae or on the mandi-

bles or the two may work in conjunction. In some Malacostraca, particularly some amphipods, the antennules and antennae function as filters, and these animals depend upon natural water currents to catch suspended particles. In general, filtering mechanisms are used in capturing plankton, or in filtering bottom detritus, which is actively disturbed by many bottom feeders. A number of Crustacea are both plankton and detritus feeders, and frequently the captured particles are aggregated into masses by mucoid material secreted by glands, a process analogous to that seen in Mollusca.

A fourth category associated with food habits involves varied symbiotic relationships. Some crustaceans apparently do no injury to the host beyond utilizing food from the mucous ribbon, as do pea crabs within the mantle cavity of lamellibranch molluscs. Frequently these pea crabs can be found among the frozen oysters obtained at the supermarket. There are a number of ectoparasites which have modified mouthparts for attachment and sustenance. Many internal parasites show extensive degeneration of structures because of their parasitism. The cirriped *Sacculina*, commonly parasitic on crabs, is degenerated to an amorphic mass and its cirriped relationships are only recog-

Fig. 15-8 *Eubranchipus*. From Schechter 1959, courtesy of Prentice-Hall, Inc.

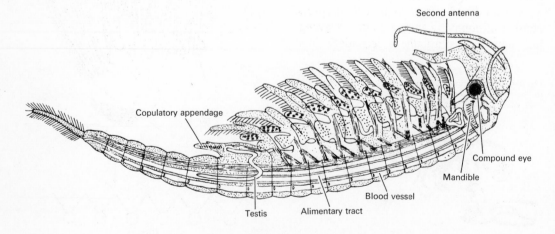

nizable during larval stages (Fig. 15-9). On the other hand, some crustaceans are parasitic only during larval stages. Copepods, cirripeds, and isopods are the principal crusta-cean groups with parasitic species.

The crustacean alimentary canal is usually a straight tube with an endodermal midgut of variable length between stomodaeum and

Fig. 15-9 (a) Nauplius and (b) Cypris stages of the parasitic cirripeded, *Sacculina.* 1,2, antennae; 3, mandible; *f*, cirrhous foot; *m*, muscles; *oc*, nauplius eye; *ov*, ovary anlagen. From Hertwig (after Delage), *A Manual of Zoology* (translated and edited by J. S. Kingsley) 1902, Holt, Rinehart & Winston, Inc.

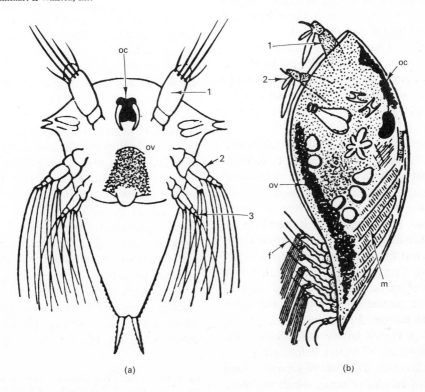

(a)   (b)

Fig. 15-10 Composite diagram of anterior portion of dissected crayfish. Teeth and denticles aid in trituration. Fine food particles are directed by the pyloric setae to the hepato-pancreas, while coarser material reaches the intestine. Adapted from various sources.

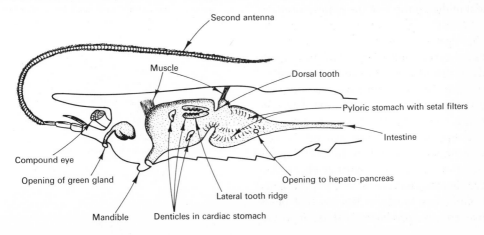

proctodaeum, both of which have a chitinous lining. The lumen of the esophagus opens to a widened chamber, which in the decapod Malacostraca is part of the stomodaeum. This chamber, called the cardiac stomach, contains the gastric mill. In the crayfish and lobster the gastric mill is mainly responsible for chewing the food (Fig. 15-10). For this purpose it is provided with three elongated teeth, two lateral and the third dorsal. The strings of food reaching the cardiac stomach are chewed by the teeth activated by the intrinsic stomach musculature, which unlike that in vertebrates is striated. Tooth action may be aided by extrinsic muscles between stomach and body wall.

The gastric mill in decapods has taken over most of the masticatory function of external mouthparts seen in many other malacostracans.

Digestive juices, principally from the *hepatopancreas,* the caeca of which open into the midgut, are active in the cardiac stomach. It is of interest that a pepsinlike enzyme is not present in Crustacea or other invertebrates, although of course other proteolytic enzymes occur. The cardiac stomach opens through a somewhat narrowed aperture to the pyloric stomach. A ventral groove in the floor of the cardiac stomach bifurcates before entry into the pyloric cavity. This pair of grooves, aided by rows of bristles or setae, direct the more finely divided food toward the paired openings of the hepatopancreatic caeca in the caudal midgut portion of the pyloric stomach. The heavily ridged wall of the pyloric stomach, together with the system of grooves and setal zones, directs large food particles directly to the intestine. Absorption of digested food occurs in the hepatopancreas and probably in the midgut in some forms. Gut contents are moved by peristalsis. In some species, antiperistalsis of the midgut is very prominent, which would aid in returning fine particles to the region of greater absorption.

The hepatopancreas is a complex gland with numerous functions besides that of digestive enzyme production. It is important in absorption, and in the storage of calcium as well as glycogen and fat. It is also responsible for metabolism related to respiratory pigments and other cellular components.

CIRCULATION

The circulatory system in Crustacea is an "open" system, which means that blood or hemolymph is not contained within discrete blood vessels throughout its circulation, but empties into venous lacunae or into sinuses with somewhat more defined limiting membranes (Fig. 15-11). Ultimately it reaches respiratory lacunae or gills. It is returned to the heart hydrostatically, since the pericardial sinus is an area having lower pressure than the more ventral sinuses communicating with it. Many of these sinuses are more or less divided by septa so that a circulation path is established. On one side of the septum blood is flowing into the appendage and on the other returning to a communicating space of lower pressure.

The simple heart is a long, tubular, contractile, dorsal vessel. It receives blood from the pericardial sinus through paired openings called ostia. The blood is discharged at the

Fig. 15-11 Diagram of crustacean circulation. Solid arrows indicate the hemolymph flow in vessels; broken arrows, the flow in unbounded sinuses. *A,* anterior median aorta; *Bp. V.,* branchiopericardial vessel; *C,* capillary bed of respiratory surface; *ca.v.,* cardioarterial valve; *G,* gut; *H,* heart; *o,* ostium; *P,* pericardium; *s.l.,* suspensory ligament; *V,* ventral venous sinus. After Maynard 1960, in *The Physiology of Crustacea,* Vol. I (T. H. Waterman, ed.), courtesy of Academic Press, Inc.

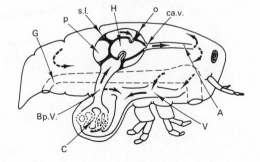

anterior end into lacunae of the hemocoele. Contraction is achieved by the striated muscle of the heart wall. Distension of the heart lumen is caused by the elastic nature of the supporting fibers.

In anostracan branchiopods (fairy shrimps) the heart extends almost to the end of the uniform trunk, and a pair of ostia is present in each segment except the first and the last. The heart tends to become reduced in length and limited to the thorax as this region gains prominence as in the Malacostraca; or it may be reduced when the abdominal region is suppressed as in the Cladocera. In some of the other small Branchiopoda there is no heart. Among Malacostraca, the leptostracan heart extends into the abdomen. It has seven pairs of ostia, none of which occur in abdominal somites. The Amphipoda have an elongated heart which is restricted to the thorax and which never has more than three pairs of ostia. In the Isopoda the heart extends into both thorax and abdomen, especially in those forms with an elongate heart. In those cases where it is more saclike, it is more frequently in the abdomen. The definitely more posterior position of the heart in Isopoda as compared with most other Malacostraca seems to be correlated with the location of the organs of respiration on the abdomen. Only one or two pairs of ostia occur in the isopod heart, but this heart gives off a median and as many as seven pairs of lateral arteries in the thorax. In the Decapoda the heart lies in the thorax, usually has three pairs of ostia, and generally gives rise to a median ophthalmic, and paired antennal and hepatic arteries anteriorly, to an unpaired sternal artery ventrally, and to the dorsal abdominal artery posteriorly. The sternal artery divides to carry blood forward or backward through subneural vesels. The Stomatopoda (mantis shrimps) possess a heart elongated through thorax and abdomen. Beginning with the first thoracic segment there are thirteen pairs of ostia and fifteen pairs of lateral arteries arising from the heart, corresponding to a segmental arrangement. The abdominal

development of the heart in this group appears to be correlated with the respiratory function of abdominal appendages, somewhat analogous to the situation in the Isopoda. Throughout the Crustacea, valves are present to aid unidirectional flow of blood. These are most common at the beginning or junction of arteries, but in some crustaceans that lack a heart, valves occur in venous sinuses.

A number of Crustacea have accessory hearts which act as blood pumps to insure adequate blood supply to all regions. Such blood pumps are usually adaptations of arteries in which extrinsic muscles are adapted specifically to squeeze a segment of the artery and hence propel the blood. Most Malacostraca have such an accessory heart on the anterior median artery shortly before it branches in the head.

Crustacean blood or hemolymph is composed of plasma and blood cells. The blood cells are frequently amoeboid, and two structural types predominate. One of these lacks granules and the average size is smaller. Somewhat larger cells contain granules thought to be stored nutrients. Since intergrades exist between the two types, different ages may account for the different morphology. Besides the storage function crustacean blood also serves to transport nutrients, hormones, and respiratory gases. Two respiratory pigments occur in the plasma of the crustaceans. Decapod and stomatopod malacostracans commonly have hemocyanin, whereas hemoglobin occurs in many other Crustacea. Another function of blood is that of coagulation, in which both cells and plasma participate. In some crustaceans the first factor of coagulation is the agglutination or clumping of blood cells. This is frequently followed by a plasma coagulation, probably induced by materials released from some fragile cells. In some groups, only one of the two types of coagulation occurs. Coagulation can be an important process in a group of animals with appendages susceptible to breakage, whether self-induced or not.

RESPIRATORY ADAPTATIONS

Respiration is a function of the integument and in many smaller crustaceans it occurs through the general body surface. In others, special adaptations have arisen, the most common of which are the gills or branchiae. Growing from the lateral aspect of the proximal segment of the generalized limb are one (or sometimes two) flattened, leaflike expansions called epipodites which may become variously lobed or laminated. Epipodite gills occur in the Branchiopoda and in the Malacostraca. In Isopoda and Stomatopoda, respiration is a function of abdominal instead of thoracic appendages. In these groups, epipodites are relatively unimportant in respiration, the principal branchial modifications being those of endopodite or exopodite or both. In Stomatopoda, an elongated extension of the exopodite develops a filamentous margin as the chief gill structure. In some terrestrial isopods, tubular *pseudotracheae* which penetrate the body from small surface cavities occur on all five pairs of pleopods or are restricted to the first two pairs. These pseudotracheae are not considered to be ancestral to the trachea of other arthropod and arthropod-related groups, but provide an interesting example of parallel or convergent evolution. Some other gill-like structures of presumed respiratory function occur. A few ostracods may have flattened platelike gills curved caudally from their dorsal attachment. Most ostracods utilize the general body surface in respiration.

EXCRETION

The principal excretory organs in Crustacea are the so-called head glands associated with antennae and with the second maxillae. They are modified coelomoducts, which probably occurred in a more extended series in ancestral Crustacea. *Hutchinsoniella,* a recently discovered primitive genus, has a series of segmental organs which might be representative of the ancestral condition. Both sets of head glands (antennal and maxillary) are not simultaneously functional in adult crustaceans, but frequently one or the other is retained in a vestigial condition. One of the two sets of glands may be functional during larval stages, while the other type becomes functional for the adult. In some of the "shelled" crustaceans in which the maxillary glands are functional, one or more loops of the coelomoduct invade the shell-fold or carapace. Such excretory glands are occasionally referred to as "shell-glands."

Both types of head kidneys have a similar basic structure with a mesodermal endsac and an elongated tubule opening to the exterior (Fig. 15-12).

The principal nitrogenous waste compound in Crustacea is ammonia. Ammonia is toxic and requires the availability of plenty of water for dilution. This well may be one of the factors hindering wide dissemination of crustaceans terrestrially. There is evidence that the excretory head glands of crustaceans function primarily to remove less soluble

Fig. **15-12** Excretory system of a larval Branchiopod, *Estheria.* These are antennal glands. After A. Vandel 1949, *Traité de Zoologie*, Tome VI (P. Grassé, ed.), courtesy of Masson et Cie.

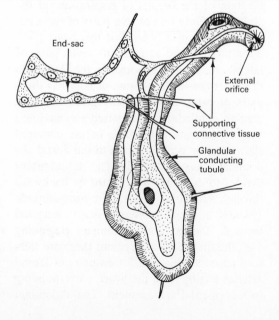

End-sac

External orifice

Supporting connective tissue

Glandular conducting tubule

wastes and for osmo-regulation. Ammonia is excreted principally through the gills as is urea. In some crustaceans, considerable amounts of nitrogenous wastes (uric acid and urea) appear in the hepatopancreas but the disposal of uric acid is not apparent. There is some evidence for its retention as solid wastes in the integument and in some phagocytic cells called *nephrocytes* and in some decapods enzymes are present which convert uric acid to ammonia. Nephrocytes are most common in axial shafts of gills and in the proximal portions of the legs.

NERVOUS SYSTEM AND SENSE ORGANS

The primitive crustacean nervous system bears close resemblance to that of annelids. There is a "brain" situated above the mouth

Fig. 15-13 Nervous system of *Branchinecta*, anterior portion. Greatly modified from Henry 1948.

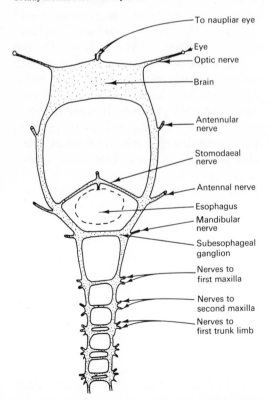

To naupliar eye
Eye
Optic nerve
Brain
Antennular nerve
Stomodaeal nerve
Antennal nerve
Esophagus
Mandibular nerve
Subesophageal ganglion
Nerves to first maxilla
Nerves to second maxilla
Nerves to first trunk limb

or esophagus from which circumesophageal commissures lead to paired ventral nerves possessing in each segment ganglionic enlargements, the most anterior of which is the large subesophageal ganglion. Segmental nerves innervate each segment, and the double row of ventral ganglia are connected usually by two transverse commissures. The Branchiopoda have this type of nervous system (Fig. 15-13). In addition, their brain is more primitive than that in other crustaceans. It is formed from the two paired ganglionic masses correlated with the paired organs of the acron or embryonic head lobe. These are the eyes and the antennules, and the ganglionic masses are designated, respectively, *protocerebrum* and *deuterocerebrum*. Most other Crustacea have a brain in which the ganglia of the antennae have moved from a postoral position. These ganglia form the *tritocerebral* lobes of the brain or cerebral ganglion.

Considerable coalescence in the ventral ganglia has occurred throughout the Crustacea. Initially there has been fusion of the paired segmental ganglia, followed frequently by fusion of the longitudinal ventral nerve cords, although these are separated around the sternal artery in crustaceans possessing this blood vessel. With increased cephalization and reduction of the abdomen there is a coalescence of ventral ganglia into various aggregates. In the Ostracoda, for example, there are from one to three such aggregates. In elongated Decapoda such as the crayfish, abdominal and most thoracic ganglia have maintained separate identity, but in the crab, *Carcinus,* with greatly reduced abdomen, the ventral ganglia have fused around the sternal artery into a single mass with nerves radiating from it (Fig. 15-14). Many variations occur between the condition seen in the Branchiopoda and that present in *Carcinus*. In larger Crustacea, such as the lobster and crayfish, which utilize abdominal flexure in swimming, the ventral nerve cords contain giant fibers analogous to those seen in annelids. These fibers provide a path for rapid transmission of motor impulses and hence facilitate an escape response.

A number of kinds of sensory receptors have been studied in Crustacea. These include receptors responsive to such factors as chemical, temperature, mechanical, or light change in the environment. The function of chemoreception has been attributed to various canals, pores, and long hairlike filaments *(aesthetascs)* associated with groups of sensory cells. Aesthetascs have been reported from most crustacean subgroups. The two sexes in many species differ in distribution and numbers of aesthetascs. Typically the aesthetascs occur in rows and are thin, tapering, hollow hairs into which dendritic processes of sensory neurons penetrate. Such structures occur most commonly on antennules, but they occur also on antennae, mouthparts, and thoracic appendages, at least in the higher malacostracans. Pores have been described from the European crayfish, *Astacus,* within the gill chamber. A pore opens into a small cavity bearing a sensory papilla. It is certain that chemoreceptors are important to Crustacea for recognition of food, for

mating, and for avoidance of noxious materials.

The evidence for distinct thermoreceptors in Crustacea is not clear-cut. Vertical migrations characteristic of many crustaceans may occur seasonally as well as diurnally. The magnitude of diurnal vertical migrations for some marine copepods is of the order of 50 to 150 meters; some decapods migrate vertically through a much greater distance. Thermoreceptors have little to do with vertical diurnal migration. Phototropic and geotropic responses are certainly more significant for diurnal migration. Seasonal migration might be in part a response to temperature change, but other factors such as the ontogenetic stage of the life cycle are important. Experimentation has shown that some crustaceans respond to temperature change if the antennae are intact, and a number move to the least unfavorable zone if subjected to a thermal gradient. Crustacea as well as most other invertebrates are usually considered to be animals whose body temperature varies closely with the environment (poikilothermic) within viable ranges. Oxygen consumption as a measure of metabolic activity is much greater for species in warm water than for closely related ones in cold water, but when placed at the same temperature, metabolism of the cold-water species is higher than that of species from warm water. This indicates that the cold-water species have some mechanism of adaptation or adjustment compensating for the temperature change. Such adaptation is evidence for the presence of thermoreceptors.

Crustacea possess a number of sensory structures that can be classified as mechanoreceptors since they are activated by pressure changes. Included here are receptors for touch, internal tensions or pressures (proprioceptors), and equilibrium. Tactile hair receptors are very numerous in crustacea with a rigid exoskeleton. Such receptors are hollow chitinous bristles extending from the surface of the skeleton. Dendritic nerve endings from bipolar neurons enter the hair lumen and are

Fig. 15-14 Nervous system of the crab, *Carcinus.* From Hertwig (after Gegenbaur), *A Manual of Zoology* (translated and edited by J. S. Kingsley) 1902, Holt, Rinehart & Winston, Inc.

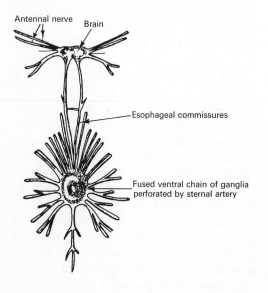

Antennal nerve Brain

Esophageal commissures

Fused ventral chain of ganglia perforated by sternal artery

stimulated when the bristle is moved. Secondary feathering of the bristle increases its sensitivity to extraneous pressure whether from currents or foreign objects. Tactile hair receptors are widely distributed over the skeleton, but are most common on appendages. In crustaceans lacking a rigid exoskeleton, as well as in the flexible joint membranes of those with such a covering, there are groups of free nerve endings subject to tactile stimuli.

Proprioceptors have been found repeatedly in larger crustaceans. In the lobster four modified muscle fibers occur dorsally in the last two thoracic and in all the abdominal segments. Dendritic endings of sensory nerves in these muscle fibers are stimulated by stretch evoked when the lobster abdomen is flexed. The more median pair of these proprioceptors in each segment undergo rapid contraction, while the outer pair undergo slow and more prolonged contraction with continued stimulation of the neuron. It has been postulated that the effect of the prolonged stimulus may be maintenance of a given posture, whereas the fast receptor may signal change. Various types of limb proprioceptors have been described. One of these is the elastic receptor activated by tension across the joint between the terminal and subterminal segments in the legs of the crab, *Carcinus* (Fig. 15-15). Another type of presumed proprioceptor is the myochordotonal organs seen in decapod malacostracans. These receptors occur in walking-leg meropodites and consist of bipolar neurons grouped in a membrane which communicates between a flexor muscle and the endoskeleton. Muscle activity varies the tension on this membrane to incite a stimulus.

Mechanoreceptors of varied structure occur in Malacostraca and function for equilibrium. These are called *statocysts* and occur in terminal regions of the crustacean. In decapods, a statocyst is located in the proximal segment of each antennule. Statocysts are in-pocketed cavities opening externally through a usually reduced pore.

Fig. **15-15** Sketch of a limb proprioceptor organ spanning the protopodite-dactyl joint in *Carcinus*. (a) Joint in flexed position. (b) Enlarged view of organ. *h*, epidermis; *N*, main leg nerve bundle; *n*, nerve bundle to organ; *o*, organ; *p*, distal attachment to protuberance; *e*, apodeme of extensor muscle; *f*, apodeme of flexor muscle; *c*, small connective tissue attachment (from Burke). After Cohen and Dijkgraaf 1961, in *The Physiology of Crustacea*, Vol. II (T. H. Waterman, ed.), courtesy of Academic Press, Inc.

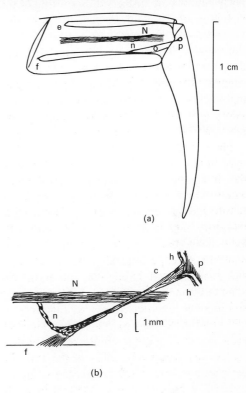

Fig. **15-16** Compensatory eyestalk and limb reflexes evoked in *Astacus astacus* by bending statocyst hairs in opposite directions (a) laterally and (b) medially, with a fine water jet (statoliths removed) (from Schöne). After Cohen and Dijkgraaf 1961, in *The Physiology of Crustacea*, Vol. II (T. H. Waterman, ed.), courtesy of Academic Press, Inc.

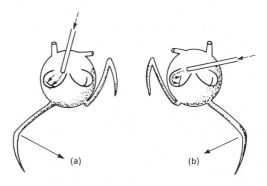

Sensory hairs project into the lumen of the statocyst and may be in contact with a *statolith*, which is a concretion secreted by the animal or formed from a clump of sand grains. The sensory hairs innervated by bipolar neurons are disturbed by shifting of the statoliths or by fluid movement. Any displacement of the animal from normal position would shift the statolith, and any sudden movement would create currents to stimulate the sensory hairs and trigger a righting reaction in the normal animal. Compensatory movement of the eyestalk and of limb reaction are shown in Figure 15-16.

Photoreceptor mechanisms are well developed in the Crustacea. Some of these involve the integument or underlying structures, within which a diffuse distribution of light-sensitive cells apparently exists. No specific receptors have been identified. Reactions to light have been noted in animals blind naturally or experimentally. In the crayfish and some related Decapoda, the sixth abdominal ganglion exhibits light-sensitivity and influences activity of the walking legs.

Commonly Crustacea possess two kinds of eyes. The median eye is simpler and appeared earlier ontogenetically. This is the type of eye characteristic of the crustacean nauplius larva. The nauplier eye is retained in adult ostracods and copepods as the only eye structure. In most Malacostracans, naupliar eyes are not retained in the adult. When they are present, usually they are somewhat vestigial. The median eyes consist of three or four symmetrically disposed simple eyes called *ocelli*. An ocellus has a few photoreceptor cells, often backed with reflective pigment. Axons from the photoreceptor cells form a median nerve leading to the protocerebrum.

The lateral or compound eyes of Crustacea bear a detailed resemblance to those of Insecta. The crustacean compound eye may be sessile or stalked; the latter condition appeared early in evolution of the group. The presence of compound eyes on movable stalks seems to be coincident with the cephalad development of the carapace to form a rostrum overlying the head.

The structural unit of the compound eye is the *ommatidium*, a cone whose truncated inner end rests on a basement membrane and whose outer end modified to a square or hexagonal shape forms with the surrounding ommatidia the faceted surface of the compound eye (Fig. 15-17). The distal end of the ommatidium is closed by a slightly convex, transparent plug, the cornea, which acts as a lens of low power. The cornea was secreted by two modified epidermal cells called corneagenous cells which lie adjacent to it. Just proximal to the corneagenous cells is a quartet of crystalline cone cells lying just distal to the crystalline cone, the principal refractive lens of the system. The crystalline cone is a semisolid or gelatinous rod or cone frequently revealing its fourfold origin. It has a varied refractive index which axially directs rays parallel to the ommatidial axis, but more peripherally refracts rays toward the surrounding absorptive pigment. Such a system would favor rays entering parallel to the ommatidial axis in contrast to rays entering obliquely. The photoreceptive portion of the ommatidium, called the *retinula*, occupies a section of the tube immediately adjacent to the basement membrane. The retinula is composed of two structures. Axially there is a *rhabdom* produced by a peripheral group of pigmented retinular cells which are modified nerve cells. Commonly seven of the retinular cells are symmetrically disposed around the rhabdom with an eighth asymmetrically placed. The rhabdom appears to be the site of initial photochemical action, at least in those crustaceans in which this structure is prominent. The nerve impulses are transmitted from the retinula by way of the axons of the retinular cells to a series of optic ganglia, which are four in number in the stalk-eyed crustaceans and fewer in other groups.

Structurally there appear to be two types of eyes. *Apposition* eyes have elongated retinulas with the rodlike rhabdom usually extending from the crystalline cone to the basement membrane. Because of the length of the crystalline cone lens a reduced inverted image is formed near the inner end of the crystalline cone. In *superposition* eyes the focal point of the image falls within the retinula, which is separated by some distance

from the shorter, spindle-shaped crystalline cone. This lens transmits a direct image to the retinula. Functionally, the more primitive ap-

Fig. 15-17 The arthropod compound eye; (a) ommatidium in longitudinal section and (b) in transverse section; (c) diagram through the entire eye. From J. A. Ramsay, *Physiological Approach to the Lower Animals*, 1952, courtesy of the Cambridge University Press.

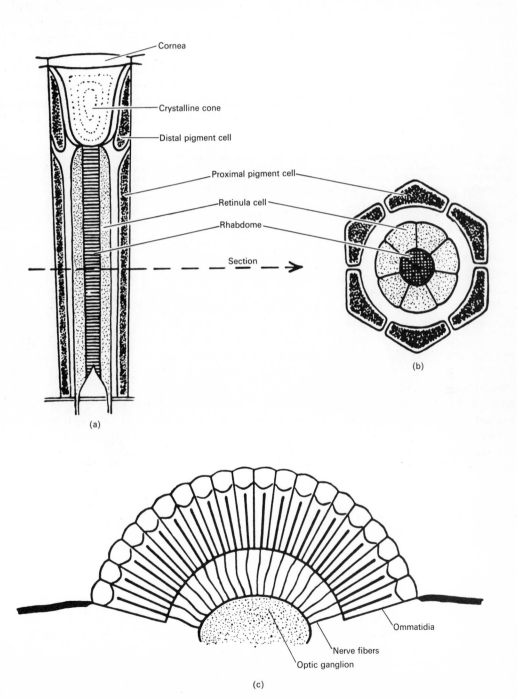

position eye casts a *mosaic* image with the axial or near-axial rays of a single ommatidium translating a single unit of the object into a single unit of the image. The total image represents a composite of the individual images received by all activated ommatidia. Actually there is some overlapping of the images from adjacent ommatidia. Since any movement of the object would activate new ommatidia, recognition of movement is a valuable function of this eye, which is most effective in relatively bright light. Superposition eyes are more characteristic of those crustaceans adapted to

habitats of relatively little light. Here a given point of light would be refracted through all the ommatidial facets within range. The refractive features of the respective conical lenses involved would transmit this same point of light across ommatidial boundaries to augment the light traversing the ommatidium whose axis is coincident with the point of light. Consequently the light received by a single retinula would be multiplied by the number of ommatidia activated. It should be borne in mind that the discussion of superposition image formation in Crustacea is based on evidence from insects and the

Fig. 15-18 Ommatidia from the eyes of light-adapted and dark-adapted *Gammarus*. The upper figures are longitudinal sections; the lower ones are transverse sections through the rhabdom. *L*, from light-adapted retina; *D*, from dark-adapted retina; *C*, cone; *RC*, retinular cell; *RP*, reflecting pigment cell; *RH*, rhabdom; *BM*, basement membrane (modified from Parker). After Kleinholz 1961, in *The Physiology of Crustacea*, Vol. II (T. H. Waterman, ed.), courtesy of Academic Press, Inc.

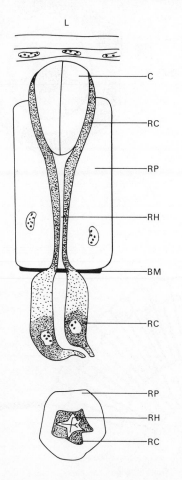
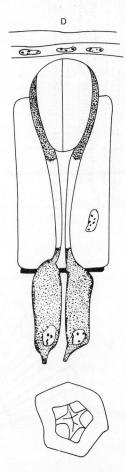

similar structural characteristics seen in some Crustacea.

The compound eye varies from species with less than 100 ommatidia to those with several thousand. More significant than numerical differences are the variations in size of ommatidia even in the same eye. This factor, together with the common absence of uniform curvature either at the external eye surface or on the basement membrane, suggests a wide range of adaptive specializations.

Many crustacean compound eyes are not restricted to the formation of either apposition or superposition images, but can undergo adaptation to lesser or greater light. In bright light, individual ommatidia are screened by pigment migration. In the fresh-water amphipod, *Gammarus,* this migration involves movement of pigment within retinular cells (Fig. 15-18). In a light-adapted retina the pigment forms a shield from crystalline cone to the basement membrane. With light restricted to axial areas of the ommatidia, an apposition or mosaic image is formed. In the dark-adapted eye the pigment migrates from the intermediate zone adjacent to the rhabdom, and the dispersal of light is further increased in this species by reflective white pigment in cells between ommatidia. In superposition eyes adaptation to darkness may involve pigment migration distally toward the cornea in a group of distal pigment cells as well as proximally toward or through the basement membrane in pigmented retinular cells. The total illumination would be enhanced by refractive spread of light from neighboring ommatidial lens systems.

REPRODUCTION

In most of the Crustacea the sexes are separate, but there are a number of attached or parasitic forms that are hermaphroditic. Parthenogenesis is common among some Branchiopoda and Ostracoda. In the Malacostraca (certain isopods and leptostracans), scarcity of males in some strains suggests the probability of parthenogenetic development. Gonads are typically paired tubes which are modified coelomoducts and which may coalesce into a single organ provided with lobes or diverticula.

The openings of the reproductive system vary among the Entomostraca. In some with little differentiation of the trunk, the male genital pore may serve to demark the posterior limit of the thorax. Another differentiation between thorax and abdomen is the frequent apodous condition of the latter. The genital aperture in females is on the same or on a more anterior segment than the male gonopore. In Branchiopoda the openings are usually far back on the trunk. In sessile and parasitic crustaceans with a reduced trunk the reproductive openings are on anterior trunk somites. In Malacostraca the male genital aperture is invariably on the eighth or last thoracic segment, while the female system opens on the sixth segment.

Typically copulatory processes result in sperm or in spermatophore transference to a seminal receptacle in the female, or externally into various protective chambers adapted for early egg development. In *Triops,* the flabellum (exopodite) provides a lid over a concavity which functions as a brood chamber on the axis of each eleventh trunk appendage. In copepods, a characteristic pair of egg-sacs develops externally on the genital segment of the female. In some bivalved Entomostraca, the eggs develop in pouches protected by the valves. In pericaridean malacostracans, such as *Mysis,* flattened plates called *oostegites* develop on the inner face of thoracic appendages. These overlap medially to form a marsupium or brood chamber. In the leptostracan malacostracan, *Nebalia,* thoracic setae form a brood basket; and in the crayfish (decapod subgroup) eggs are fastened to the abdominal swimmerets (pleopods) by a gluelike substance called glair, through which sperm from previously deposited spermatophores penetrate for fertilization.

METAMORPHOSIS

The young crustacean typically hatches in an immature stage that must undergo metamorphosis, through a series of ecdyses, to achieve the definitive adult structure. The stage prior to each molt is known as an *instar;* as many as ten instars may occur before the definitive adult condition is reached. The typical first larva is a free-swimming stage called *nauplius* characterized by a median eye, three pairs of functional appendages, and absence of segmentation in the thorax (Fig. 15-19). The three pairs of appendages consist of uniramous antennules, biramous antennae, and according to Sanders (1963) uniramous or biramous mandibles. The successive increase in number of segments after hatching is known as anamorphic development and is well represented in the ontogeny of many entomostracans. The nauplius elongates and new segments develop from a growth zone immediately anterior to the terminal telson. When some of this new segmentation is apparent beneath the cuticle of the newly hatched embryo, the stage is

designated as a metanauplius (Fig. 15-19). In a number of crustaceans, often correlated with larger amounts of yolk in the egg, the early larval stages may be telescoped in the embryology so that fewer additional segments are added after hatching. The crayfish is representative of epimorphic development in which the definitive number of segments is present at hatching. In most malacostracans the nauplius is not a free-living stage and the young hatch in a more advanced larval condition. A larva called *zoea,* characteristic of many malacostracans, has a pair of lateral eyes in addition to the median or naupliar one. Six pairs of functional appendages and a segmented abdomen are other distinguishing characteristics. Various other larval stages may occur in the metamorphosis of crustaceans. Stages which follow naupliar or zoeal larvae are usually called postlarvae and are designated by special names.

Although ecdysis and metamorphosis are common features of crustacean ontogeny, there are many forms, of which the lobster *Homarus* is a well-known example, in which molting and growth continue after the defini-

Fig. 15-19 (a) Nauplius and (b) metanauplius of *Triops* (*—Apus*). 1 *Ant*, first antennae; 2 *Ant*, second antennae; *Md*, mandibles; *tbSegs*, appendages of teloblastic segments. After Snodgrass 1956, courtesy of the Smithsonian Institution.

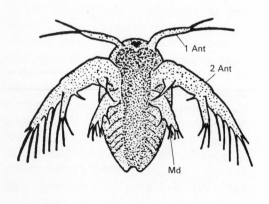

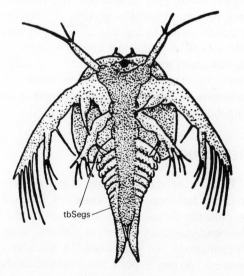

(a)   (b)

tive adult condition is reached. In other crustaceans a constant number of molts is characteristic.

Among Branchiopoda a free-swimming nauplius or metanauplius is characteristic, but in the bivalved forms the nauplius is retained in the brood chamber and development is more direct. In Ostracoda, a nauplius larva enclosed in a bivalved shell occurs within the brood chamber, or hatches directly when eggs are freed externally. The free-living Copepoda metamorphose through as many as six naupliar stages and an equal number of so-called copepodid stages with less change between instars. In the life cycle of a parasitic copepod such as *Lernaea,* the naupliar instars are free-living, but during the copepodid

stages, temporary parasitism occurs on the gills of fish where paedogenetic copulation occurs. The fertilized females become free-living briefly, but then become ectoparasites of fish, losing all resemblance to typical copepods.

Cirripedia hatch to a naupliar stage, but metamorphose through a so-called *cypris* stage with bivalved shell, superficially reminiscent of Ostracoda. During this stage, great changes occur in the appendages, the body is reoriented, and attachment characteristic of adult barnacles occurs. Parasitic forms exhibit even greater change. *Sacculina,* parasitic on some decapod crabs, has characteristic naupliar and cypris stages (Fig. 15-9). A cypris stage attaches and penetrates the host, and as

Fig. 15-20 Parasitic castration in crabs caused by *Sacculina.* (a) Normal male, *Inachus*; (b) normal female; (c) male infested by *Sacculina* (final stage); (d) abdomen of infested female; (e) infested male in an early stage of its modification. After G. Smith 1904, courtesy of the original publishers of *Cambridge Natural History*, Vol. IV, Macmillan & Co., Ltd.

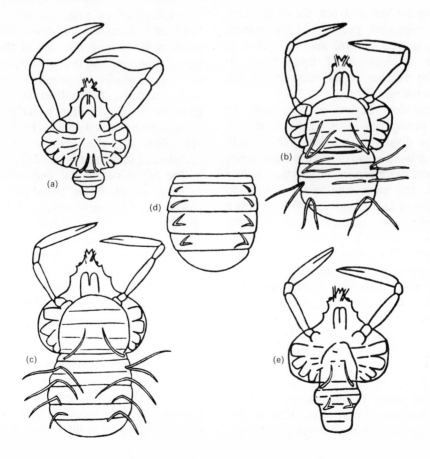

a somewhat amorphic mass, it eventually reaches the lower side of the host's intestine. Since its presence prevents cuticle formation in that area following the next host ecdysis, the parasite is exposed. The new skeleton of the host shows marked change in structure, males approaching female conformity and females appearing more juvenile. Because of these sexual changes crab parasitism by *Sacculina* results in what is called "parasitic castration." This is somewhat of a misnomer, since the gonad is not destroyed. The changed appearance may be due to a modification of the sex-hormone-producing androgenic gland attached to the vas deferens and situated adjacent to the coxal muscles of the last walking leg (Fig. 15-20).

EMBRYOLOGY OF NEBALIA

Among the Malacostraca, the embryology of the somewhat primitive Leptostracan, *Nebalia,* is well known, and will serve to illustrate development of those forms in which the naupliar stages occur in the egg before hatching.

Segmentation begins in the centrally located protoplasm of a large-yolked egg. Soon the dividing cytoplasm joins a thin peripheral layer in two or three isolated areas, only one of which carries the cleaving nuclear material. The latter continues to divide to form a cap of four blastomeres from which a blastodermic layer spreads around the yolk. This blastoderm is particularly thin at the vegetal pole. The germinal disc develops as a thickened plate on the ventral face of the egg, and this plate alters to a horseshoe-shaped distribution with a common junction around the future blastoporal area. The arms of the horseshoe become lobated, the lobes representing primordia of the naupliar structures (Fig. 15-21). Most anterior are the optic lobes, followed by antennular, antennal, and mandibular lobes. The next lobes to appear are the primordia of the first maxillae; behind them a transverse furrow develops which is the caudal furrow (Fig. 15-22). Behind this furrow the germinal disc bulges forward to form the caudal papilla. The papilla elongates to reach the labrum, which arises from fusion of median processes developing from the optic lobes. When the papilla has extended to this point, the embryo hatches (Fig. 15-23) and straightens from the constriction of the vitelline membrane. Two ecdyses separate three embryonic stages before the larva escapes from the brood chamber.

Within the blastoporal area of the early embryo mesoderm differentiates in front of the endoderm. All internal structures originate in the blastoporal area except the preantennulary mesoderm. Two mesodermal bands grow forward between the yolk and the germinal disc, eventually giving rise to the mesoderm of the naupliar segments. Caudally, the mesendodermal cell mass gives rise to endodermal cells which become yolk cells or vitellophags by yolk absorption; others form an endodermal epithelium. These two components enclose the yolk at the end of gastrulation, and the cephalad-oriented yolk cells are gradually transformed into epithelium. Caudally, the endodermal epithelium gives rise to a diverticulum which pushes into the elongating caudal papilla. Eventually this epithelium will give rise to the definitive endodermal midgut (Fig. 15-23).

The *Nebalia* larva has only a brief free-living stage outside the brood pouch and it already has the form of a small adult. Among the Peracarida, most larval stages occur within the brood chamber, and the embryo that leaves the brood pouch bears close resemblance to the adult, although the last pair of thoracic appendages may not have appeared. Some of the Amphipoda exhibit a greater degree of metamorphosis.

DECAPOD METAMORPHOSIS

Marine Decapoda show considerable metamorphosis after hatching. The most complete series is seen in the shrimp, *Penaeus*. It

Fig. 15-21 Early embryology of *Nebalia*. (a) Sagittal section through egg to show formation of germinal disc. (b) through (f) development of the germinal disc from a surface view (with a slightly exaggerated long axis). After Manton 1934, courtesy of the author and the Royal Society of London.

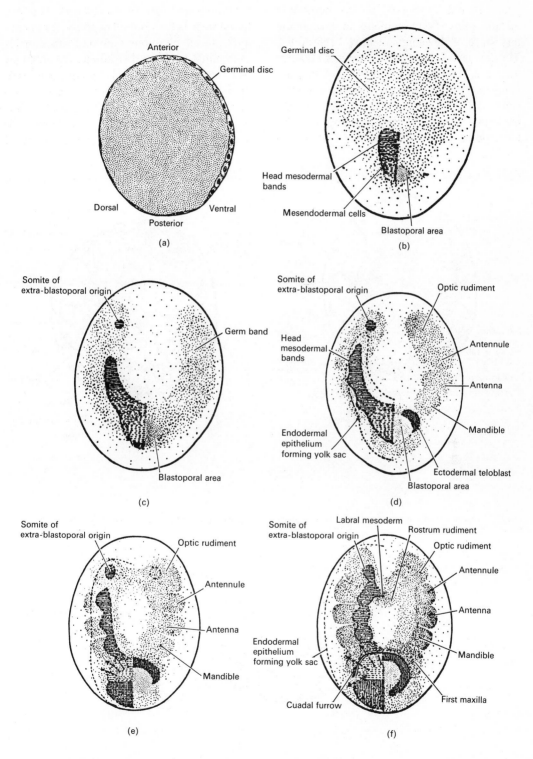

is representative of the only subgroup of Decapoda to produce a free-swimming nauplius. It undergoes ecdysis to become a metanauplius. Four segments in a rudimentary stage of development have been added. The next larval stage, *protozoea,* has a definite carapace. Three additional pairs of thoracic appendages have appeared but the abdomen still lacks segmentation. At the next ecdysis, metamorphosis to the zoeal stage occurs. This larva possesses movable stalked eyes, devel-

ops a rostral spine, and has a segmented limbless abdomen with only the last segment exhibiting well-formed appendages. The final larval stage is the *mysis.* The thoracic appendages are all biramous now and function for swimming. In the earlier larvae, the antennae were the natatory appendages. In the lobster, *Homarus,* the life cycle is telescoped and a mysis stage appears at hatching, while in the crayfish the hatched embryo resembles the adult and goes through a short series of

Fig. 15-22 Side views of the developing *Nebalia* embryo. After Manton 1934, courtesy of the author and the Royal Society of London.

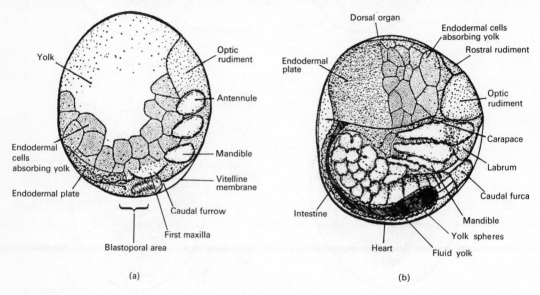

(a)

(b)

Fig. 15-23 Lateral view of a *Nebalia* embryo nearly ready to shed the first cuticle. After Manton 1934, courtesy of the author and the Royal Society of London.

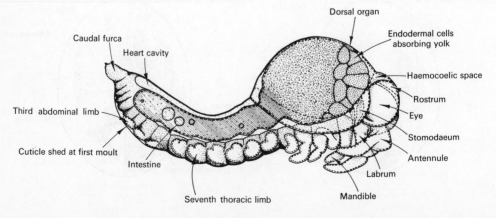

instars before reaching the definitive condition. In the blue crab, *Callinectes,* the first larval stage is a quiescent, bottom-dwelling form called a *prezoea* (Fig. 15-24). It metamorphoses to the first of five zoeal stages. Early zoeal stages (Fig. 15-25) tend to be near the water surface, while later ones are at the bottom. The last zoeal molts to a larval stage called *megalops* (Fig. 15-26), which has a closer conformity to the adult but still possesses a prominent abdomen having six

segments and likeness to macrurous decapods.

SUBPHYLUM CRUSTACEA— SYSTEMATIC ACCOUNT

The crustacea are fundamentally aquatic organisms respiring by gills or through the unspecialized body surface. They are the only arthropods with two pairs of antennae. The body is covered with a chitinous cuticle, com-

Fig. 15-24 Prezoea larva of the blue crab, *Callinectes sapidus.* After Churchill 1942, courtesy of the Chesapeake Biological Laboratory.

Fig. 15-25 Third zoeal larval stage of the blue crab, *Callinectes sapidus.* After Churchill 1942, courtesy of the Chesapeake Biological Laboratory.

Fig. 15-26 Megalops larva of the blue crab, *Callinectes sapidus.* After Churchill 1942, courtesy of the Chesapeake Biological Laboratory.

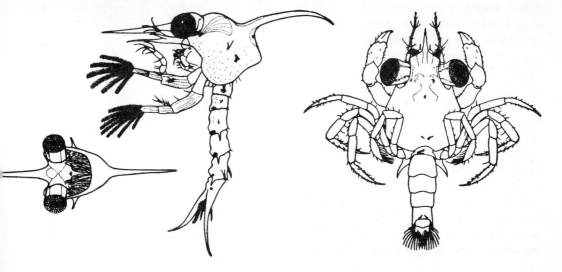

monly thickened intrasegmentally and strengthened with calcium salts to form a series of relatively rigid plates called *sclerites*. The sexes are separate. A nauplius larva is characteristic, and development usually involves ecdysis. Muscle in the crustacea is striated, including that around the intestine, and cilia are absent. There is a single class, Crustacea, with all the characteristics of the subphylum.

SYSTEMATIC AND DESCRIPTIVE ACCOUNT OF ENTOMOSTRACAN CRUSTACEANS

Although the term, Entomostraca, no longer has validity as a taxonomic category, it is convenient to consider the subclasses composing it separately from the mostly larger crustaceans of subclass Malacostraca.

Subclass Cephalocarida

The continued discovery, description, and evaluation of new species of animals frequently reaffirms or supports phylogenetic hypotheses. Just as frequently it provides new direction or clarifies the apparent sequence of phylogenetic progression. In 1955, crustaceans less than three millimeters in length were found subtidally in soft mud in Long Island Sound. Two genera with a total of three species were found. These genera are *Hutchinsoniella* and *Lightiella*. The most complete descriptions are those of a species named *Hutchinsoniella macracantha* (Fig. 15-27).

Hutchinsoniella exhibits a number of intriguing features. There is marked structural similarity of the appendages beginning with and posterior to the second maxillae. These limbs show structural features that are intermediate between the phyllopodial and the stenopodial types. Although the exopodite is four-jointed, it has a foliaceous form and bears laterally a pseudepipodite which also is foliaceous. The endopodite is a segmented

cylindroid structure, ambulatory in function. The protopodite bears endites medially. It has been suggested that this tripartite limb (pseudepipodite, exopodite, and endopodite) implies affinity to trilobites. The head structures bear some resemblance to Copepoda and Mystacocarida. The feeding pattern and dorsoventral thoracic trunk muscles are very similar to primitive Malacostraca (Leptostraca), and the stomatopodan malacostracans possess similar muscles. The structural features prior to the acquisition of the caridoid facies in Malacostraca show marked similarity to cephalocarid morphology.

Hutchinsoniella is hermaphroditic with gonads not united into an ovotestis. During the summer months these animals are ovigerous with a pair of egg-sacs each of which contains one embryo. The egg-sacs are attached to the limb rudiment of the ninth or genital segment. Feeding is associated with metachronal beat of the limbs, which begins with the posterior trunk limbs and sweeps cephalad (Fig. 15-28). Detritus suspended by the limb action is carried to a median

Fig. 15-27 The cephalocaridan, *Hutchinsoniella macracantha*. After Waterman and Chace 1960, in *The Physiology of Crustacea* (T. H. Waterman, ed.), courtesy of Academic Press, Inc.

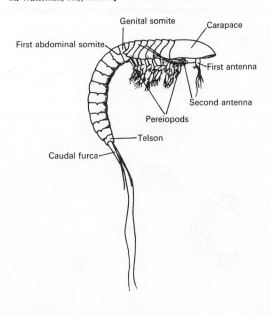

chamber between limb bases. Spines and setae filter the detritus and successively comb it forward toward the mouth. *Hutchinsoniella* is blind, but there appears to be a compensating enlargement of the brain, apparently associated with presumed olfactory function of antennules.

Subclass Branchiopoda

This subclass containing about 800 species is subdivided into four orders as follows:

Order Anostraca
Order Notostraca
Order Lipostraca
Order Diplostraca
    Suborder Conchostraca
    Suborder Cladocera

Order 1 Anostraca These branchiopods, which average about a centimeter in length, lack a carapace, and the eyes are stalked (Fig. 15-8). Unlike Cephalocarida, the sexes are separate. The antennae are somewhat reduced triangular structures in the female, but stout and modified as claspers with a copulatory function in the male. Anostraca have an elongated trunk, the first eleven or more segments bearing limbs which are structurally all alike. Trunk segments behind the male genital pore are apodous. The rami of the caudal furca are unsegmented. The geologic history goes back to the Silurian or Devonian Period. *Artemia, Branchinecta, Eubranchipus, Chirocephalus.*

Anostraca are essentially fresh-water crustaceans of cosmopolitan distribution, occurring in temporary ponds and small pools. They are absent from lakes and running waters and rare in more permanent ponds containing predators. While there are no true marine species, *Artemia salina* occurs in salt lakes and marshes as well as in high salt concentrations in water undergoing evaporation in basins for the production of salt commercially.

Artemia salina has a world-wide distribution. In Europe it shows more structural variability, and parthenogenesis is more frequent. *Artemia* hatches as a nauplius and probably undergoes molting twice after reach-

Fig. 15-28 The metachronal cycle of trunk appendages in *Hutchinsoniella*. These limb movements create water currents used in locomotion and in feeding. The arrows above each trunk limb indicate the relative movement, and the thickness of the stippled lines indicates the intensity of the resultant water currents during that phase of the metachronal oscillation. From Sanders 1963, *The Cephalocarida*, Mem. Conn. Acad. of Arts & Sci., Vol. XV, courtesy of the Conn. Acad. of Arts & Sci.

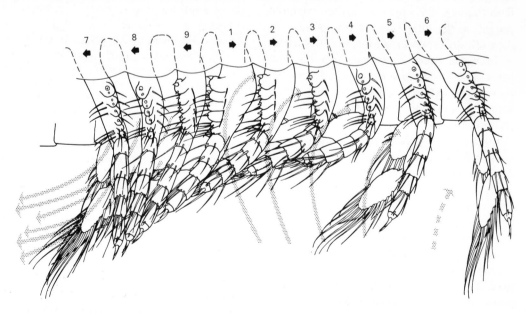

ing sexual maturity at the twelfth instar.

Other Anostraca occur most commonly in temporary ponds and may reappear at the same site for many years, although unaccountably absent in some seasons. Many of them typically swim with the ventral side up, which appears to be the result of a phototropic response. The limb movement, which is usually metachronal, functions for locomotion and in food gathering, as well as for respiration.

The food includes flagellates and other microorganisms in the water as well as bottom detritus. In the filter-feeding metachronal pattern, each limb is activated just prior to the one anterior to it. At the beginning of the stroke, the limbs approximate a position parallel to the ventral body surface. As the limb moves forward, water is pulled into the space enlarged behind the limb-base. This space is walled laterally by the exopodite and other foliacious structures, so that the water with its contained suspensions is forced medially and suspended material is caught by the filtering setae on the median edge of the limb (Fig. 15-7). Before the limb reaches a somewhat perpendicular position at the end of the forward stroke, a stream of water is forced forward in the gully separating the limb bases. This stream washes material caught on the filters toward the mouth. On the back stroke, water is forced ventrolaterally from the decreasing spaces behind limb bases, so that this current propels the animal forward. Sticky secretions near the mouth help to capture the food delivered by the forward stream.

Both parthenogenetic and bisexual reproduction may occur in the same population at the same time. The eggs are carried in an oval brood sac during early development. Two kinds of eggs are produced. Thin-shelled eggs soon hatch, but thick-shelled or "resting" eggs are capable of withstanding very adverse conditions of temperature and dryness. Such resting eggs have been kept for years in dried mud. The habitats of Anostraca in temporary pools, which are without water during dry seasons, necessitate some method of species survival, which is accomplished by the resistant resting eggs.

Order 2 Notostraca These Branchiopoda, commonly called tadpole shrimps, possess sessile compound eyes frequently placed very close together. There is a large carapace which covers much of the body. There are 35 to 71 pairs of legs, but these cannot be equated to a like number of segments, since some anterior segments bear two pairs of limbs and some posterior segments as many as ten pairs. The elongated caudal furca are filamentous and segmented. The proximal endite, particularly on the more anterior limbs, is enlarged to form a gnathobase.

The order Notostraca contains some 15 species in two genera: *Triops* (*Apus*) and *Lepidurus* (Fig. 15-3). The carapace forms a broad, flat shield which covers the head and about half of the trunk. Tadpole shrimp swim in a somewhat wavelike motion and also creep along the substrate. The presence of gnathobases is an aid to eating larger particles than is generally characteristic of Anostraca, and the food may include material scavenged from small dead metazoa.

Males are rare and the male reproductive ducts open by simple pores. Parthenogenesis is normal and the female carries eggs in a kind of marsupium capped by the flabella on the eleventh trunk segment.

Order 3 Lipostraca The single species, *Lepidocaris rhyniensis,* is placed in this order. *Lepidocaris* occurred in the mid-Devonian Period, and bears considerable resemblance to Cephalocarida and to other branchiopods. The biramous antenna resembles this appendage in the Cladocera. Sanders considers *Lepidocaris* to be the closest known relative of *Hutchinsoniella,* with the latter containing some more primitive features. *Lepidocaris* has a stenopodial limb structure. Apparently the first maxillae were modified as clasping organs rather than the antennae as in the Anostraca. The presence of gnathobases suggests that *Lepidocaris* fed on detritus, probably on the pond floor. This animal was blind, minute, and lived in fresh water.

Order 4 Diplostraca These Branchiopoda have a laterally flattened bivalved carapace which encloses the trunk and, in one subgroup, the head also. The compound eyes are sessile and frequently fused. The antennae are large and biramous. The suborder, Conchostraca, commonly called clam shrimps, possess 10 to 32 pairs of trunk limbs; the carapace halves articulate through a fold and are provided with an adductor muscle. The carapace generally encloses the head. A nauplius larva is char-

acteristic of conchostracan development.

The second suborder is the Cladocera or "water fleas." Most Cladocera are less than 3 mm in length. Segmentation is reduced with five or six phyllopodous trunk appendages. Usually the carapace covers only the trunk. The large head, bearing prominent biramous antennae, minute antennules, a single ocellus,

Fig. 15-29 *Daphnia.* From Hertwig, *A Manual of Zoology* (translated and edited by J. S. Kingsley) 1902, Holt, Rinehart & Winston, Inc.

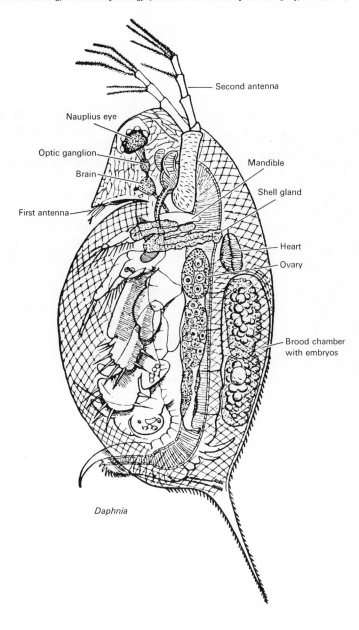

Daphnia

and a single compound eye formed by fusion, protrudes beyond the anterior edge of the carapace. The carapace lacks a hinge and an adductor muscle and is frequently projected as a spine. Cladocerans develop directly and without a nauplius stage, except in the genus *Leptodora.*

The common water flea, *Daphnia,* is the best-known representative of the Cladocera (Fig. 15-29). Some species of Cladocera are marine, but most are fresh-water organisms. The latter occur in a considerable variety of habitats, in temporary and permanent ponds and in less disturbed water along river and lake margins.

The food of *Daphnia* includes bacteria, protozoa, algae, and organic detritus. A few cladocerans are predaceous on other small crustacea and rotifers. Most cladocerans are filter feeders; suspended material is caught on the setal combs of the appendages and subsequently moved forward along the midventral gully between the bases of the appendages to the mouth.

Antennae are the chief natatory organs, and swimming in some forms is a kind of saltatory progression of successive leaps or hops. Cladocerans resting on the bottom are apt to fall on one side when the antennae are not beating. In addition, some bottom feeders propel themselves along the substrate by "kicking" with a posterior-ventral body extension called the postabdomen.

Reproduction is commonly by parthenogenesis during much of the year. Usually few to many males appear in later phases of the spring reproduction peak, apparently due to some combination of ecological factors which instigates metabolic changes resulting in production of parthenogenetic male eggs. Some but not all females are able to copulate with the males, and the reproductive activity of parthenogenetic females may continue side-by-side with bisexual reproduction in the population. In many cladocerans, a second male population may appear in late fall.

Parthenogenetic eggs complete development by hatching in the brood chamber, which is a space between the carapace valves dorsal to the trunk. A dozen or more of these eggs may occupy the brood chamber at one time. Hatched young are released from the brood chamber by depression of the postabdomen. In bisexual reproduction, the eggs are larger and fewer in number. These so-called "resting" or dormant eggs pass to the brood chamber where fertilization occurs. The brood-chamber walls produce a thick-walled capsule called an *ephippium.* At the next molt of the female, the ephippium is released attached to or free from the remains of the castoff shell. Ephippia provide for survival during unfavorable conditions. This may be the drying up of a temporary pond or rigors of over-wintering. It appears probable that some cladocerans acclimated to large permanent ponds reproduce entirely by parthenogenesis.

Typical cladocerans do not have a nauplius. The first juvenile instar resembles the adult, and it is during this stage that the young crustacean is released from the brood chamber. Growth is pronounced during the three to six instars (depending upon the species) that follow. During the last of these immature instars, eggs in the ovary reach maturity, and during the first adult instar this batch of eggs is deposited in the brood chamber, and a new batch reaches maturity in the ovary.

Fig. 15-30 Diagrammatic representation of cyclomorphosis in *Daphnia* caused by seasonal changes (especially temperature) and by genetic factors. After Coker 1939, the *Quart. Rev. Biol.,* courtesy of the American Institute of Biological Sciences and of the author.

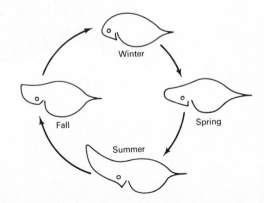

The phenomenon of cyclomorphosis (seasonal change in morphology) is well known for cladocerans, but not well understood. The most pronounced change is in head shape, but frequently there is marked change in size of the compound eye and in extension of the spine at the posterior end of the carapace. During part of the year (late fall to early spring) the head tends to be rather smoothly rounded on its anterior surface, but as the waters become warmer, the anterior head surface tends to become peaked so that the longitudinal axis of the head is greatly elongated, forming a so-called helmet. While increased temperature or marked change in temperature during the development of the first instar within the brood chamber appears to be the critical factor, the amount of vertical migration of the parent or turbulence affecting the temperature of the surface water might be factors causing modification of the environmental temperature. The family Daphnidae particularly has been studied for cyclomorphic changes (Fig. 15-30).

Subclass Ostracoda

This subclass contains over 2000 species and the geologic history goes back to the Ordovician Period. This group is divided into four orders as follows:

Order Myodocopa
Order Cladocopa
Order Podocopa
Order Platycopa

Ostracoda are mostly minute, marine or fresh-water crustaceans whose bivalved calcareous carapace resembles that of a mussel as well as that of the clam shrimps (Conchostraca) but differs from both in lacking the concentric growth lines. The ostracod valves are joined dorsally by a noncalcified hinge whose elasticity causes the valves to gape open. The valves can be closed by adductor muscles which join the inner valve faces. The insertion scars of these muscles are of taxonomic importance (Fig. 15-31)

The body is divided into head and trunk and is completely contained within the closed

Fig. 15-31 *Philomedes*, Ostracoda. After Snodgrass 1956, courtesy of the Smithsonian Institution.

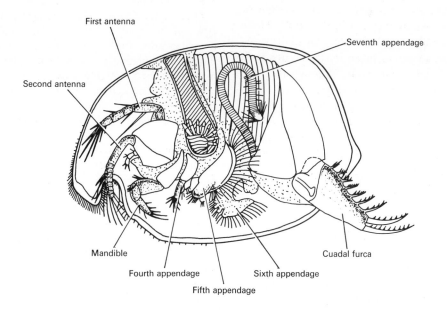

First antenna

Seventh appendage

Second antenna

Mandible

Cuadal furca

Fourth appendage

Sixth appendage

Fifth appendage

carapace. The head carries four pairs of appendages: the first and second antennae, the mandibles, and the maxillae. Because the next pair of appendages bears strong similarity to the maxillae, they have sometimes been interpreted as second maxillae, but since segmentation behind the mandibles is obscure, they may represent a more posterior pair of appendages. Regardless of interpretation, there are never more than four pairs of appendages behind the mandibles. Terminally, the trunk carries an elongated caudal furca, usually reflected ventrally against the abdomen.

Both pairs of antennae are usually provided with prominent setae which function in swimming. Probably crawling progression in the soft substrate in either running or standing water is aided by the robust antennae and by "kicking" with the reflected caudal furca.

Ostracods are mostly filter feeders, utilizing algae, bacteria, and molds as well as dead organic matter. Large food particles are manipulated by the head appendages. In some ostracods, a gastric mill is developed in the anterior part of the foregut.

Most crustaceans have either antennal or maxillary glands retained in the adult. These glands, of presumed excretory or hydrostatic function at least in juvenile stages, are both present in adult ostracods, although they appear to lack external openings.

Respiration is accomplished through the general body surface. Only rarely are true branchiae found. The flattened portions of appendages function primarily to maintain a water current.

The nervous system is composed of a ganglion (the brain) above the esophagus and this is connected by commissures to an abbreviated ventral chain of no more than two pairs of ganglia. A median or nauplius eye is characteristic of ostracods, and one marine subgroup have paired sessile compound eyes, probably convergently similar to other compound eyes among crustacea.

Reproduction is bisexual or parthenogenetic, and males are unknown or rare for some species. In both sexes the reproductive systems are paired. In the male the sperm ducts open through paired penes or medially between the penes, which occur in front of the reflected caudal furca. The female gonopores occur ventrally between the last pair of appendages. The second antennae of the male function as clasping structures during copulation. Eggs are quite resistant to adverse climatic conditions, but they hatch readily in favorable conditions. A few ostracods retain the eggs until hatching in a dorsal brood chamber. At hatching, the larva is a shelled nauplius. Sexual maturity is reached at the ninth and final instar.

Order 1 Myodocopa In this group, the shell has a persistent notch serving as an aperture for the antennae which have an enlarged natatory exopodite. There are four pairs of postmandibular limbs. This marine order possesses two characteristics not found in other ostracods. These features are a heart with paired ostia and sessile compound eyes. The order name is derived from the enlarged muscle activating the antennae. *Philomedes, Asterope, Cypridina.*

Order 2 Cladocopa These marine ostracods lack an antennal notch, and both pairs of antennae are natatory. Two pairs of postoral limbs occur behind the mandibles. The order name is derived from the presence of two rami on the second antennae (clado-branched). *Polycope.*

Order 3 Platycopa This marine group contains one genus. There is no antennal aperture, and the name is derived from the broad rami of the second antennae. There are three pairs of limbs posterior to the small mandibles. *Cytherella.*

Order 4 Podocopa This order is well represented in both marine and fresh-water environments. There is no antennal notch. The endopodite of the second antennae is pediform and clawed, while the exopodite is reduced. The mandibles bear four-segmented palps, and four pairs of limbs occur more caudally. *Cypris, Darwinula.*

Subclass Mystacocarida

In 1943, small crustaceans were found in Long Island Sound living in the interstitial water between sand grains on the beach. These crustaceans were placed in a new genus, *Derocheilocaris,* and other species found on the shores of other continents have been added since. Although the copepods appear to be their nearest relatives, sufficient differences occur to justify the erection of a new subclass.

Derocheilocaris is usually less than one millimeter in length (Fig. 15-32). The body is differentiated into head and trunk areas and is composed of fifteen segments, but the trunk is not as sharply differentiated into thorax and abdomen as with copepods. *Derocheilocaris* lacks the fusion between the head

Fig. 15-32 Metanauplius of mystacocarid, *Derocheilocaris remanei* adapted from Delamare Deboutteville (1954). From Sanders 1963, *the Cephalocarida,* Mem. Conn. Acad. of Arts & Sci., Vol. XV, courtesy of the Conn. Acad. of Arts & Sci.

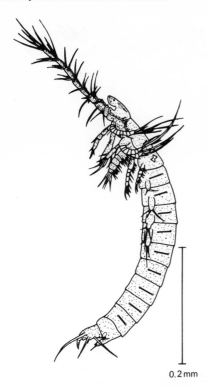

0.2 mm

and the first trunk segment bearing maxillipeds characteristic of copepods. It has a more uniformly elongated body with prominent head appendages. Compound eyes are absent, but the naupliar eye is retained. The second antennae and the mandibles are biramous structures and both antennal and maxillary glands persist, presumably for excretion. The mystacocarids are probably filter feeders, but the mandibles bear robust gnathobases and the space between them is walled ventrally by the large overlapping labrum so that sizable pieces of organic detritus apparently can be utilized. Behind the segment bearing the maxillipeds, the next four segments carry rudimentary appendages and these are followed by six apodous segments. Terminally the two robust rami of the caudal furca face each other like pincers. The sexes are separate. The metanauplius is the earliest larval stage known (Fig. 15-32). During an extended series of molts, the number of segments increases rather uniformly, but there is less regularity in the appearance of appendages.

Subclass Copepoda

The Copepoda constitute the largest subclass among the Entomostraca. The subclass contains over 4,500 described species, most of which are under 2.0 mm in length. The majority of copepods are marine. In both fresh and salt water they are represented by free-living, commensal, and parasitic species. Copepoda are numerous in littoral, benthonic, and planktonic habitats.

Shape varies from the inverted pear typical of many free-living species, with pronounced segmentation frequently regionated into head, thorax, and abdomen, to elongate distorted parasitic forms in which segmentation and frequently appendages are reduced or absent. Most copepods are inconspicuous, but some in littoral habitats or at high altitudes are brilliantly colored. A distinctive characteristic is the presence of a median naupliar eye, but compound eyes are absent. Copepods have no geologic history. The subclass is divided into seven orders as follows:

Order Calanoida
Order Harpacticoida
Order Cyclopoida
Order Notodelphyoida
Order Monstrilloida
Order Caligoida
Order Lernaeopodoida

The first three orders are large and mostly free-living. The other orders are smaller in number and mostly parasitic or commensal during at least part of the life cycle.

In typical free-living species the broadly ovoid cephalic shield, sometimes called a carapace, extends about a third of the animal's length. It is sometimes projected as a rostrum, and in any case it serves as a cover for the cephalothorax which is composed of five thoracic segments fused with the first and sometimes also the second thoracic segment (Fig. 15-33). The head carries a pair of antennules, antennae, mandibles, and two pairs of maxillae. A pair of maxillipeds occur on the first thoracic segment while the following five thoracic segments carry swimming legs. The next segment, considered by some authors to be the seventh thoracic, and by others to be the first abdominal segment, contains the genital openings. In female copepods it is usually fused with the next segment, here considered to be the first abdominal segment. Usually there are two or three additional abdominal segments which lack appendages. The anal segment or telson bears paired caudal rami which are provided with pinnately haired setae of varying length.

The free-living copepod with segmented

Fig. 15-33 *Cyclops*, a copepod. From Schechter 1959, courtesy of Prentice-Hall, Inc.

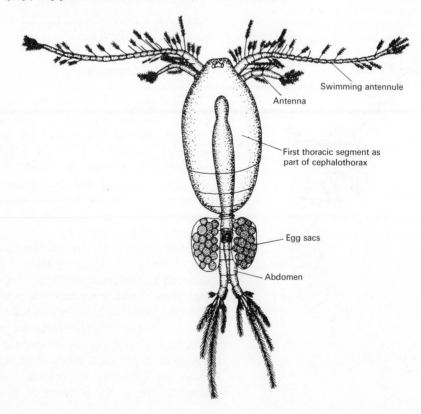

Swimming antennule

Antenna

First thoracic segment as part of cephalothorax

Egg sacs

Abdomen

body has a special articulation, often apparent because a difference in width divides the body into two regions, an anterior *metasome* and a posterior *urosome*. The site of this special joint is not uniform. In some copepods the urosome begins with the genital segment; in others it includes the next anterior segment.

Order 1 Calanoida In these large, free-living copepods the metasome-urosome articulation shows marked constriction and occurs between the genital and the pregenital segments. Antennules in the female have twenty-three to twenty-five segments. A single egg-sac is carried medially. The antennae are biramous. Typically the habitat is planktonic. *Calanus, Diaptomus, Epischura.*

Order 2 Harpacticoida These mostly benthonic-copepods occur in fresh and salt water. The urosome begins with the pregenital segment but there is little or no constriction separating it from the metasome. Antennules are short with five to nine segments in the female and antennae are biramous. There is a single median egg-sac. A few harpacticoids are parasitic. *Attheyella, Harpacticus.*

Order 3 Cyclopoida These are planktonic and benthonic copepods found in fresh and salt water. The urosome includes the pregenital segment and it is separated from the metasome by a marked constriction. Antennules have less than seventeen segments and the antennae are uniramous. There is a pair of egg-sacs. A number of species in this order are parasitic. *Cyclops, Ergasilus, Eucyclops.*

Order 4 Notodelphyoida The urosome includes the pregenital segment in males but is more caudal in females. There is a dorsal egg-sac just anterior to the genital segment. These copepods are commensal in the ascidian pharynx, but may leave the tunicate occasionally. *Doropygus, Notodelphys.*

Order 5 Monstrilloida The free-swimming marine adults lack mouth parts, alimentary canal, and antennae. After the free-swimming nauplius parasitizes a polychaete or a mollusc, the subsequent larval stages absorb sufficient nutrients (apparently by way of modified antennae) to carry the adults through reproduction. *Monstrilla.*

Order 6 Caligoida The urosome includes two pregenital segments in the typical species ectoparasitic on the skin or in the gill chambers of fresh- and salt-water fish. The antennae are modified for attachment, but this is not permanent as the adults can leave the host. *Caligus, Eudactylina, Lepeophtheirus.*

Order 7 Lernaeopodoida Morphology is greatly modified in the adults (especially females) of these ectoparasites of fresh- and salt-water fish. The nauplius moults to a copepodid which becomes parasitic on fish gills. At sexual maturity the copepods leave the host and copulation occurs. The female seeks a second fish host, usually a member of the cod family. Here she changes into an elongate wormlike form with slight or no trace of segmentation, serving as a brood chamber and providing nourishment for the developing eggs. *Brachiella, Lernaea, Lernaeocera.*

Many of the appendages have more than one function. Antennae are sensory and locomotor and in males of some species modified for copulation. Second antennae are primarily sensory. The next four pairs of appendages are used principally for gathering food. The pinnately haired setae of the second maxillae form a screen or filter which catches food particles in the current produced by action of antennae, mandibular palps, and first maxillae, whether these actions be locomotor, respiratory, or specifically to create a food-carrying current (Fig. 15-7). The current is aided or increased by the action of more posterior thoracic limbs. Food caught by the filter is combed out and carried to the mouth by action of spines or setae of other limbs. In some copepods the maxillary filters are utilized actively as scoop or dip nets. Many species of copepods are predaceous or browsers with mouthparts adapted to such behavior. Some predatory copepods can also obtain food by filter mechanisms.

The relatively uniform digestive tract is often provided with as many as three caeca. There is evidence that caudal areas of the digestive tract have excretory and respiratory functions, with water being periodically drawn in and evacuated.

Originally, gonads were probably paired but many copepods have retained only a sin-

gle testis or ovary. Paired, median, or unilateral genital ducts and pores are frequent.
Copulation involves the transfer of spermatophores, a unique condition among ento-

mostracans. The spermatophores adhere to
the opening of the female seminal receptacle
where the sperm are stored. In most female
copepods the seminal receptacles communi-

Fig. 15-34 Fourth copepodid larval stages of *Lernaea*, (a) female; (b) male. After Wilson 1915-16, courtesy of the United States Bureau of Fisheries.

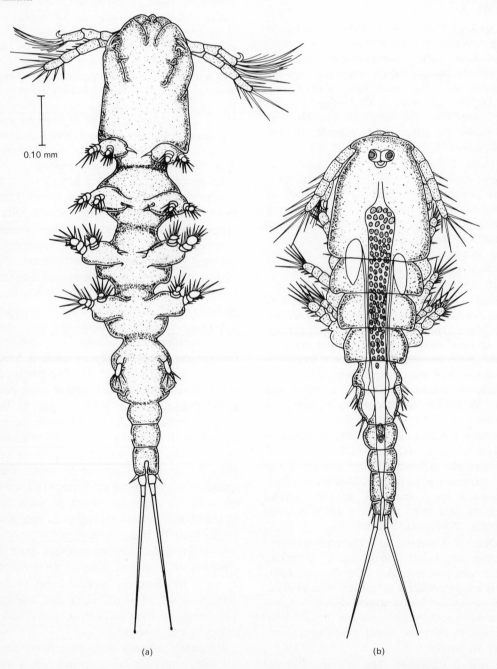

0.10 mm

(a)   (b)

cate with the oviducts. Subsequently, when eggs are produced, sperm are available for fertilization. The developing zygotes are retained in single or paired egg-sacs secreted by the oviducts and attached to the genital segment. Depending upon the species, the young hatch in from one-half to five days and the ovisacs disintegrate to free the larvae. In some species there is immediate release of a new batch of eggs, which are fertilized and retained in a new ovisac without further copulation. This event can be repeated many times. Parthenogenetic development is very rare among copepods.

The egg hatches to free a nauplius larva and in subsequent molts, which may number as many as five, additional naupliar instars occur. At the next molt, the larva loses its ventral curvature and shows a sharper regionation between segmented anterior and unsegmented posterior areas. Because of closer structural similarity to the adult, this larval stage is called a *cyclops* or *copepodid* stage. At subsequent molts, a series of five additional copepodid stages occurs before attainment of the definitive adult condition (Fig. 15-34).

Some Parasitic Copepod Life Histories Parasitism is well developed among the copepods, occurring occasionally in Cyclopoida and Harpacticoida, while the Caligoida, Monstrilloida, Lernaeopodoida, and Notodelphoida are exclusively parasitic or commensal. The genus *Ergasilus* is a relatively unmodified member of the Order Cyclopoida. The parasitism is limited to adult females which attach to the gills of fresh-water fish. *Ergasilus* resembles *Cyclops,* but differs in the greatly enlarged antennae used for attachment (Fig. 15-35). Except that the female is attached, the life cycle is typical of free-living copepods.

Lernaea is a genus belonging to the Order Caligoida. Some thirty species are parasitic on fish, and seven of these are known only from an ancient lake (Nyasa) in southern Africa. One species has been reported in the United States from frog tadpoles. Free-living

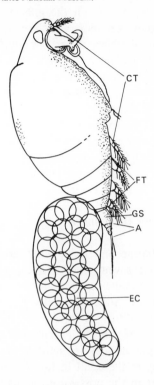

Fig. 15-35 Lateral view of the female of the parasitic copepod, *Ergasilus*. *A*, abdomen; *CT*, cephalothorax; *EC*, egg cases; *FT*, free thorax; *GS*, genital segment. After Wilson 1911, courtesy of the United States National Museum.

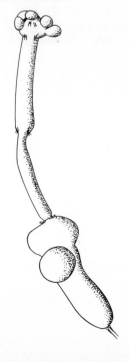

Fig. 15-36 Adult female copepod, *Lernaeocera*, highly modified by parasitism. Modified after Wilson 1915-16, courtesy of the United States Bureau of Fisheries.

naupliar and metanaupliar stages occur in most lernaean life cycles. Upon molting to the first copepodid stage the larvae commonly become parasitic on the gills of fish, although they do not attach permanently during larval stages. After the fourth copepodid state has been reached, (see Fig. 15-34) sexual union occurs. The female immediately seeks a final host into which she bores until the anterior section of her body is buried. An extensive transformation occurs with extreme elongation of the thoracic segments and the development of lateral processes from the cephalothorax to anchor the parasite (Fig. 15-36).

Subclass Branchiura

This marine and fresh-water group contains about seventy-five species, of which some fifteen in the genus *Argulus* occur in the United States. Although related to copepods, Branchiura differ in the following ways. They lack the copepodid larval stages and have a gradual development with molting continuing in the adult instar. Anatomically they differ in the possession of sessile compound eyes. Branchiura are markedly flattened dorso-ventrally with a broad shield-like carapace covering the head and thorax and with a reduced, unsegmented, bilobed abdomen. In *Argulus,* the first maxillae are replaced by a pair of large suckers. Such structures are absent in the genus *Dolops.* Few species of Branchiura are more than twenty-five millimeters long. The adults, known as fish lice, attach to the fish host within the branchial chamber or near the base of eyes or fins. Some amphibia have been recorded as hosts.

Argulus possesses a median hollow spine located preorally just in front of a cylindrical proboscis within which is the mouth. The carapace is specialized ventrally for respiration, and an ostiate heart emptying to an anterior artery is the circulatory organ (Fig. 15-37).

Sexes are separate with the gonoducts from a usually single ovary and paired testes opening at the bases of the last pair of thoracic appendages. The last three pairs of thoracic appendages in the male are modified for copulation and structurally are important in identification of species. In both sexes these three pairs of appendages function in swimming, since the adult crustaceans leave the host at breeding times and on other occasions.

The eggs are attached in rows to hard substrate in the water. They hatch in two weeks or more. In some species the hatched larva is a nauplius, but in others this stage is missing or occurs within the egg before hatching. The animal reaches sexual maturity after six or seven molts.

Subclass Cirripedia

This exclusively marine subclass contains somewhat more than 800 species. The more familiar cirripeds are known as barnacles and there is relatively little in their adult structure to suggest their inclusion with the Crustacea. They are the only crustaceans that as a group are typically attached. The geologic record goes back to the Silurian or possibly the Ordovician Period.

Barnacles hatch as nauplius larvae, and metamorphose through a cypris stage indicating a relationship to the Ostracoda. As adults most barnacles possess a calcareous shell of plates or scales. Such standard crustacean appendages as the antennae are usually absent and antennules are inconspicuous and apparently oddly located. Many of the parasitic cirripeds are so highly modified that their relationship to other arthropods is unrecognizable. The subclass is commonly divided into the following five orders:

Order Thoracica
Order Acrothoracica
Order Apoda
Order Rhizocephala
Order Ascothoracica

Order 1 Thoracica The species in this

Fig. 15-37 (a) Ventral and (b) dorsal views of *Argulus japonicus*, and (c) antennae of *A. pugettensis*. After Meehean 1940, courtesy of the United States National Museum.

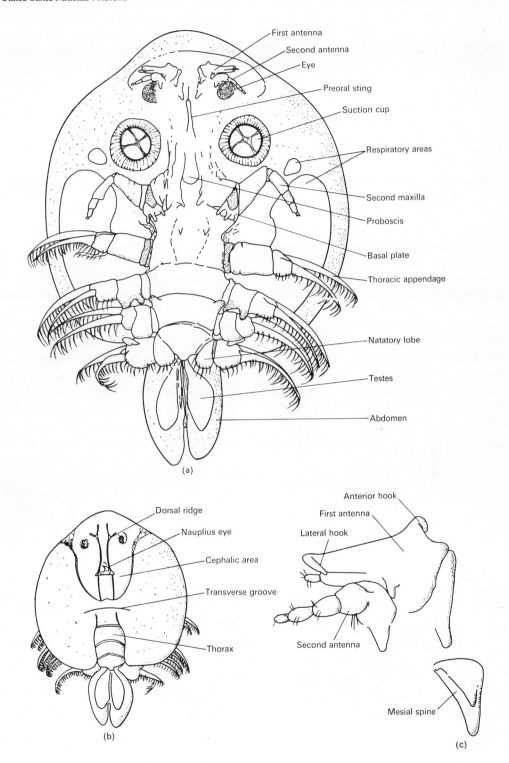

First antenna

Second antenna

Eye

Preoral sting

Suction cup

Respiratory areas

Second maxilla

Proboscis

Basal plate

Thoracic appendage

Natatory lobe

Testes

Abdomen

(a)

Dorsal ridge

Nauplius eye

Cephalic area

Transverse groove

Thorax

(b)

Anterior hook

First antenna

Lateral hook

Second antenna

Mesial spine

(c)

group, including the familiar barnacles, are permanently attached by the preoral region by a cement within which are found the reduced antennules. Antennae are lacking in the adults and there are six pairs of thoracic limbs called *cirri* (Fig. 15-38). Abdominal segments are absent. The Thoracica are divided into subgroups based in part on the presence or absence of a prominent stalk or peduncle. Pedunculate forms are commonly called goose barnacles, while sessile types are known as acorn barnacles. *Balanus, Conchoderma, Coronula, Lepas.*

Many barnacles are attached to pilings and other periodically submerged substrates between tide levels. Water turbulence is an important factor in the distribution of barnacles on such pilings and results in a distribution in zones: some species are limited to a strip near the high-tide mark, others occur in intermediate areas, and still others are restricted to areas just above or below the low-tide mark. Some are adapted to living well below low-tide level. Many barnacles are attached to floating objects including boat bottoms, which they may foul to such an extent as to impede progress. One species of the genus *Lepas* has its own float composed

of gas-filled bubbles in the cement. Many barnacles are parasitic and others are commensal on whales and other animals both vertebrate and invertebrate. An interesting relationship is that of an acorn barnacle, *Coronula diadema,* attached to a whale; with a goose barnacle, *Conchoderma auritum,* in turn attached to the acorn species (Fig. 15-39). This species of *Conchoderma* possesses extensions called "rabbit-ears" which serve as exits for the water which the cirri have filtered for food.

Most barnacles feed by filter method, sweeping the water with the extended cirri and thereby collecting detritus or plankton which is propelled to the mouth.

The goose barnacle, *Lepas,* has a worldwide distribution, which might be expected from its attachment to floating objects (Fig. 15-38). Its peduncle represents the preoral region and contains the adhesive glands which open on the minute antennules at the base of the stalk. The remainder of the body, at the distal end of the stalk, is the *capitulum.* It is enclosed with a fleshy carapace called the *mantle* which secretes five calcareous plates. The *scuta* are paired plates proximal to the

Fig. 15-38 Cirripedia (barnacles): (a) *Balanus*; (b) and (c) *Lepas*. After Snodgrass 1956, courtesy of the Smithsonian Institution.

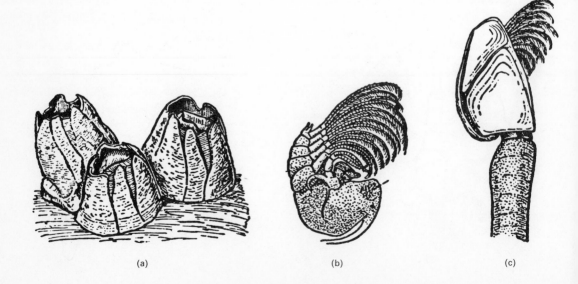

(a)   (b)   (c)

ventral face of the stalk. More distally on this same side of the capitulum are the paired *terga*. On the side opposite to the paired plates is a single median *carina*. This term is somewhat a misnomer since it means keel, a structure associated with the underside of a ship, whereas the carina is on the dorsal or upper aspect in barnacles.

The mantle cavity opens ventrally between the paired plates, and this cavity can be closed by an adductor muscle joining the two scuta. The mouth opens behind the adductor muscle between the paired mandibles and first maxillae. The second maxillae edge the mouth behind. The mouth leads into an esophagus which joins an expanded midgut provided with several caeca. Caudally, the midgut tapers to an anus, opening into the mantle cavity behind the base of the last cirri.

In *Lepas* the ovaries are in the stalk. Paired oviducts open into the mantle cavity between the maxillae and the first thoracic appendages or cirri. Testes lie in the bases of the cirri and extend to the region around the midgut. Paired ducts join at the penis, which extends from a position between the last pair of cirri and the anus.

Pedunculate barnacles are considered to be more primitive than sessile ones. An early ancestor might have been a stalked form with rows of overlapping plates covering the entire animal. Reduction in the number of plates appears to be characteristic of the evolution of barnacles.

Sessile or acorn barnacles are attached broadly at the base or *basis* which may become calcareous. Infolding of the mantle when the shell is being formed may leave radial canals in the basis as well as in other portions of the shell. In *Balanus,* more or less at right angles to the basis, is a whorl of six calcareous plates, forming a truncated cone. One of the plates, which is on the dorsal aspect of the animal, is the carina and opposite it is the rostral plate. Two pairs of lateral plates complete this whorl in *Balanus.* Within the open end of the cone, the paired scuta on the rostral side and the paired terga opposite serve as the skeletal support closing the mantle cavity. When these plates are retracted, the cirri can be protruded through the opening for feeding. Retraction is accomplished by depressor muscles which connect these plates to the basis (Fig. 15-38).

In the acorn barnacles the ovaries occur in the basal portion of the mantle and may extend into the mantle adjacent to the rostrum. The testes are embedded in the tissue along the greater curvature of the midgut and may extend into the basal areas of the cirri.

Respiration is accomplished primarily through the mantle surface, facilitated by water currents through it. Circulation is accomplished principally by a blood sinus subject to pressures between midgut and rostral adductor muscle. This sinus can be dilated. A one-way flow is controlled by

Fig. 15-39 Whale barnacles. The barnacle, *Coronula diadema* attaches to the skin of whales, and the rabbit-eared barnacles, *Conchoderma auritum* attach to other whale barnacles. The "rabbit-ears" serve as egress funnels for water going through the feeding structures. After MacGinitie and MacGinitie 1949, courtesy of the McGraw-Hill Book Company.

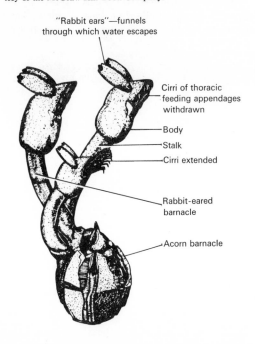

"Rabbit ears"—funnels through which water escapes

Cirri of thoracic feeding appendages withdrawn

Body

Stalk

Cirri extended

Rabbit-eared barnacle

Acorn barnacle

valves. Blood flows into the mantle and also into the stalk in pedunculate forms. In adult cirripeds maxillary glands are retained for excretion. An abbreviated arthropod-type nervous system is characteristic.

Most free-living barnacles are gregarious and they constitute the only large group of crustaceans which are hermaphroditic. Nevertheless cross-fertilization is the usual if not the only method leading to impregnation. Sexual reproduction is favored by the gregarious habit, by the unusual elongation of the penis, and (in some pedunculate species) by production of dwarf males which are attached within the mantle cavity of normal hermaphroditic animals. A condition of protandry or protogyny would tend to insure cross-fertilization.

Fertilization occurs within the mantle cavity. Dislodgment of the eggs by currents within the cavity is prevented by an egg-sac or ovisac of gelatinous secretions produced by the oviduct. A nauplius larva hatches from the egg. This nauplius has a large triangulate dorsal shield characterized by the antero-lateral projection of a pair of hollow horns through which glands discharge. During later larval stages (metan, naupliar) six paired rudiments are apparent on the ventral aspect of

the caudal region. These are the primordia of the six pairs of thoracic appendages (cirri).

Subsequent molting produces a *cypris* larva which bears resemblance to an ostracod. This larva has a large bivalve shell, paired eyes in addition to the median naupliar eye, antennules provided with adhesive glands, and greatly reduced antennae. The larva finally attach permanently in the region of the antennules. By extension of dorsal and ventral folds, the thoracic region with its appendages and alimentary tract becomes connected by a stalk with the mantle and attached preoral portion. The extension of the folds allows the trunk to rotate about ninety degrees, so that the longitudinal axis of the intestine changes from the earlier position continuous with the longitudinal axis of the preoral body to an orientation at right angles to it. This new position leaves the thoracic appendages extending distally (Fig. 15-40). Some of the plates of the adult shell appear before loss of the bivalved larval shell. In later molting the definitive shell plates are not lost, but the uncalcified cuticle adjacent is shed.

Order 2 Acrothoracica These atypical barnacles have a mantle but lack a shell. The mantle in the female possesses teeth which are

Fig. 15-40 Diagrams of metamorphosis of a stalked barnacle from the free-swimming cypris stage (a) to attached stages in (b) and (c). Extension of dorsal and ventral folds is associated with the orientation change in the principal axis. Greatly modified from Kaestner, after Korschelt.

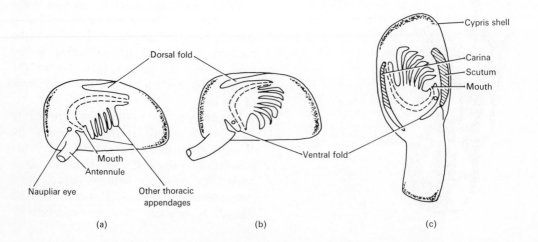

used in excavation of molluscan shells within which the animal lives. Others live in coral. There are only four pairs of thoracic appendages (cirri) and these are less well developed than those in typical barnacles. Dwarf males are characteristic, living attached to the female usually within the mantle cavity. These males lack a digestive system and all appendages except the antennules, which are used for attachment. The male is little more than a sac containing the reproductive system provided with a penis that can extend as much as four times the body length. About a dozen species are known. *Cryptophialus, Trypetesa.*

Order 3 Apoda *Proteolepas bivincta* is the only established species. It was found by Darwin parasitic in the mantle cavity of a pedunculate barnacle from the West Indies. Later some nauplius larvae were tentatively referred to the Apoda. *Proteolepas bivincta* is a distinctly segmented, maggotlike animal narrowing to a cone at either end. Antennules occur at the tip of paired filaments on the dorsal surface. Thoracic appendages and a mantle are lacking, and the alimentary canal is greatly reduced apparently to a stomodaeal portion.

Order 4 Rhizocephala These cirripeds are parasitic on decapod crustaceans and more rarely on tunicates. The degenerate adults lack an alimentary canal, paired appendages, and segmentation. There is no shell, but the mantle is persistent. There is both a nauplius and cypris stage in the development (Fig. 15-9 and Fig. 15-20). The cypris larva is attached to the host by antennules. A system of absorptive roots is characteristic of the adult degeneration. *Parthenopea, Peltogaster, Sacculina.*

Order 5 Ascothoracica This group of parasitic cirripeds lack shells, but a bilobed or saccular mantle containing arborescent diverticula of the digestive tract persists in the adult. Ascothoracica occur as internal parasites in Asteroidea, Echinoidea, and in the black or thorny corals, and as external parasites of stalked crinoids and ophiuroids. *Synagoga,* ectoparasite of crinoids, has pointed first and second maxillae and smaller mandibles adapted for piercing. Endoparasites obtain nourishment from the host through absorptive mantle lobes or papillae terminating in stellate diverticula.

There is a pair of preoral appendages provided with hooks in most genera. These structures have been interpreted as antennules or as antennae, but in any case the cement glands present in most cirripeds in association with antennules are absent. Only in *Synagoga* are the thoracic appendages biramous and functionally segmented. A nauplius larva has been observed in some life cycles, but *Dendrogaster,* parasitic in starfish, hatches as a modified cypris larva. *Dendrogaster, Laura, Synagoga.*

SUBCLASS MALACOSTRACA

The subclass Malacostraca contains about seventy per cent of all known crustaceans. It is in this group that we find the crayfish, lobsters, crabs, and shrimp, familiar from the seafood market or from beginning biology. But all of these familiar animals plus many others belong to the order Decapoda, which contains less than half of the known malacostracan species. The nondecapod malacostracans are a diverse group as indicated by their arrangement into many orders. Generally they are less familiar because they are mostly small, mostly marine, and unimportant commercially. Some of these orders have nonmarine representatives, with the only truly terrestrial crustaceans occurring in order Isopoda.

It is generally accepted that the Malacostraca represent a natural group, with a constancy of structural characteristics grouped in the caridoid facies representing a generalized type of malacostracan (Fig. 15-5). Sanders (1963) has pointed out that the caridoid morphology appeared relatively late in ontogeny and that the structural characteristics prior to its appearance are close to those in the Cephalocarida *(Hutchinsoniella)*. This structural relationship suggests that the Malacostraca are less isolated from other Crustacea than has frequently been assumed. See the discussion of the caridoid morphology earlier in this chapter. Although adaptation has resulted in diversity from the caridoid pattern in many Malacostraca, the familiar crayfish illustrates a number of the basic features. On the head are the compound eyes on movable stalks projecting from beneath the carapace. The antennules (first antennae of some authors) have two elongate, multiarticulate flagella. Antennae are biramous, with a scalelike exopodite and a long, segmented endopodite. The mandible carries a palpus. The crayfish lacks the caridoid feature of natatory exopodites on thoracic limbs but does show a carapace, an elongated, ventrally-flexed abdomen, and the flattened biramous appendages (uropods) of the last abdominal segment. Other abdominal appendages typically are also biramous. These appendages, called pleopods, do not have natatory function in the crayfish, although this action is common for many malacostracans. In the Decapod subgroup to which the crayfish belongs, sexual dimorphism is evident, with the first two pairs of pleopods in the male modified for copulation. Finally, the crayfish has the caridoid pattern of gonopore location. Genital aperture in the female is on the sixth, in the male on the eighth thoracic segment.

Malacostraca are commonly divided into two series: Eumalacostraca exhibiting caridoid morphology; and Leptostraca, a small group of seven known species with a number of divergent features. The following are some of the more evident features by which the Leptostraca differ from other Malacostraca. A movable rostrum articulating with the anterior dorsal edge of the carapace is projected over the head in front of the antennae; a large bivalved carapace is joined by an adductor muscle above the second maxillae of the thoracic segments, and covers all thoracic and most abdominal segments; thoracic limbs are foliaceous and structurally uniform; seven segments occur for the abdomen with the first four provided with robust natatory appendages, the next two with reduced appendages, and the seventh lacking appendages; a telson terminates in a movable caudal furca (Fig. 15-41).

Superorder Phyllocarida (Leptostraca)

There is a single superorder (Phyllocarida) and a single order (Nebaliacea) in the Leptostraca. Most Nebaliacea are small crustaceans under 12 millimeters, and are benthonic in shallow coastal waters, but the genus *Nebaliopsis* may reach a length of 40 millimeters and occurs at depths of over six thousand feet (Fig. 1-2). Nebaliacea are

Fig. 15-41 *Nebalia bipes*, a primitive malacostracan. *h*, heart; *i*, intestine; *o*, ovary; *a*, adductor of carapace; *b*, brain; *r*, rostrum. From Hertwig (after Sars), *A Manual of Zoology* (translated and edited by J. S. Kingsley) 1902, Holt, Rinehart & Winston, Inc.

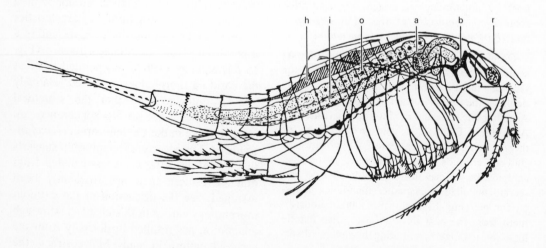

filter feeders. The water current produced by the thoracic limbs carries food particles but also serves the respiratory surfaces of the epipodites of thoracic limbs and of the interior surface of the shell.

Feeding in Nebaliacea is very similar to the pattern in some Branchiopoda, with water currents caused by the beat of thoracic limbs, caught by setae on these same limbs and transferred to the ventral groove between bases of the thoracic appendages. *Nebalia bipes* lacks a current in this ventral groove, and food is pushed toward the mouth by the action of successive gnathobases. The alimentary canal has a stomodaeal enlargement, commonly called the stomach, which is divided into a proventriculus or cardiac portion provided with masticatory ridges and a more caudal pyloric section possessing setae which appear to direct the flow of minute food particles into the midgut. The midgut extends through the sixth abdominal segment and at its anterior end is provided with hepatic and other caeca.

Respiration is accomplished by the broad epipodites of thoracic appendages, and by the inner carapace surface. The heart extends from the head to the fourth abdominal segment and carries seven pairs of ostia. The nervous system has a complex brain similar to that in other Malacostraca. Thoracic ganglia are crowded together, and the adult shows six abdominal ganglia, but a seventh transitory ganglion occurs during development. Nebaliacea differ from most other crustaceans except ostracods in retaining both maxillary and antennal excretory glands, but both are vestigial in the adult and eight pairs of ectodermal glands in the thorax are considered to have excretory function. The gonads are paired tubular structures that open externally on the same segments characteristic of the caridoid facies pattern. Development is direct within the brood chamber of the female. The embryo hatches from the egg membrane with all thoracic and usually some of the abdominal appendages evident (Fig. 15-23). Recent genera include *Nebalia,*

Nebaliopsis, and *Paranebalia,* and a fossil nebaliid has been identified from the Upper Permian.

Superorder Hoplocarida (Stomatopoda)

This group of Eumalocostraca is limited to a single order, Stomatopoda, which contains about 180 species. The name means "mouth-foot" and refers to the large number of appendages modified for feeding. The species, varying in size between that of the shrimp and that of the lobster, are strictly marine and possess a number of distinctive features (Fig. 15-42). There is a flat, shield-like carapace fused with the first two or three thoracic somites and not extending caudally much beyond this region. In front of the carapace are two movable pseudosegments, the more anterior of which bears stalked eyes, while the second bears the antennules distinctive in possessing three rami. A movable rostrum, articulating with the carapace, extends dorsally over the antennular segment. The antenna has a setose exopodite larger than the segmented endopodite, and this appendage is smaller than the antennule. Mandibles and the two pairs of maxillae are structurally quite diverse from these appendages in the familiar crayfish. The first five pairs of thoracic appendages are six-segmented rather than seven as in *Cambarus,* the crayfish. The second pair are exceptionally large and raptorial and their orientation on the body is suggestive of that odd but familiar insect, the praying mantis. Because of this similarity, the name of mantis shrimp is applied to these animals. This appendage is also known as a *jackknife claw,* since the terminal segment has a serrate or bladelike edge that fits into a groove in the large penultimate segment similar to a nearly closed jackknife. Action of this 'jackknife" in larger species can cut a shrimp or other food in two with a single slashing movement. The abdominal segments are biramous, with flattened endopodite and exopodite. In development the orientation of these two structures may be partly reversed so that the exopodite is more median. It bears a narrow stalk, on one side of which is a series of long gill filaments. The only other malacostracans possessing abdominal gills are the isopods. The terminal segment of the broad abdomen bears uropods which with the median telson form a tail-fan. The uropod differs from that in the crayfish with a flat forked extension of the protopodite projecting between endopodite and exopodite.

Tropical coastal waters have the greatest number of different stomatopod species, but some occur in more temperate zones such as *Pseudosquilla bigelowi* on the Pacific Coast and *Squilla empusa* on the Atlantic Coast of the United States. They are often highly colored animals with various oranges mixed with greens and azures. Stomatopods seek protective cavities in which to live. These may involve excavations on the bottom, crevices in coral, or burrows formed by other animals. In some species, the armored telson serves as an effective operculum when the animal is "home." Swimming by use of the abdominal appendages is usually restricted to areas near the burrow, into which the animal retreats when alarmed.

All Stomatopoda are predatory and feed on various small animals (both vertebrate and invertebrate) which they are able to capture. Food is dispatched by means of the jackknife claw and devoured in the burrow. Initial mastication is accomplished by the mandi-

bles. The proventriculus has two pairs of lateral ossicles, the more dorsal pair operating against a ventral median plate which extends into the pyloric region. Action of this "gastric mill" completes the triturating process. The stomatopod digestive gland communicates with the pyloric stomach and is probably homologous with the hepatopancreas of other malacostracans, but differs in its extension in the abdomen even into telson and uropods. Respiration is accomplished by the gills on abdominal appendages, and blood (which contains the respiratory pigment, hemocyanin, at least in some forms) reaches the pericardial cavity through afferent canals in the abdomen.

The heart is unique among Malacostraca in extending through most of the thorax and abdomen. It is provided with thirteen pairs of segmentally arranged ostia, the first pair occurring in the maxillary somite. Behind this pair of ostia there are fourteen pairs of segmental arteries leaving the heart, as well as a median terminal artery extending into the telson. Maxillary glands are the excretory organs of adult stomatopods. The gonoducts open on the same segments characteristic of the caridoid pattern, but all of the testes and most of the ovaries occur as paired masses in the abdomen. In both sexes the gonads are united in the telson. The small eggs are clumped and either carried by the female with the thoracic appendages which are chelate (actually subchelate by the flexion of

Fig. 15-42 *Squilla mantis* (Hoplocarida, Stomatopoda). After Snodgrass 1956, courtesy of the Smithsonian Institution.

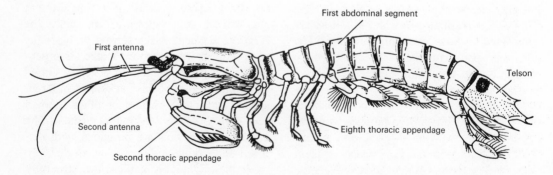

First abdominal segment

First antenna

Telson

Second antenna

Eighth thoracic appendage

Second thoracic appendage

the terminal with the subterminal segment) or kept in the burrow.

There appear to be two general variations in metamorphosis of the hatched larvae. One type hatches in a form similar to an early zoeal larva, in which the only segmentation apparent is in the thorax, with a large carapace enveloping most of the body excepting the unsegmented tail-plate representing the abdomen. Later changes involve relative reduction of the carapace, fusion of anterior thoracic segments with the carapace, and the formation of segments and appendages in the abdomen. It is noteworthy that the abdominal appendages appear prior to the appendages on the last three thoracic segments. In some species of stomatopods, the larva that hatches already has several pairs of abdominal appendages or pleopods and the last five or six thoracic somites are still devoid of appendages. Fossil stomatopods have been traced from the Mississippian Period. Recent species include *Squilla, Pseudosquilla,* and *Coronida.*

Superorder Syncarida (Anaspidacea)

These Eumalacostraca include a few species of primitive crustaceans reported from various continents not including North America. These primitive features include a head structure reminiscent of that in Anostraca (Snodgrass, 1951). Another distinctive feature is the absence of a carapace. The first thoracic segment is fused with the head or demarked from it by a furrow. There is an elongate tubular heart extending through most of the body. The first pair of thoracic appendages are modified as maxillipeds in *Anaspides* (Fig. 15-43). The next five pairs of appendages are walking legs composed of an endopodite of seven segments, a smaller exopodite with annulated flagellum, and two leaflike epipodites which function as gills (Fig. 15-2). Endopodites are reduced or missing on most abdominal appendages, but in *Anaspides* and *Koonunga* the first two function for copulation in the male. Uropods occur on the terminal segment and with the telson form a tail-fan. *Bathynella* is a related species often placed in a separate order. It was first found in a deep well in Prague in 1882. It and a related species, *Thermobathynella,* are blind, cave-dwelling species, smaller than most Anaspidacea. *Anaspides* reaches a length of four to five centimeters, while *Koonunga* is about one centimeter long. The head of *Bathynella* suggests relationship to Pericarida to be discussed later, but this genus possesses a caudal furca as well as uropods.

Anaspides and *Paranaspides* are known from Tasmanian lakes. *Paranaspides* is a filter feeder, but lacks a forward current in the ventral groove. The feeding current is a wave action lacking the rotary movement characteristic of many filter feeders. *Anaspides* is provided with a filter-feeding mechanism, but is principally a raptorial feeder. It grovels in

Fig. 15-43 *Anaspides* male, lateral view. After Snodgrass 1952, courtesy of the Comstock Publishing Associates.

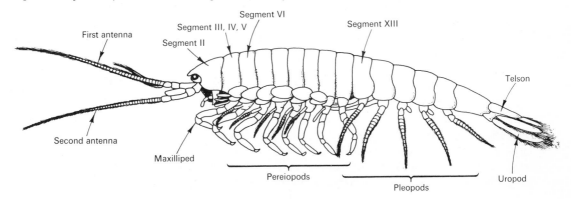

the substratum and scrapes up detritus as well as small animals. Minute material is caught on the maxillary filter and larger food is chewed with the mandibles. *Anaspides* has stalked, *Koonunga* sessile compound eyes. A statocyst is present on the antennular base. Both testes and gonads extend from the thorax into the abdomen. The respective gonopores open on the thoracic segments characteristic of the caridoid pattern. Sperm of *Anaspides* are enclosed in horseshoe-shaped spermatophores, and presumably are attached to the seminal receptacle on the last thoracic segment of the female. Eggs leaving the female are fertilized as they pass adjacent to the spermatophores. Eggs are shed directly into the water or upon water plants, where they develop directly with no known free-living larval stages. Recent genera include *Anaspides, Paranaspides,* and *Koonunga.* The fossil record goes back to the Pennsylvanian Period.

Superorder Peracarida

The Peracarida, a large group with over 9,000 species, is composed of five well-known but diverse orders: Mysidacea, Cumacea, Taniadacea, Isopoda, and Amphipoda, and one obscure order, Spelaeogriphacea, containing a single species. *Spelaeogriphus lepidops* was described from caves in South Africa in 1957. It possesses a carapace covering only the first thoracic segment and in this feature stands between the first three orders with larger carapaces and the Isopoda and Amphipoda which have none. Another order, the Thermosbaenacea, containing four species is sometimes placed in the Peracarida, but its brood pouch or marsupium does not have the characteristic pericarid structure and location. The brood pouch in the Thermosbaenacea is formed from a pocket of the carapace. In order to introduce eggs into this marsupium, the female lies on her back while egg-laying. *Thermosbaena mirabilis* lives in warm springs in northern Africa; it can tolerate a temperature of 47° centigrade, and

a temperature of 35° is apt to be fatal. Siewing has proposed that the Thermosbaenacea be placed in a superorder, Pancarida.

The most distinctive feature of the Peracarida is the brood pouch or marsupium in females formed from large, horizontal plates called oostegites, which project medially from thoracic coxopodites to form an imbricated floor. The carapace, when present, is never fused with the last four thoracic somites whereas the first thoracic segment is always fused with the head. The heart is elongate and sometimes situated in the abdomen. Hepatic caeca are few and unbranched. Consistently, the peracarids have tended to extend the embryonic period with the consequent elimination of free-swimming larval stages. In some forms, the larva that leaves the brood pouch has the primordia of all the definitive appendages; in others, the last pair of thoracic appendages and the pleopods are not evident, but otherwise the young closely resemble adults.

Order 1 Mysidacea   This group retains the general caridoid features. The carapace, which does not fuse with more than the first three thoracic segments, covers most of the thorax, although in some forms it is recessed dorsally to leave the last two or three thoracic somites uncovered. Frequently the carapace projects forward as a rostrum. The last seven pairs of thoracic segments in the females of some species bear oostegites, while in others only the last two or three somites form the marsupium. The compound eyes, when present, are movable and pedunculate.

The first pair of thoracic appendages are modified as maxillipeds, and in family Mysididae the second pair (sometimes also called maxillipeds) are inclined toward the mouth, and lack the terminal claw. In most Mysidacea the last seven thoracic appendages are similar. In some families, fimbriated lobed gills develop near the bases of most of the thoracic appendages, but in Mysididae the inner surface of the carapace is the principal respiratory surface.

Some variation of filter feeding is considered to be the primitive mode for crustaceans, and the variation found in Mysidacea is probably primitive for the Malacostraca. In *Gnathophausia,* a primitive marine mysid, the abdominal limbs (pleopods) are natatory, the thoracic limbs create a respiratory current by spiral rotation, and the second maxillae are the principal filters. These maxillae cause a current to flow forward through a filter on the median edge of the appendage. Food caught is pushed forward toward the first maxillae by setae projecting from the first thoracic appendage, and a similar action carries it to mandibles and mouth. Here the functions of locomotion, respiration, and feeding are mainly independent. In *Hemimysis,* the pleopods are no longer natatory and thoracic appendages function for both swimming and feeding. Both of these genera utilize larger food particles caught by other means than the filter, and these are masticated by the mandibles. The stomodaeal region of the alimentary canal has a cardiac and pyloric "stomach," both of which are internally armed with spines and setae so that a gastric mill for trituration is evolving. The heart is elongate, restricted to the thorax, and provided with two pairs of ostia. Siewing (1963) thinks that the Mysidacean circulatory system provides a connecting link to the Eucarida. The definitive excretory organ in this order is the antennal gland, but groups of excretory cells at the bases of the thoracic limbs are reminiscent of those in the Leptostraca. Ganglia of the ventral chain in front of the abdomen may be fused, or separate; six abdominal ganglia are distinct. In addition to the compound eyes, other prominent sense organs are the statocysts which occur on the uropods in Mysidacea; these have nerve communication with the last pair of abdominal ganglia. Gonopores occur on the segments typical of the caridoid facies. Development is direct and occurs within the brood chamber.

Most Mysidacea are about two or three centimeters in length, but one species of *Boreomysis* may reach a length of about eight centimeters and some *Gnathophausia* may be four or five times larger. Some Mysididae are planktonic or benthonic in relatively shallow water, but most members of the order are bathypelagic. A few species have become adapted to fresh water. *Mysis oculata relicta* is a fresh-water form occurring in the United States in deep, cold northern lakes, such as the Great Lakes and some of the Finger Lakes, where it is probably the chief source of food of commercial fish such as lake trout. On the west coast of North America, *Neomysis mercedis* occurs in some strictly freshwater lakes and rivers near the coast, but is probably more common in brackish water. There are about 450 species of Mysidacea, and geologic history of the group goes back to the Pennsylvanian Period. Some recent genera are *Hemimysis, Neomysis, Mysis,* and *Gnathophausia.*

Order 2 Cumacea This order contains several hundred Recent species, but no fossil history is known. The carapace is fused with the first three or four thoracic somites and it extends ventrally on either side to form branchial cavities. Paired latero-dorsal horns extend forward and usually meet in the mid-dorsal line to form a forked pseudorostrum. The cephalothorax is bulbous and tapering caudally, to be sharply demarked from a slender, rather uniformly segmented abdomen. The eyes when present are sessile and united medially in a loose aggregation of ocelli. Antennules appear to be uniflagellate, with the inner flagellum reduced or absent. Antennae show marked sexual dimorphism, being vestigial in the female, and with a robust base and a long flagellum in the male. The first one or two pairs of thoracic appendages have epipodites modified as gills. Oostegites are well developed on the third, fourth, fifth, and sixth thoracic segments. Abdominal appendages are absent in the female, but from one to five segments in the male are provided with prominent, biramous pleopods. The telson is often somewhat reduced and may be fused with the terminal segment, but the uropods are elongate, rodlike, and furnished with rows of spines.

Cumacea are found exclusively in salt water. A large number of species in the genus *Pseudocuma* are limited to the Caspian Sea, in which the average salinity is only about one-third that of the Mediterranean Sea. Most Cumacea are detritus feeders; a few browse on organic matter on sand grains. The respiratory current in some of the more primitive malacostracans moves forward through the branchial chamber propelled by the action of epipodites or exopodites on appendages behind the mouth. In the lower Pericarida this involves the first and sometimes the second thoracic appendage (maxillipeds). *Diastylis* has a burrowing habit, the body being embedded in the substrate with only the extremities protruding. Since much of the carapace is buried, posterior or ventral entry of the respiratory current, which in Cumacea is also the food-bearing stream, is limited or impossible. The water current enters at the front end of the carapace, and the first maxilliped which is principally responsible for the current is modified to form an exhalant siphon emptying just below the pseudorostrum. Food is filtered from this current by the setae on the second maxillae. The stomodaeum has a primitive gastric mill. Cumacea possess from one to four hepatic caeca. The tubular or globular heart is confined to the thorax and has two ostia. The well-developed excretory glands are on the maxillae. Gonads are tubular, and the eggs develop to a postlarva stage called *manca.* Genera include *Cumopsis, Diastylis,* and *Pseudocuma.*

Order 3 Tanaidacea   This order, containing somewhat over 250 species, is typically marine, although nonmarine species of *Tanais* have been reported from Argentina and from the Kurile Islands off Siberia. Body form resembles that of Isopoda. The carapace is abbreviated and is fused with the first two thoracic segments. The eyes when present are located on short stationary stalks. Other distinctive features are the presence of two instead of three segments in the antennal

protopodite or peduncle; the second pair of thoracic appendages are enlarged and typically chelate; exopodites are absent on most thoracic appendages; uropods are elongate and slender, and the telson is fused with the terminal segment.

Water movement in the branchial chamber is effected by the maxillipeds with the inner carapace surface functioning as the principal respiratory surface. The water current carries food particles, but the maxillary setae are less important than setae on appendages closer to the mouth. Raptorial feeding is common in these burrow and tube dwellers. The tubular heart is confined to the thorax and has two to four ostia. Maxillary excretory glands are well developed. Gonads are simple, but gonopores are often paired. One species of *Apseudes* is hermaphroditic; and two types of males have been reported for *Leptochelia*. The eggs develop in a marsupium formed from one to five pairs of oostegites in different species.

Most Tanaids in shallow water are under one centimeter long, while deep-water forms (*Neotanais* and *Herpotanais*) are commonly two or three times bigger. Characteristic of many Tanaids is the utilization of the abdomen as a kind of vaulting or undulating action to escape enemies or to rise off the ocean bottom. No fossil Tanaidacea are known. Recent genera include *Apseudes, Neotanais,* and *Tanais.*

Order 4 Isopoda   This large order with over 4,000 described species is predominantly marine, but has important fresh-water and terrestrial representatives. A large number of Isopoda are parasitic—externally on some fish hosts, externally and internally on other crustacea. Parasitism has resulted in many modifications and in some cases intensive degeneration. Typically Isopoda are flattened dorso-ventrally, but some marine forms are elongate and cylindrical, and *Phreaticus,* a fresh-water isopod of South Africa and Australia, is flattened laterally, a condition generally characteristic of Amphipoda. The flattened abdominal appendages, some of which are used in respiration and in the male are modified for copulation, differentiate isopods from the amphipods.

A carapace is absent in isopods but the first thoracic segment (and sometimes the second) is fused with the head, which is somewhat shield-shaped (Fig. 15-44). Compound eyes, absent in some marine forms, are sessile or on short nonmovable stalks and vary from few to many ommatidia. Antennules are short or vestigial and typically do not show a biflagellate structure. Antennae vary from vestiges to great length, represented almost exclusively by the endopodite. Mandibles of more typical species show close conformity with other Peracarida, but these appendages have undergone great modifications coincident with varying food habits and particularly with parasitism. The first and second maxillae have two and three prominent endites respectively, and the former is armed with stout spines. The first pair of thoracic appendages are maxillipeds and are associated with the other mouthparts. The rest of the thoracic appendages are typically ambulatory and uniform in size and structure, but frequently these are modified in natatory species. Some legs may be subchelate and function as grasping organs. In most isopods, the coxal leg segment is incorporated into the lateral wall of the segment and in

some it is expanded as a shield covering the leg articulation. Since oostegites are lateral expansions of the coxopodite, in many isopods oostegites appear to develop from the body wall of the segment in question. Pleopods are typically biramous and flattened. In the primitive condition, both exopodite and endopodite are respiratory. Various divisions of labor occur, however, with more anterior pleopods fringed for natatory function (particularly in immature stages) and respiration limited to more posterior appendages. Frequently, the respiratory structures are protected by a cover called an operculum which may be derived by modification of the first pair of pleopods; from more caudal exopodites; and in the marine suborder, Valvifera, from the uropod endopodites.

In the suborder Oniscoidea, which embraces amphibious and terrestrial isopods including those known as wood lice, the exopodites of the pleopods contain lunglike cavities or tubelike, chitinous-lined pseudotrachea. Oniscoids are also commonly called sow bugs or pill bugs, the latter name derived from the protective habit in *Oniscus* and *Armadillidium* of rolling up into tight spheres. In American fresh-water species in the suborder Asellota, the last four abdominal segments are fused with the telson to form a shieldlike plate, whereas in our terrestrial

Fig. 15-44 Isopoda: (a) *Asellus* and (b) *Cymothoa*. From Hertwig (a, from Ludwig-Luenis; b, after Gerstäcker), *A Manual of Zoology* (translated and edited by J. S. Kingsley) 1902, Holt, Rinehart & Winston, Inc.

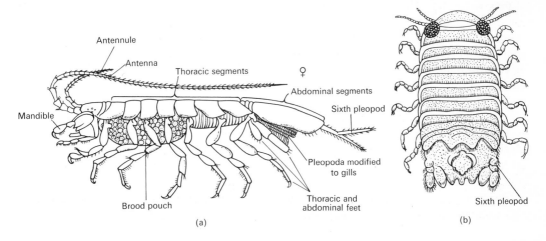

species (suborder Oniscoidea) abdominal segments are usually not fused. Uropods are usually biramous, but there are numerous cases in which either the exopodite or the endopodite is missing.

Marine isopods occur at a variety of depths, some having been found in water more than 10,000 meters deep. As with other crustaceans, larger species are apt to occur in deeper water. *Bathynomus* may be more than a foot long but most isopods are well under an inch in length. Isopods are omnivorous generally, including scavenging, but some are largely herbivorous, such as *Idotea* which eats seaweed. Crawling is a common method of locomotion and may be quite rapid. *Cruregens* is able to run backward or forward with equal facility. The order includes a number of tube-dwellers and in these, water must be circulated to obtain oxygen. *Limnoria lignorum,* the gribble, is a wood-boring isopod less than three millimeters long. It is a serious pest because of the tunnels it makes in submerged wood and is largely responsible for the "pinched waist" on pilings at tide level. The presence of fungi growing on submerged wood is an important factor in gribble infestation, but the presence of cellulose-splitting enzymes indicates that the gribble can utilize the wood for nourishment.

The heart commonly extends into or is located in the abdomen. This appears to be correlated with the respiratory function of abdominal appendages whether through gills or pseudo-trachea. The heart has two to four ostia. The ventral nerve cord may show its paired origin with ganglia corresponding to segmentation, but it reaches a great degree of concentration in those isopods with reduced and fused abdominal segments. Compound eyes, when present, are sessile or on short, immovable stalks. Statocysts have been reported on the telson in a few species. Maxillary glands are commonly retained in adult isopods and are considered to be excretory.

Gonopores are typical of the caridoid pattern usually, but in males of some species

fusion of segments appears to displace the openings to the first abdominal somite. Two pairs of oviducts with corresponding openings have been reported in some Epicaridea. In the fresh-water genus, *Lirceus,* copulation occurs after the female has lost the posterior half of her exoskeleton at ecdysis. The male moves to a latero-dorsal position and with the aid of modified pleopods transfers sperm to the seminal receptacle on that side. The process is repeated to introduce sperm into the opposite seminal receptacle. Fertilization occurs in the oviducts. The young develop within the brood chamber to a late stage called manca, which is similar to the adult structure except that the last thoracic appendages have not appeared. In parasitic forms, hermaphroditism is common. Some isopods are parasites of parasites. *Peltogaster,* a barnacle, causes some gonadal degeneration in its host, the hermit crab. A somewhat similar effect occurs in *Peltogaster,* parasitized by the isopod *Liriopsis*. In another family of the Epicaridea, the first immature stage to infect the gill chamber of its decapod host invariably develops into a female and later arrivals will develop into males.

The Isopoda are divided into a number of suborders. The names of representative species precede the suborder for the ones listed: *Cruregens* (Anthuridea), *Sphaeroma* (Flabellifera), *Idotea* (Valvifera), *Asellus* and *Lirceus* (Asellota), *Liriopsis* and *Probopyrus* (Epicaridea), and *Armadillidium, Ligia, Oniscus,* and *Porcellio* (Oniscoidea). The geologic history of the isopods goes back to the Devonian, but the earliest evidence of terrestrial species is from the Upper Eocene.

Order 5 Amphipoda The Amphipoda is a large group of Peracaridea, containing nearly as many species as the Isopoda, and resembling them in lacking a carapace, and with the first (and sometimes the second) thoracic segment fused with the head. The amphipod body tends to be laterally compressed (Fig. 15-45). The sessile compound eyes are lateral and prominent, except in subterranean species in which they may be degenerate or absent. Antennules are usually biramous and robust. The antennae as well as thoracic limbs lack exopodites. Mandibles structurally are typical peracaridan. The first pair of maxillae are larger than the second pair. The first pair of thoracic appendages are maxillipeds with their coxopodites fused into a single plate. The second and third appendages are usually prehensile, being subchelate or chelate, and are frequently called gnathopods since they assist in food collection. The other thoracic appendages are locomotor. The first two of these are often flexed forward at the principal joints with a backward-projecting dactylopodite, but in the last three these features are reversed. In the suborder Caprellidea there is a breakage plane at which site the limb breaks at autotomy as an escape provision. Some Caprellidae are called skeleton shrimp because of the attenuated structure of successive segments. The coxopodites of the walking legs or periopods tend to be enlarged plates whose flat surface emphasizes the lateral compression of the body.

Gills are attached to the mediad surfaces of thoracic appendages behind the first gnathopods. Gills are platelike or hollow, frequently with the surface increased by folds and vary in number from two to six pairs. Proximal to the gills, oostegites develop on the coxopodites of females on the third, fourth, fifth, and sixth periopods, but this number may be less. Five pairs of pleopods are typical. The first three pairs are fringed, turned forward, and function to produce a respiratory current over the gills and for swimming. The last two pairs of pleopods are biramous, turn backward, and structurally are like the uropods. No pleopods show distinctive copulatory modifications as they do in isopods. A distinct telson is characteristic.

Of the four suborders comprising the Amphipoda, only the Gammaridea have successfully radiated into fresh waters. They include over fifty American species occurring in unpolluted surface and subterranean waters. Both marine and fresh-water Amphipoda may be brilliantly colored and common species exhibit a considerable range of color. Most amphipods are well under an inch in length, the smallest being in the neighborhood of one to two millimeters. Calman re-

Fig. 15-45 *Orchestia,* an amphipod. Redrawn from Hertwig (after Nebeski), *A Manual of Zoology* (translated and edited by J. S. Kingsley) 1902, Holt, Rinehart & Winston, Inc.

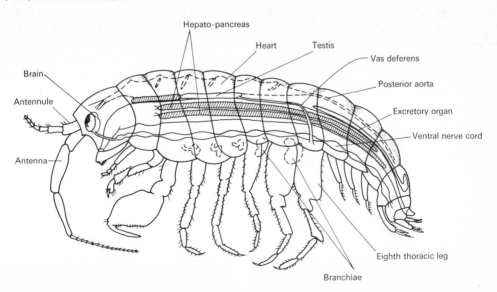

ports the largest is *Alicella gigantea* which may reach a length of 140 millimeters. Many amphipods occur in marine shore waters; others occur at great depths. Some have been dredged from Pacific floor trenches at depths exceeding 10,000 meters. Over three hundred species of Amphipoda have been reported from the littoral waters of the Antarctic and seventy per cent of these appear to be restricted to that region. Lake Baikal, a large body of water in southern Siberia, has nearly three hundred species of *Gammarus,* only one of which has been reported elsewhere.

Members of the suborder Hyperiidea are pelagic, but most amphipods are bottom dwellers. *Talorchestia longicornis,* one of the sand hoppers or beach fleas—which are amphipods that live in sand just above high-water line—can run, climb, jump, and burrow with great facility and it can swim if forced to do so. It has been known to jump fifty times its body length of about two centimeters. Jumping is usually accomplished by sudden extension of the abdomen with springing action of posterior legs. This species digs with gnathopods, having folded the long antennae out of the way. The body is supported by the second and third pairs of thoracic legs, while the next two pairs act as pushers. Sand reaching the posterior abdominal appendages is thrown clear by rapid extension of the abdomen. Some other amphipods, which are littoral, move the sand back hydraulically by a current created by the pleopods, and antennae instead of gnathopods are utilized in digging by *Urothoe.* In addition to sand hoppers, another terrestrial amphipod is *Talitroides alluaudi,* which lives in soil in the forest and has become established in greenhouses in Europe. Many amphipods construct temporary or permanent burrows. *Cerapus longirostris* is interesting because of its mobile home, which is a cylindrical tube. This animal can crawl or even swim carrying its home with it. It does this by projecting sufficient appendages to accomplish these functions. A number of Amphipods characteristically swim on their side or even on their back.

Most amphipods have biting mouthparts, with the first maxillae armed with stout spines. Food is held and pieces bitten off. Chelate and subchelate appendages if present aid in securing the food. One amphipod, *Chelura,* bores into wood, but not with the efficiency of the isopod *Limnoria.* Most amphipods are omnivorous, including scavenging, but some eat blades of seaweed and other vegetation. *Hyperia galba* lives in the genital pits on medusoid jellyfish, and at least occasionally takes a bite out of the host. Some members of the suborder Caprellidea are usually attached to small colonial coelenterates. These feed on copepods or other small animals which wander within reach. In this same suborder there is a small group called whale lice which live on the skin of whales. A number of amphipods are filter feeders, with setae on antennules, antennae, or gastropods acting as filters. *Haustorius arenarius* is one of the few amphipods to utilize a maxillary filter. Food is swept from the filter by a setal comb on the maxilliped palps.

The stomodaeum has a triturating stomach akin to the gastric mill of decapods. Generally the large midgut has four hepatic caeca plus a median dorsal caecum. Some amphipods have two or more caeca arising from the midgut and thought to be excretory in function. The antennal gland, retained in most adult amphipods, is also excretory. In most members of this order a respiratory current flows caudally, usually activated by anterior pleopods. In some tube dwellers, antennae are responsible for this function. The ventral nerve cord is paired and connected with twelve ganglia in most Gammaridea, but in the other suborders there is considerable fusion of ganglia. The compound eyes when present vary greatly in size, but generally lack the corneal lens and hence the faceted appearance of most compound eyes. Negative phototropism is correlated with night feeding and is probably also a protective device against excessive desiccation. Anterior statocysts have been reported for some species.

Simple tubular gonads open on the segments, characteristic of the caridoid facies. Spermatozoa, usually not encased in spermatophores, are deposited near the female gonopore and are carried by currents into the marsupium where fertilization occurs. Development is usually direct and the young hatch with all appendages, but do not leave the brood pouch until the next ecdysis.

Fossil records for Amphipoda are certain from the Tertiary; more doubtful records go back to the Silurian Period. Recent genera include *Alicella, Gammarus, Haustorius, Orchestia,* and *Talorchestia* (Gammaridea); *Hyperia* and *Phronima* (Hyperiidea); *Caprella* and *Cyamus* (Caprellidea); and *Ingolfiella* (Ingolfiellidea).

Superorder Eucarida

This group, with more than 8,600 species, contains most of the larger and more familiar crustaceans. It differs from the other superorders in having a well-developed carapace fused with all thoracic somites. It differs from the other large Eumalacostracan superorder, Peracarida, in lacking a well-developed accessory blade on the mandible, in having the basal antennal segment composed of two instead of three segments, and in the absence of oostegites. Development typically is metamorphic, with free naupliar stages occurring in some primitive species and with a zoeal larva stage very common. The Eucarida is subdivided into two orders, the Euphausiacea and the Decapoda.

Order Euphausiacea   The eleven genera including some ninety species are placed in the single family Euphausiidae, and are all marine. This group possesses the primitive caridoid features with all thoracic appendages biramous and structurally alike, and with podobranch gills uncovered by the carapace. The pleopods are flattened, fringed with setae, and generally natatory in function, but with the first two pairs in the male modified for copulation. The uropods and telson are elongate, the latter carrying a pair of large movable spines which are not homologous with the caudal furca of the Leptostraca.

Euphausiids are pelagic animals of the open ocean and some occur at great depths. They range in size from fifteen to fifty millimeters. One of the larger species, *Euphausia superba,* is a brilliant red, occurs in surface waters, and is the principal food of whalebone whales. Luminescent species occur in all the genera except one, which in the latter case appears to be correlated with blindness. The light is produced by special organs called *photospheres* which are provided with lenses, reflectors, and light-producing cells. Light production is intermittent. Photospheres are located on eyestalks, on the seventh pair of thoracic coxae, and ventrally mediad on some abdominal plates.

Euphausiids are commonly filter feeders, but some of the larger are predators on other small pelagic animals. At copulation, sperm are transmitted in flask-shaped spermatophores. Eggs may be carried briefly either free among thoracic setae or glued to the ventral surface. Free naupliar, zoeal, and postlarval stages are characteristic of the metamorphosis. There is no known fossil history. Recent genera include *Euphausia, Nematoscelis,* and *Thysanopoda.*

Order Decapoda   Most of the Eucarida belong in the Order Decapoda, which contains some 8,400 living species including the familiar crayfish, crabs, lobsters, and shrimp. Distinctive features are modification of the three anterior pairs of thoracic appendages to structures called maxillipeds; usually more than a single series of gills; lateral projections of the carapace over the gills to form branchial chambers; and enlargement of the exopodite of the second maxilla as a flattened scoop called scaphognathite or bailor. The name Decapoda is derived from the posterior five pairs of thoracic appendages which have leg structure. Unfortunately, an order of molluscan cephalopods is also often called Decapoda.

The decapod crustaceans are divided into two suborders: Nantantia and Reptantia. As the name indicates, Nantantia are adapted for swimming, having a laterally compressed body and five well-developed pairs of pleopods which are natatory. There is a pronounced rostrum, also laterally compressed and usually with a serrate dorsal edge. The legs tend to be slender, but frequently one of the first three pairs is stoutly chelate. The Nantantia includes all shrimp and is usually separated into three series (Penaeidea, Caridea and Stenopodidea) based on certain structural features, but a number of penaeids are noteworthy in hatching as free-swimming nauplii, a larval stage seen elsewhere in the Euphausiacea and in many Entomostraca. The Reptantia are more likely to be flattened dorso-ventrally with legs adapted for crawling or walking. The first pair of legs are usually modified as large chelipeds; the rostrum tends to be reduced and flat dorsally, and pleopods are usually reduced or absent. Phylogenetically, Reptantia appear to be the more successful, since nearly seventy-five per cent of Decapods are included in it.

Crabs, crayfish, and lobsters belong in Reptantia, a group that is commonly subdivided into three sections. The Macrura, as the name suggests, have a prominent abdomen with large uropods and telson. One of the superfamilies in the Macrura contains the American lobster *Homarus* and freshwater crayfish *Astacus* and *Cambarus.* The Anomura exhibit either a soft, asymmetrical abdomen or an abdomen flexed beneath the thorax. Well-formed uropods are characteristic, although the tail-fan is usually reduced or absent. *Paralithodes,* the commercial king crab of the supermarket, and *Coenobita,* one of the hermit crabs, and the terrestrial robber crab, *Birgus,* are included here. The true crabs belong in section Brachyura. The reduced abdomen is always flexed beneath the thorax, and uropods are usually absent. The carapace is fused at least laterally with a sternal plate in front of the mouth called episternum, a fusion absent in Anomura. The cancer crab *Cancer,* the commercial crab of the Atlantic Coast *Callinectes,* the fresh-water

crab *Potamon,* the commensal pea crab *Pinnotheres,* and the fiddler crab *Uca* are brachyurans (Fig. 15-46).

Decapod Habitats Habitats of decapods are extremely varied (Fig. 1-2). A great many decapods belong to the plankton. For many of these and for pelagic crustaceans diurnal vertical migration has been an extensively studied subject. Considerable data show that bathypelagic decapods have vertical migrations of the order of 300 to 400 meters daily, and average speed of migration for decapods has been estimated at 25 to 125 meters per hour. Upward migration begins toward sunset and downward movement near dawn. Seasonal and age differences introduce additional factors in study of vertical migration. Various decapods show considerable horizontal migration. The commercial shrimp of the east coast, *Penaeus setiferus,* has seasonal shoreward migrations, in winter seeking the more stable environment found in deeper waters. Some littoral Crustacea show an inshore-offshore cycle. In some cases this provides for a more suitable environment and adequate food source for young stages. Many decapods are benthonic, although some of these can propel themselves off the bottom. Some of the benthonic forms dig their own retreats; others utilize natural crevices in coral and rock. Hermit crabs are adapted for comfortable living in the coiled

Fig. 15-46 *Uca,* a fiddler crab. From Schechter 1959, courtesy of Prentice-Hall, Inc.

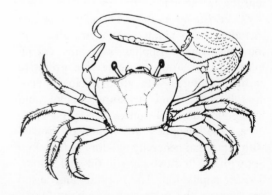

shells of gastropods, and hermit crabs experimentally reared without access to coiled shells still developed in the normal asymmetrical pattern. As the hermit crab grows, the need for a bigger gastropod shell becomes imperative. Since only empty shells are used, a prospective home is probed for debris or other occupant before the crab forsakes his old home. There are about 150 species of freshwater decapods in the United States. Crayfish, also known as crawdads, are generally found in fresh water less than five feet deep. They tend to feed at night, remaining hidden in debris on the bottom, or in burrows when light intensity is high. Many crayfish dig extensive burrows recognized by the extensive mud pellets which are built up as chimneys at the burrow entrance. Some portion of the burrow goes below the water table, so that the inhabitant has access to water to keep gills moist. *Birgus,* the robber or coconut crab of the South Sea Islands, is a large terrestrial decapod, a tree-climbing crab which as an adult is restricted to land and is incapable of swimming. Unlike some other tree-climbing crustacea, such as *Orchestia, Birgus* comes down the tree backward.

Most decapods are predators and scavengers. Food is captured with the chelate appendages and pushed forward to the gnathal structures where suitable-sized pieces are chewed or torn off. Subsequent trituration is done in the stomodaeal gastric mill (Fig. 15-10). Special structures in some species, such as the large cheliped of the pistol shrimp, are used to stun prey (Fig. 15-6). Decapods have utilized some unusual food supplies. A shrimp of the genus *Spirontocaris* will feed on tunicates. Lobsters in captivity are reported to eat sand dollar (echinoderm) tests. *Birgus* will pursue the crab *Cardisoma* to its burrow, grab its large defensive cheliped, and pull until it is autotomized. Such a source of food parallels that in crab fisheries in southern Spain, where the large chela of the local crab *(Uca)* is pulled off and the original owner returned to the sea to grow a new one. Some predator crabs can swim rapidly enough to capture small fish and other prey. A number of decapods have returned to filtration, although this more often involves filtering detritus containing organic matter than catching plankton. One species of *Upogebia* is a tube dweller, and produces a current within the tube from which food is caught on a filter on the first leg. The sand or mole crabs, *Emerita,* use antennules for filters. These shore crabs burrow backward into wet sand using the uropods. Antennules protrude to catch food in suspension where water from breaking waves will flow by them for the maximal length of time. As the tide comes in the whole population emerges, hurries up the beach, and reburies along an optimal zone. As the tide recedes, the local migration is reversed.

Decapod Locomotion Locomotion in Decapoda involves a wide variety of complex actions as is apparent in the tree-climbing activities of *Birgus* and in various burrowing patterns in other species. Jumping or leaping is often an escape mechanism. In Decapoda strong and sudden flexure of the abdomen propels the animal backward as in the crayfish *Cambarus.* Some shrimp achieve sufficient force to carry them out of the water. Walking and swimming are more fundamental patterns of locomotion and frequently these methods follow a metachronal rhythm, but variation is almost as common as conformity. Most decapods use four pairs of legs in walking, and three pairs are essential to provide a tripod for stable support in sequence. In a group of animals in which loss of limbs by autotomy is common, adaptive measures for adequate locomotion are well developed. Many crabs walk sideways, the legs in front pulling and those behind pushing. A number of decapods, such as the crayfish *Astacus* and the robber crab *Birgus,* can walk backward. Swimming is accomplished usually in one of two ways: (1) there is a backward-forward beat of natatory appendages similar to the use of oars, and (2) there is a vortex beat in which the appendage describes a cone. There are various modifications adapted for steering. In all types of locomotion, changes in the center of gravity, as when food is carried, involve automatic adaptive response in the crustacean.

Decapoda are well known for the exhibition of a variety of colors and color changes. Some of these appear to be functionless, and others unquestionably involve concealment. A number of species can recognize and respond to colors at one or the other end of the visible spectrum, but various grays elicit no response. The familiar difference in color between a living lobster and a boiled one is due to heat breakdown of the link between the color and an appropriate protein. The ghost crab, *Ocypode,* is so called because of its apparent disappearance. Its color approximates the sand of its habitat and its visibility is due to the shadow cast. When the crab is alarmed, its body is brought prone on the sand, and with the loss of its shadow the ghost crab apparently disappears. Color of some crustaceans is a long-term adaptation involving increase or decrease of pigment. A rapid response involves changes in concentration of pigment already present. These changes occur in pigment contained in stellate cells called *chromatophores.* Under the right stimulation, pigment granules in these cells disperse into the radiating processes or contract centrally as the case may be. Some Nantantia have as many as four different pigments in the same chromatophore. Since these pigments can move independently, these shrimp can adapt to a wide variety of background colorations.

Respiration and Circulation The penaeid shrimp, *Lucifer,* is the only decapod without gills, and in this crustacean respiration is assumed to occur through the integument. Other decapods have developed a multiple series of gills named from their orientation to certain structures. From the proximal segment of thoracic limbs a single podobranchia is formed. On the lateral wall (pleuron in arthropod terminology) of the thoracic segment and dorsal to the leg articulation a pleurobranchia develops, and

extending from the membrane joining the limb base and body wall, two arthrobranchiae are found. Although this is the assumed primitive pattern, no living decapod has thirty-two gills. One of the penaeid shrimp has retained twenty-four, the lobster *Homarus* has twenty, and the pea crab *Pinnotheres* has only six. In *Penaeus* the early development of the gills is well known. Three buds appear on the proximal segment of the limb. The more distal of these is the podobranch primordium. It soon becomes bilobed; the anterior lobe forms the gill and the posterior lobe becomes a slender process called the mastigobranchia which becomes a support for the gill in some decapods. The other two buds are the primordia of the arthrobranch gills. The pleurobranch bud arises nearby. In decapods, water flows forward through the gill chambers, propelled by action of the scaphognathites. This current empties near the antenna base, helping to remove excretory products. Gills are cleaned by the action of maxilliped epipodites, and by current reversal.

Decapod Gills Three gill types occur. The dendrobranchiate type is restricted to Penaeidea and consists of a double lamella which may be variously twisted and with the outer faces of the lamellae covered by a thick pile of secondary filaments. Trichobranchiate gills are paired primary filaments arising from a central axis. Phyllobranchiate gills are paired lamellar plates diverging from a common base. These two gill types occur widely in nonpenaeid decapods, but a gill type is constant for a given species. Afferent and efferent blood channels course along gill axes and septa divide the filaments, at least in some forms, so that a circulation can be maintained through the filament. Blood goes from the efferent vessels through ill-defined sinuses to the pericardial sinus, entering the heart through three pairs of ostia when that organ is expanded by suspensory ligaments after contraction (Fig. 15-11). Pathways from the heart were discussed earlier under crustacean circulation.

Hormones and Molting Integrative activities, at least in more complex animals, have long been considered to be controlled by the nervous and endocrine systems, but in many phases of this control the two systems are inseparably related. Two examples from vertebrate zoology suffice. Acetylcholine is released by parasympathetic nerve fibers, and posterior pituitary hormones are produced by neurosecretory cells of the brain and stored until used in the posterior lobe of the pituitary. A similar interrelationship between nervous and endocrine systems occurs for the complex phenomenon of molting in Malacostraca and probably for all crustaceans. With a limiting exoskeleton, molting is essential for growth. In some crustaceans, molting ceases when an upper size limit is reached, while in others *(Homarus)* molting and growth continue throughout the active life of the animal.

Growth in vertebrates is concerned with total normal physiology during the growing years. The same premise can be assigned to crustacean molting, which is intimately associated with growth. The actual exuviation of the old skeleton (molting or ecdysis in the strict sense) involves about one-half of one per cent of the time for completion of the total physiological changes associated with the molting cycle. These changes are discussed in detail by Passano in The Physiology of Crustacea.

In Crustacea and pterygote insects a number of nerve centers closely associated with the forebrain occur in the head and are called optic ganglia. In stalk-eyed malacostracans there are four optic ganglia and these are located in each eyestalk. Other Malacostraca have three pairs of optic ganglia, entomos-

Fig. 15-47 Diagram of the anterior central nervous system with four optic ganglia, characteristic of decapod crustaceans. Adapted from various sources.

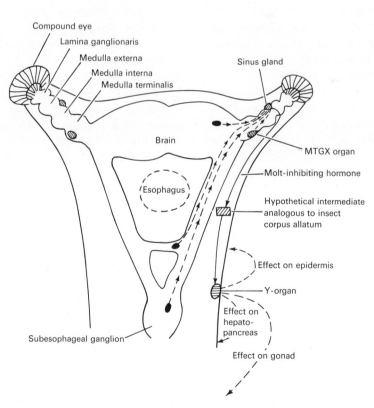

tracans have two pairs, while pterygote insects never have more than three pairs. Beginning distally in the decapod eyestalk, these ganglia are called lamina ganglionaris, medulla externa, medulla interna, and medulla terminalis (Fig. 15-47).

In Brachyura, located between the medulla externa and the medulla interna is an organ called the *sinus gland,* which appears to be a reservoir for neurosecretions transmitted along axons from neurosecretory cells in the forebrain, post-esophageal commissure, ventral ganglia, and from a center in the proximal optic ganglion called the *Medulla Terminalis Ganglionic X-organ,* henceforth called MTGX. The neurosecretions from the various sites seem to differ qualitatively, indicating that the sinus-gland complex may well be responsible for several hormones, and may influence chromatophore behavior and retinal pigment migration among other things. A molt-inhibiting hormone is produced by the MTGX organ. Removing the sinus glands and MTGX organs leads to early ecdysis, whereas implantation of this complex into animals from which both eyestalks have been removed blocks the onset of ecdysis.

Molting is under the control of the central nervous system, which is activated by a complex of stimuli involving adequate conditions of temperature, humidity, light, nutrition, stage in the sexual cycle, and privacy. Privacy is significant in the sense of isolation from predators, since the crustacean is particularly helpless before the new skeleton is hardened. With the right proportion of stimuli (and perhaps initially set in motion by a distended hepatopancreas), release of molt-inhibiting hormone is reduced, its blood level drops, and the *molting gland* or *Y-organ* situated beneath the cuticle on each side of the face is activated. Presence of the molting gland is essential to initiate *proecdysis,* the immediate preparatory changes leading to ecdysis. During proecdysis (part of which is a fasting period) there are epidermal changes involving secretion of new cuticle, accumulation of glycogen or glucose as a precursor of chitin,

and softening and partial resorption (particularly along suture lines) of the old skeleton. There are changes in the biochemical content of the hepatopancreas, which must release some materials for nutritional requirements and to build up the new skeleton. It also serves as temporary storage for calcium and magnesium phosphates. Continued mitotic activity of the gonad may be enhanced or at least is not blocked by molting hormone.

The diagram follows Passano's suggestion of the presence of a hypothetical intermediate, equivalent to the insect corpus allatum, since some of the other molt-control mechanisms are so parallel between Crustacea and Insecta (see Fig. 15-47).

Excretion The segmental excretory organs in decapods are the antennal or green glands. Typically there is an end-sac, commonly partitioned or ramified to increase its surface, an excretory canal often enlarged distally as a bladder, and an aperture opening on a small papilla on the proximal antennal segment. Evidently the urine is formed principally by secretion by both end-sac and canal, modified by some reabsorption of glucose and some ion regulation for osmotic balances. There is some evidence that filtration is a factor in urine production.

The terrestrial crab *Birgus* is able to regulate salt content of the blood. If this animal is limited to fresh water, salt concentration drops to an average of 68 per cent of sea-water concentration; if limited to sea water, the salt concentration may reach about 120 per cent.

Reproduction and Development Gonads are located principally in the thorax, except for hermit crabs in which they are displaced to one side in the abdomen. Considerable sexual dimorphism occurs in decapod species. In *Cambarus* there are size and proportion differences, and the first two pairs of pleopods are modified for copulation in the male. Sperm, usually in spermatophores, are transferred to the ventral surface of the female, which in many species has seminal receptacles. Among some crabs various courtship procedures occur before copulation, but in some crayfish the male is unable to recognize the opposite sex and consequently approaches all other crayfish during the breeding season with equal fervor. Receptive females are turned on their back to effect copulation.

The development of some penaeid shrimp goes through an extensive metamorphosis beginning with a nauplius, but this free-living stage does not occur in other decapods. A later larval stage, zoea, although given special names in some species, is the nearly universal larval type seen among decapods (Fig. 15-25). Among crabs metamorphosis includes a later postlarval stage, called megalops (Fig. 15-26).

Autotomy and Regeneration A remarkable phenomenon called *autotomy* occurs in decapod crustaceans. Proximal on the ischiopodite is a breaking plane at which point the animal, by reflex contraction of special muscles, can self-amputate an injured or caught limb (Fig. 15-48). In the American lobster, *Homarus,* this autotomy reflex is limited to the chela, but the other legs have a preformed breakage plane and the limb can be severed by the animal's strug-

Fig. **15-48** Autotomy in the lobster. From Fig. 17, F. D. Wood and H. E. Wood II, 1932, *J. Exp. Zool.,* 62:53, courtesy of the editors of the *J. Exp. Zool.*

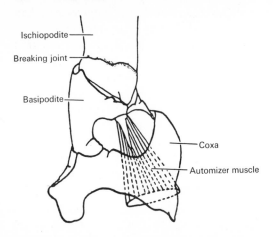

gles if the leg is caught in a crevice or by an enemy. This type of escape response also occurs in a number of other crustacea. In some decapods at least, a double membrane exists at the breaking plane with a single perforation for nerves and blood-vessels which break at autotomy. The proximal fold of the membrane is retained and the perforation is closed by blood pressure. This mechanism, plus coagulative properties of crustacean blood, reduce blood loss to a minimum.

Regeneration is a well-established process among crustaceans. Following autotomy, there is development of a bud beneath the scab formed at point of rupture. This bud represents the primordium of the regenerating limb. In a series of ecdyses, the limb bud which has already undergone considerable differentiation, ultimately attains normal size. Regeneration occurs on appendages severed at other than the breaking plane, although usually less rapidly. In general, the regenerating process is more rapid in younger animals. Regeneration experiments involving extirpation of a degenerate eye in blind crayfish resulted in organs resembling antennae. Similar results were found on the prawn (Caridea) after eye removal. Such an effect has been interpreted to mean that the eye belongs in the segmental series of appendages, but more probably the regenerating tissue included cells carrying a potential for antennae regeneration.

PHYLOGENETIC CONSIDERATIONS

The phylogenetic origin of Crustacea is lost in Precambrian antiquity. Most authorities accept the group as being monophyletic, characteristically developing through a nauplius and with two pairs of antennae. While these features are unique for the Crustacea, the group shares with other arthropods and with annelids a set of features indicative of a related ancestral pattern. The architecture of the nervous system, the serially segmented body, coelomic formation, distribution of muscle, and other features form this composite group of characteristics.

Arthropods show many special features superimposed on the generalized annelid structure. Perhaps the most distinctive of these characteristics are the increasingly rigid chitinous exoskeleton, the jointed appendages (from which the group name is derived), and the development of the hemocoele.

Discovery of the Onychophora, having such annelid similarities as paired nephridia and ciliated genital ducts, and such apparent arthropod affinities as the derivation of jaws from limbs, the fate of the coelom, the formation of the hemocoele, and especially the development of trachea, focused attention on *Peripatus* and its allies as intermediate. Particularly the middle Cambrian marine onychophoran, *Aysheaia,* provided a presumed more primitive stock from which the extant terrestrial Onychophora evolved. On the commonplace acceptance of the hypothesis that the arthropods are monophyletic, various theories have been advanced to show phylogenetic succession from annelids to arthropods via Onychophora. The diplopod myriapods with their body shape, an unregionated trunk of many segments, and a tubular alimentary canal with ectodermal fore and hindgut are arthropods closest to Onychophora. Diplopods established themselves during the Silurian Period, but ostracod crustaceans appeared in the upper Cambrian and there is geologic evidence for other entomostracans and for leptostracans from the middle Paleozoic Era. Tiegs and Manton (1958) point up the difficulty of attempting to derive Crustacea from myriapods, and the difficulty is nearly as great if one seeks to derive insects (considering their undoubted myriapod affinities) from Crustacea. The close affinity of myriapods and insects will be discussed in a later chapter.

Snodgrass (1958) suggested, primarily on the basis of mandible origin, that crustaceans and the myriapod-insect group arose from a protomandibulate ancestor. Such a theory accounts for the striking similarity between the insect and crustacean compound eye. The alternate explanation (if Crustacea and Insecta are not derived from the same stem) is to account for the eye similarity by convergence, a case well argued by Tiegs and Manton, who point out that the Snodgrass theory accepts convergence to explain trachea in Arachnida and in the myriapod-insect line.

A great deal of speculation about the early evolution of crustaceans hinges on the character of the appendages. The biramous appendage is a specialty of Crustacea. Some investigators consider a foliaceous phyllopodial structure, others, a slender, jointed stenopodial structure as primitive. If the primitive appendage was ambulatory, and the ancestral crustacean was a detritus feeder utilizing coarser particles moved by enditic processes, the stenopodial structure was first to appear. Furthermore there is no embryological evidence among Crustacea, indicating that a phyllopodium was ancestral. Sanders (1957, 1963) emphasizes that in the recently discovered cephalocarid *Hutchinsoniella,* the limb has three prominent rami (pseudoepipod, foliaceous exopod, and stenopodial endopod), and that there is at least duality of function in such limbs. Such a generalized limb might well be ancestral to the phyllopodial limb of Branchiopoda as well as to the stenopodial limb seen in the mid-Devonian lipostracan *Lepidocaris.* Sanders also shows how the phyllopodial appendages of *Nebalia* might be derived from the cephalocarid type. *Lepidocaris,* as well as the recently found *Derocheilocaris* (Mystacocarida), suggests affinity among Branchiopoda, Copepoda and Malacostraca.

Sanders has postulated that the triramous cephalocarid appendage shows a structural relationship to that of trilobites, and further, that the endopodite has eight segments, counting the terminal mid-claw as a segment homologous with the trilobite pretarsus. Such a theory supports the monophyletic origin for Crustacea and Trilobita. However, Størmer (1944) indicated that the biflagellate trilobite appendage could not be homologous since the lateral branch arose from a precoxal leg segment and therefore was not an exopodite. At present, the question of trilobite-crustacean relationship is unresolved.

The entomostracans appear to have the following relationships (Fig. 15-49). Ostracoda stand apart. They bear some resemblance to conchostracan branchiopods, but differ in having a mandibular palp and an indistinctly segmented trunk with not more than four pairs of limbs behind the mandibles. The Copepoda, Branchiura, Mystacocarida, and Cirripedia can be grouped as Maxillopoda with five or six thoracic segments, mandibles with palps, both pairs of maxillae well devel-

oped for filtering, and the absence of gnathobases on thoracic segments. Anostraca are clearly separated from the other Branchiopoda, which are grouped under the name Phyllopoda. The Cephalocarida stand near the middle with a combination of features overlapping with such other groups as Mystacocarida, Copepoda, Anostraca, and Malacostraca. They are unique in having eight-segmented limbs and second maxillae closely similar to other thoracic appendages. They differ from Branchiopoda in trunk limb muscle pattern, head appendages, and naupliar features.

Malacostraca probably arose simultaneously with entomostracans (Fig. 15-49). The

Fig. 15-49 A phylogenetic tree for crustacea, derived primarily from Dahl 1963, Siewing 1963, and Waterman 1961.

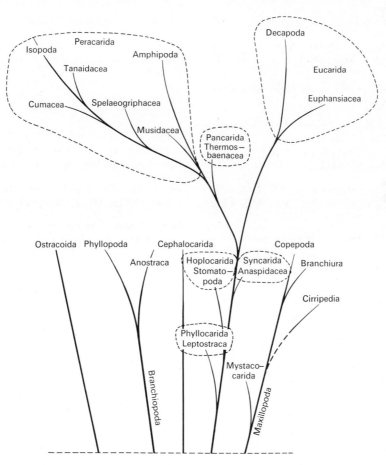

extinct early Devonian genus, *Nahecaris,* bears real resemblance to Decapoda. The Leptostraca is probably the most primitive group of Malacostraca, although the phyllopodous thoracic appendages are probably convergent. The bivalved carapace unattached to thoracic segments, seven abdominal segments, a caudal furca, and development through a naupliar stage are indicative of a primitive position. General head structure confirmed by muscle homology in that region and the evidence from blood vessels and nerve cord for a seventh abdominal segment indicate that Stomatopoda are near the Leptostraca. Although Anaspidacea show relationships to the decapods in the antennal statocyst, they lack a carapace and they share the simplest crustacean head structure with Anostraca, although other features confirm placement diverging from the main Malacostracan stem. The phylogenetic tree shows divergence into two main branches: the Eucarida and the Pancarida-Peracarida group (characterized by presence of a brood chamber). The Thermosbaenacea have a dorsal brood chamber and must be separated from Peracarida in which the marsupium is formed from oostegites. Peracarida culminate in Isopoda and Amphipoda, groups showing convergency in carapace loss. Decapods probably diverged from a penaeidlike ancestor into Nantantia on one hand and Reptantia on the other.

REFERENCES

Borradaile, L. A., Notes upon crustacean limbs. Amer. Mag. Nat. Hist., 17:193, 1926a.

———, On the primitive phyllopodium. *Ibid.,* 18:16, 1926b.

Brown, F. A. Jr., Physiological rhythms (pp. 401-430). *In* (T. H. Waterman, ed.) The physiology of Crustacea, Vol. II. New York: Academic, 1961.

Calman, W. T., Crustacea. *In* (R. Lankester, ed.) A treatise on zoology, Part VII, Fasc. III, 1909.

Cannon, H. G., On the feeding mechanisms of the Branchiopoda. Philos. Trans. Roy. Soc. London, (B) 222:267, 1933.

Churchill, E. P., The zoeal stages of the blue crab, *Callinectes sapidus* Rathbun. Chesapeake Biol. Lab. Publ. No. 49 (1942), 25 pp.

Cohen, M. J., and S. Dijkgraaf, Mechanoreception (pp. 65-108). *In* (T. H. Waterman, ed.) The physiology of Crustacea, Vol. II. New York: Academic, 1961.

Dahl, E., Main evolutionary lines among Recent Crustacea (pp. 1-15). *In* (H. B. Whittington and W. D. I. Rolfe, eds.) Phylogeny and evolution of Crustacea. Cambridge: Mus. Comp. Zool., 1963.

Glaessner, M. F., Evolutionary trends in Crustacea (Malacostraca). Evolution, 11:178, 1957.

Green, J., A biology of Crustacea. Chicago: Quadrangle Books, 1963.

Hansen, E. D., Animal diversity (2nd ed.) (Foundations of Modern Biology Series). Englewood Cliffs, N.J.: Prentice Hall, 1961.

Heath, H., The external development of certain phyllopods. J. Morphol. 38:453, 1924.

Henry, Laura, The nervous system and the segmentation of the head in the Annulata. Microentomology, 13:1-26, 1948.

Herrick, F. H., Natural history of the American lobster. U. S. Bur. Fish. Bull., 29:149, 1911.

Hertwig, R., A manual of zoology (5th ed.; trans. and ed. by J. S. Kingsley). New York: Holt, Rinehart & Winston, 1902.

Kaestner, A., Lehrbuch der Spezieller Zoologie. Lief 4, Tiel I (659-979) Wirbellose. Stuttgart: Gustav Fischer, 1959.

Kleinholz, L. H., Pigmentary effectors (pp. 133-169). *In* (T. H. Waterman, ed.) The physiology of Crustacea, Vol. II. New York: Academic, 1961.

MacGinitie, G. E., and N. MacGinitie, Natural history of marine animals. New York: McGraw, 1949.

Manton, S. M., On the embryology of the crustacean *Nebalia bipes*. Philos. Trans. Roy. Soc. London, (B) 223:163, 1934.

Marshall, S. M., and A. P. Orr, Feeding and nutrition (pp. 227-258). *In* (T. H. Waterman, ed.) The physiology of Crustacea, Vol. I. New York: Academic, 1960.

Passano, L. M., Molting and its control (pp. 473-536). *In* (T. H. Waterman, ed.) The physiology of Crustacea, Vol. I. New York: Academic, 1960.

Pearson, J. C., The early life histories of some American Penaeidae, chiefly the commercial shrimp, *Penaeus setiferus* Linn., U. S. Bur. Fish. Bull. 30 (1939), 73 pp.

Pennak, R. W., and D. J. Zinn, Mystacocarida, a new order of Crustacea from intertidal beaches of Massachusetts and Connecticut. Smithson. Misc. Coll., 103:1, 1943.

Sanders, H. L., The Cephalocarida. Mem. Conn. Acad. Arts and Sci., Vol. XV (1963), 80 pp.

Sars, G. O., An account of the Crustacea of Norway, 9, Ostracoda. Bergen Museum (1928), 277 pp.

Shrock, R. R., and W. H. Twenhofel, Principles of invertebrate paleontology (2nd ed.). New York: McGraw, 1953.

Siewing, R., Studies in Malacostracan morphology: results and problems (pp. 85-103). *In* (H. B. Whittington and W. D. I. Rolfe, eds.) Physiology and evolution of Crustacea. Cambridge: Mus. Comp. Zool., 1963.

Smith, G., and W. F. R. Weldon, Crustacea. *In* (S. F. Harmer and A. E. Shipley, eds.) The Cambridge natural history, Vol. IV. London: Macmillan, 1904. (Reprint edition, Wheldon & Wesley, 1958.)

Smith, S. I., The early stage of the American lobster, *Homarus americanus* Edwards. Trans. Conn. Acad. Arts and Sci., 2:351, 1871-1873.

Snodgrass, R. E., Evolution of the Annelida, Onychophora, and Arthropoda. Smithson. Misc. Coll., 97 (6) (1938), 159 pp.

———, Comparative studies on the head of mandibulate arthropods. Ithaca: Comstock, 1951.

———, Crustacean metamorphoses. Smithson. Misc. Coll., 131 (10) (1956), 78 pp.

Tiegs, O. W., and S. M. Manton, The evolution of the Arthropoda. Biol. Rev., 33:255, 1958.

Waterman, T. H., and F. A. Chace, Jr., General crustacean biology (pp. 1-33). *In* (T. H. Waterman, ed.) The physiology of Crustacea, Vol. I. New York: Academic, 1960.

Waterman, T. H. (ed.), The physiology of Crustacea, Vols. I and II. New York: Academic, 1960 and 1961.

Welsh, J. H., Neurohumors and neurosecretion (pp. 281-311). *In* (T. H. Waterman, ed.) The physiology of Crustacea, Vol. II. New York: Academic, 1961.

Whittington, H. B., and W. D. I. Rolfe (eds.), Phylogeny and evolution of Crustacea. Cambridge: Mus. Comp. Zool., 1963.

Wood, F. D., and H. E. Wood II, Autotomy in decapod Crustacea. J. Exp. Zool., 62:1, 1932.

16

LABIATA

The subphylum Labiata includes those arthropods having a distinct head capsule; a single pair of antennae corresponding to the first antennae of Crustacea; an absence of appendages on the next segment; and gnathal or feeding appendages on the subsequent three segments. The first of these is a sometimes segmented but always uniramous mandible. Following the mandibulate segment are two pairs of maxillae, commonly with median fusion of the second pair to form the lower lip or labium from which the subphylum name is derived.

Like Crustacea, Labiata are mandibulate, but following Tiegs and Manton this similarity represents convergence, with the labiate mandible derived from a uniramous appendage. Food manipulation is by the mandible tip in this group and not by the base as with the biramously derived crustacean mandible.

The affinities of the Myriapoda (particularly Symphyla) with Insecta appear to be well substantiated, although they continue to be given separate and equal rank with Crustacea and Arachnomorpha in some authoritative systems. Head segmentation and appendages are correlated similarly with divisions of the brain in both groups. The insectan and symphylan labia appear to be homologous structures formed from fused second maxillae. In both groups the alimentary canals are similar and lack the prominent digestive organ characteristic of Crustacea. Segmentally arranged spiracles and trachea occur in both myriapods and insects, as do Malpighian tubules arising from the ectodermal proctodaeum. The greatest obstacle to acceptance of a prosymphylan form as ancestral to the Insecta is the presence of anterior genital pores in Symphyla. However, Tiegs (1940, p. 159) says that "the embryological evidence (of Symphyla) points to an originally opisthogoneate condition." For these and other reasons, the Myriapoda and Insecta will be joined in subphylum Labiata.

SUPERCLASS MYRIAPODA

The Myriapoda is a group of tracheate, mandibulate arthropods with the body divided into two tagmata, the head and the trunk, with the latter bearing many pairs of legs. Most myriapods are elongate, possess a single pair of antennae, and are provided with Malpighian tubules arising from the ectodermal proctodaeum. This combination of characteristics appears in a variety of organisms possessing too many divergent features for inclusion in a single class. Accordingly, the Myriapoda will here be considered a superclass, with a monophyletic origin implicit for the classes included.

The myriapod head lacks uniformity among the four classes, which are Chilopoda, Symphyla, Pauropoda, and Diplopoda. In the first two the posterior head segment is the second maxillary metamere and is homologous to the insect labium; but in diplopods and pauropods the most caudal head appendage is the gnathochilarium derived from the first maxillary segment. There are no second maxillae, and this metamere is incorporated not into the head but into the trunk, forming the collar or *collum*.

In three of the four classes peculiar sensory structures of unknown function, known as the organs of Tömösvary, occur in concavities near the antennae. However, these organs are absent in some diplopods. Epimorphic development with segmentation complete at hatching occurs among some Chilopoda. In all other myriapods the development is ana-morphic, that is, segments are added after hatching. Among Chilopoda the genital pores are posterior on the abdomen, a condition called opisthogoneate. Other Myriapoda are progoneate.

Myriapoda are terrestrial animals living in loose soil or often hidden beneath decaying logs and under rocks. Distribution, particularly for the large classes, is world-wide.

Class 1 Chilopoda

The common name for the animals included in this class is centipede (Fig. 16-1), and over 1800 species have been described. While the number of pairs of legs may vary from 15 to over 100, none has an even number of pairs. Centipedes are nocturnal animals and are usually found in dark and moist habitats. They are unprotected from considerable water loss, since their cuticle lacks a waxy coat. A few centipedes are marine (Geophilids) and several are cave-dwellers. Centipedes are primarily carnivorous, feeding principally on insects, slugs, and worms, but some of the larger tropical forms will capture small vertebrates. One group, Geophilomorpha, will feed on vegetation occasionally, and in sufficient numbers may be injurious to crops.

The common house centipede *(Scutigera)*, which has a world-wide distribution, has an arched dorsal surface, but most centipedes are flattened dorso-ventrally. *Scutigera* belongs to a group characterized by long legs, considerable agility, a reduced number of

Fig. 16-1 Chilopoda, *Lithobius*, lateral view of a common centipede. After Snodgrass 1952, courtesy of the Comstock Publishing Associates.

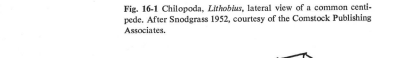

tergal as compared with sternal plates, compound or pseudo-compound eyes, and spiracles opening dorsally on the first seven tergites. The first pair of trunk appendages arise from a reduced segment. These are the segmented poison claws perforated by poison ducts and are used for food-getting and for protection. The condition of a single pretarsal muscle is uniquely shared by myriapods and insects. These appendages in the chilopods are often called maxillipeds (Fig. 16-2) because of their association with food-getting.

A pair of walking legs occurs on each of the subsequent trunk segments except the last one or two. These legs have seven segments rather than the six characteristic of insect legs. The additional segment is a second trochanter, and between the two trochanters is a common site of fracture which may function as an escape mechanism if a leg is caught. In a number of centipedes the last pair of legs has an additional segment.

The trunk segment immediately anterior to the anus-bearing telson bears the opening of the reproductive system and is called the genital segment. It usually carries a pair of reproductive structures called gonopods, generally more prominent on the female. In a number of centipedes there is evidence of a reduced or transitory pregenital segment which may carry rudimentary gonopods.

Centipedes are carnivorous and they capture the prey, principally small arthropods, with the poison claws. The digestive tract is a straight tube with salivary glands opening to the foregut and one or two pairs of Malpighian tubules arising from the hind gut.

The nervous system is typical of arthropods. The paired condition of the ventral nerve cord is particularly distinct. In addition to organs of Tömösvary present in many centipedes, groups of ocelli occur laterally on the head. Some chilopods (Order Scutigeromorpha) have bulging compound eyes

Fig. **16-2** *Lithobius* maxillipeds and first leg-bearing segment, ventral view. After Snodgrass 1952, courtesy of the Comstock Publishing Associates.

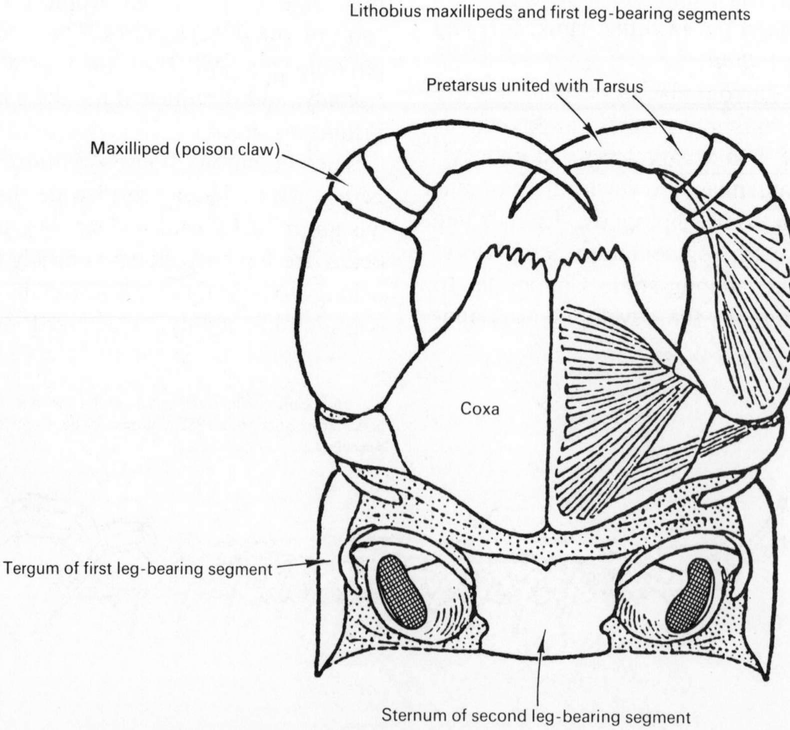

Lithobius maxillipeds and first leg-bearing segments

Pretarsus united with Tarsus

Maxilliped (poison claw)

Coxa

Tergum of first leg-bearing segment

Sternum of second leg-bearing segment

which are similar to those of Crustacea and Insecta; but the similarity may well be the result of detailed convergence rather than homologous origin.

Respiration is by means of trachea opening segmentally through lateral spiracles. Some segments lack spiracles and there is considerable anastomosis of trachea. In one group of centipedes median spiracles open into dorsal chambers on most trunk segments. From these chambers two masses of fine branching trachea radiate laterally, forming well-defined so-called tracheal lungs (Fig. 16-3).

The elongate dorsal heart opens from the pericardial cavity (Fig. 16-4) by segmental paired ostia. In many centipedes a pair of lateral arteries arise from the heart in each segment and blood passes to the hemocoele, eventually reaching the pericardial cavities through the transverse perforate membrane isolating the dorsal portion of the segment.

The gonad in these dioecious animals lies dorsal to the intestine. It is usually unpaired, more commonly in the female than in the male; but paired genital ducts pass around the gut to open ventrally on the genital segment. In the male this gonopore usually is located on a median penis which is flanked by reduced gonopods (Fig. 16-5).

In the female the larger gonopods are lateral to the vulva and in some cases appear to be used for egg transport. Eggs are deposited singly or in groups. Some centipedes (Scolopendromorpha) brood both eggs and young. The mother coils around them and holds them in a space between her two leg rows. The brooding period may take several weeks. Other centipedes deposit eggs in the soil encased in a sort of cocoon formed by adhesion of debris to the gelatinous egg surface. The following account of development is based on Johannsen and Butt.

The large-yolked egg in *Scolopendra* undergoes cleavage of the central protoplasm followed by partial cleavage of the peripheral yolk into pyramids. Cells appear at the lateral walls of the yolk pyramids and migrate to the surface to form a blastoderm. Rapid proliferation in one area gives rise to a germinal disc which marks the ventral side. The germinal disc thickens, and from its posterior aspect two mesodermal bands grow forward

Fig. 16-3 Tracheal lungs in posterior end of tergum, seen from below. After Snodgrass 1952, courtesy of the Comstock Publishing Associates.

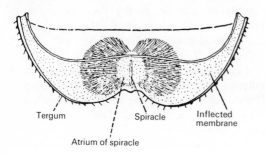

Tergum   Spiracle   Inflected membrane

Atrium of spiracle

Fig. 16-4 Chilopoda, *Scolopendra* diagrammatic cross-section. Compare with cross-sections of onychophoran, Fig. 13-3. After Johannsen and Butt 1941, courtesy of McGraw-Hill Book Company.

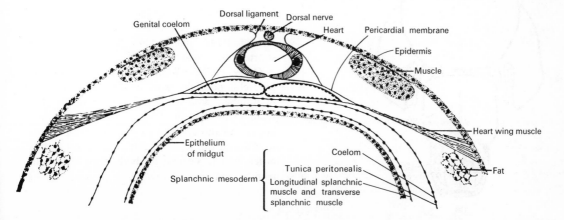

Dorsal ligament   Dorsal nerve

Genital coelom   Heart   Pericardial membrane

Epidermis

Muscle

Heart wing muscle

Epithelium of midgut   Coelom

Fat

Splanchnic mesoderm   Tunica peritonealis

Longitudinal splanchnic muscle and transverse splanchnic muscle

below the advancing surface ectoderm, giving rise to the germ band. Endoderm is apparently formed from cells, either by isolation from the germinal disc earlier as an indefinite layer, or by migration from the peripheral layer.

Segmentation and the formation of appendage primordia begins at the anterior end. A peculiarity of the germ band is the marked separation of the two mesodermal bands halfway between the anterior end and the telson, with a commensurate increase in the ectodermal membrane separating these bands. Owing to sharp flexure of the two

germ-band halves, the labrum and telson come into close juxtaposition, but a deep transverse furrow divides the ectodermal membrane separating them. The separated halves of the lateral germ bands develop medially as sternites and laterally as tergites to encompass the yolk already covered by endodermal epithelium. *Scolopendra* is epimorphic and the characteristic 23 segments appear before hatching. The developing embryo is dependent upon the contained yolk and not until after the third molt can the young centipede leave the brooding mother to forage.

The fossil history of the chilopods is meager. Some Recent orders have representatives in the Tertiary, and a few unrelated Chilopoda were found in the Pennsylvanian Period.

Fig. 16-5 Chilopoda, *Lithobius*, terminal body segments of (a) male and (b) female. After Snodgrass 1952, courtesy of the Comstock Publishing Associates.

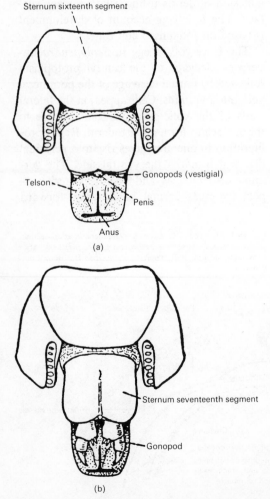

Sternum sixteenth segment

Gonopods (vestigial)

Telson

Penis

Anus

(a)

Sternum seventeenth segment

Gonopod

(b)

Chilopod Classification

Order 1 Scutigeromorpha This group is anamorphic in development. Representatives are characterized by 15 pairs of long legs, compound eyes, and very long antennae which arise behind the anterior extremity of the head. The dorsal surface of the head is arched. There is a median spiracle on the dorsal surface of most trunk segments. *Scutigera.*

Order 2 Lithobiomorpha These anamorphic chilopods have 15 pairs of short legs. The antennae arise from the anterior head margin. The dorsal surface of the head and the trunk terga tend to be flattened. The spiracles are lateral. *Lithobius.*

Order 3 Scolopendromorpha These chilopods are epimorphic. They are stout-bodied and have 21 or 23 pairs of legs. Spiracles are situated laterally in the anterior part of the trunk. Longer tergal plates tend to alternate with shorter ones. *Scolopendra.*

Order 4 Geophilomorpha In these epimorphic chilopods the pairs of legs are inconstant in number, with the number of pairs varying from 35 to 181. Short legs, a slender wormlike body, and the absence of eyes are adaptations to a life in the soil. Spiracles are lateral in this order which occurs in both temperate and tropical regions. *Geophilus.*

Class 2 Symphyla

This is a group of small, centipedelike arthropods containing about 50 species. Some are herbivorous, feeding on saprophytic growth on decaying vegetation as well as on living plants, while others are omnivorous.

These myriapods have a prognathous head with mouthparts directed forward. The head of *Hanseniella* (Fig. 16-6) bears elongate, many-segmented antennae, an inverted Y-shaped groove on the antero-dorsal aspect that resembles the epicranial suture characteristic of many primitive insects; an organ of Tömösvary near the base of each antennae; and a pair of spiracles. As with insects the second maxillae are fused and form the labium.

The trunk of 14 segments in the adult carries 12 pairs of legs, and a pair of dorsal cerci on the thirteenth segment. On most leg-bearing segments there is a pair of styles and an eversible vesicle, both of uncertain function. The fourteenth metamere bears the anus, and paired coelomic pouches occur in the development of this segment. A telson is lacking. In most Symphyla the number of terga is greater than the number of segments since the tergal plates are duplicated for some metameres (Fig. 16-7).

The alimentary canal is a straight tube with salivary glands opening to the mouth cavity, an enlarged midgut, and a proctodaeum from which a pair of Malpighian tubules arise. The paired gonads lie ventral to the intestine, and in the adult animal the gonoducts open on the fourth trunk segment (Fig. 16-8). A pair of straight, tubular spinning glands lie in the posterior dorsal body cavity and open at the tips of the cerci. The paired condition of the ventral nerve cord is not sharply defined. It originates from a single median and paired lateral ectodermal thickenings. Tiegs (1940) draws a parallel between these lateral cords and the nervous system of the Onychophora.

The respiratory system is remarkable among myriapods, since the only spiracles occur on the head, with trachea limited to the three anterior trunk somites and to the head.

Tiegs (1940) describes symphylan embryology. The large-yolked eggs are spherical and cleavage is total. Eventually the egg surface is covered by a blastoderm, thicker on the ventral face in which a deep transverse cleft develops. The two areas adjacent to the cleft mark the anterior and posterior ends of the germ band with the intermediate U-shaped area recessed into the interior. All developing segments are correlated with paired coelomic cavities. Of particular interest is the labial segment which appears to arise as a trunk metamere, later to be incorporated into the head. Tiegs provides evidence that the developing reproductive system has a transitory connection with a caudal coelomoduct, and that the progoneate condition of the adult arises secondarily. This evidence alleviates the obstacle of a progoneate myriapod being ancestral to an opisthogoneate insect.

The so-called garden centipede, *Scutigerella immaculata,* occurs in California and elsewhere in greenhouses where it may cause

Fig. 16-6 Symphyla *Hanseniella* head, lateral view. Outline from Tiegs 1940, *Quart., J. Micros. Sci.* 82:1, completed drawing after Snodgrass 1952, courtesy of the Comstock Publishing Associates.

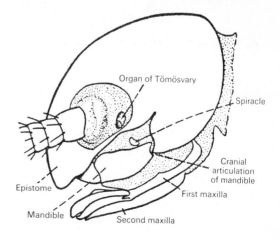

Fig. 16-7 Symphyla, Scutigerella immaculata. Adult garden centipede: (a) dorsal, (b) lateral, and (c) ventral views. *cs,* coxal sac; *pao,* post-antennal organ; *sex aper,* sexual aperature ♂; *sh,* sensory hair; *st pl,* sternal plate; *sty,* stylus; *tel,* telson; *scut,* scutum, *spin,* spinneret. After Michelbacher 1938, courtesy of Hilgardia.

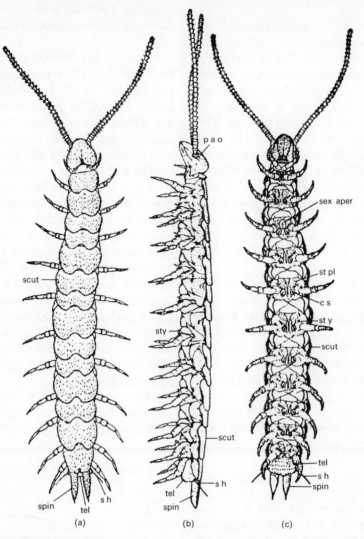

Fig. 16-8 Symphyla: sagittal diagram to show internal anatomy of *Scutigerella immaculata.* After Williams 1907, courtesy Boston Soc. of Nat. Hist., Proceedings.

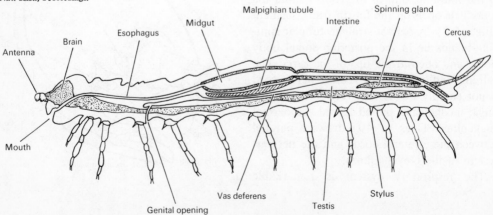

considerable damage to the plants. According to Michelbacher it is anamorphic and hatches with six pairs of legs. New segments are added at subsequent molts, until the definitive number is achieved (Fig. 16-9). However, this species continues to molt throughout life.

The Symphyla appear to provide a key to myriapod-insectan relationship. The number of trunk segments, the fused second maxillae forming a labium, the ventral abdominal styles, and according to Manton (1953) the locomotory gait are some of the symphylan features that support this possible relationship.

Class 3 Pauropoda

These small myriapods averaging about one millimeter in length are characterized by the relatively few legs (nine pairs in typical adults). They may feed on decaying humus or on the saprophytic organisms present in such an environment.

The pauropod head has five segments, the second maxillary segment being absent. The first maxillae are fused into a structure called a *gnathochilarium*. The head is unique in having branched antennae and a pair of ovoid areas which in location and superficial appearance suggest eyes but lack the histological

Fig. 16-9 Symphyla: (a) Egg and (b) through (h) seven instars in the development of *Scutigerella*.   *ch.Pl.*, chitinous plate· After Michelbacher 1938, courtesy of Hilgardia.

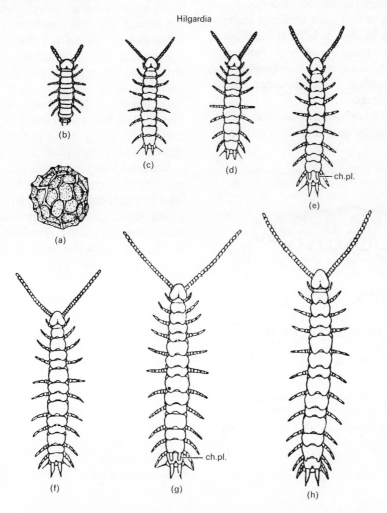

Hilgardia

(b)

(c)

(d)

(a)

(e) ch.pl.

(f)

(g) ch.pl.

(h)

structure of the compound eyes of arthropods.

The trunk has twelve segments with legs absent on the first and the last two. The first trunk segment, called a *collum,* is reduced and is equivalent to a similar segment in Diplopoda. In some pauropods, a lesser number of tergal plates apparently reduces the number of segments dorsally.

Pauropoda are definitively progoneate, anamorphic myriapods, hatching with three body segments (Fig. 16-10). Their nearest relatives appear to be the Diplopoda.

Class 4 Diplopoda

These myriapods, commonly called millipedes, are mostly elongated, segmented worms in which the dorsal or tergal plates are coalesced so that each apparent segment has two pairs of legs. It is from this feature that the class name is derived. Internally, nerve ganglia, coelomic development, and heart ostia confirm the coalescence of two adjacent segments.

Diplopoda have world-wide distribution, but are especially prevalent in the tropics.

Fig. 16-10 Pauropoda: (a) second, (b) third, and (c) fourth instars of *Pauropus.* After Tiegs 1947, *Quart. J. Micros. Sci.,* **88**: 165.

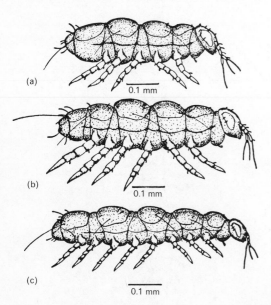

(a)

0.1 mm

(b)

0.1 mm

(c)

0.1 mm

Some of the approximately 8,000 species are brightly colored in life. Diplopods are found beneath logs, stones, or leaf debris where they are sheltered from light and humidity is higher. Their rather sluggish gait is sufficient to penetrate light soil and humus. Occasionally millipedes are found in cellars and basements; sometimes they arrive on earth adhering to such vegetables as potatoes and squash, but these arthropods are known to migrate and especially in dry years they may seek haven in cooler, usually damper, surroundings such as cellars. Most millipedes are vegetarians, feeding on fallen and especially on decaying leaves. Many of them will vary their diet with dead animal matter. Attacks on such crops as sugar beets and potatoes are possible only because of prior injury in the roots or tubers, since millipede mouthparts are too weak to effect entry. Strawberries, especially if they are touching the ground, are often subject to injury by diplopods. Other crops are also subject to millipede attack.

Diplopoda are divided into two subclasses. The subclass Pselaphognatha includes a single order containing two widely distributed genera. These diplopods are minute. They lack a hard integument and gonopods. Postmandibular appendages have not fused to form a gnathochilarium but have retained a leglike structure. The soft integument of many Pselaphognatha is armed with rows and festoons of scales and bristles.

The second subclass (Chilognatha) is very large. Members of this group have a hard integument, and one or both pairs of the immediately postmandibular appendages are fused to form a gnathochilarium. In this subclass one or two pairs of legs in the male are modified to transmit sperm to the sperm receptacle situated on the third segment in the female. These special legs called *gonopods* are usually found on the seventh or on the terminal segment.

Among more familiar diplopods, the terga are so convexly arched as to give these arthropods a cylindrical shape; but one order and one family of a second order of Chilognatha are flat-backed. The ventral or sternal plates are commonly somewhat flattened in most millipedes. Some species have a defense mechanism consisting of tight coiling, thus presenting only a smooth, tough surface to the attackers.

The head (Fig. 16-11) carries a pair of seven-segmented antennae, and behind their base most diplopods possess a pair of organs of Tömösvary of some undetermined sensory function. In millipedes as in Pauropoda, the head is composed of only five segments, the floor of the mouth being the *gnathochilarium,* derived from fusion of the first maxillae. The next segment, homologous to the second maxillary or labial segment of chilopods and insects, in Symphyla was seen to arise as the first trunk somite, but it was subsequently incorporated into the head in that group. In Diplopoda as in Pauropoda this metamere is retained as the anterior trunk segment and is enlarged dorsally to form the collum. This segment carries no legs. The second, third, and fourth trunk somites each carry one pair of legs. A single pair of legs also occurs on the fifth trunk somite in some diplopods. The last one or two trunk segments are legless.

The alimentary canal is a straight tube provided with salivary glands opening to the mouth, one pair of Malpighian tubules arising from the proctodaeum, and an anus opening between lateral lobes called paraprocts

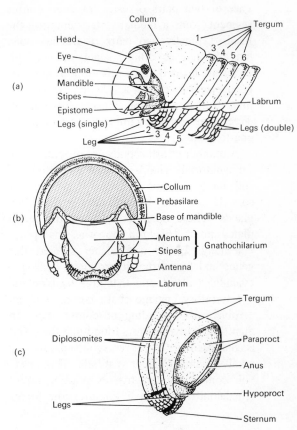

Fig. 16-11 Diplopoda: (a) lateral and (b) ventral view of the head of a diplopod, and (c) posterior end of a diplopod. After Beck and Braithwaite, *Invertebrate Zoology Laboratory Workbook,* 1962, courtesy of the authors and Burgess Publishing Company.

Fig. 16-12 Diplopoda, *Fontaria*; diagrammatic longitudinal section of the head. After Snodgrass 1952, courtesy of the Comstock Publishing Associates.

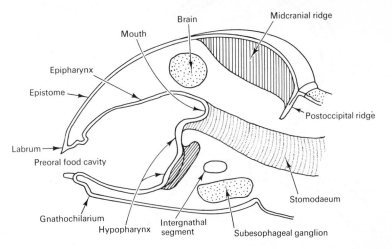

(Fig. 16-12). Millipedes are herbivorous, feeding on decaying humus.

The dorsal heart, noteworthy for the presence of two pairs of ostia for each double segment, joins a median artery entering the head. Typically two pairs of trachea open laterally in each double segment. The spiracles are located at the tips of internal skeletal projections called apodemes, whose primary function is for muscle attachment. Trachea are generally unbranched and do not anastomose.

A number of arthropods are provided with repugnatorial glands whose secretion is sufficiently noxious or even fatal to aggressors. Three orders of millipedes possess such glands. These open laterally on the tergal plates and in *Apheloria* appear as small pores externally. Eisner and Eisner studied this genus and found that it produced hydrogen cyanide, a compound that kills by blocking a respiratory enzyme chain common to all aerobic cells, including of course those in man. These investigators found that the gland is composed of a larger reservoir separated by a valve from a smaller vestibule. This reservoir contains an inactive cyanogenic liquid (madelonitrile). When compression forces

this fluid through the valve, substances (presumably enzymatic) release the HCN and it as well as the residue following the reaction have repellant action. The residue has a more prolonged but less toxic action. Not all millipedes produce HCN. Other repellants produced include quinones and iodine, some of which may have a tanning or even a caustic effect on tissue. The various repellants are undoubtedly more effective and prolonged in the cramped or confined spaces where millipedes are apt to occur.

The gonads lie ventral to the intestine. Millipedes are progoneate and the genital ducts open ventrally on the third trunk segment. In some diplopods the last pair and sometimes the last two pairs of legs function as clasping organs at copulation. In others, one or both pairs of legs, typically on the seventh segment, are modified as gonopods to effect (Fig. 16-13) sperm transference to the female. Millipede eggs are fertilized at laying.

Although some diplopods deposit eggs directly in the earth, others make a sort of cocoon or capsule of earth bound together with salivary secretion or built up from excrement.

Fig. 16-13 Diplopoda: (a) diplosegment from middle part of body of *Arctobolus*, anterior and (b) gonopods and sternum of seventh segment, *Arctobolus*, anterior. *Gpd*, gonopod; *S*, sternum. After Snodgrass 1952, courtesy of the Comstock Publishing Associates.

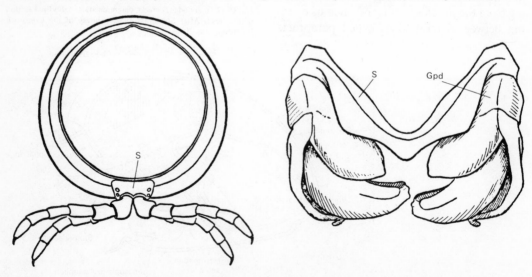

The eggs are rich in yolk and early nuclear division may occur centrally, followed by migration to the surface, or it may be peripheral from the start. Some cells remain dispersed in the yolk or migrate back to the yolk from the peripheral cells, many of which appear to have processes connecting with the surface layer. The endoderm is derived from these cells, but apparently some of them join in mesodermal structures.

By proliferation the surface becomes covered with a layer of cells called the blastoderm, which thickens on the ventral side to form the germinal disc or germ band. The germ band elongates and is composed of two layers, surface ectoderm and underlying mesoderm. Segmentation begins first anteriorly and then near the posterior end with the intermediate area last to show segmentation. Coelomic sacs appear in segmenting mesoderm and these push into the appendages as they are formed. At a very early stage the future double segments show double coelomic pouches.

As with the Chilopoda a median flexure of the germ band occurs which brings anterior and posterior ends of the developing embryo into close apposition at the surface, while the intermediate portion forms a narrow loop into the yolk. Such a U-shaped regression into the yolk is similar to what occurs in Apterygota, and particularly in Collembola.

Millipedes are anamorphic. At hatching, the body has seven visible segments and three pairs of rudimentary trunk appendages. Most millipedes pass through seven ecdyses as larvae, but the added number of segments and leg pairs may reach 100 depending on the species.

Some 6,500 species of Diplopoda have been described. Only a few of these are fossils. The oldest millipede fossils, which date from the Devonian, are placed in extinct orders and are older than any Chilopoda. More recent fossils found in the early Tertiary are placed in modern families.

Comments on Diplopod Classification

The Diplopoda are usually grouped into two subclasses. The subclass Pselaphognatha has world-wide distribution and includes a single order of the same name. These are small millipedes. They possess 13 trunk segments with legs lacking on the last two somites. Pselaphognatha do not have gonopods or a gnathochilarium. Hairlike clumps of scales occur dorsally and laterally on these diplopods. The second subclass is Chilognatha, which contains six orders. Two of these, Oniscomorpha and Limacomorpha, are sometimes grouped in a superorder (Opisthandria) in which the last pair of legs are modified as gonopods in the male. Distribution tends to be tropical for this superorder. In the second superorder, Proterandria, one or both pairs of legs on the seventh trunk somite (or the second pair of the seventh and the first pair on the eighth segment) are modified as gonopods. The four orders included in this superorder are Proterospermophora, Opisthospermophora, Colobognatha, and Ascospermophora. The last order lacks the repugnatorial glands present in the others, and also differs in the possession of silk-producing glands that discharge through dorsal projections on the last segment. The Proterospermophora differ from other Proterandria in having a markedly flattened dorsal surface. *Julus* is a common European genus and *Narceus* (= *Arctobolus*) is widely distributed in the United States. *Apheloria* is a flat-backed millipede also present in the United States.

SUPERCLASS HEXAPODA

Class 1 Insecta

The name insect, like other designations such as bug and worm, is a common term of wide and often erroneous usage by the individual unfamiliar with invertebrate zoology. Each of these designations has special meaning for the zoologist; although worms (Vermes) is no longer considered a taxonomic category, it continues to be used as a convenience in discussing some quite unrelated groups of animals. The Insecta (Hexapoda) is a category with an established grouping of structural characteristics. These features are so constant that, as Calman pointed out, it is far easier to draw a generalized insect than a typical crustacean. The Hexapoda constitute better than 75 per cent of described species of animals. The group is estimated to be at least ten times larger in number of species than the second largest phylum, Mollusca, with over 80,000 described. True bugs represent a subdivision of Insecta, and their species number in the thousands. The largest order of insects is the Coleoptera (beetles) containing over 275,000 described species. Other large orders include Lepidoptera (moths and butterflies) 112,000, Hymenoptera (wasps, ants, and bees) 103,000, and Diptera (flies and mosquitoes) with 85,000 species.

The majority of insects range in length from an eighth to one and one-fourth inches. Only a few contemporary species are larger; one orthopteran (*Pharnacia serratipes*) measures about ten inches in length, and some moths have a wingspread of nearly eleven inches. Fossil insects have been found with a wingspread of over 30 inches and a body length of 15 inches. On the other hand, some beetles are only about 250 micra long —well within the size range of the protozoan, *Paramecium caudatum*.

The insects are a most successful group because they are able to adapt to a great variety of habitats. Only the ocean depths have eluded their radiation. Most major orders of insects are nearly cosmopolitan in distribution, and a few species are almost as widely dispersed.

Geographically, insects are widely distributed. A number of butterfly species are common within the Arctic circle. Some northern mosquitoes breed in the icy water of puddles on glacier surfaces. Lesser vegetation at the South Polar regions seems to bear correlation to fewer insect inhabitants, but some Collembola and Diptera have been found there. The largest numbers of insect species occur in the tropical zone. While lesser numbers of species occur in temperate zones, the number of individuals of a species

Fig. 16-14 External anatomy of a grasshopper. After Herms 1923, courtesy of The Macmillan Company.

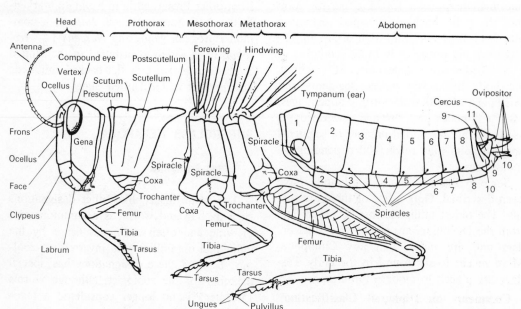

often is greater. The presence of larger numbers of insectivorous predators is a contributing factor to the adaptive radiation of species in tropical environments.

Perhaps the simplest precise definition of a typical adult insect is that it is an arthropod with the body divided into three tagmata (head, thorax, and abdomen) (Fig. 16-14), with one pair of legs on each of the three thoracic segments, with a pair of wings on the second and third thoracic segments, with a single pair of antennae, and with metameric spiracular orifices opening to a tracheal respiratory system. It should be kept in mind that some Hexapoda are primitively or secondarily without wings.

The generalized insect is considered to have additional features commonly. It is opisthogoneate, that is, the reproductive pores are posterior; six Malpighian tubules arise from the inner end of the ectodermal proctodaeum and function in excretion; and each

tagma is composed of a definite number of segments.

Three features supply fundamental evidence of metamerism in insects. Externally paired appendages are indicative of segmentation, and internally the serial arrangement of nerve ganglia (Fig. 16-15) and the presence of paired coelomic cavities provide proof. Since all of these features may be modified in development of the adult insect, recourse is made to comparative embryology.

The Insect Head   Although it is generally accepted that the insect head is composed of six segments (Fig. 16-16), interpretations vary on how these originate. The beginning biology student from study of crayfish and grasshopper finds it convenient to associate paired appendages with segments. In the insect head this makes for some difficulty. The antennae, mandibles, and maxillae are obviously paired, and it is relatively easy to see the derivation of the labium from paired

Fig. **16-15** Seven stages in the development of the nervous system in a waterbeetle. After Kellogg 1908 (enlarged after Brandt), courtesy of Holt, Rinehart & Winston, Inc.

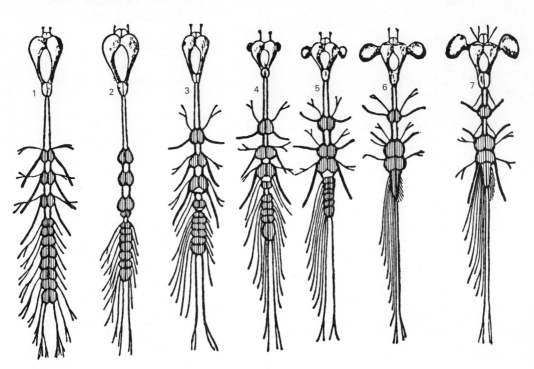

primordia. Thus four segments are accounted for, but to coordinate the other two metameres with existing appendages is not possible in the adult. The labrum is the unpaired anterior pole of the arthropod; and the insect hypopharynx is a variant development from mandibles and possibly from maxillae so it cannot represent an additional segment (Fig. 16-17). The compound eyes of hexapods cannot be considered as derivatives of paired appendages, but their innervation paralleling that of the simple lateral eyes of immature stages gives support for their origin from a separate neuromere and hence a separate segment. With acceptance of this hypothesis, five segments are accounted for in the insect head.

The insect antennae might better be called

Fig. 16-16 Head and mouthparts of the cockroach. From Belding, *Textbook of Clinical Parasitology*, 1942 (second edition, 1952), adapted from Miall and Denny 1886. By permission of Appleton-Century-Crofts and Miall and Denny, as modified in Belding.

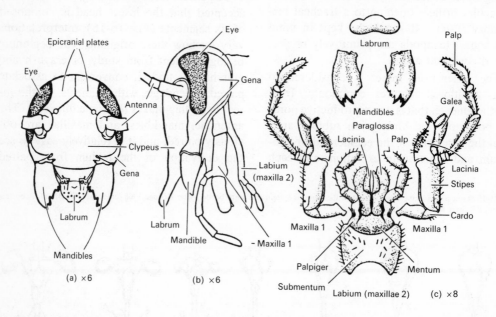

Fig. 16-17 Diagrams illustrating theories of segmentation of the arthropod head and composition of the brain. (a) The primitive head region as commonly supposed to include the prostomium (*Prst*) and six somites (I-VI); the brain formed of the prostomial archicerebrum (*Arc*) and preantennal and first antennal ganglia, with the second antennal ganglia added later. (b) The head region supposed to include the prostomium and only four postoral somites; the brain formed from the archicerebrum differentiated into protocerebrum (1 *Br*) and deutocerebrum (2 *Br*), with the first postoral, or second antennal, ganglia finally added to form the tritocerebrum. *PrntGng*, preantennal ganglion; *AntGng*, antennal ganglion; *FrGng*, frontal ganglion; *LmNv*, labral nerve; *RNv*, recurrent nerve; *E*, eye; *Mth*, mouth; *Stom*, stomodaeum. After Snodgrass 1935, courtesy of the McGraw-Hill Book Company.

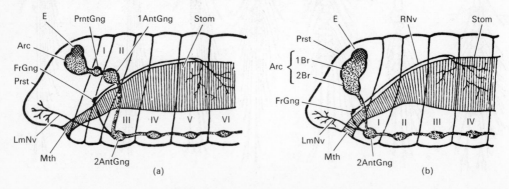

antennules since they are analogous to the structures of this name (first antennae) of Crustacea, and these were correlated with a brain lobe called the deutocerebrum in that group. A more anterior brain lobe called the protocerebrum was associated with the eyes, while the tritocerebrum, innervating the second antennae, originated postorally as the anterior ganglion of the ventral nerve chain and commonly shifted to a supraesophageal position (Fig. 16-17). The insect brain is composed of these same three structures, but

Fig. 16-18 Piercing-sucking mouth parts of a female mosquito. (In (b) the cross-section and isometric projection of the stylets as described by Howard, Dyar, and Knab.) After Metcalf and Flint 1932, courtesy of the McGraw-Hill Book Company.

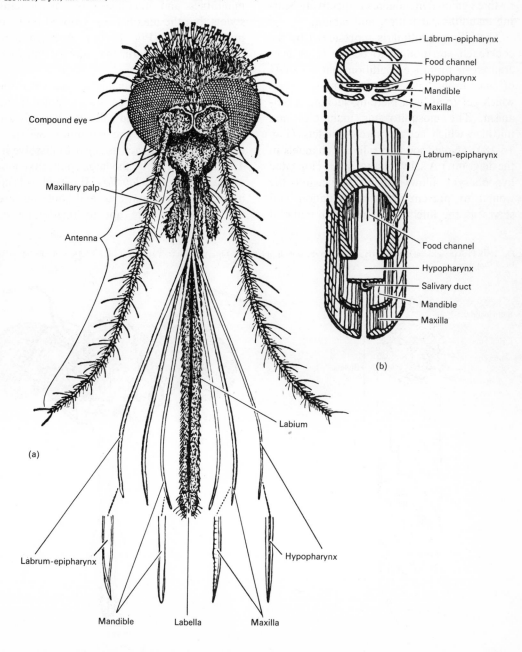

appendages associated with the tritocerebrum are missing in the adult insect and only a few embryonic studies show the presence of a transitory appendage.

The insect head is composed of two primitive segments represented by an ocular and an antennal section, possibly analogous to the annelid prostomium; by the tritocerebral segment without external appendages; and by three gnathal metameres respectively bearing mandibles, maxillae, and labium.

The biting mouthparts represented by the cockroach are thought to be the more generalized or primitive condition, but a variety of adaptations have occurred among insects which get food by a piercing-sucking mechanism. The mosquito has mandibles and maxillae which act as piercing stylets (Fig. 16-18). (Note food and salivary channels in the diagram.) A salivary duct in the elongated hypopharynx allows entry of saliva into the wound to prevent blood coagulation and serves as the infective channel for malarial organisms. Blood is taken into the mosquito through a channel formed by a ventral groove in the labrum, the inner side of which is labeled epipharynx. This groove forms a tube by apposition with the flat surface of the hypopharynx.

In the piercing-sucking mouthparts characteristic of true bugs and their allies, including the bedbug, stink bug, and cicado, the mandibles and maxillae serve as piercing stylets, but the maxillae are grooved on their inner surfaces (Fig. 16-19). Apposition of the two maxillae form the salivary and food channels.

The house fly is unable to bite since the mandibles and maxillae are atrophied (Fig. 16-20). The food and salivary channels are similar to those of the mosquito. Saliva is extruded on food such as sugar to dissolve it. This is facilitated by the large spongelike end of the labrum (the *labella*). It is well to keep in mind that many insects, and houseflies are not exceptions, are apt to regurgitate or

Fig. 16-19 Piercing-sucking mouth parts as occur in the squash bug and cicado. After Metcalf and Flint 1932, courtesy of McGraw-Hill Book Company.

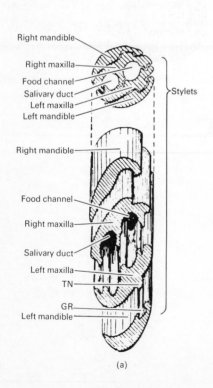

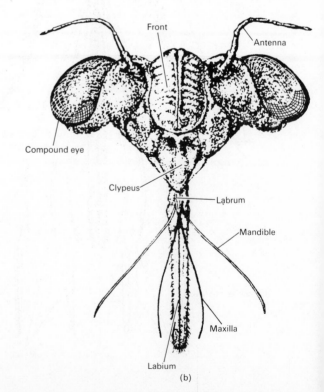

(a)

(b)

defecate while feeding. Such processes result in flyspots and in wound contamination for some biting insects.

Typically two kinds of eyes occur in adult Insecta, but only simple eyes called *ocelli* or *stemmata* occur in larval stages and these are lateral and paired. Lateral ocelli and com-

pound eyes are both innervated through the optic lobe section of the brain. This differs from the innervation of dorsal ocelli when the latter are present in adult insects.

The compound eye of insects (Fig. 16-21) is composed of individual elements called ommatidia. An ommatidium is an elongate

Fig. 16-20 Head and proboscis of the house fly, *Musca domestica*. After Snodgrass 1935, courtesy of the McGraw-Hill Book Company.

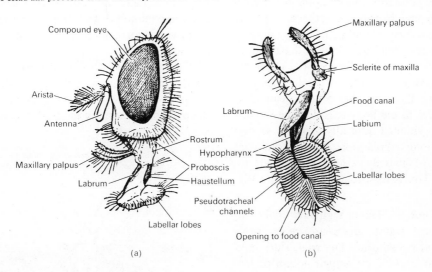

(a)　　　　(b)

Fig. 16-21 The insect compound eye, diagrammatic. (a) vertical section of part of eye, (b) typical structure of an ommatidium, (c) horizontal section of ommatidium through cone, and (d) same through retinula. *a*, eccentric retinula cell; *BMb*, basement membrane (membrana fenestrata); *CgCl*, corneagenous cell; *Cn*, crystalline cone; *Cor*, corneal lens; *l*, lamina ganglionaris; *IPgcl*, iris pigment cell; *Nv*, nerve; *OCh*, outer chiasma; *OR*, ocular ridge; *os*, ocular suture; *OSc*, ocular sclerite; *PgCls*, pigment cells; *Ret*, retinula; *Rhb*, rhabdom; *RPgCl*, retinal pigment cell; *SCl*, sense cell (retinula cell). After Snodgrass 1935, courtesy of the McGraw-Hill Book Company.

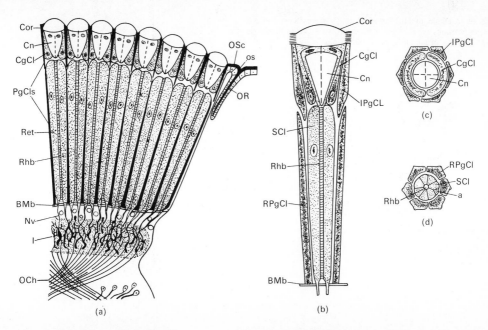

(a)　　　　(b)

cylindrical structure whose external lens forms a facet. Below the lens is an inverted conical structure called the crystalline cone, and below the latter is a secreted rodlike rhabdom surrounded by a concentric ring of retinular cells. Separate layers of pigment cells surround the retinular ring and the cone. An extreme degree of evolutionary convergence has been advanced to explain the remarkable similarity of compound eyes in Crustacea and Hexapoda, arthropod groups not otherwise closely related.

Attention should be called to the relationship of the head to the long axis of the body. There are two general types. In the hypognathous type the long axis of the head is at right angles to the body axis and the mouthparts are situated ventrally. In the second type the long axis is more or less continued in the line of the body axis and mouthparts are anterior. This is the prognathous head. (Fig. 16-22).

The Thorax Three segments make up the thoracic tagma; these are called pro-, meso-, and metathorax. The roof, sides, and floor of the thorax are named notum or tergum, pleura (singular pleuron), and sternum, respectively. The term pronotum refers to those fused sclerites (hardened plates of the exoskeleton) composing the prothoracic roof.

Similar terminology is applied to other areas. It is to be remembered that in the generalized insect the pleura are typically membranous and flexible and remain so in the abdomen, but in the winged insect they are sclerotized in the thoracic segments to support flight.

Two theories have been advanced to explain wing origin. The tracheal gill theory presents two obstacles to acceptance. It implies an aquatic ancestor for winged forms, and the common distribution of tracheal gills lacks good correlation with the site of wing formation.

The more widely accepted theory is based on the presence of so-called *paranotal lobes* (Fig. 16-23) projecting horizontally from the prothoracic tergum in fossil insects which

Fig. 16-23 A primitive insect, *Stenodictya*. Note the prothoracic lobes. After Berry (after Schuchert) 1929, courtesy of the McGraw-Hill Book Company.

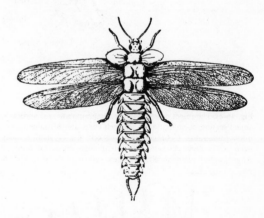

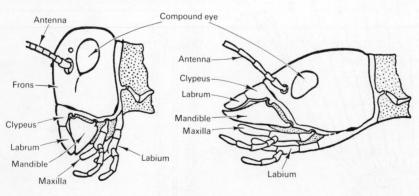

Fig. 16-22 Diagrams illustrating (a) the hypognathous and (b) the prognathous types of insect head structure. After Snodgrass 1935, courtesy of the McGraw-Hill Book Company.

possessed wings on meso- and metathorax. While prothoracic wings never developed from these lobes, it is thought that similar lobes gave rise to true wings. This theory is supported further by a not unrelated method of wing formation among some more primitive winged insects.

If the early wings were rather rigid lateral extensions, they probably served as gliders to keep the insect airborne longer. Subsequently flexibility at the base and coordinated muscular action were developed. Since the wing is attached both to the tergum and to the pleuron, the relative arching or flattening of the tergum, controlled by appropriate antagonistic muscles, respectively depresses or elevates the wings (Fig. 16-24).

Based upon the assumption that all insect wing venation arose from the same primitive ancestral pattern, a hypothetical archetype has been formulated. Utilizing the Comstock-Needham nomenclature, Snodgrass presents a slightly modified archetype correlated with functional regions of the wing. Wings arose as thin, outfolding expansions of the body wall with the two layers of epithelial cells forming the upper and lower surfaces of this wing primordium fusing. So-called veins form around the trachea already incorporated in the wingfold. In some insects with complete metamorphosis, this sequence of vein and tracheal appearance is reversed. The hypothetical wing prototype (Fig. 16-25) serves as an important basis for study of wing evolution and therefore is a significant factor in the classification of pterygotes.

The characteristic three pairs of legs (hence hexapod) occur on the thoracic segments in insects. Such legs typically are composed of six segments. Beginning proximally these are coxa, trochanter, femur, tibia, tarsus, and pretarsus. The last segment is reduced in arthropods generally, and in the insects is represented usually by a pair of claws and certain median structures. The insect pretarsus apparently corresponds to the dactylopodite of crustaceans; but opinions diverge as to whether the limbs of various arthropods have an ancestral prototype in-

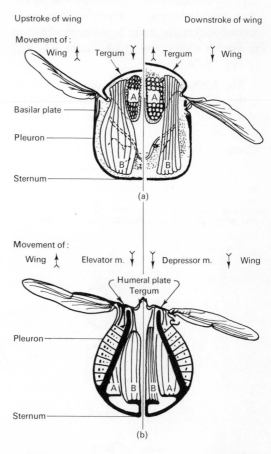

Fig. 16-24 Comparison of gross wing mechanics among insects. (a) Typical modern pteryogote (modified from Snodgrass), (b) Dragonfly (*Epiaeschna*). After Sargent 1951, courtesy of *Biol. Rev. City College of New York.*

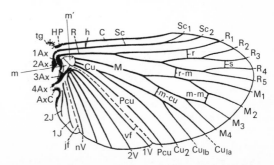

Fig. 16-25 Hypothetical wing venation. *A*, anal veins; *Ax*, axillary sclerites (first, second, third and fourth); *AxC*, axillary cord; *C*, costa; *Cu*, cubitus; *h*, humeral cross-vein; *HP*, humeral plate; *J*, jugal veins; *jf*, jugal fold; *M*, media; *m,m'*, median plates; *m-m*, median cross-vein; *m-cu*, mediocubital cross-vein; *Pcu*, postcubitus (first anal); *R*, radius; *r*, radial cross-vein; *r-m*, radial-medial cross-vein; *Rₛ*, radial sector; *s*, sectorial cross-vein; *tg*, rudiment of tegula; *V*, vannal veins (anal veins except the first); *1V*, first vannal vein; *2V*, second vannal vein; *nV*, last vannal vein (there may be as many as 12 vannal veins, so *nV* represents the last one of the series; *vf*, vannal fold. After Snodgrass 1935, courtesy of the McGraw-Hill Book Company.

dicating a strict homology. The typical insect walks by moving the fore and aft legs on one side, synchronized with the middle one on the other side. In keeping with extensive environmental variations insect legs are modified in numerous ways, some of which are indicated in Fig. 16-26.

The Abdomen The last tagma of insects is the abdomen, characterized by the general absence of paired appendages. In typical adult insects the abdomen is composed of eleven segments (Fig. 16-27) plus the area

around the anus (periproct) which might be interpreted as analogous to the telson of other arthropods. In the Protura the so-called twelfth segment is well developed, and in the embryology of some more generalized pterygote insects there also appear to be twelve segments. The telson, customarily interpreted for arthropods as the anus-bearing, terminal lobe, is not considered to be a segment.

In anamorphic development characteristic of many Myriapoda and of Protura the zone

Fig. 16-26 Some insect leg modifications. (a) digging leg of mole cricket, (b) walking leg of an ichneumon wasp (note the two-segmented trochanter), (c) clinging leg of the hog louse, (d) swimming leg of a predaceous diving beetle, (e) grasping leg of a praying mantis, and (f) foot of the house fly. This last figure is after Kellogg 1908, courtesy of Holt, Rinehart & Winston, Inc. Composite, after Metcalf and Flint 1932, courtesy of the McGraw-Hill Book Company.

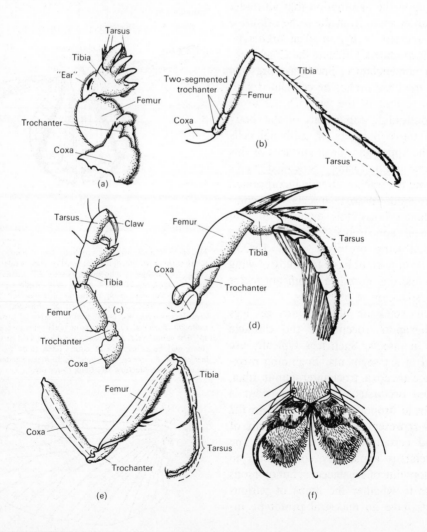

Fig. 16-27 Sagittal section of the body of a roach showing most of internal structures except tracheae. After Metcalf and Flint 1932, in part after Miall and Denny, courtesy of the McGraw-Hill Book Company.

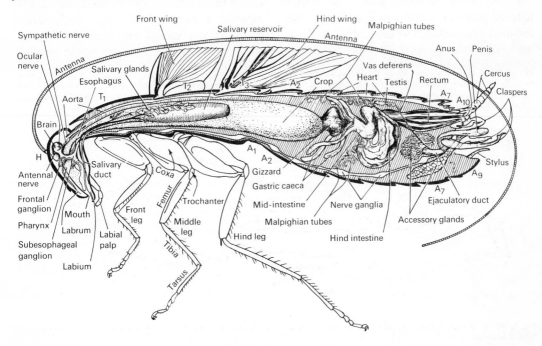

Fig. 16-28 Abdomen of the cockroach (*Blatta orientalis*). (a) Ventral view of male, (b) lateral view of male, (c) lateral view of female, and (d) tracheal system, showing dorsal tracheal communications after removal of ventral integument and viscera. From Belding, *Textbook of Clinical Parasitology*, 1942 (Second edition, 1952). Redrawn from Miall and Denny 1886. By permission of Appleton-Century-Crofts, and Miall and Denny, as modified in Belding.

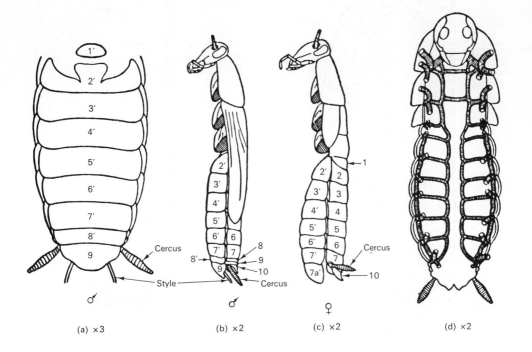

(a) ×3   (b) ×2   (c) ×2   (d) ×2

of new segment formation is immediately anterior to the terminal lobe. The newly hatched proturan has nine segments with the terminal lobe included as the ninth, and three new segments are eventually added between it and the eighth. In the proturan the twelfth segment represented by tergal and sternal plates is not completely incised from the

Fig. 16-29 The insect alimentary canal, diagrammatic. *AInt*, anterior intestine; *An*, anus; *BuC*, buccal cavity; *Car*, cardia; *Cln*, colon; *Cr*, crop; *GCa*, gastric caecum; *Il*, ileum; *Mal*, Malpighian tubules; *Ment*, mesenteron (ventriculus); *Mth*, mouth; *Oe*, oesophagus; *Phy*, pharynx; *PInt*, posterior intestine (rectum); *Prox*, proctodaeum; *Pvent*, proventriculus; *Py*, pylorus; *Rect*, rectum (*rect*, rectum proper *rsc*, rectal sac); *Stom*, stomodaeum; *Vent*, ventriculus. After Snodgrass 1935, courtesy of the McGraw-Hill Book Company.

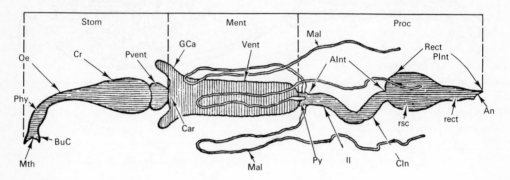

Fig. 16-30 (a) Cleavage and (b) blastoderm formation in an insect egg. After Johannsen and Butt 1941, courtesy of the McGraw-Hill Book Company.

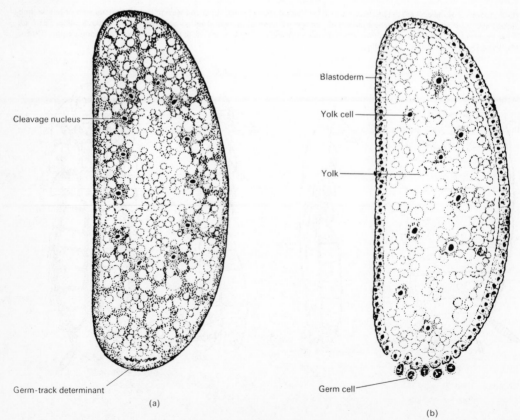

periproct or telson. This same condition occurs in the epimorphic development of generalized insect embryos.

In many insect orders only nine or ten abdominal segments are evident, and even in groups still retaining eleven segments identity of posterior segments may be obscured by adaptation for reproduction. Compare the diagrams of the grasshopper (Fig. 16-14) with those of the cockroach (Fig. 16-28).

One of the chief functions of the abdomen is respiratory movement (Fig 16-28). In many larger insects there are expandable air sacs in the tracheal system and the tracheae are ventilated by abdominal movement. The spiracular valves of the trachea function mainly to control water loss, a major advance over Onychophora. Most of the viscera of the digestive and reproductive systems are also housed in the abdomen (Fig. 16-29).

Embryology and Metamorphosis Although some small-yolked eggs (e.g., Collembola and some parasitic Hymenoptera) exhibit total or holoblastic cleavage in development, most insect eggs have extensive yolk and undergo a meroblastic segmentation which is commonly labeled centrolecithal superficial cleavage. Early nuclear divisions begin in the centrally situated protoplasm which is surrounded by yolk. The resultant cleavage products largely move to the periphery (Fig. 16-30) to give rise to a surface layer of cells called the blastoderm. This stage is analogous to a blastula. The oösome or germ tract in some insect eggs appears as a more granular area and gives rise to germ cells.

Some cells called yolk cells or vitellophags appear in the yolk. These cells are derived completely or in part from the blastoderm, function to assimilate yolk, represent an endodermal primordium, and may be incorporated into the mesenteron or midgut.

The blastoderm undergoes change to form a ventral plate of columnar cells which is continuous with a flat epithelium over lateral and dorsal areas. The latter is called the dorsal or extraembryonic blastoderm. In reality the

ventral plate marks the germ band or primitive streak. Lengthwise on the germ band a pair of slight folds or ridges develops, dividing the embryonic area into two lateral plates and a median plate. The immediate fate of this elongated median plate involves a modified pattern of gastrulation and the appearance of mesoderm. In many insects the middle plate recesses to form a groove. This groove is homologous to blastopore formation as seen in Onychophora. The lateral plates proliferate to close the groove with or without leaving a tubular cavity. In some insects the middle plate does not produce a groove, but overgrowth of the lateral plates displaces it from the surface. In a few hexapods cells proliferate from the inner face of the middle layer and spread laterally to produce a two-layered embryo.

Fig. 16-31 Diagrams of the formation of the Pteryogote definitive alimentary canal. (a) The germ layers in longitudinal section, including the three regenerative endodermal rudiments of the mesenteron (*AMR, IMR, PMR*) and envelopment of the yolk by the growth of the mesenteron rudiments to form the stomach (*Ment*), and the ingrowth of the ectoderm stomodaeum (*Stom*) and proctodaeum (*Proc*). *Ecd*, ectoderm; *Msd*, mesoderm; *Lm*, labrum; *Mth*, mouth; *An*, anus; *Y*, yolk. After Snodgrass 1935, courtesy of the McGraw-Hill Book Company.

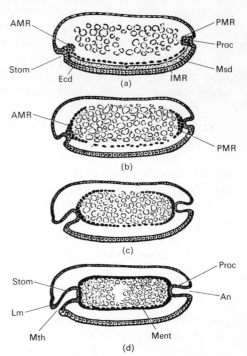

Although gastrulation is customarily considered to be a process delineating endoderm from ectoderm with subsequent derivation of mesoderm from one or both of the primary layers, in Hexapoda endoderm origin is obscure. In the insect endoderm forms the midgut or mesenteron. Gastrulation involving relocation of the midplate, as just described, shows that the latter is primarily mesoderm.

Several theories, all partly substantiated by embryological evidence, contribute to an explanation of the endodermal mesenteron. Among some apterygotes, endodermal cells remain scattered in the yolk rather than joining the cells that become surface blastoderm. Later these dispersed endodermal cells form into a layer to produce the midgut. Among most winged insects some of the cells at either end of the transposed middle plate are considered to be endoderm (Fig. 16-31). These, carried inward by the developing stomodaeal and proctodaeal invaginations, give rise to the mesenteron with or without the addition of scattered endodermal cells (vitellophags) migrating from the yolk. In a few instances the anterior and posterior endodermal primordia are in continuity by way of a strand of endodermal cells. Some evidence shows a proliferation of cells from the middle plate and their subsequent dispersion into the yolk. Such cells might be additional vitellophags which may subsequently contribute to mesenteron formation.

In the embryology of pteryogote insects after gastrulation, embryonic membranes form in one of two ways. In the overgrowth method, amniotic folds of the dorsal blastoderm encompass the surface-lying ventral embryo. These folds fuse to produce an outer serosa and an inner amnion ventral to the embryo. Yolk may be forced between amnion and serosa in some cases where the developing embryo sinks deeper into the yolk mass.

In several insect orders a process which might be termed inversion occurs. The posterior end of the germ band begins an invagination into the yolk, carrying with it the thin-walled extraembryonic blastoderm.

This invagination continues to move toward the anterior end, resulting in an inversion or somersaulting of the entire developing embryo into the yolk. At completion, the invaginated blastoderm loses connection with the external section, the latter being called serosa and the former, amnion. Some insects fail to complete inversion so that a portion of the embryo retains a superficial position, but in those which do the developing embryo subsequently reverses the somersault to regain its original orientation. These changes are termed blastokinesis (Fig. 16-32).

About the time that the lateral plates extend to cover the median plate in gastrulation, the beginning of segmentation appears. The first indication is a division into two embryonic tagmata, a primitive head called protocephalon and a primitive trunk region called protocorm. The protocephalon includes the ocular, antennal, and intercalary metameres, with the latter rarely carrying transitory appendages. The first three protocormic segments are potential gnathal metameres and will be incorporated into the insect head (Fig. 16-33). The next three segmental appendages will become thoracic legs. In adult pterygotes abdominal appendages do not persist except as cerci on the last or pretelsonic metamere. Some abdominal appendages are retained among apterygotes and on various immature stages of winged insects. The more prominent first pair are called *pleuropodia* and are considered to have a glandular function.

The characteristic exoskeleton of arthropods is a confining encasement and is periodically shed to accommodate growth. This process of shedding is called molting or ecdysis. The immature insect stage prior to a molt is termed an *instar*. Ecdysis is limited to the developing period of most insects so that the final molt produces the adult or *imago*.

Varying degrees of change or metamorphosis occur at ecdysis. A number of descriptive terms have been advanced to differentiate type or degree of metamorphosis. In primi-

Fig. 16-32 Blastokinesis in Odonata (*Calopteryx-Agrion*). In (a) the ventral plate is formed; in (b) and (c) the embryo invaginates into the yolk and the blastoderm has thinned out to form the serosa; (d) and (e) show beginning of visible metamerism and the developing appendages; in (f) through (h) the embryo has reversed its position and faces the ventral surface and the amnion has been lost during this process. After Harold R. Hagen, *Embryology of the Viviparous Insects.* Copyright 1951, the Ronald Press Company. Modified from Brandt, 1869.

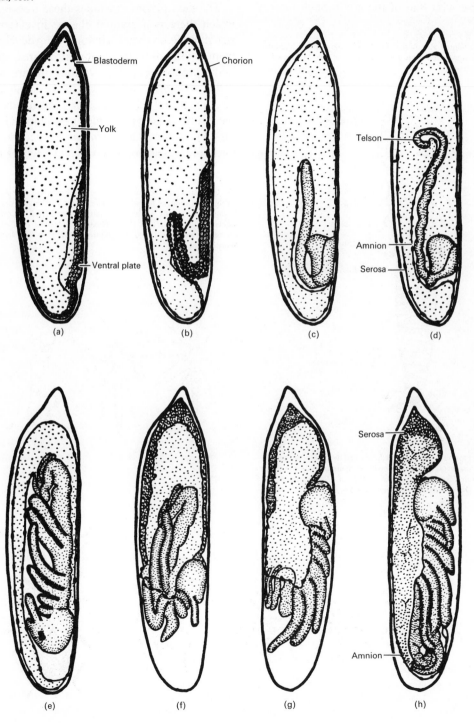

tive apterygote insects, as well as in some secondarily wingless forms, the external structure of the newly hatched stage is nearly identical with that of the adult. Such insects are called *ametabolous*. Among pterygote insects this condition occurs in Anoplura, Mallophaga, and wingless Notoptera.

The next division includes those insects in which there is a gradual change in external structure. Such changes involve wing development, maturation of genital structures, and body proportions. The various instars are called *nymphs*. They occur in the same environment and have the same food habits as the adults. This type of metamorphosis (Fig. 16-34) called *paurometabolous* occurs in Orthoptera, Dictyoptera, Cheleutoptera, Em-

Fig. 16-33 Ventral view of insect embryo, diagrammatic. Adapted from Johannsen and Butt 1941, courtesy of the McGraw-Hill Book Company.

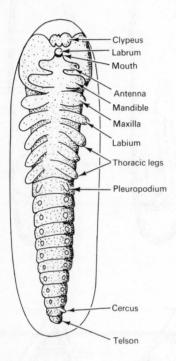

Clypeus
Labrum
Mouth

Antenna
Mandible
Maxilla
Labium

Thoracic legs

Pleuropodium

Cercus

Telson

Fig. 16-34 Paurometabolous growth; gradual development through nymphal stages. (a) Egg, (b) through (f) nymphal stages, and (g) adult. From *Insect Life and Insect Natural History*, by S. W. Frost, by Dover Publications, Inc., New York.

Fig. 16-35 Hemimetabolous development in *Perla*; metamorphosis through an aqueous larval stage (naiad). (a) Wingless larva, (b) larva with wing pads, 1,2, and (c) adult. I, II, and III, are thoracic segments. From Hertwig (from Huxley), *A Manual of Zoology* (translated and edited by J. S. Kingsley) 1902, Holt, Rinehart & Winston, Inc.

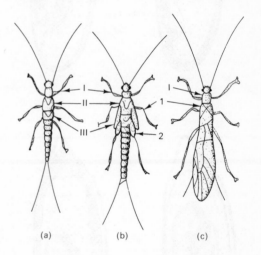

(a)   (b)   (c)

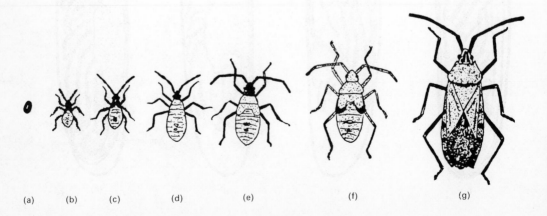

(a)   (b)   (c)   (d)   (e)   (f)   (g)

bioptera, Thysanoptera, Dermaptera, Psocoptera, Homoptera, Heteroptera, Isoptera, and Zoraptera. Metamorphosis in these last two orders is so slight as to approach an ametabolous condition.

In three insect orders the immature stages are aquatic and are called *naiads*. There are marked changes in structure involved in the change from aqueous to aerial-terrestrial environment. This has been called *hemimetabolous* metamorphosis (Fig. 16-35), and is found in Odonata, Ephemeroptera, and Plecoptera. The Ephemeroptera are unique in undergoing a molt to attain adulthood after the development of functional wings.

Many insects undergo striking change in the transformation from the immature form to the adult. A so-called resting or pupal stage (Fig. 16-36) is interposed between the last larval instar and the adult. During this nonfeeding and usually inactive period extensive reorganization occurs. This is characteristic of complete or *holometabolous* metamorphosis (Fig. 16-37) and occurs in Coleoptera, Megaloptera, Raphidioptera, Planipennia, Mecoptera, Trichoptera, Lepidoptera, Diptera (Fig. 16-38), Siphonaptera, Hymenoptera, and Strepsiptera, that is, in the orders included in Section Oligoneoptera. Among some of these orders successive larval instars are sharply differentiated structurally from each other.

Fig. 16-36 Larva and pupa of May beetle. From Hertwig, *A Manual of Zoology* (translated and edited by J. S. Kingsley) 1902, Holt, Rinehart & Winston, Inc.

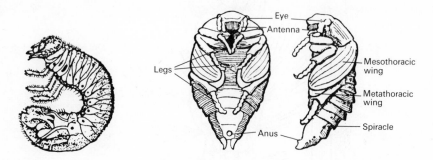

Fig. 16-37 Holometabolous development, typically involves feeding larval stages and a non-feeding pupal (e) stage. (a) Egg, (b) through (d) larval stages, (e) pupa, and (f) adult. From *Insect Life and Insect Natural History*, by S. W. Frost, by Dover Publications, Inc., New York.

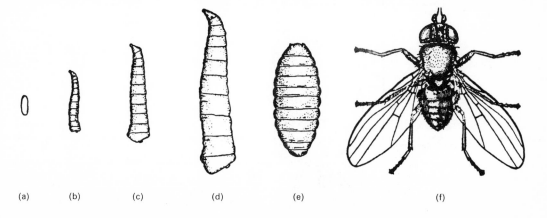

(a)　　　(b)　　　(c)　　　(d)　　　(e)　　　　　(f)

CLASSIFICATION OF SUPERCLASS HEXAPODA, CLASS INSECTA

SUBCLASS 1 APTERYGOTA These minute primitive insects are primitively wingless and possess terminal cerci. Metamorphosis is absent.

Superorder 1 Entognatha In this group the labium fuses with the cranium laterally to conceal mandibles and maxillae.

Order 1 Protura Anamorphic insects hatching with nine abdominal segments add three segments in subsequent molts. Antennae are absent. *Eosentomon, Acerentomon.*

Order 2 Collembola Insects with six abdominal segments. Malpighian tubules always and tracheae usually are absent. Possible collembolan fossils occurred in the Devonian. *Sminthurus, Podura.*

Order 3 Diplura These Entognatha have an eleven-segmented abdomen terminating in cerci or forceps. Malpighian tubules are rudimentary or absent. Their geologic history goes back to the Middle Tertiary. *Campodea* (Fig. 16-39), *Heterojapyx.*

Superorder 2 Ectognatha In this group the mandibles and maxillae are not concealed

Fig. 16-38 Mosquito larva (Order *Diptera*), dorsal view showing dorsal tracheal trunks opening through posterior spiracles only, and lateral trunks along the line of closed adult spiracles. After Snodgrass 1935, courtesy of the McGraw-Hill Book Company.

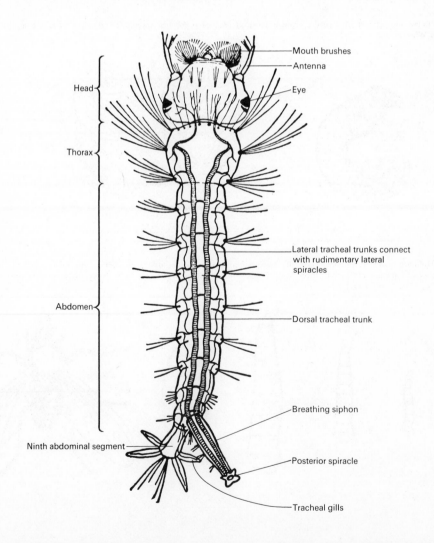

and show similarity to pterygote mouthparts.

Order 4 Thysanura These insects have an abdomen of eleven segments terminating in a median filament and paired cerci. Malpighian tubules and compound eyes are present. They are known from Triassic to Recent. *Lepisma* (Fig. 16-39), *Machilis.*

The insects (and especially the winged ones) constitute a majority of animal species. Their size, duration of reproductive processes, and ease of laboratory maintenance make them unusually suitable as research material. Their importance in pollination as well as their economically significant destructive habits have particularly drawn attention to them.

There is an immense volume of literature being published on physiological processes in insects, and many if not most of these processes have applications to physiology of other groups. Patton gives a brief summary of the history of insect physiology and points out that the literature of the group is second only to that of mammalian physiology.

Fig. 16-39 (a) *Lepisma*, a silverfish (Thysanura) and (b) *Campodea* (Diplura-Dicellura). From *Insect Life and Insect Natural History* by S. W. Frost, by Dover Publications, Inc., New York.

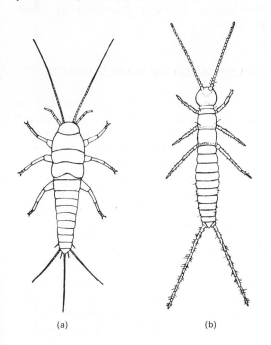

(a)   (b)

Only a few brief annotated examples can be cited here. The predaceous mantids capture their prey, such as a fly, from ambush, detecting it by sight with the aid of their large fixed compound eyes. When the prey is within reach, the speed of the capturing stroke of the great prothoracic legs is comparable to the flash of a frog's tongue in snatching flying insects; but the performance is also analogous to that of a good tennis player accurately judging and effectively returning a fast serve. However, the tennis player requires months and even years of learning to judge speed, direction, and possible richochet of the ball in order to achieve the necessary coordination. In the necessity of survival the mantid cannot depend upon a learning process, although it has been shown that performance can improve slightly.

In food capture, the mantid turns its head, so that both eyes receive the prey image symmetrically. Thus movement of the head corrects for deviation of the target from the head axis; the changing head position stimulates neck touch receptors and muscle proprioceptors which supply information on the amount of head-axis deviation from the body axis, which in turn determines the deviation of strike axis from body axis. Mittelstaedt found that mantids normally were about 85 per cent effective, but with unilateral denervation of neck receptors strikes were only about 25 per cent successful.

Another area of insect physiology extensively studied is the relationship to cold. In the metamorphosis of some insects an extended quiescent period occurs during cold weather. This is one phase of a phenomenon of dormancy called *diapause*. In nature, insects in northern climates are subject to periods of cold temperature. Some of these insects such as the Japanese beetle will continue in an inactive state even when brought into the laboratory. Wigglesworth has demonstrated that the immediate cause of diapause is the absence of essential growth and molting hormones, and that at least some of these factors occur in the brain. If the brain of a pupa (Lepidoptera) resuming activity after diapause is transplanted into another pupa in diapause, the second animal also reverts to the active state. In part at least what is involved is some biological clock system that regulates onset and return from dormancy, and which is most probably related to the constant variable of day length. Diapause is certainly a survival factor in the life cycle of many insects which are thus protected from becoming active in winter during unseasonable warm spells only to succumb to subsequent cold.

A different relationship to cold is illustrated by Dubach and co-workers at the University of Minnesota. They demonstrated that the carpenter ant, *Camponotus pennsylvanicus,* contained about 10 per cent glycerol by weight in winter. The glycerol was lost when these insects became active. If they were returned to a state of dormancy, glycerol reappeared. Salt reported the presence of glycerol in a number of immature stages of species that are freezing-tolerant (i.e., that can survive the formation of ice in their tissues). However, he found one freezing-susceptible species with glycerol. Sømme reported that representatives of a number of species containing glycerol were killed by the same freezing procedure in which other species containing glycerol survived, and one species was found that was freezing-tolerant without a trace of glycerol. It is apparent that glycerol increases the cold-hardiness of some insects, but that other factors also are involved.

Other studies of physiological interest are the resistances shown by insects to various insecticides such as DDT. These phenomena have both genetic and economic implications.

Still another phase of intensive physiological research is that associated with localization of nervous-system functions and with neurohumors. The chapter on Crustacea presented this latter subject particularly in relationship to molting and metamorphosis. The results of such studies are better known for insects than for Crustacea, but space does not permit their inclusion. Related to nervous system function is the well-known dance and waggle of bees. A circle dance pattern communicates the presence of relatively nearby food; a figure-of-eight pattern refers to more distant food sources; and direction of the abdominal waggle indicates direction of the food source correlated with the position of the sun.

The honeybee performs the dance pattern usually within the hive. Since movement up the comb indicates direction of the sun (or source of polarized light on a cloudy day) the honeybee must be able to correlate gravity with the sun's position. Gravity is perceived through the agency of sensory hairs between body tagmata or between appendage joints. Sensory neck hairs are asymmetrically stimulated when the insect is not horizontal. Other sensory hairs occur between thorax and abdomen. Immobilizing the head or weighting it or destroying the innervation of the neck sensory plates modifies or destroys the ability to recognize gravity changes and therefore the ability to communicate accurately by this means.

The incipient physiologist could do worse than get a thorough grounding in insect physiology.

CLASSIFICATION OF WINGED INSECTS

SUBCLASS 2 PTERYGOTA   These winged or secondarily wingless insects lack abdominal appendages except for cerci. Development is epimorphic, and metamorphosis varies. Malpighian tubules are characteristic.

SECTION *I Paleoptera*   These differ from all other pterygotes in the possession of wings which cannot be folded parallel to the abdomen in repose. These wings, sometimes described as fluted because of a tendency to longitudinal creases, were thickened along these creases often in correlation with veins. The wings developed from external buds, a process referred to as *exopteryogote.* Malpighian tubules were numerous. Two of the orders included in this section have persisted to the present. These are the Ephemeroptera (Mayflies) which are unique in undergoing ecdysis after wing formation, and the Odonata (dragonflies and damselflies).

Order 5 Palaeodictyoptera These fossil insects were heavybodied and possessed biting mouthparts. Their fossil record begins with the Lower Pennsylvanian and persists through the Permian. They resemble Mayflies and are probably ancestral to Ephemeroptera and Odonata as well as to some extinct groups.

Order 6 Protohemiptera These fossil insects had sucking mouthparts. Although their name suggests ancestry to Hemiptera, most authorities do not consider this probable. They occurred in the Upper Pennsylvanian and Permian Periods.

Order 7 Megasecoptera This group of fossil insects had slender bodies, long cerci, and biting mouthparts, and were probably carnivorous. They were prominent during the Permian Period.

Order 8 Protephemerida A single large specimen from the Upper Pennsylvanian Period had an orthognathous head with biting mouthparts and terminal cerci. It may represent a link between Palaeodictyoptera and Ephemeroptera.

Order 9 Ephemeroptera (Plectoptera) These present-day Mayflies (Fig. 16-40) have atrophied mouthparts, and wings unequal in size. Larvae are aquatic. The last immature stage possesses wings, after which the final ecdysis occurs. Two long cerci and a median filament are characteristic. The hind pair of wings may be atrophied. The fossil history can be traced to the Lower Permian Period. *Hexagenia, Ephemera.*

Order 10 Meganisoptera These large fossil insects possessed wings of equal size, with a wing structure that could be ancestral to that of the Odonata. They are found from the Carboniferous into the Jurassic Periods.

Order 11 Odonata These large insects with an ancestry back to the Lower Permian have equal-sized wings extending laterally at rest or extended unfolded over the abdomen. Larval stages are aquatic. Dragonflies and damselflies (Fig. 16-40) belong here. *Aeschna, Libellula, Lestes.*

SECTION *II Polyneoptera* These Neopteran insects possess a richly veined jugal section of the wing. The wings are folded over the abdomen at repose. Wing development is exopterygote and many Malpighian tubules are characteristic. In this section are found the orders that include cockroaches and mantids; termites, grasshoppers and crickets, and several smaller groups.

Fig. 16-40 (a) Mayfly, (b) damselfly, and (c) dragonfly. After Muesebeck 1952, courtesy of the author and the *Yearbook of Agriculture.*

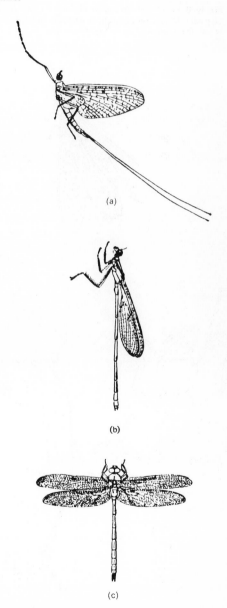

(a)

(b)

(c)

Order 12 Dictyoptera This group of running insects has jointed cerci, pentamerous tarsi, and an orthognathous head and produces eggs in a capsule called ootheca. Cockroaches and mantids (Fig. 16-41) belong here. They are mid-Pennsylvanian to Recent. *Blaberus, Periplaneta, Mantis.*

Order 13 Protoblattoptera These fossils are similar to roaches, but possessed a smaller pronotum which did not hide the prognathous head. They existed in the last half of the Paleozoic Era.

Order 14 Isoptera These polymorphic insects are the termites (Fig. 16-41) or "white ants." In the winged forms the wing has a suture line near the base for autotomy. The equal-sized wings have a longitudinal venation only slightly modified from the generalized form, but possessing a chitinized network between the long veins. Isoptera are known from the Lower Tertiary to Recent. *Termes.*

Order 15 Zoraptera These minute insects are polymorphic. Males are often wingless, and females can lose the wings by fracture at a basal joint. The tarsi are two-jointed. These insects are related to Psocids. No fossils are known.

Order 16 Protorthoptera These well-represented fossils of the late Paleozoic Era possessed running legs not adapted for leaping. The head was prognathous and the pronotum elevated. The abdomen carried cerci. *Gyrophlebia.*

Order 17 Plecoptera These are the stoneflies. They have aquatic larvae which develop through hemimetabolous metamorphosis.

Fig. 16-41 (a) Winged termite, (b) wingless termite, (c) cricket, (d) praying mantis, and (e)earwig. After Muesebeck 1952, courtesy of the author and the *Yearbook of Agriculture.*

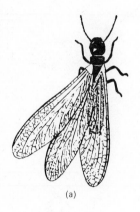

(a)

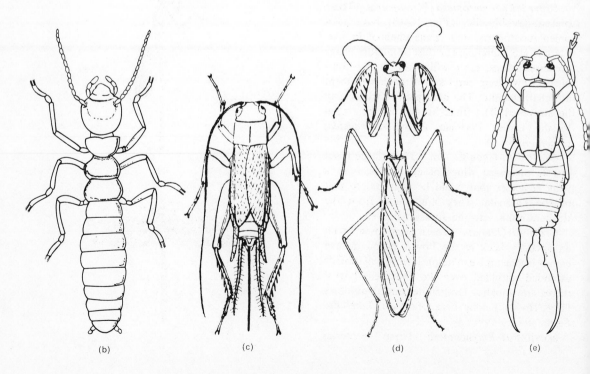

(b)　　　　　　　(c)　　　　　　　(d)　　　　　　　(e)

Prominent cerci and elongate antennae are characteristic. They are known from the Upper Permian to Recent. *Perla, Isoperla.*

Order 18 Notoptera This is a small group of wingless insects with ametabolous development. The development of the ovipositor suggests a relationship to Orthoptera. *Grylloblatta.*

Order 19 Cheleutoptera These stick-insects and leaf-insects, so called because of their adaptive structure, have a prognathous head. The winged forms are paurometabolous, the wingless nearly ametabolous. They are known from the Early Carboniferous to Recent. *Carausius, Phyllium.*

Order 20 Orthoptera The grasshoppers and crickets belong here (Fig. 16-41). They have an orthognathous head and metathoracic legs adapted for leaping. The ovipositor is well developed. *Melanoplus, Gryllotalpa, Gryllus.*

Order 21 Embioptera These small tropical insects are prognathous. Tarsi are three-jointed and those on the prothoracic legs have silk glands. Silk lines the tunnels in which these insects live. They are Lower Permian to Recent. *Embia.*

Order 22 Protelytroptera These fossil insects from the Permian Period have thickened forewings resembling elytra of beetles, a similarity probably due to convergence.

Order 23 Dermaptera These are known as earwigs (Fig. 16-41) and possess elytra-like mesothoracic wings. The metathoracic wing folds transversely as well as longitudinally. Cerci are modified as a pair of large forceps. Earwig history dates from the Lower Permian. *Forficula.*

SECTION *III Oligoneoptera* These holometabolous insects have a single vein in the jugal area behind the jugal fold (Fig. 16-25) of the wing. Malpighian tubules are few. Mouthparts are for biting or modified for sucking. The wings develop from internal buds, a condition called *endopterygote.* Four very large orders occur in this neopteran group. These include beetles (Coleoptera), moths and butterflies (Lepidoptera), flies and mosquitoes (Diptera), and ants, bees, and wasps (Hymenoptera). In addition several smaller groups occur and include such familiar insects as fleas, dobson-flies, and ant-lions.

Order 24 Coleoptera In this very large order, the prothorax is freely movable and the mesothoracic wings are *elytra,* which have a hard structure and meet along the middorsal line over the abdomen when the insect is not in flight. The head is prognathous with biting mouthparts and metamorphosis is holometabolous. The Coleoptera (Fig. 16-42) date from the Lower Permian. *Dytiscus, Carabus, Popillia.*

Order 25 Megaloptera These insects have a short prothorax, a prognathous head, and biting mouthparts. Longitudinal veins tend to bifurcate at the wing periphery. The metamor-

Fig. 16-42 (a) Lady beetle, (b) larder beetle, and (c) longhorned beetle. After Muesebeck 1952, courtesy of the author and the *Yearbook of Agriculture.*

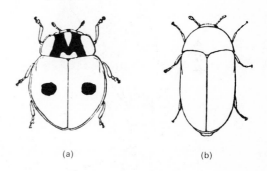

(a)   (b)

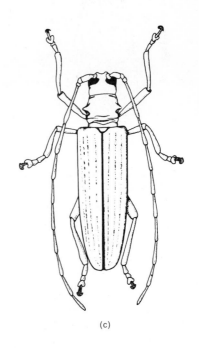

(c)

phosis is holometabolous and larvae are aquatic. These are the alderflies and dobsonflies (Fig. 16-43), and they have existed from the Lower Permian Period. *Sialis, Corydalis.*

Order 26 Raphidioptera The long prothorax and narrow head suggest a long, snakelike neck. These snake-flies are holometabolous with terrestrial larvae and primitive pupae. *Raphidia.*

Order 27 Planipennia These prognathous insects are holometabolous and the adults have biting mouthparts. The predaceous larvae have sucking mouthparts. Modified Malpighian tu-

bules in the last larval instar produce silk to form a cocoon. The common names of these insects are lace-wings and ant-lions, and they have a history from the Lower Permian. *Mantispa, Myrmeleon.*

Order 28 Mecoptera These are the scorpion-flies, whose name is derived from the upward curvature of the male abdomen. The mouthparts occur at the end of a beaklike prolongation of the orthognathous head. The membranous wings are alike. It has been suggested that this small order holds a key position, and its Permian ancestry probably gave

Fig. 16-43 (a) Dobson-fly, (b) blowfly, (c) butterfly, (d) ant, and (e) flea. After Muesebeck 1952, courtesy of the author and the *Yearbook of Agriculture.*

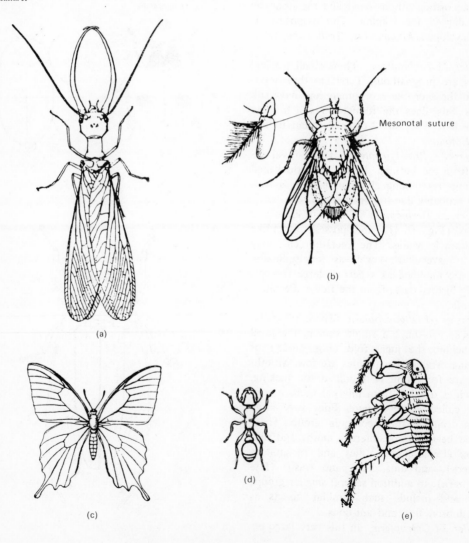

(a) (b) Mesonotal suture (c) (d) (e)

rise to Trichoptera, Lepidoptera, and Diptera. *Panorpa.*

Order 29 Trichoptera These medium- to small-sized insects are known as caddis-flies. They have a mothlike appearance due to the presence of long hairs on the body and wings. Biting mouthparts on the orthognathous head are reduced with loss of mandibles. Wings at rest form a rooflike peak. The aquatic larvae construct characteristic cases of silk and various foreign materials. These holometabolous insects date from the Middle Jurassic. *Rhyacophilia, Mayatrichia.*

Order 30 Lepidoptera These are the moths and butterflies (Fig. 16-43) with wings and body customarily clothed with overlapping scales. The larvae are known as caterpillars and have chewing mouthparts, but in the adult the mandibles are vestigial and the maxillae are modified to form a sucking tube. This group can be traced back to the Eocene. *Pieris, Samia, Vanessa.*

Order 31 Diptera These holometabolous insects have sparsely veined mesothoracic wings, and the second pair of wings is reduced to balancers called halteres. Mouthparts are adapted for piercing and sucking or are solely suctorial as in the common house fly. Mosquitoes and flies (Fig. 16-43) belong in this group, which is known from the upper Triassic Period. *Anopheles, Musca.*

Order 32 Siphonaptera (Aphaniptera) These are the fleas (Fig. 16-43), which as adults are wingless, laterally compressed external parasites of warm-blooded hosts. The coxal leg segments are very large. Mouthparts are adapted for piercing and sucking. The fossil record of the group begins with the Oligocene. *Pulex, Ctenocephalus.*

Order 33 Hymenoptera This large group includes the ants (Fig. 16-43), bees, and wasps. Two pairs of membranous wings are interlocked by hooks or *hamuli* on the anterior margin of the hind wing. Mouthparts range from a generalized biting type to a highly specialized sucking structure. The first abdominal segment called *propodeum* is fused to the thorax. Females bear an ovipositor, sometimes modified as a sting. Metamorphosis is holometabolous and the group is represented from Middle Jurassic to Recent. *Apis, Formica, Vespa.*

Order 34 Strepsiptera Degenerate wingless females are endoparasites in other insects. Mesothoracic wings of free-living males are reduced to halteres. The hind wings lack crossveins and fold fanwise at rest. The holometabolous metamorphosis is modified by two larval stages. The group traces from the Oligocene. *Stylops.*

SECTION *IV Paraneoptera* These insects are exopterygote, that is, the wings develop from external buds. The jugal lobe of the wing is little developed. Malpighian tubules are few and metamorphosis varies from an ametabolous to a primitive holometabolous condition. This neopteran section includes biting (Mallophaga) and sucking lice (Anoplura), the latter including a vector of typhus fever of man. A great many garden and farm plant pests occur here as well as that ubiquitous parasite of man, the bedbug, *Cimex lectularius,* which belongs to the true bugs (Heteroptera) —a group including some 40,000 species.

Order 35 Psocoptera (Corrodentia) These so-called booklice have an orthognathous head and biting mouthparts. These minute insects are variously winged or wingless, and cerci are absent. There is a very slight metamorphosis. The group has an ancestry from the Lower Permian. *Psocus.*

Order 36 Mallophaga These are the biting or bird-lice (Fig. 16-44) and have somewhat reduced biting mouthparts carried on an orthognathous head. They have a dorso-ventrally flattened (depressed) body, short antennae, and no wings. Bird-lice are ametabolous and no fossils are known. *Menopon.*

Order 37 Anoplura Mouthparts for piercing and sucking are carried on the prognathous head. These lice (Fig. 16-44) are external parasites of most mammals, but have not been found on bats or on marsupials. They are dorso-ventrally flattened, lack wings, and are ametabolous. Typhus fever is transmitted by lice. They are known from the Pleistocene to Recent. *Pediculus.*

Order 38 Thysanoptera These insects known as thrips (Fig. 16-44) have sucking mouthparts tilted caudally on an orthognathous head. They are serious economic pests on many plants. Wings when present are exceedingly narrow and carry long marginal setae.

Fig. 16-44 (a) Bedbug, (b) biting louse, (c) sucking louse, (d) thrips, and (e) cicada. After Muesebeck 1952, courtesy of the author and the *Yearbook of Agriculture*.

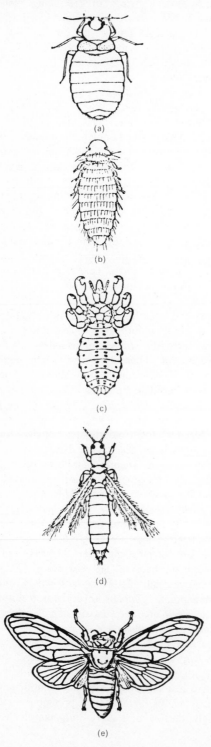

(a)

(b)

(c)

(d)

(e)

Thrips have a primitive holometabolous metamorphosis. They have existed from Upper Permian to Recent. *Heliothrips.*

Order 39 Homoptera The sucking mouthparts face caudally on these orthognathous insects (Fig. 16-44e). The pronotum is small and the membranous wings assume a rooflike position at rest. The metamorphosis is usually paurometabolous, rarely holometabolous. Their ancestry goes back to the Lower Permian. *Cicado, Aphis.*

Order 40 Heteroptera These orthognathous insects have sucking mouthparts often directed caudally. The pronotum is large and the wings usually overlap at rest. The mesothoracic wings are thickened and pigmented on the basal half. Metamorphosis is paurometabolous and the fossil history begins with the upper Triassic Period. *Anasa, Belostoma, Cimex* (Fig. 16-44a), *Triatoma.*

PHYLOGENETIC CONSIDERATIONS

The Arthropoda constitute an assemblage of animals related by a unique combination of characteristics, including a specialized hard exoskeleton, paired jointed appendages correlated with body segmentation, and a lacunar or open circulatory system with dorsal tubular heart. Additional features are shared with Annelida and Onychophora and include arrangement of the central nervous system, and such embryological aspects as elongation with median closure of the blastopore, development of additional segments from a pretelsonic growth zone, and teloblastic mesoderm formation with schizocoelic development of coelomic sacs.

The total picture indicates marked affinities of these three groups, but the divergence of characteristics among arthropod subgroups suggests either the absence of a monophyletic origin or an exceedingly remote branching from a primitive wormlike ancestor. Of the three groups, only the annelids retained spiral cleavage.

The Onychophora and Arthropoda possess a number of features in common, so that the former is sometimes included as an arthropod subdivision. In addition to most of the characteristics already related for arthropods, the Onychophora possess jaws adapted from segmental appendages, reduced coelom with similarity of reproductive organs, trachea (probably a convergence), and the process of ecdysis.

The major Arthropoda fall into three main groups. These are the Trilobita-Arachnomorpha, the Crustacea, and the Myriapoda-Insecta groups. The presence of tracheae in some arachnids and in myriapods and insects at one time suggested a common ancestry for these diverse groups. However, some Arachnids respire by means of book lungs, others utilize book lungs as well as tracheae, and in still others tracheae are the sole respiratory organs. In the Arachnida, tracheae were probably derived from book lungs. The establishment of the marine horseshoe crab, *Limulus,* as an arachnomorph supported the proposition that the Arachnida had an aquatic origin. This generally accepted ancestry for Arachnomorpha established the proposition that tracheae in terrestrial arthropods originated at least twice, and that the tracheae of Acarina and the myriapod-insect group are the result of convergence.

The insects show several important differences from Crustacea besides the presence of tracheae. The biramous appendage of Crustacea has no counterpart among the Hexapoda. The antennae of the latter are comparable not to the crayfish antennae, but to the antennules. The tubular insect intestine has no hepatopancreatic organ so characteristic of crustaceans. Ectodermal Malpighian tubules are characteristic of insects and absent in Crustacea, and there is lack of correlation of gonopore location. These factors are real obstacles to acceptance of a close affinity in the two groups.

While cephalization among arthropods supports the divergence seen in the larger arthropod subdivisions, it is a unifying factor emphasizing myriapod-insect affinity. The protocerebrum has the same correlation with sessile eyes, deutocerebrum with antennae,

and tritocerebrum with the first true segment which lacks persistent appendages in both groups. The gnathal segments show more variation, with Diplopoda and Pauropoda apparently lacking the second maxillary or labial segment in the head tagma. In both myriapods and insects the mandible does not retain a palps.

Snodgrass points out that in both Insecta and Myriapoda the foot musculature to the pretarsal segment is identical. The myriapods are a less concise group and sometimes one, sometimes another class shows best correlation with insectan structure, but the total picture supports the myriapod-insect relationship.

The Myriapoda are a tracheate group with Malpighian tubules and with marked similarity to the insectan head. Behind the head the body with homonomous metamerism and the widespread occurrence of anamorphic development are both suggestive of a group closer to the primitive than are Insecta. Among myriapods, the Diplopoda have a fossil history dating from the Lower Devonian, whereas the other major group, Chilopoda, show a geologic record more contemporaneous with Insecta.

Among Arthropoda, the Myriapoda provide the best candidates for derivation from Onychophora, although there is a tremendous void between the mid-Cambrian *Aysheaia* and the early Devonian diplopod.

Papers by Imms (1936, 1945), Calman (1936), and Tiegs and Manton (1958) discuss insect phylogeny. Of the various theories the so-called Symphylan Theory links the small myriapod order, Symphyla, with pterygote insects by way of the hexapod orders, Diplura and Thysanura.

Imms (1945) enumerates similarities between Symphyla and Diplura, such as structural features of head and legs, mandibular articulation, abdominal segments bearing movable styles, and the presence of cerci; and Manton (1953) points out the uniquely similar gait of Symphyla and Insecta.

Attention must be drawn to one major

difference. This is the progoneate condition of Symphyla as compared with opisthogoneate Hexapoda. Tiegs and Manton suggest that this difference can be minimized if correlation is made with the anamorphic development of Symphyla. The investigations of Tiegs (1940, 1945) indicated that the location of the symphylan gonopore (Fig. 16-45) is a secondary adaptation from a transitory, potentially opisthogoneate larval condition.

The Symphyla agree with Thysanura in being ectognathous rather than having the entognathous or hidden mouthparts characteristic of Collembola and Diplura. This variation is cause for dispute, unless, as has been suggested by Imms, the Diplura secondarily developed the labial mouth cover. Possibly radiation from a primitive apterygote resulted in the current distribution of features among the orders of wingless insects, the pterygotes retaining a new combination of features not unique for any apterygote.

Fig. 16-45 Comparison of genital systems: (a) *Lepisma* (Thysanura) male and (b) *Japyx* (Diplura) female. After Vandel 1949, in *Traité de Zoologie*, Tome VI (P. Grassé, ed.),courtesy of Masson et Cie.

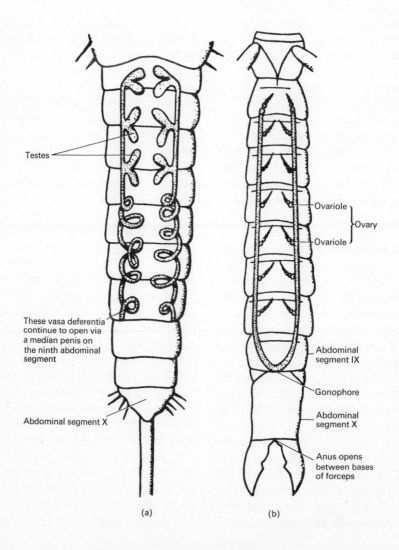

(a)   (b)

Thousands of species of fossil insects have been described. Pterygote insects were derived from the primitive Apterygota, but links between the two groups are tenuous. The earliest winged insects were unable to fold their wings caudally over the abdomen. Most of such groups are extinct, but dragonflies and mayflies have survived. Among insects able to fold their wings, cockroaches are the elite, since their ancestors left a fossil record from the Pennsylvanian Period. Although holometabolous insects include many of the most advanced and specialized orders, Carpenter (1952) has pointed out that lace-wings and scorpion flies with such metamorphosis were contemporary with heterometabolous orders surviving from the Lower Permian.

The ability to fold the wings caudally is a favorable adaptation, and correlated with it is the frequent modification of the meso-thoracic pair to provide a protective cover for the flight wings. About 87 per cent of modern insects can fold their wings, and nearly 85 per cent of our insects have complete metamorphosis. In the evolution of winged insects, these two processes have had a profound effect.

REFERENCES

Belding, D. L., Textbook of clinical parasitology (2nd ed.). New York: Appleton, 1952. (A third edition is dated 1965).

Berland, L., and others, Insectes. *In* (P. Grassé, ed.) Traité de zoologie, Tome X, Fasc. I and II. Paris: Masson et Cie, 1951.

Berry, E. W., Paleontology. New York: McGraw, 1929.

Calman, W. T., The origin of insects. Proc. Linn. Soc. London, 148:193, 1936.

Carpenter, F. M., Fossil insects. *In* Insects: the yearbook of agriculture, U.S.D.A., 1952.

Carthy, J. D., The behavior of arthropods. Edinburgh: Oliver and Boyd, 1965.

Chen, C. H., Evolution of the insect larva. Trans. Roy. Ent. Soc., London, 97:381, 1946.

Chu, H. F., How to know the immature insects. Dubuque, Iowa: Wm. C. Brown, 1949.

Cloudsley-Thompson, J. L. Spiders, scorpions, centipedes, and mites. New York: Pergamon, 1958.

Comstock, J. H., An introduction to entomology (9th ed.). Ithaca: Comstock, 1949.

Dubach, P., D. Pratt, F. Smith, and C. M. Stewart, Possible role of glycerol in the winter-hardiness of insects. Nature, 184: 288, 1959.

Eisner, T., and H. E. Eisner, Mystery of a millipede. Natural History, 74:30, 1965.

Hagen, H. R., Embryology of the viviparous insects. New York: Ronald, 1951.

Handlirsch, A., Arthropoda (pp. 211-276). *In* (W Kükenthal and T. Krumbach, eds.) Handbuch der zoologie, (3) 1. Berlin: Walter de Gruyter, 1926-1927.

Imms, A. D., The ancestry of insects. Trans. Soc. Brit. Ent., 3:1, 1936.

———, The phylogeny of insects. Tijdschr. Ent., 88:63, 1945.

———, A general textbook of entomology (7th ed.). New York: Dutton, 1948.

Jaques, H. E., How to know the insects. Dubuque, Iowa: Wm. C. Brown, 1947.

Lanham, U., The insects. New York: Columbia U. P., 1964.

Manton, S. M., Locomotory habits and the evolution of the larger arthropodan groups. Symp. Soc. Exp. Biol., 7:339, 1953.

———, The structure, habits, and evolution of the Diplopoda, Part 4. J. Linn. Soc. Zool., London, 42:299, 1954.

———, Habits of life and evolution of body design in Arthropoda. J. Linn. Soc. Zool., London, 44:58, 1958.

————, Concerning head development in the arthropods. Biol. Rev., 35:265, 1960.

Martynov, A. B., Studies on the geological and phylogenetic history of the orders of pterygote insects. Trav. Inst. Palaeont. Acad. Sci. USSR, Vol. VII, Fasc. IV, 1938.

Miall, L. C., and A. Denny, The structure and life history of the cockroach, *Periplaneta orientalis*, Kent, England: L. Reeve and Co., 1886.

Michelbacher, A. E., The biology of the garden centipede, *Scutigerella immaculata*. Hilgardia, 11:55, 1938.

Mittelstaedt, H., Prey capture in mantids (pp. 55-71). *In* (B. T. Scheer, ed.) Recent advances in invertebrate physiology. Eugene: U. of Oregon, 1957.

Muesebeck, C. F. W., What kind of insect is it? *In* Insects: the yearbook of agriculture, U.S.D.A., 1952.

Patton, R. L., Introductory insect physiology. Philadelphia: Saunders, 1963.

Remington, C. L., The Apterygota. *In* A century of progress in the natural sciences 1853-1953 (495-505). Calif. Acad. Sci., San Francisco, 1955.

Roeder, K. (ed.), Insect physiology. New York: Wiley, 1953.

Salt, R. W., Principles of insect cold-hardiness (55-74). *In* (E. A. Steinhaus and R. F. Smith, eds.) Ann. Rev. Entom., Vol. 6. Palo Alto, Calif.: Ann. Rev., Inc., 1961.

Sargent, W. D., The flight of the dragon fly. Biol. Rev. (City College of New York), 13:8, 1951.

Shrock, R. R., and W. H. Twenhofel, Principles of invertebrate paleontology (2nd ed.). New York: McGraw, 1953.

Snodgrass, R. E., Evolution of the Annelida, Onychophora, and Arthropoda. Smithson. Misc. Coll., 97:(6)1, 1938.

————, Comparative study of the head of mandibulate arthropods. Ithaca: Comstock, 1951.

————, A textbook of arthropod anatomy. Ithaca: Comstock, 1952.

————, Insect metamorphosis. Smithson. Misc. Coll., 122(9):1, 1954.

Sømme, L., Effects of glycerol on cold-hardiness in insects. Can. J. Zool., 42:87, 1964.

Tiegs, O. W., The embryology and affinities of the Symphyla, based on a study of *Hanseniella agilis*. Quart. J. Microsc. Sci., 82:1, 1940.

————, The post-embryonic development of *Hanseniella agilis* (Symphyla). *Ibid.*, 85: 191, 1945.

————, The development and affinities of the Pauropoda, based on a study of *Pauropus silvaticus*. *Ibid.*, Part I 88:165, Part II 88:275, 1947.

————, and S. M. Manton, The evolution of the Arthropoda. Biol. Rev., 33:255, 1958.

Tillyard, R. J., The evolution of the class Insecta. Papers, Roy. Soc. Tasm., (no vol.) 1-89, 1930.

Vandel, A., Généralités sur les Arthropodes. *In* (P. Grassé, ed.) Traité de zoologie, Tome VI. Paris: Masson et Cie, 1949.

Wheeler, W. M., The embryology of *Blatta germanica* and *Doryphora decimlineata*. J. Morphol., 3:291, 1889.

Wigglesworth, V. B., Insect physiology. London: Methuen, 1956.

————, The hormonal regulation of growth and reproduction in insects (pp. 247-336). *In* (J. W. L. Beament, J. E. Treherne, and V. B. Wigglesworth, eds.) Advances in insect physiology, Vol. 2. London: Academic, 1964.

Williams, S. R., Habits and structure of *Scutigerella immaculata* (Newport), Proc. Bos. Soc. Nat. Hist., 33:461, 1907.

Yonge, C. M., Evolution and adaptation in the digestive system of the Metazoa. Biol. Rev., 12:87, 1937.

Zenkevitch, L. A., The evolution of animal locomotion. J. Morphol., 77:1, 1945.

17

THE LOPHOPHORATE COELOMATES

Three small phyla will be discussed briefly in this chapter. These phyla are linked by the possession of a structure called a *lophophore,* defined by Hyman (V, p. 229) as a circumoral crown of tentacles not encompassing the anus and containing a coelomic diverticulum. All of these animals have a coelom septate between the lophophore-bearing anterior end and the lumen of the posterior body cavity. The digestive cavity loops to bring the anus near but external to the lophophore. A more general definition of lophophore permits inclusion of the Entoprocta, in which, as indicated by the name, the anus opens within the tentacle ring.

The three phyla considered here are the Phoronida, the Bryozoa (Ectoprocta), and the Brachiopoda. A number of authorities combine the Endoprocta and Ectoprocta under either the name Polyzoa or Bryozoa, but more frequently the name Ectoprocta is used as a synonym for Bryozoa.

The Phoronida, Bryozoa, and Brachiopoda all undergo holoblastic cleavage, and the division products in each case are approximately equal. A coeloblastula occurs in all three groups. In subsequent development, the mouth of the adult arises from or in the vicinity of the larval blastopore (this relationship is less clear for Ectoprocta) so that these groups belong with the protostomate coelomate animals.

Cleavage in these three phyla is commonly radial in pattern, but some Phoronida show indications of a spiral cleavage characteristic of phyla which develop a trochophore larva, and the *Actinotrocha* larva (Fig. 17-1) of the Phoronida is considered to be a modified trochophore. Ectoproct larvae are of various types. One of these, the *Cyphonautes* larva (Fig. 17-2) is often considered to be a highly modified trochophore, but other larval types bear little resemblance to the trochophore structure. The larvae of Brachiopoda (Fig. 17-3) bear still less resemblance to a trochophore. In this phylum, the origin of the coelom as indicative of phylogenetic

Fig. 17-1 Actinotroch larva with portion of body wall removed to show internal structure. After Goodrich 1904, *Quart J. Micros. Sci.* 47: 103, courtesy of the Company of Biologists Limited.

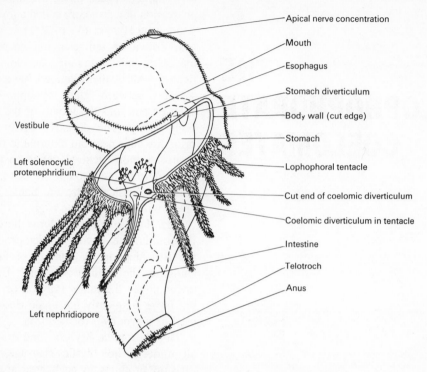

- Apical nerve concentration
- Mouth
- Esophagus
- Stomach diverticulum
- Body wall (cut edge)
- Stomach
- Lophophoral tentacle
- Cut end of coelomic diverticulum
- Coelomic diverticulum in tentacle
- Intestine
- Telotroch
- Anus

Vestibule

Left solenocytic protenephridium

Left nephridiopore

Fig. 17-2 (a) Mature cyphonautes larva (modified after Prouho 1892) and (b) early metamorphosis of cyphonautes larva (modified after Kupelweiser 1906). Both after Shrock and Twenhofel 1953, courtesy of the McGraw-Hill Book Company.

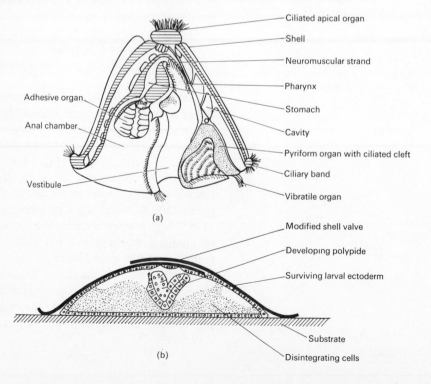

- Ciliated apical organ
- Shell
- Neuromuscular strand
- Pharynx
- Stomach
- Cavity
- Pyriform organ with ciliated cleft
- Ciliary band
- Vibratile organ

Adhesive organ

Anal chamber

Vestibule

(a)

- Modified shell valve
- Developing polypide
- Surviving larval ectoderm
- Substrate
- Disintegrating cells

(b)

relationships provokes controversy. In one subdivision, the coelom arises from gut evaginations, the enterocoelous condition generally found in Deuterostomate phyla, while in the other subdivision the coelom is schizocoelous in formation as is generally characteristic of Protostomates.

PHYLUM PHORONIDA

Phoronida are a small group of noncolonial, benthonic tube-dwellers typically in marine coastal waters of both tropical and temperate climates. They are well known on the Atlantic and Mediterranean coasts of Europe and both eastern and western shores of the United States. *Phoronis ovalis* of South America and New Zealand is the smallest species known, being about 6 mm long, while *Phoronopsis viridis* of the California coast is the largest, sometimes reaching a length of 200 mm. *P. ovalis* is well known for its bur-

rowing ability in molluscan shells and calcareous rocks, but such burrows do not replace the close-fitting secreted tube characteristically produced by phoronids. Phoronids feed on organic debris and plankton gathered by the ciliary currents of the tentacles and subsequently coated with mucus. Undesirable material can be rejected. The current flowing toward the mouth escapes at the base of the tentacles and also serves to remove wastes extruded at the anal papilla.

The Phoronida are elongated vermiform animals inhabiting a chitinous tube (usually marked by adhering sand granules and debris) produced by the secretion of epidermal glands. Phoronida are of small size, ranging from one-half to 20 centimeters in length. At the posterior end the body bulges into an end bulb, and at the anterior end a double row of tentacles often is coiled into a double scroll (Fig. 17-4). The double row of tentacles constitutes the lophophore. At the midpoint of the inner row between the scrolls,

Fig. 17-3 Generalized diagrams to illustrate brachiopod embryology. Modified after Kowalevsky 1874, from Hertwig, *A Manual of Zoology* (translated and edited by J. S. Kingsley) 1902, Holt, Rinehart & Winston, Inc.

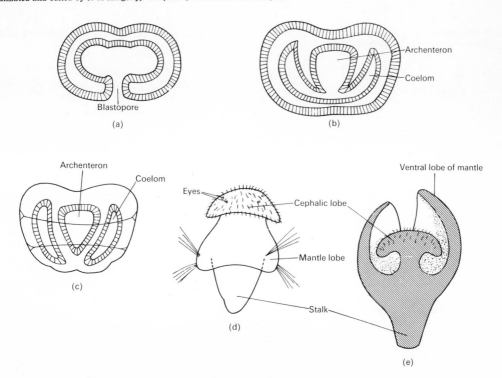

the inner row of tentacles is broken by a short proliferation zone where new tentacles are added. Between the two rows of tentacles lies the lunar-shaped mouth opening, shielded dorsally by an upper lip or *epistome*. Immediately dorsal to the tentacle-proliferation zone there is a concavity bounded laterally by the metanephridiopores and dorso-medially by the anus. This concavity functions as a brood chamber in some forms. Fertilization occurs either in the coelom or after the germ cells exit by way of the nephridia, which function as gonoducts.

The coelom is divided by a septum between a smaller anterior chamber, associated with the lophophore and provided with coelomic branches in the tentacles, and the elongate posterior chamber of the trunk (Fig. 17-5). The gonads are closely associated with the peritoneum of the trunk coelom, and the paired metanephridia lead from this chamber.

The descending limb of the alimentary canal is strongly ciliated anteriorly and becomes more weakly ciliated before it makes a U-turn in the coelom of the end bulb to run forward suspended from the dorsal wall. It opens on the anal papilla dorsal to the lophophore. Unicellular organisms compose the principal food. The nervous system is not extensively developed. A nerve net lies in the base of the epidermis and is connected with sensory cells extending to the periphery. In the region of the coelomic septum, the nerve net forms a nerve ring near the base of the lophophore somewhat concentrated beneath the area of the brood chamber. The tentacles are innervated from the nerve ring. The circulatory system is composed of a ring or horseshoe-shaped vessel beneath the lophophore, a diverticulum into each tentacle in which the blood flow is tidal, and an afferent median and an efferent lateral vessel in communication through a plexus in the neighborhood of the alimentary canal flexure. Phoronida are mostly hermaphroditic. Fertilization may be within the coelom or external, and early development may occur in the brood chamber or in sea water. The developing larva eventually becomes a ciliated, planktonic Actinotrocha feeding on microscopic marine life.

Fig. 17-4 Phoronida, diagrammatic representation of a transverse section cut through tentacle bases. After Benham 1889, *Quart. J. Micros. Sci.* 30:125, courtesy of the Company of Biologists Limited.

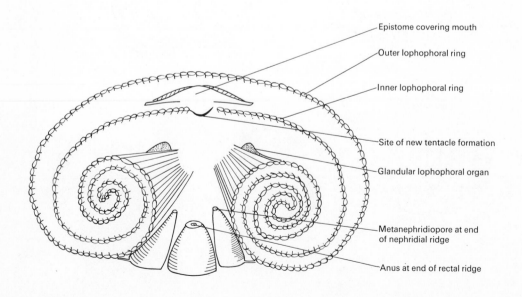

Epistome covering mouth

Outer lophophoral ring

Inner lophophoral ring

Site of new tentacle formation

Glandular lophophoral organ

Metanephridiopore at end of nephridial ridge

Anus at end of rectal ridge

PHYLUM BRYOZOA

The Bryozoa or Ectoprocta constitute a large group (nearly 4,000 living species and nearly four times as many extinct ones) of minute lophophorates living a typical sessile and colonial tubiculous existence. Only about one per cent are not marine, and Pennak reports that about fourteen species are re-

ported from fresh waters of the United States. Although most colonies are permanently attached, a few fresh-water species can move slowly. Marine colonies are attached to rocks, shells, pilings, or seaweed, and are usually found in the littoral zone below the low-tide level, although a few are found in very deep waters. The marine forms have a world-wide distribution and are common in both tropical

Fig. 17-5 Phoronida, diagrammatic representation of a sagittal section. The main features of the circulatory system are indicated by broken lines. Lateral mesenteries are not shown. Adapted from various sources.

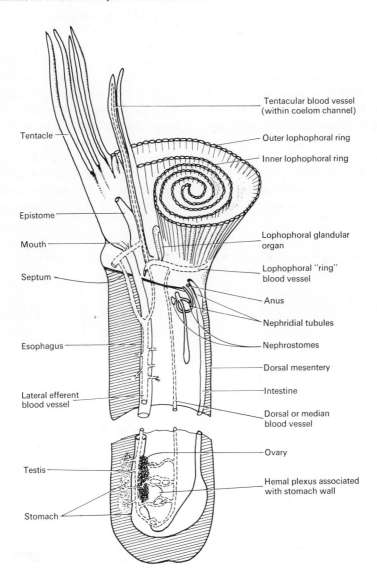

and polar coastal waters. Fresh-water species occur in shallow unpolluted waters of ponds and lakes or in streams where the current is sluggish. Bryozoa are ciliary feeders capturing plankton such as diatoms, other algae, protozoa, and minute metazoa, and rejection of larger particles has been observed. Unlike phoronids, Bryozoa are not reported to encase food particles in mucus.

The Bryozoa are minute, colonial lophophorates with a coelom divided by a somewhat incomplete septum near the base of the lophophore. Each individual or zooid of the colony has a nonliving secreted external case called the *zooecium* (Fig. 17-6), permanently fastened to the substrate or to adjacent zooecia. In many forms a zooecium is in communication with adjacent zooecia directly through pores or through intervening chambers. The chitinous walls of zooecia are usually hardened with calcium carbonate, and various devices in addition to simple thickening are used to strengthen the walls. The living portion of the zooid is called the *polypide*. It has an anterior end bearing the loph-

ophore which is retractile into the zooecium. In some ectoprocts, polymorphism results in highly modified zooids. One of these types is a beaked or jawed structure called an *avicularium*, and another type is the *vibraculum*, with a movable bristle. Both apparently function to keep the body surface free from epizoic guests. In the Class Gymnolaemata, composed almost exclusively of marine species, the lophophore or crown of tentacles is disposed as a simple ring around the eccentrically placed mouth (Fig. 17-7). In the Class Phylactolaemata, which is restricted to fresh water, the tentacles form a continuous curved row infolded on itself so that the lophophore is a double-walled horseshoe. The mouth opens centrally between the inner and outer row of tentacles, while the anus is partly encompassed by the loop of the infolded inner row. In both classes the tentacles have a coelomic lumen and lateral longitudinal tracts of cilia. The coelomic diverticula in the tentacles communicate with a ring coelom in Gymnolaemata and with a horseshoe-shaped coelomic cavity in Phylactolaemata, lying in

Fig. 17-6 Diagram of an Ectoproct, *Flustra* (c), (a) avicularium and (b) vibraculum. From Hertwig (a and b, after Claparéde; c, after Nitsche), *A Manual of Zoology* (translated and edited by J. S. Kingsley) 1902, Holt, Rinehart & Winston, Inc.

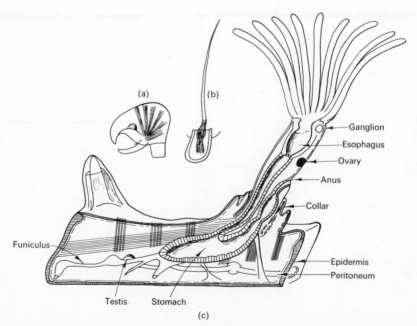

(c)

the lophophore base. The latter class differs from the former in the possession of an extension dorsal to the mouth called an *epistome*. It contains a coelomic extension considered by some authorities to be the equivalent of the head coelom (protocoel) of the tripartite coelom of deuterostomes.

Behind the retractable portion of the polypide the cavity of the zooecium is lined with a double wall: an outer epidermis and an inner coelomic peritoneum. The regionally differentiated alimentary canal is U-shaped with the stomach often extended as a caecum situated at the canal flexure. A cord called the *funiculus* attaches the stomach to the posterior wall of the coelom. The most prominent muscles are the lophophore retractors running from the lophophore to the posterior

Fig. 17-7 Diagram to illustrate some zooid features in ectoprocts.

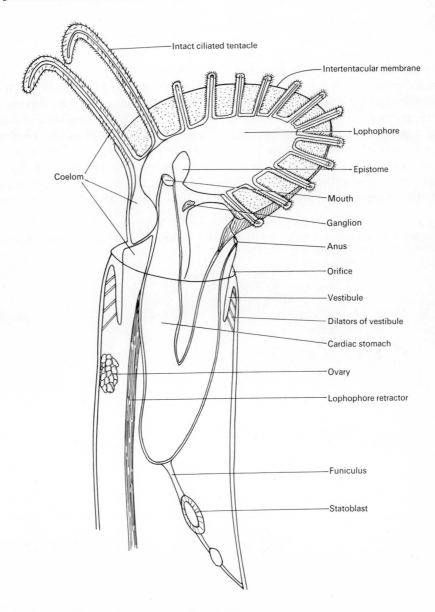

part of the zooid coelom. Other muscles function on the motile tissues of the polypide at the zooecium orifice. Most ectoprocts are monoecious. They lack gonoducts, and the gonads bulge into the coelom with the ovaries usually on the parietal peritoneal wall and the testes on the funiculus (Fig. 17-7). Fertilization occurs in the coelomic fluid, but since the gonads in hermaphroditic zooids do not usually ripen simultaneously, sperm must be introduced in some unexplained fashion from other zooids. Brooding of developing young is common in brood chambers within the coelom with embryos subsequently escaping through degeneration of the parent zooid or through rupture of the body wall. Fresh-water ectoprocts, besides budding, reproduce asexually by the production of statoblasts (Fig. 17-8). These are biconvex discoidal capsules composed of paired shell-valves and sometimes armed with hooks.

The nervous system consists of a ring enlarged dorsally as a so-called ganglion in the base of the lophophore supplying the tentacles with efferent and afferent tracts. The nerve ring is in communication with a sub-epithelial nerve net and with nerves in the digestive tract. Nephridia do not occur in Bryozoa. Reddish-brown masses, which are waste products, do occur in stomach epithelial cells and in coelomic and peritoneal cells. Accumulation of such material, known as brown bodies, is often present in the coelom and is associated with degeneration of part of the polypide.

PHYLUM BRACHIOPODA

Because of their shape in profile, which bears a similarity to ancient lamps, the Brachiopoda are known by the common name of lamp shells. They were once considered to be molluscs because of the bivalved shell, but the valves are respectively dorsal and ventral rather than lateral as in the Lamellibranchia. The shell with its muscle scars (and in one class (Articulata) hinge teeth and

Fig. 17-8 Ectoprocta, *Cristatella mucedo*: (a) colony, (b) colony enlarged, (c) statoblast (ventral view), and (d) statoblast (profile). After Rogick in *Fresh-Water Biology* 1959, courtesy of John Wiley & Sons, Inc.

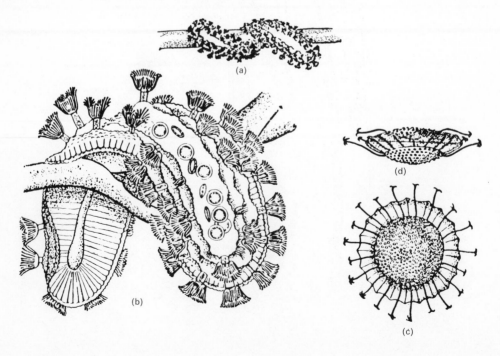

sockets), lophophoric support internally, and its shape and sculptured features externally, is of paramount importance in identification. These features survive well in fossilization. Only about 250 living species have been described, but one hundred times as many fossil species are known. There are some debatable Precambrian records of Brachiopod fossils. Roger (Traité de Zoologie) lists 34 superfamilies of which 27 are extinct. Brachiopods were most numerous in the Middle Paleozoic Era.

All brachiopods are sessile or pedunculate marine animals, although the lingulids do not have the permanent attachment characteristic of the others. Brachiopoda have a world-wide distribution mostly in continental shelf waters below low tide, but a good many occur in very deep water. These animals are ciliary feeders, with water entering the shell laterally and being expelled medially. The food current is directed along the lophophoral spirals with tentacular cilia serving as continuous filters. Eventually the adjacent lophophoral cilia direct the food current into the median brachial groove within which the mucus-coated particles are carried to the mouth. During this process, larger particles have fallen through the tentacular current to be discarded by ciliary action of the ventral mantle lobe. The food consists of various

suspended organisms, with diatoms most important for many brachiopods, but the more active lingulids accept a much wider variety of food or have less success in discarding unwanted material. Lingulids have complete ciliation of the tentacles not present in other brachiopods, and lateral ciliary currents are accessory for discharge of some products. The foregoing account is adapted from Hyman.

Brachiopods (Fig. 17-9) are for the most part firmly affixed to the substrate, usually cemented at the end of the stalk or peduncle, or by the ventral valve if the peduncle is reduced or missing. They vary in length from

Fig. 17-10 Brachiopoda, a living *Lingula* in its burrow and extended. After Berry 1929, courtesy of the McGraw-Hill Book Company.

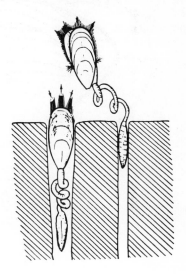

Fig. 17-9 Brachiopoda, *Magellania* (-*Waldheimia*) shell cut away to show internal organs. From Hertwig (from Zittel), *A Manual of Zoology* (translated and edited by J. S. Kingsley) 1902, Holt, Rinehart & Winston, Inc.

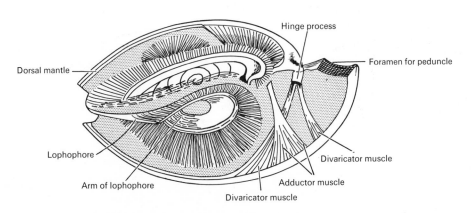

Hinge process

Dorsal mantle

Foramen for peduncle

Lophophore

Divaricator muscle

Arm of lophophore

Adductor muscle

Divaricator muscle

a few millimeters to nearly a foot and many are wider than they are long, but the majority are under three inches in their greatest dimension.

The phylum is divided into two classes based on the presence or absence of a hinge at the posterior end formed by tooth-and-groove modifications of the two valves. This feature is characteristic of Class Articulata. In the other class (Inarticulata) such a hinge is lacking and the valves are attached to each other by muscles, resulting in a greater flexibility in movement. In the inarticulate genus *Lingula* (Fig. 17-10) the animal lives in a vertical burrow anchored semipermanently by an elongate peduncle. The shell may pro-

Fig. 17-11 Brachipoda, *Magellania*, showing the muscle system of a modern articulate brachiopod: (a) left lateral view of the shell, with part removed. The muscle scars of the brachial valve are shown as though they could be seen through a transparent shell, and the scars of the pedicle valve are shown on the imaginary mirror surface directly beneath the shell; (b) through (c) diagrams showing the actions of the muscles when the valves are pulled together and apart, respectively. After Shrock and Twenhofel 1953 (modified from Hancock 1859), courtesy of the McGraw-Hill Book Company.

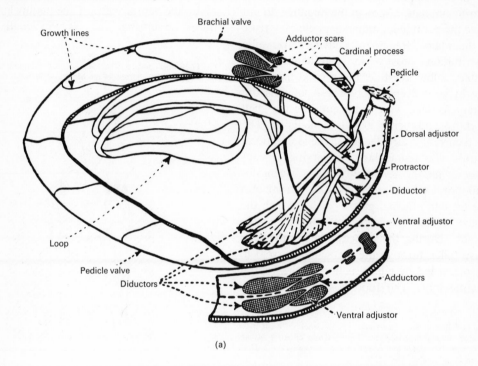

(a)

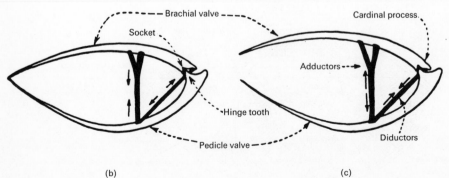

(b)

(c)

trude slightly, but can be retracted if the animal is disturbed. Of necessity, the muscle system in the Inarticulata is much more complex than in the hinged group.

Within the shell, the body of the animal is concentrated near the pedunculate or posterior end. Where the body itself is not in contact with the shell, the body wall projects as a double-walled sheet, the *mantle,* to line both shell valves. The mantle secretes the shell, and since it frequently has elongate papillae on its outer surface, vertical channels are formed in the shell which extend to the outer layer called the *periostracum.* Coelomic diverticula remain in the mantle as pallial or mantle sinuses and their distribution is often evident on fossil shells.

In the Articulata an internal skeleton, the *brachidium,* commonly projects forward from an attachment near the hinge of the dorsal valve (Fig. 17-11). The brachidium may vary from a pair of prongs to a variously recurved loop in existing brachiopods.

The lophophore develops on the anterior aspect of the brachiopod body. In its simplest form it is composed of a ring of ciliated tentacles surrounding the mouth. As is characteristic of lophophorates, the anus is not encompassed by the tentacular ring in members of the class Inarticulata, while in the Articulata the alimentary canal ends blindly so that there is no anus. Usually the base of the lophophore follows an undulating or sinuous course to produce lobations. Rarely a

Fig. 17-12 View of the left half of *Cistella(-Argyrotheca).* After Shipley 1895, courtesy of the original publishers of *Cambridge Natural History,* Vol. III, Macmillan & Co., Ltd.

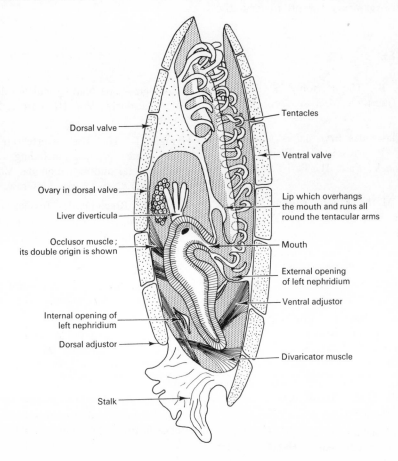

Dorsal valve

Tentacles

Ventral valve

Ovary in dorsal valve

Liver diverticula

Lip which overhangs the mouth and runs all round the tentacular arms

Occlusor muscle; its double origin is shown

Mouth

External opening of left nephridium

Ventral adjustor

Internal opening of left nephridium

Dorsal adjustor

Divaricator muscle

Stalk

simple bilobate condition is retained, but more commonly the lateral lobes elongate enormously and may be thrown into spirals. In some species a median lobe also develops extensively. The median mouth has a dorsal lip called the brachial fold or epistome. This brachial fold extends laterally in the lateral lobes of the lophophore. A portion of the coelomic cavity occurs in the brachial fold of inarticulates but is usually obliterated in Articulata. Medially there is a coelomic cavity in the lophophore with branches into the tentacles, into the lateral lobes or arms of the lophophore, and into somewhat discontinuous channels in the mantle. A septum may or may not be present between the lophophoric coelom and the body coelom, which contains the usual coelomic organs and through which course the muscles to the shell.

The food of brachiopods is composed of microscopic organisms swept toward the mouth by the cilia on the tentacles. A large digestive gland opens into the cilia-lined alimentary canal not far behind the mouth (Fig. 17-12). A pair of metanephridia (rarely two pairs) opens to the mantle cavity. In addition to excretory function, they serve as gonoducts for these commonly dioecious animals. A few brachiopods brood their young, usually in the base of the lophophore or in the mantle cavity. The nervous system consists of a small ganglion above and a larger ganglion below the foregut connected by commissures. From these ganglia various nerves run to tentacles, muscles, and other organs. A contractile tube in a mesentery dorsal to the anterior gut represents the heart of the circulatory system. It connects with lacunae around the digestive tract and has branches into the tentacles, mantle lobes, and gonads.

REFERENCES

Benham, W. B., The anatomy of *Phoronis australis*. Quart. J. Microsc. Sci., 30:125, 1889.

Brien, P., Classe des Bryozoaires (pp. 1053-1335). *In* (P. Grassé, ed.) Traité de zoologie, Tome V, Fasc. II. Paris: Masson et Cie, 1960.

Bulman, O. M. B., Muscle systems of some inarticulate brachiopods. Geol. Mag., 76: 434, 1939.

Dawydoff, C., Classe des Phoronidiens (pp. 1008-1053). *In* (P. Grassé, ed.) Traité de zoologie, Tome V, Fasc. I. Paris: Masson et Cie, 1959.

de Beauchamp, Classe des Brachiopodes (pp. 1380-1430). *In* (P. Grassé, ed.) Traité de zoologie, Tome V, Fasc. II. Paris: Masson et Cie, 1960.

Hancock, A., On the organization of the Brachiopoda. Philos. Trans. Roy. Soc. London, 148:791, 1859.

Helmcke, J., Brachiopods. *In* (W. Kükenthal and T. Krumbach, eds.) Handbuch der Zoologie—eine Naturgeschichte der Stämme des Tierreichs, Vol. III, Part 2, 2:139-262, 1939.

Hyman, L. H., The invertebrates: smaller coelomate groups, including Phoronida, Ectoprocta, and Brachiopoda, Vol. V. (pp. 228-609). New York: McGraw, 1959.

Roger, J., Brachiopodes fossiles (pp. 1431-1499). *In* (P. Grassé, ed.) Traité de zoologie, Tome V, Fasc. II. Paris: Masson et Cie, 1960.

Rogick, M. D., Bryozoa (pp. 495-507). *In* (W. T. Edmondson, ed.) Ward and Whipple's Fresh-water biology (2nd ed.). New York: Wiley, 1959.

Shrock, R. R., and W. H. Twenhofel, Brachiopoda (pp. 260-349). *In* Principles of invertebrate paleontology (2nd ed.). New York: McGraw, 1953.

Williams, A., The calcareous shell of the Brachiopods and its importance in their classification. Biol. Rev., 31:243, 1956.

18

ECHINODERMATA

Nearly everyone who has visited a natural history museum, taken high school biology, or walked along the seashore will remember starfish or sea stars. The beautiful, typically pentamerous symmetry of starfish etches the observer's memory, while the durability and convenient size of the starfish skeleton makes it easy to collect and handle them. One sees the radial, five-armed symmetry and feels that the skeleton is knobby or studded with spines. In the living starfish, epidermis covers the skeleton and follows the contour of the spines, so that actually the skeleton is internal. The phylum name, Echinodermata, meaning spiny skin, was first applied not to starfish but to a related group.

Examination of the dried starfish skeleton fails to reveal another unique characteristic of the phylum. This feature is the presence of fluid-filled *tube-feet* or *podia* which project through the skeleton from channels of coelomic origin and which usually can be modified terminally to form suction cups useful in locomotion or in opening a mollusc for a seafood dinner. In some starfish whose habitat is loose sand or mud, the tube-feet taper to blunt diverticula and these cannot form suction cups.

Since adult starfish have radial symmetry, there is an absence of head structures usually evident in bilaterally symmetrical animals. Consequently, the terms anterior and posterior are not applicable. The mouth opening designates the oral aspect of the animal, and in the usual position, this is on the animal's lower side and against the substrate. The tube-feet protrude along grooves or zones called *ambulacra* radiating from the mouth. The upper aspect is called the aboral surface; in typical starfish the anus opens centrally on it. Another order of star-shaped echinoderms have slender snakelike arms (hence the name of Ophiuroidea) sharply separated from a central disc. In this group tube-feet or podia occur on the oral side of the arms, which lack ambulacral grooves. The primary function of the podia is sensory. The mouth opens from a pentagonal jawed cavity into a short esophagus. The stomach is a caecum and has no communication with the aboral surface. Because ophiuroid arms break readily, the name of brittle-star is often applied to members of this order.

The Echinoidea (sea urchins, sand dollars, and relatives), with about 800 living species, vary from a spheroid to a flattened discoidal shape. They can best be compared to a starfish with its five arms recurved and fused terminally around a relatively small aboral disc. The pentaradiate grooves with tube-feet radiate from the oral mouth up to the aboral area. Some echinoids have developed a tertiary bilateral symmetry.

Starfish belong to the order Asteroidea containing about 1,600 living species, which is somewhat less than one-third the total number of extant species in this phylum. Remarkable variation in structure has already been noted in our brief comparison of Asteroidea, Ophiuroidea, and Echinoidea, but the remaining two orders with living representatives show even greater differences. The Crinoidea contains about 70 living species, but it has a vast if not well-delineated family tree of fossil relatives. Crinoids are attached during part or all of their life cycle. The attached forms of about 75 species are somewhat flowerlike echinoderms with the oral surface on the upper side. The arms and small side branches called *pinnules* are grooved on the upper surface. Suitable organic detritus falling through the water is directed by the tube-feet into the grooves, in which it is swept toward the mouth in mucus activated by cilia. Once again ciliary feeding is seen, and in the Echinodermata it is almost certainly the primitive method of feeding.

As Nichols points out, crinoids not only are the first echinoderms in the paleontological record, but were sufficiently conservative to retain a primitive morphology. While some extant crinoids retain the stalk throughout life, in others (the *comatulids*) the stalk is early discarded for an unattached existence. This latter group is most abundant in the relatively shallow waters of southeastern

Asia. Stalked crinoids and some comatulids occur in much deeper water and have a wider distribution. Whereas comatulids are found among coral formations and other rocky substrates, stalked forms are more often found where the ocean bottom is silt-covered. Crinoids are also found in Arctic and Antarctic waters.

The fifth order is called Holothuroidea. These are elongate cylindrical animals which are pear-shaped, wormlike, or with about the proportions of a cucumber. This last similarity has supplied the common name for the group. The mouth is at one end and the anus is at the other. The skeleton is reduced to spicules embedded in a tough, leathery skin. Five radii of tube-feet extend back from the mouth. One of these might be described as medioventral in position. The tube-feet on this radii and on the ones immediately adjacent often terminate in suckers, while the two dorsal ones are more in the form of papillae.

Echinodermata are marine animals which, lacking mechanisms to accommodate salinity change, are restricted to a sea-water habitat. The body fluids are in balance with the sea water, and even brackish water cannot be tolerated. This is a very old phylum, well substantiated by fossils, but its embryological development brings it to or near the stem leading to the Chordata.

Echinoderm species tend to be gregarious, as evidenced not only by studies of living forms but also by fossil collections. Hyman gives an extensive discussion of geographical distribution for each of the living classes and has pointed out the interesting fact that intertidal or littoral species in all classes with the possible exception of the Asteroidea are in greatest concentration at the conjunction of the Indian and Pacific Oceans. In general, Echinodermata are widely distributed both geographically and bathometrically. As is to be expected in animals with stout skeletal parts, there is a rich fossil history, naturally sparse in the Holothuroidea which lack a skeleton of fused plates. Among crinoids, some 700 living and 5,000 fossil species have been described. Many more fossil species than modern also are known for the Echinoidea. For both the Asteroidea and the Ophiuroidea, modern species greatly outnumber those from the fossil record. For the phylum as a whole, about 5,300 living species have been described.

Echinoderms are coelomate animals. The coelom is derived from outpockets of the archenteron, and these together with mesenchyme give rise to the mesoderm. In most echinoderms the coelom is large and within it lie various organs, particularly the digestive tract and gonads. These, encased in coelomic epithelium, are suspended by mesenteries in development, although the mesenteries are frequently obliterated to some degree in adults. Coelomic fluid is kept in motion by cilia.

A particularly distinctive feature in this phylum is the water-vascular system. It is a derivative of the developing coelom and frequently continues to communicate with the definitive coelom. Qualitatively and osmotically, fluids in the two systems are very similar.

In the adult echinoderm, a tube of the water-vascular system surrounds the pharynx. This so-called water ring arises from the asymmetrical development of a portion of the left anterior coelom of the bilateral larva. It communicates with the external environment through a canal which opens to the aboral surface except in Ophiuroidea. Later, the canal is commonly thickened with calcareous accumulation and is then called the *stone canal*. In many echinoderms the stone canal opens to the exterior through a perforated surface plate called the *madreporite*, eccentrically located on the aboral aspect in Asteroidea and Echinoidea. In Holothuroidea and in Crinoidea the terminal end of the canal is lost and a newly formed madreporic body opens from the shortened canal directly into the coelom.

The most consistent feature of the water ring in echinoderms is the presence of the radial canals which lie under the ambulacral

rays or grooves. Branches from each radial canal pass through the body wall to terminate as podia on the oral face of the *ambulacrum*. In Crinoidea each lateral branch subdivides to give rise to a group of three podia. Among most other echinoderms, locomotor podia often with a terminal suctorial disc are each supplied internally with an *ampulla*, which is a small spherical or elongate reservoir whose contraction forces water into the *podium* or tube-foot. In the Holothuroidea, locomotory tube-feet are apt to persist only along those ambulacra against the substrate, with the others reverting to a papillary shape. Most asteroid and echinoid podia are locomotory in function and are provided with *ampullae*. In the Echinoidea, podia not in contact with the substrate are apt to be papillate. Ampullae associated with podia are absent in the Ophiuroidea, and the podia function as small sensory tentacles.

The nervous system of adult echinoderms does not show the specialized concentrations characteristic of bilaterally symmetrical animals. It consists of three radially distributed networks. The superficial oral network, which is the principal system of most echinoderms, is concentrated into radial strands adjacent to or a part of the epidermis of the ambulacral grooves connected with a ring around the mouth. The radial distribution of the deep oral or hyponeural network in many echinoderms is separated from the superficial oral network only by a thin layer of connective tissue or by narrow sinuses. It appears to be primarily motor and is associated with wall muscle in Holothuroidea, muscles in the arms of Ophiuroidea, and with *Aristotle's lantern* in the Echinoidea, particularly. The aboral system is well developed only in the Crinoidea, presumably the most primitive of living echinoderms. In the crinoids it occurs as a concave disc in the bottom of the *calyx* and it innervates the stalk, cirri, arms, and pinnules. This system is absent in Holothuroidea. Although reduced in both Echinoidea and Ophiuroidea, part of it appears to persist to innervate the gonads. In asteroids, a third network occurs which sends branches to the gonads, but Hyman points out that it may not be homologous to the aboral system of crinoids.

CLASS CRINOIDEA

This group of echinoderms occurs in two closely related structural forms. Stalked forms called sea lilies (Fig. 18-1) compose less than 13 per cent of living crinoids and are found from the lower edge of the neritic zone and on into very deep water (Fig. 1-2). Conditions here approach uniformity with minimal light, constant temperature, and slight water agitation.

Most crinoids possess a stalk only during developmental stages, and a common name

Fig. 18-1 Crinoid Echinoderm, sea-lily. From Schechter 1959, courtesy of Prentice-Hall, Inc.

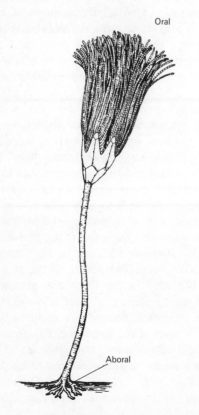

Oral

Aboral

for the stalkless adult is feather star (Fig. 18-2). In development of crinoids the principal viscera develop in a pentagonate enlargement called the crown, which varies from a discoid to an ovoid shape. The transitory or permanent stalk is attached to the aboral aspect of the crown. The pentagonal stalk consists basically of a series of endoskeletal elements called *columnals,* and alternately these usually carry a whorl of projections called *cirri.* Most crinoids which have lost the stalk nevertheless retain a whorl of cirri connected with the aboral surface. These cirri may function as attachment devices, or if spread out, they would serve to keep the feather star from sinking into soft substrate.

The aboral portion of the crown is the cup-shaped calyx. Jointed pentamerous arms or *brachia* (Fig. 18-3) arise from its rim. Dichotomous branching and irregular replacement of lost arms account for some asymmetry in the group. Side branches called *pinnules* occur in alternate fashion on the brachia of many crinoids. Ambulacral grooves with underlying canals of the water-vascular system occur on the oral faces of the arms and many of the pinnules. The crown is roofed by a somewhat flexible membrane called the *tegmen,* analogous to the oral structure of fused plates in the theca of many fossil echinoderms. The tegmen contains various unfused plates or small ossicles and from its upper surface a multitude of tiny pores open to ciliated canals leading to underlying coelomic cavities. The water canals converge from the brachia into typically five radial canals which approach the mouth symmetrically

Fig. 18-2 Crinoid Echinoderm, feather-star. From Schechter 1959, courtesy of Prentice-Hall, Inc.

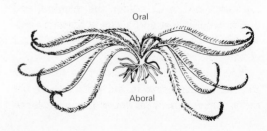

Oral

Aboral

when the latter is central on the tegmen. When the mouth is displaced laterally, asymmetry of the converging radial canals occurs.

The radial canals join a ring or pentagonal canal which surrounds the mouth. Tubes called *stone canals* open from the ring canal into the coelom, but there is no *madreporite* opening externally. Buccal podia also arise directly from the ring canal.

Crinoids fundamentally are sessile animals dependent for their food upon the organic detritus that is sinking through the water above them. Normally, the food-collecting area faces this "rain." The food grooves which occur on arms and pinnules in Crinoids are lined with tube-feet and cilia. In *Antedon,* these tube-feet occur in

groups of three of descending length. Apparently under stimulation from food, these tube-feet or podia whip about, throwing out strings of mucus to entrap the food. Subsequently the food-laden mucus string is passed medially to the successively shorter tube feet and eventually to the cilia whose action transports it to the mouth. Contamination of waste from the anus is reduced for some comatulids since this aperture is at the end of a flexible papilla. In some crinoids, food grooves that are near the anus are largely nonfunctional.

The mouth leads to a short esophagus which runs aborally to join the intestine. The latter moves to the periphery of the calyx cavity and forms a loop of one or four coils around the cavity before again turning

Fig. 18-3 Transverse section through *Antedon* arm, Crinoidea. After Cuénot 1948, in *Traité de Zoologie,* Tome XI (P. Grassé, ed.), courtesy of Masson et Cie.

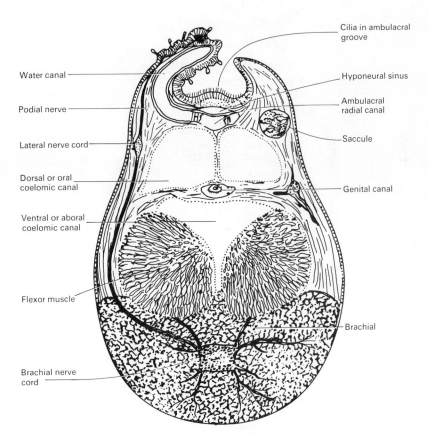

toward the aboral surface. The rectum opens through a prolongation of the body wall called the anal tube. Water can be forcibly ejected through this exit by contraction.

There do not appear to be any special organs of excretion or respiration. The communication of the coelom with the water-vascular system through the stone canals on the one hand, and with the external environment via the ciliated canals of the tegmen on the other, probably provides amply for respiration. It has been suggested that the ejection of water by the anal tube may also serve a respiratory function. Excretion is

likely accomplished by phagocytic coelomocytes for nonsoluble wastes, and soluble wastes may be discharged into water-vascular and coelomic channels.

Genital cells occur in the arms or more commonly in specialized pinnules located midway on the arms (Fig. 18-4). Spawning occurs with marked periodicity. Pinnules break to release the germ cells into the sea where fertilization occurs. Holoblastic, radial cleavage eventually gives rise to a *doliolaria* larva, which is an oval or barrel-shaped stage with four or five bands of cilia. This larva attaches during metamorphosis (Fig. 18-5).

Fig. 18-4 Transverse section of a pinnule, female *Antedon*. After Cuénot 1948, in *Traité de Zoologie*, Tome XI (P. Grassé, ed.), courtesy of Masson et Cie.

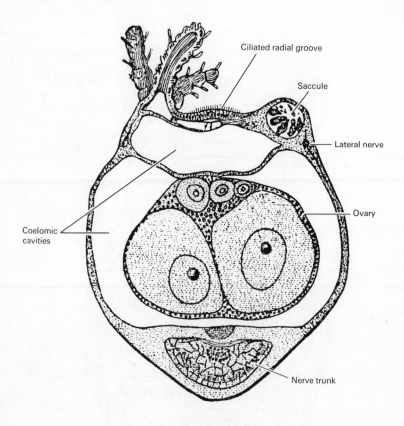

Ciliated radial groove

Saccule

Lateral nerve

Ovary

Coelomic cavities

Nerve trunk

CLASS HOLOTHUROIDEA

The echinoderms in this class are elongated along the oral-aboral axis and vary from robust to slender wormlike cylinders (Fig. 18-6). A common name for representatives in this class is sea cucumbers. Typically, they recline on one side with a median and two latero-ventral ambulacral rays against the substrate. The other two rays are latero-dorsal in position. At the oral end of the sea cucumber a ring of retractile buccal tentacles, which are modified podia, frame the mouth. The anus is at the aboral end of the animal and like the mouth may be displaced dorsally or ventrally. A single dorsal gonopore, sometimes supported by a genital papilla, opens on or near the base of the buccal tentacles. In most holothuroids the hydropore is not retained as an external opening of the water-vascular system, but in those forms in which it persists, the location is near the gonopore. More commonly one or more newly formed madreporic bodies open directly to the coelom.

Some sea cucumbers exhibit the pentaradiate distribution of ambulacra characteristic of echinoderms by the presence of five

Fig. 18-5 Development of *Antedon bifida.* (a), (b), and (c) Larva prior to attachment; (d) shortly after attachment; (e) pentacrinoid stage of larva immediately after complete separation of oral plates, with cup closed; (f) pentacrinoid larva immediately after complete separation of orals, expanded, with some of the arms shown; (g) theca, showing how the calyx can be closed by folding of the oral plates: (h) a stemless adult, provided with basal cirri. After Shrock and Twenhofel 1953 (adapted from A. H. Clark 1921, (a, b, c, d, e, and f) chiefly after W. Thomson 1865, Vol. 155 and (g) after W. B. Carpenter 1866, Vol. 156, *Philos. Trans. Roy. Soc.,* London)

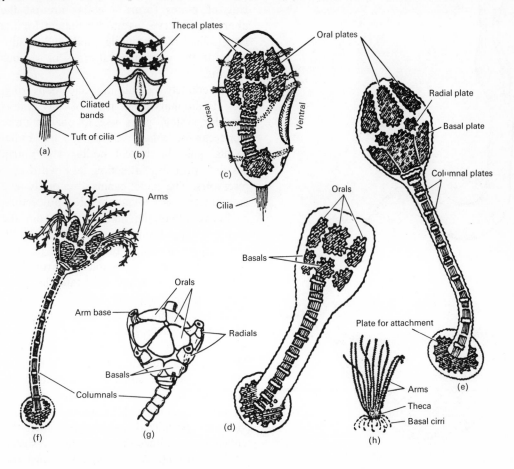

rows of tube-feet. These are locomotor podia, often modified by the presence of a terminal sucking disc or concavity. More commonly, the podia of the latero-dorsal rays have reverted to a papillate (or sometimes a wartlike) structure and with the spread of podia into the interradii, the distribution of rays is obscured.

. While the body wall is very thin in a few holothuroids, typically it has a thick, somewhat leathery consistency, and is supported

Fig. 18-6 (a) Holothuroidea, *Synapta roseola* and (b) *Thyone briareus*. After Coe 1912, courtesy Conn. Geol. and Nat. Hist. Survey.

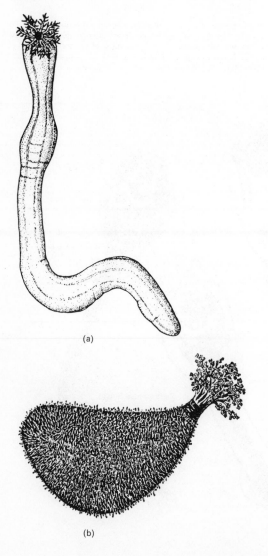

(a)

(b)

internally by radial muscle bands. Externally it may exhibit radially or generally distributed warts and papillate or locomotor podia. Pigment granules, mostly in dark shades, are present in the skin. So-called ossicles or spicules which form the embryological remnants of the endoskeleton occur in the skin. The ossicles vary from monoactinal rod types through numerous antler, pedestal, and wheel shapes. Variously perforated discs and cylinders often form components of these bizarre structures. Ossicles are generally minute. Taxonomists have developed an extensive terminology naming them, since each species develops a characteristic assortment.

An additional skeletal element in Holothuroidea occurs as a calcareous ring at the oral end of the animal (Fig. 18-7). This ring of plates forms a collar around the pharynx. It serves as an attachment for the longitudinal radial muscle bands and as support for the circumbuccal rings of various systems.

Immediately behind the calcareous ring, the circumpharyngeal ring of the watervascular system gives rise to one or more stone canals, *polian vesicles,* the five radial canals, and the buccal podia. The polian vesicles probably function as hydrostatic reservoirs. The radial canals loop orally past the calcareous collar before proceeding backward along the ambulacra. From the oral loop large branches, each provided with a diverticulum which functions as an ampulla, lead into the tentacles. From the radial canals, branches penetrate the body wall to supply the podia.

Sea cucumbers employ one of two general methods of feeding. Some of them feed on plankton or organic matter living and dead on the surface of the ocean floor around them. The tentacles, which are actually dendritic tube-feet, are swept over the adjacent area and food is garnered by mucus on these specialized appendages. Then the tentacles, sometimes in very orderly fashion, are bent around and wiped off against the

Fig. 18-7 Sagittal section through anterior region of *Cucumaria*. After Cuénot 1948, in *Traité de Zoologie*, Tome XI (P. Grassé, ed.), courtesy of Masson et Cie.

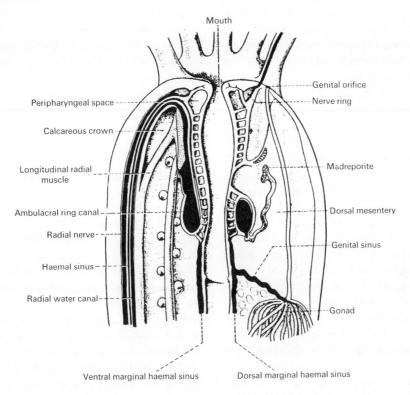

Mouth

Peripharyngeal space

Calcareous crown

Longitudinal radial muscle

Ambulacral ring canal

Radial nerve

Haemal sinus

Radial water canal

Genital orifice

Nerve ring

Madreporite

Dorsal mesentery

Genital sinus

Gonad

Ventral marginal haemal sinus

Dorsal marginal haemal sinus

Fig. 18-8 Composite diagram of a sea-cucumber such as *Cucumaria* (order Dendrochirota) dissected from the right ventro-lateral aspect.

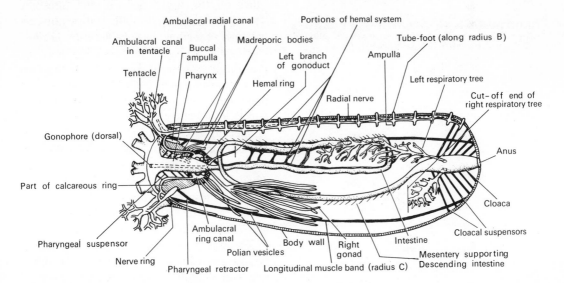

Ambulacral radial canal

Portions of hemal system

Ambulacral canal in tentacle

Buccal ampulla

Madreporic bodies

Tube-foot (along radius B)

Left branch of gonoduct

Ampulla

Tentacle

Pharynx

Hemal ring

Left respiratory tree

Radial nerve

Cut-off end of right respiratory tree

Gonophore (dorsal)

Anus

Part of calcareous ring

Cloaca

Pharyngeal suspensor

Ambulacral ring canal

Body wall

Right gonad

Intestine

Cloacal suspensors

Nerve ring

Polian vesicles

Mesentery supporting Descending intestine

Pharyngeal retractor

Longitudinal muscle band (radius C)

oral ring. Other holothurians simply push the surface substrate material into the mouth, while burrowing forms swallow much of the material through which they are progressing. Food may include protozoa, algae, nematodes, small crustacea, and bits of dead organic matter.

The mouth opens into a tubular pharynx supported within the calcareous collar by suspensors (Fig. 18-8). Following successively are a short esophagus, a muscular stomach, a long thin intestine, and a short rectum which opens to the exterior or to a terminal enlargement supported by suspensors and called a cloaca. Slight constrictions occur immediately behind the pharynx and the stomach. The anterior part of the intestine lies adjacent to the dorsal interradius, where it is supported by the dorsal mesentery (Fig. 18-9). In the posterior third of the animal the intestine loops to run forward along the right side. It is also supported by a mesentery. The alimentary canal loops again to run caudally along the lower left side.

Evaginated from the cloaca, sometimes with a common stem, is a pair of highly branched tubules known as *respiratory trees*. They are supported by remnants of mesen-

teries and may extend well forward in the body cavity. Arising from the base of the respiratory trees many holothuroids possess simple tubular diverticula called *tubules of Cuvier*. These can be everted through the anus by way of a fissure which develops in the cloacal wall, and apparently function to retard enemies either by an entangling adhesive action or by liberation of a toxin. Toxin formation has been repeatedly demonstrated, and in fact some primitive people used crushed sea cucumbers to aid in catching fish, which appear to be drugged into inactivity. The source of the toxin is not limited to Cuvierian tubules. Sea cucumbers are able to regenerate the eviscerated and broken-off tubules as well as to repair the cloacal fissure.

Echinoderms possess a system of channels or sinuses in connective tissue, encased in coelomic epithelium, which is usually called a blood lacunar or hemal system. It is well developed in Holothuroidea. An irregular hemal ring encircles the pharynx in the vicinity of the water ring. Radial lacunae, giving off branches to tentacles and podia, parallel the radial water-vascular canals. Lacunae run backward from the ring along the intestine, one on the ventral and the other on the dorsal side of the intestine. The dorsal lacuna exhibits contractility. A network of lacunar tufts called *rete mirabile* carries blood from the ascending intestine into the dorsal sinus. The gonad is supplied by a branch from the dorsal lacuna. Depending on the species, the fluid in this system is increasingly colored with hemoglobin in special cells, and it will coagulate. It has marked similarity to coelomic fluid and the two systems often communicate directly. The special functions of the hemal system are the transport of nutrients from the intestine and the production of cells called coelomocytes.

Respiration in sea cucumbers is a function of the respiratory trees. Water is forced into and evacuated from the trees by their own contractility and by the pumping action

Fig. 18-9 Transverse section of *Holothuria tubulosa*. From Hertwig (after Ludwig) *A Manual of Zoology* (translated and edited by J. S. Kingsley) 1902, Holt, Rinehart & Winston, Inc.

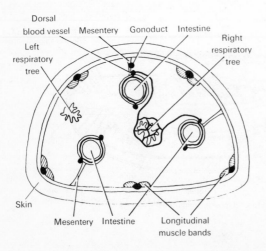

of the cloaca. Excretion is accomplished by diffusion directly, or into body fluids, or into cavities which communicate with the exterior. Coelomocytes are active in the transfer of insoluble materials. In the order Apoda special ciliated funnels called *urns*, situated along mesenteries, are loci for phagocytic coelomocytes and function in excretion. Some insoluble wastes may be retained in the coelom as so-called brown bodies.

Sea cucumbers possess a single multitubular gonad, usually attached to the dorsal mesentery, with a single gonoduct opening dorsally. Spawning is seasonal and fertilization occurs in sea water. Except for the few species which brood the young, the freefloating egg is relatively yolkless. It undergoes holoblastic cleavage which ultimately develops into a free-swimming larva, possessing a long, undulating, symmetrical band of cilia or flagella. This larval stage (Fig. 18-10) is an *auricularia*. Later this ciliary band becomes discontinuous, with some fragments realigning to form a series of circumferential bands around an ovate larval stage similar to that of the Crinoidea and, like it, named *doliolaria*. The ventral stomodaeal invagination which forms the mouth is recessed by invagination of the

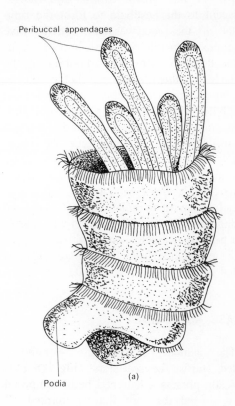

Fig. 18-10 Metamorphosis of Holothuroidea. (a) Pentactula of *Holothuria*, (b), (c), and (d) transformation of an auricularia to a doliolaria. After Dawydoff 1948, (a through c, after Semon; d, after J. Müller) in *Traité de Zoologie*, Tome XI (P. Grassé, ed.) courtesy of Masson et Cie.

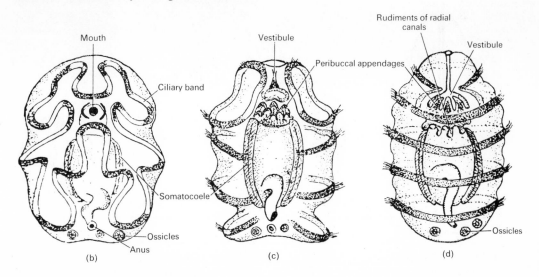

thickened wall. This second invagination, common in echinoderms, is called the *vestibule*. A larval coelomic element called the *hydrocoel* has grown around the foregut adjacent to the vestibule to form the ring-canal of the water-vascular system. Five lobations from this ring push into the vestibular floor to form the primordia of the tentacles. In this metamorphosis the body of the larva is reoriented, the originally ventral vestibule being shifted to the anterior end, with simultaneous loss of the preoral portion of the larva. In the meantime the radial canals have started to develop, the future median ventral one well in advance of the others. It develops one or two podia well ahead of the other radial canals. This stage, with an expanded vestibule from which arise five primary tentacles, and with one or two podia protruding from the posterior end, is called a *pentactula* (Fig. 18-10).

CLASS ASTEROIDEA

The members of this class, commonly called starfish or sea stars (Fig. 18-11), typically possess a flattened body composed of a central disc not sharply marked off from five symmetrical arms. The anus lies centrally on the aboral disc, except in those forms in which the digestive tract ends blindly. The madreporic plate occurs off

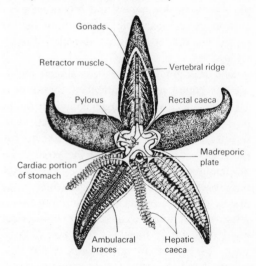

Fig. 18-11 Anatomy of starfish, *Asterias vulgaris*. After Coe 1912, courtesy Conn. Geol. and Nat. Hist. Survey.

Fig. 18-12 Calcareous plates of *Asterias* Pedicellariae. The jaws are activated by appropriate muscle insertions. (a) Major pedicellaria, *Asterias vulgaris*, (b) minor pedicellaria, *Asterias tenera*, (c) major pedicellaria, *Asterias forbesi*, and (d) minor pedicellaria, *Asterias forbesi*. After Coe 1912, courtesy Conn. Geol. and Nat. Hist. Survey.

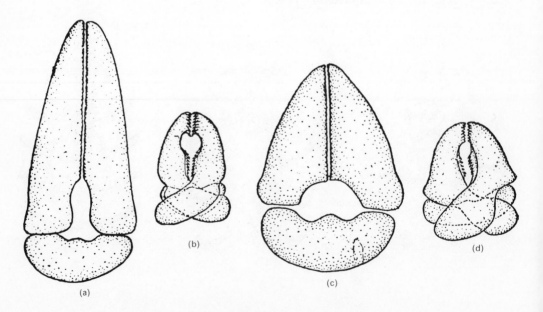

center on the disc near the junction of two arms. Ambulacral grooves with tube-feet occur on the oral surfaces of the arms, and converge at the mouth located in the middle of the central disc. At the end of each arm the water-vascular system terminates in a small tentacle at the base of which is a simple eye, often red, composed of a group of ocelli.

The asteroid skeleton, lying beneath the ciliated epidermis, consists of closely fitting or overlapping calcareous plates, with connective tissue bonds allowing for flexibility. Variously shaped spines protrude from it, particularly on the aboral surface. Small retractile gills called *dermal branchiae* or *papulae* are diverticula of the coelomic wall, and these extend to the exterior through interstices between ossicles or calcareous plates. Many starfish possess *pedicellariae* (Fig. 18-12), which are movable spines usually modified as a pair of jaws. Pedicel-

lariae are variously stalked or sessile and may occur grouped around spines. Various functions have been ascribed to these organs, such as debris removal, defense, and food-getting.

On the oral surface, series of paired ossicles called ambulacral plates form an angular roof to the ambulacral groove, and internally protrude as a ridge into the coelom of the arm. Canals to the *ampullae* of the tube-feet penetrate between calcareous plates through pores formed by the conjunction of recesses along the edge of the adjoining ossicles.

The ring canal of the water-vascular system lies around the esophagus and is supported by the ring of calcareous plates forming the principal oral endoskeleton of the disc, and by the peristomial membrane around the mouth (Fig. 18-13). From the water ring the stone canal arises from the inner side and runs aborally to open exter-

Fig. **18-13** Water-vascular system of starfish. After Coe 1912, courtesy Conn. Geol. and Nat. Hist. Survey.

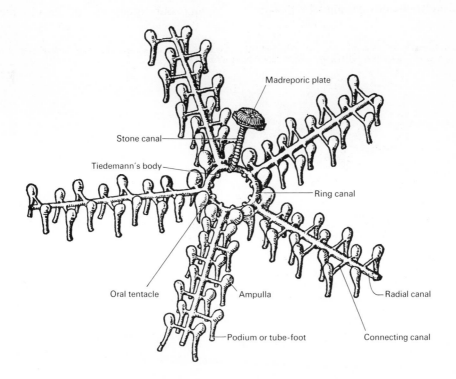

Madreporic plate

Stone canal

Tiedemann's body

Ring canal

Oral tentacle

Ampulla

Radial canal

Podium or tube-foot

Connecting canal

nally through a series of pores in the madreporite. The stone canal is attached by mesenteries to the inside of a tubular coelomic chamber called the axial sinus. A series of small interradially spaced lobations called *Tiedemann's bodies* of unknown function also arise from the water ring. Many sea stars possess *polian vesicles,* which are globular diverticula arising from the inner surface of the water ring and which presumably are effective in controlling turgor within the water-vascular system. Radial canals course into each arm from the ring canal. These canals lie immediately oral to the ridge formed by the convergent ambulacral ossicles. Branches arise from the radial canals, each branch dividing to terminate externally as a podium or (via ambulacral pores) internally as an ampulla (Fig. 18-14). Ampullae are commonly bilobed and they have an extensive musculature consisting of a series of rings of smooth muscle fibers. The muscle of the tube-foot is a sheath of longitudinal fibers adjacent to the lining epithelium. The alternating contractions of ampulla and tube-foot account for the protraction and retraction of the tube-foot.

The alimentary canal of asteroids is short. The mouth, surrounded by peristomial membrane, opens into a short, sometimes radially lobate, esophagus which broadens into a large pouch with folded walls, the eversible cardiac stomach. Paired gastric ligaments anchor the cardiac stomach to the ambulacral ridge proximally in each arm. This remarkable organ can be insinuated between the valves of clams through minute slits, to digest the internal soft structures. If the mollusc valves fit too snugly, the starfish is able to apply suction with the tube-feet to force open a small gap. At this point the starfish becomes a ciliary feeder, with cilia or flagella on the stomach surface sweeping digested material toward the mouth.

Starfish are carnivorous and commonly feed on bivalves, gastropods, and other echinoderms. Also they will eat dead or sickly animals which normally they could not capture. It has already been pointed out that many starfish secondarily use cilia in feeding, but some sea stars utilize mucus-

Fig. 18-14 Starfish, (a) cross-section of an arm and (b) ambulacral plates, showing ambulacral pores. Modified from Hertwig, *A Manual of Zoology* (translated and edited by J. S. Kingsley) 1902, Holt, Rinehart & Winston, Inc.

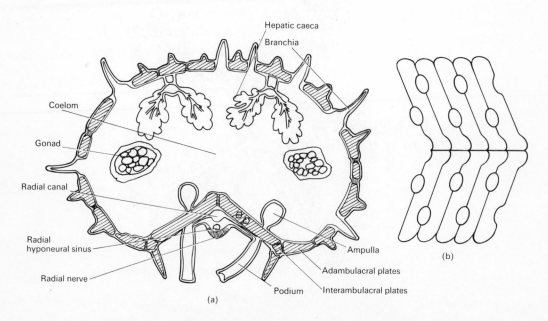

Hepatic caeca
Branchia
Coelom
Gonad
Radial canal
Radial hyponeural sinus
Radial nerve
Ampulla
Adambulacral plates
Interambulacral plates
Podium
(a)
(b)

ciliary methods almost exclusively. Some experimental animals whose only access to food was plankton in flowing sea water thrived on the food obtained. Other species grovel in mud and silt on the ocean floor, obtaining a variety of organisms and organic matter on mucus strings which subsequently are transferred to the mouth.

The cardiac stomach occupies most of the disc coelom. Aborally, it opens to a flattened pouch, the pyloric stomach. A pair of glandular pyloric or hepatic caeca lie laterally in each arm and join the pyloric stomach. In some asteroids a secondary caecum, called Tiedemann's diverticulum, is attached to the lower side of each pyloric caecum and apparently functions in some sea stars to circulate contents in the pyloric compo-

Fig. 18-15 (a) Diagrammatic section through central disc and one of the rays of the starfish with hemal system indicated by dotted areas and (b) enlargement to show hemal channels in the peribuccal region.

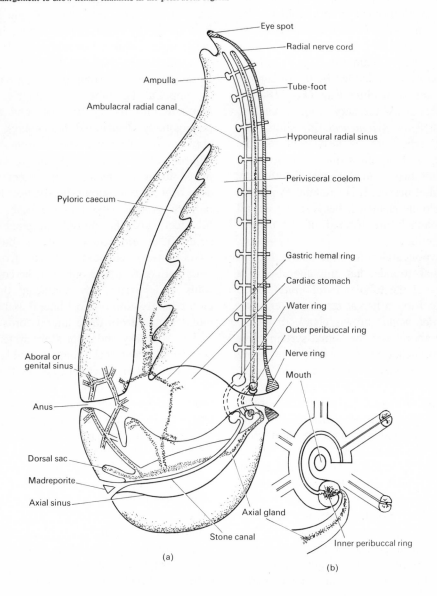

Eye spot

Radial nerve cord

Ampulla

Tube-foot

Ambulacral radial canal

Hyponeural radial sinus

Periviseral coelom

Pyloric caecum

Gastric hemal ring

Cardiac stomach

Water ring

Outer peribuccal ring

Nerve ring

Aboral or genital sinus

Mouth

Anus

Dorsal sac

Madreporite

Axial sinus

Axial gland

Stone canal

Inner peribuccal ring

(a)

(b)

nents of the digestive system. From the pyloric stomach a short intestine runs directly to the aboral anus. En route, a varying number of small pouches called rectal or intestinal caeca attach to the intestine.

The hemal system in starfish is not as extensively developed as in Holothuroidea and Echinoidea, but for the most part it is contained in coelomic channels as is generally characteristic of the phylum. Immediately aboral to the water ring and to the water radial canals, two coelomic elements have joined to produce a somewhat tubular cavity or sinus. The fused walls of these two elements remain as a more or less complete mesentery. The circumoral ring, called the *peribuccal sinus,* is divided by the mesentery into an inner and outer ring (Fig. 18-15). Since it lies below the nerve ring, it has also been named the *hyponeural* ring sinus. The adjective hyponeural is also used for the radial canals radiating from the ring sinus, but in fact these radial canals lie aborally to the radial nerves. It is essential to picture these coelomic elements, because the aboral hemal channels are formed in the mesenteries described.

The hyponeural ring sinus communicates with hemal strands that run aborally in a mesentery of the tubular *axial sinus.* These enlarge to form a hemal structure variously called *axial gland,* brown gland, or heart. Near the aboral end the hemal system gives off two branches to an inconspicuous ring plexus that branches to the pyloric caeca. Near the aboral wall a coelomic diverticulum houses hemal strands. This organ, called the *dorsal sac* or *madreporic vesicle,* like the axial gland appears to be contractile. Aborally, the axial gland joins an aboral hemal ring contained in a coelomic cavity called the genital sinus. Radiating channels carry hemal strands to the gonads.

The nervous system of asteroids has three diffuse but interrelated components. The most prominent portion is the oral system with a peribuccal ring beneath the epithelium of the peristome, and radial nerve

bands which are V-shaped ectodermal thickenings lying between the bases of the tube-feet. These radial nerve cords (Fig. 18-16) are covered externally by a layer of cuticle continuous with that which covers the body generally. The radial nerve band is sensory and associative. Coordination of tube-feet is achieved by centers pentagonally arranged on the peribuccal ring at the junctions of the radial nerves. Lying immediately oral to each radial nerve, from which it is separated by connective tissue, is a motor tract incorporated into the coelomic epithelium of the hyponeural sinus above it. This nerve tract is called *Lange's nerve.* It innervates the transverse muscles of the ambulacral ossicles, and some of the musculature of ampulla and tube-foot. Lange's nerves continue into the central disc and exhibit pentagonally distributed thickenings, probably responsible for motor coordination of adjacent limbs. Lange's nerves are also referred to as the hyponeural system or the deep oral system. Along the edge of the ambulacral groove, lateral to the bases of the tube-feet, are the paired marginal nerve cords. They are primarily motor, but have some sensory elements. Nerves from the marginal cords spread out over the coelomic walls. It is particularly significant that the motor innervation of most lateral and aboral muscles arise from these lateral cords.

The excretory and respiratory systems are very simple in starfish. Some insoluble waste is transported by coelomocytes to the exterior either through papulae or into channels which communicate with body openings. Coelomocytes have been seen to aggregate at the apex of a papula. Later this tip is pinched off. Respiration in most sea stars is a function of the *papulae,* which are retractile evaginations of the coelom, covered by surface epithelium.

Sea stars are typically dioecious. The gonads occur in pairs (Fig. 18-14) near the base of each arm, and open to the exterior interradially. The gonad is composed of branching tubules and tapers plumelike to the distal end. Gametes are freed into sea water and subsequent development is left to chance, although a few starfish brood the developing eggs.

Holoblastic cleavage gives rise to a coeloblastula by invagination. The coelom arises enterocoelously, either as paired outpockets which subsequently fuse anterior to the archenteron or as a median sac which grows caudally on either side of the primitive intestine. At hatching, the larva is rather uniformly ciliated. The rounded contours of the larva are changed by the formation of blunt lobes, and the more angular shape is accentuated by localization of cilia into an elongated loop whose ends cross transversely in front of and behind the larval mouth. The ventral preoral loop of cilia is pinched off to form a band not in continuity with the original loop. Various lobations in the larval contour extend as arms edged by the ciliary band. This larva is called *bipinnaria*. Later, three

new projections called brachiolar arms surrounding an adhesive sucker develop from the surface anterior to the preoral loop. This larva is called a *brachiolaria*. It attaches by the brachiolar arms and sucker. A pentagonal development, early evidenced by five primary podia which are the anlage of the radial canals, forms at the free end. With the formation of tube-feet along the developing radii, the young starfish is soon ready for free existence, and it pulls free from the attaching stalk.

Starfish have a marked capacity for regeneration. Injured arms are cast off adjacent to the disc. One intact arm, however, plus a varying portion of the central disc, is the minimal structure that can successfully regenerate in most cases. Such regenerative ability suggests that asexual reproduction is possible in some starfish, and usually involves a portion of the central disc, as indicated for *Linckia* by A. M. Clark.

Fig. 18-16 Schematic transverse section of a starfish arm, showing distribution of sensory, association, and motor components of the nervous system. *A, B, C, D,* and *E*, systems of motor neurons. After Smith 1945, courtesy of *Biological Reviews*, the Cambridge Philosophical Society and the author.

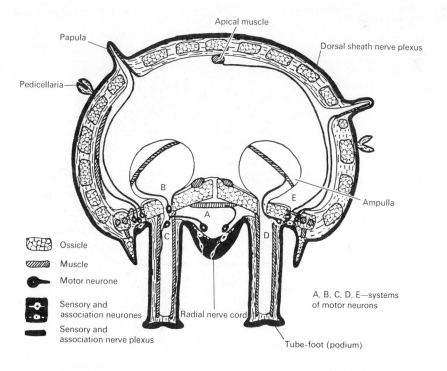

Apical muscle

Papula

Dorsal sheath nerve plexus

Pedicellaria

B

E

Ampulla

A

C   D

Ossicle

Muscle

Motor neurone

Sensory and association neurones

A, B, C, D, E—systems of motor neurons

Sensory and association nerve plexus

Radial nerve cord

Tube-foot (podium)

CLASS ECHINOIDEA

This class includes marine animals which are globular to discoidal in shape, and are known as sea urchins, sand dollars, and heart urchins. Many of these have a precise radial symmetry. In others, the anus and periproct is translocated from the center of the aboral disc into one of the interradii to set up a slight bilateral symmetry.

The living sea urchin shell or test is composed of firm, closely fitted plates terminating at the oral and aboral poles in membranous walls called peristome and periproct, respectively. The test is thickly beset with movable spines, usually differentiated into larger or primary spines and smaller or secondary spines (Fig. 18-17). Close examination of a living sea urchin will usually reveal a higher concentration of spines along five meridional rows. Between these rows, the lesser number of spines are edged by rows of tube-feet which outline the edges of the ambulacra. The meridians between ambulacra are termed interradii or interambulacra. The mouth opens centrally on the peristome, and five toothlike ossicles of *Aristotle's lantern* are visible in the opening. In many sea urchins ten small plumose structures called gills occur at the conjunction of ambulacral and interambulacral meridians where these meet the peristome. At the aboral pole, the anus opens often eccentrically on the periproct. Encircling the periproct is a ring of ten plates alternating in size. The larger genital plates bear the five gonopores. One of these, perforated by many pores, is the madreporite. The smaller ocular plates, which fail to reach the edge of the periproct in some sea urchins, are aligned with the ambulacral rays. Each ocular plate bears a pore for the terminal podium, homologous with the tentacle at the extremity of the starfish arm. Sea urchins possess numerous stalked, usually three-jawed, *pedicellariae* situated on the test between the spines and on the peristome. Some pedicellariae are equipped with poison glands. These small organs may be used to secure food, ward off enemies, and to remove debris.

Fig. 18-17 A sea-urchin, *Arbacia*; oral view showing spines, rows of tube feet, gills, and "teeth" of Aristotle's lantern. From Schechter 1959, courtesy of Prentice-Hall, Inc.

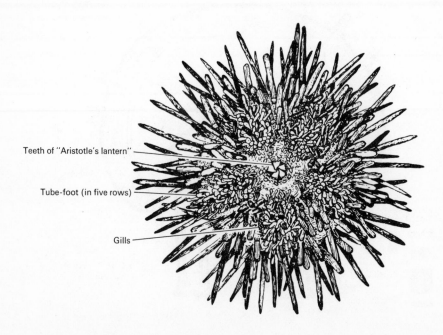

Teeth of "Aristotle's lantern"

Tube-foot (in five rows)

Gills

In the sea urchin test cleaned of spines, the arrangement of ambulacra and interambulacra is clear-cut. Pores for the tube-feet rim the ambulacral rays (Fig. 18-18). Small cone-shaped protuberances arise from the test. These are called tubercles. Each is topped by a knob. The base of the spine fits around the knob, so that the spine is movable over this ball-and-socket joint in many directions. Longitudinal muscle fibers attached to the base of the spine can sustain contraction to keep the spine immobile. This muscle action can be inhibited by appropriate sensory stimulation. Spines are locomotory and protective. Sometimes the latter function is accentuated by poison glands.

The mouth opens in the middle of the peristome, with the teeth usually projecting slightly from it. These teeth represent the only portion of Aristotle's lantern visible externally. The teeth pass through the wall of the buccal chamber. Their aboral ends diverge and pass along the somewhat grooved median face of broad, V-shaped pieces called *pyramids* which act as supports and guides.

At the broad pentagonal base of the cone-shaped lantern, five *compasses* lie radially. Each of these is composed of two ossicles. Bracing plates called *rotules* lie radially beneath the converging ends of the compasses. Epiphyses are sutured horizontally to the aboral ends of the arms of the V-shaped pyramids. Aristotle's lantern (Fig. 18-19) is composed of 40 skeletal pieces, and these are controlled by 60 muscles. Teeth are constantly renewed by growth at the soft aboral end. A separate unit of the coelom, called peripharyngeal cavity, encloses Aristotle's lantern. The lantern serves primarily for mastication, but certain of its muscular contractions modify the coelomic chamber to force water in and out of the gills.

Echinoid food habits are of course related to benthonic life in the ocean. Many sea urchins occur in crevices in rocky or coral substrates. They may enlarge these spaces by their own action, and a number of urchins can make deep burrows in rocks. The burrowing is apparently accomplished by rotary or spiral action of spines rather than with the

Fig. 18-18 Aboral view of *Arbacia* test. After Beck and Braithwaite, *Invertebrate Zoology Laboratory Workbook* 1962, courtesy of the authors and Burgess Publishing Company. (Copyright held by authors.)

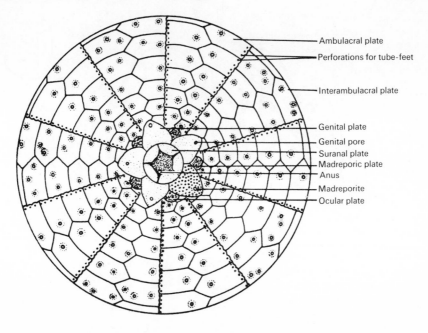

Ambulacral plate
Perforations for tube-feet
Interambulacral plate
Genital plate
Genital pore
Suranal plate
Madreporic plate
Anus
Madreporite
Ocular plate

teeth of Aristotle's lantern. Hyman cites one reference in which sea urchins made concavities in steel pilings. Animals within burrows depend upon water action to bring suitable food, so it appears that some food is taken by mucus-ciliary action. However, normal feeding includes chewing action by the lantern, and the shells of most animals are no deterrent. Some food is immobilized by action of poison from specialized pedicellariae, which also aid in holding food. Sea urchins are somewhat omnivorous, but some seem to prefer animal, some plant food. They will also eat dead animal matter. Some of the heart urchins are normally buried in surface burrows. Specialized tube-feet or podia extend through a small surface aperture of the burrow and by the aid of sticky secretions pick up food from the surrounding ocean floor. The podia are then retracted and the food delivered by way of spines to the mouth.

The pharynx runs aborally in the center of the lantern. It enters the esophagus, which loops orally before joining the stomach. The stomach, supported by mesenteries, pursues an undulating course around the coelomic cavity (Fig. 18-20). It loops into the intestine, which reverses the encirclement, before passing aborally to the anus. In most echinoids a short caecum of unknown function occurs at the esophagus-stomach junction. A smooth, slender tube with ciliated lumen arises near the caecum and runs along the inner curvature of the stomach, into which it empties distally. This tube is called the *siphon* and carries water, which thereby is shunted past an important digestive chamber.

The ring canal of the water-vascular system surrounds the esophagus just aboral to the peripharyngeal cavity enclosing Aristotle's lantern. The radial canals run radially beneath the rotules. They then pass to the oral wall, cross the peristome, and follow the inner curvature of the test up to the terminal podia in the ocular plates. En route,

Fig. 18-19 (a) Internal view of Aristotle's Lantern *Euchinus esculentus*. After Cuénot 1948, in *Traité de Zoologie*, Tome XI (P. Grassé, ed.), courtesy of Masson et Cie.

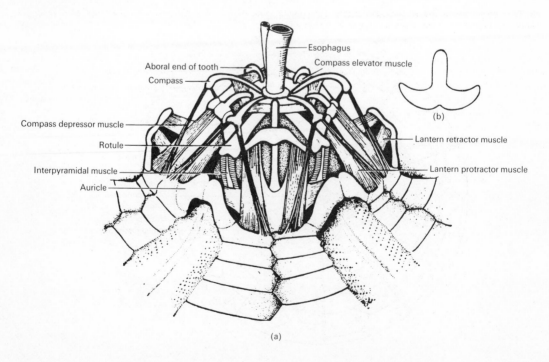

Fig. 18-20 Internal anatomy of *Arbacia punctulata*. From Schechter 1959, courtesy of Prentice-Hall, Inc.

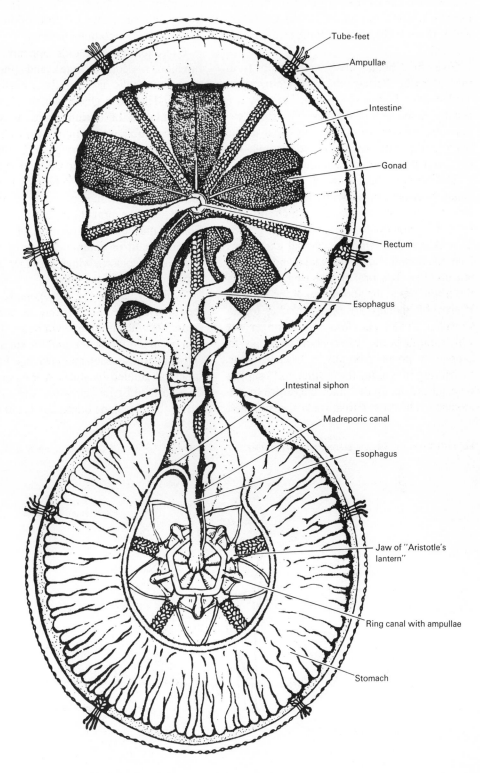

Tube-feet

Ampullae

Intestine

Gonad

Rectum

Esophagus

Intestinal siphon

Madreporic canal

Esophagus

Jaw of "Aristotle's lantern"

Ring canal with ampullae

Stomach

valved branches communicate with the ampullae. Two canals from an ampulla join externally to form the lumen of the tube-foot, which in most echinoids is long, slender, and retractile.

Five small bodies arise interradially from the water ring. Perhaps they are analogous to Tiedemann's bodies in starfish, but they are usually called Polian vesicles. The stone canal runs aborally from the ring canal to the madreporic plate. In its course through the coelom it is supported by mesentery.

The spindle-shaped *axial gland, brown gland,* or *heart* runs aborally from the hemal ring to join an aboral ring which in turn branches radially to the gonads (Fig. 18-21). A terminal sinus or dorsal sac arises from the aboral end of the axial gland in some sea urchins. The oral hemal ring surrounds the esophagus at the aboral end of the lantern. It gives off radially arranged branches to the so-called Polian vesicles, and a longer set which parallels the water-vascular canals to supply the podia. Aborally, a branch of the hemal ring runs along the esophagus to supply a hemal plexus on the inner curvature of the stomach. The outer curvature is also supplied by a hemal plexus whose point of origin is uncertain. The hemal system serves as a communication between food absorption sites and areas of high metabolic activity.

Excretion in echinoids appears to be a function of coelomocytes and possibly of phagocytic cells in the walls of coelomic elements. The axial gland, which often shows accumulation of coelomocytes, may absorb some insoluble wastes in its own walls or may throw off wastes through communicating channels with the water-vascular system.

Respiration in many echinoids is mainly a function of the five pairs of aboral gills, which are like branching *dermal branchiae.* Certain muscular contractions of Aristotle's lantern result in volume change of the peripharyngeal coelom, which provides a kind of ebb-and-flow into the gills.

Typically, there are five gonads opening separately. This number may be reduced in echinoids with modified symmetry. Fertilization occurs in sea water, and the small-yolked eggs undergo holoblastic cleavage to form a spherical ciliated blastula. A long archenteron is formed by invagination, and a coelomic cavity that develops bilaterally is cut off from

Fig. 18-21 The hemal system of *Echinus.* After Cuénot 1948, in *Traité de Zoologie,* Tome XI (P. Grassé, ed.),courtesy of Masson et Cie.

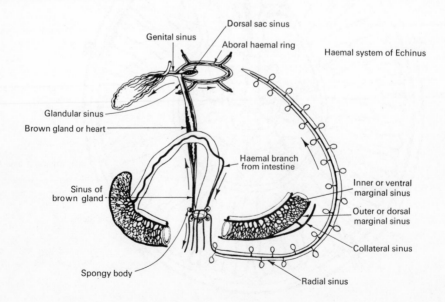

Dorsal sac sinus
Genital sinus
Aboral haemal ring
Haemal system of Echinus
Glandular sinus
Brown gland or heart
Haemal branch from intestine
Sinus of brown gland
Inner or ventral marginal sinus
Outer or dorsal marginal sinus
Collateral sinus
Spongy body
Radial sinus

the primitive intestine. The gastrula changes to an elongated cone which develops a slight concavity on one side. The concavity is later accentuated by the development of two pairs of arms arising respectively near the base and near the apex of the cone. Between these arm pairs, the stomodaeum develops to join the intestine. This larval stage is called a *pluteus*. Three additional pairs of arms develop: two anterior and one posterior to the stomodaeum. Sometimes a stubby pair appear caudally. All arms are rigid structures, since each contains a calcareous rod.

On the left side of the pluteus, an ectodermal invagination is cut off to form a thick-floored flat vesicle. This structure is the *vestibule,* mentioned in a more characteristic form in the embryology of sea cucumbers. Coordinate development of the coelomic primordium of the water ring gives rise to the pentaradiate lobations in the vestibular floor. These lobations are the primary podia. Later the roof over the vestibular cavity breaks and the strictly larval structures are resorbed or lost to complete the changes to radial symmetry initially evidenced in the vestibular floor.

CLASS OPHIUROIDEA

The Ophiuroidea are echinoderms with long snakelike arms which may be readily broken. Because of these features, members of this group are frequently called serpent stars and brittle stars (Fig. 18-22). Sometimes they are classified with starfish or sea stars, but they differ markedly in certain features. The arms, always much longer than the disc diameter, are sharply demarked from the disc, and insert on its aboral surface near the periphery. Taxonomic subdivision is based on articulation of adjacent arm ossicles (so-called vertebrae) which limits arm movements to a horizontal plane in one order, whereas in the other both vertical and horizontal movements allow for increased versatility. Some of the latter group possess arms

that branch repeatedly. These intertwining branches account for the name, basket star.

Brittle stars differ from asteroids as well as other echinoderms, as they lack ambulacral grooves. In asteroids, the radial nerve lies adjacent to the epithelium in the roof of the ambulacral groove. In the ophiuroids, the radial nerve is internal (Fig. 18-23), running in a

Fig. 18-22 Ophiuroidea, serpent star or brittle star. From Schechter 1959, courtesy of Prentice-Hall, Inc.

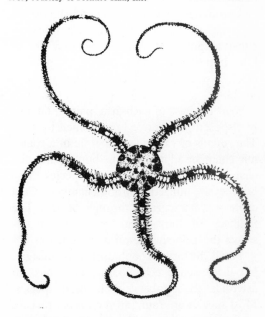

Fig. 18-23 Section through an Ophiuroid arm. From Hertwig, *A Manual of Zoology* (translated and edited by J. S. Kingsley) 1902, Holt, Rinehart & Winston, Inc.

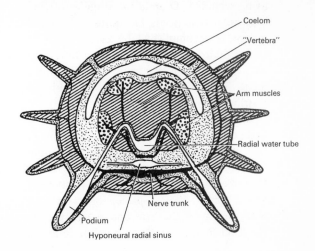

furrow on the oral side of the vertebral ossicles. Correlated with each vertebral ossicle or vertebra is a series of calcareous shields lying superficially on the oral, aboral, and lateral surfaces. The oral shield thus serves as a protection to the radial nerve, which lies immediately aboral to an ectodermal cavity called the epineural sinus.

Ophiuroids do not possess pedicellariae or the dermal papulae present on many starfish. Small spines may occur on the aboral disc, and prominent ones on the lateral shields of the arms. Podia, or tube-feet, do not possess either ampullae or suckers and they are of little importance in locomotion. A podium emerges near the oral edge of each lateral shield.

Near the base of each arm, paired, laterally disposed pouches or bursae open by slits. The gonads of varying number lie in a coelomic chamber adjacent to the bursae, and discharge through them. In some species these pouches are utilized as brood chambers. Cilia cause a water current through bursae. The intimacy of bursal and coelomic cavities serves the principal respiratory function.

Fossil history of ophiuroids is meager, but these active echinoderms rank next to asteroids in numbers of modern species. Most species are found in the deeper reaches of the neritic zone and in the bathyal zone (Fig. 1-2). Serpent stars are common in the littoral zone but they avoid light and tend to be secluded. Despite the fragility of their long arms ophiuroids are quite agile. Locomotion is accomplished by use of the arms rather than by podia, although a few forms with suckers use the tube-feet for movement. The brittle stars have a world-wide distribution in marine waters.

While ophiuroids are carnivorous, most of them depend largely on ingesting bottom silt with its mixture of living and dead animals for food. MacGinitie reports that a laboratory specimen of *Ophioderma panamensis* would grasp offered pieces of clam meat with the tip of the arm and would transfer the food to the mouth by a spiral-coiling of the arm. Another feeding method is employed by a sand-dwelling species, which lies submerged in sand except for the arm tips. These explore the adjacent area to collect food, small particles of which are transferred to the mouth by podial action and large ones directly by arm retraction. Since adult ophiuroids lack an anus, the mouth serves as a waste exit. Buccal podia are adapted not only for rejection of unusable food material but also for fecal deposits. Ophiuroids lack the cilia necessary for a mucus-ciliary feeding method seen in other echinoderms. Considering the great similarity between the larval *plutei* of this group and the Echinoidea, failure of an anus to be formed in adult serpent stars is of real interest.

The coelom is confined to the disc and to the aboral bases of the arms (Fig. 18-24). The mouth lies at the base of the cavity formed by the rings of ossicles called jaws. A short esophagus joins a blind cavity, the stomach, which lobes laterally into pouches confined to the disc coelom. The ring canal of the water-vascular system, in addition to the usual radial canals and the stone canal, gives rise to the peribuccal podia or tentacles and to one or more polian vesicles. The stone canal opens by an external madreporite which embryologically is aboral, but is displaced during growth to an oral position. The radial canals lie in the aboral furrows of the vertebra, oral to the coelomic element called the hyponeural radial sinus, which in turn is oral to the radial nerves. Branches of the radial canal may loop aborally before running to the latero-orally disposed podia.

The circulatory or hemal system has oral and aboral rings connected by the axial gland (brown gland or heart). In general, the system is very similar to that of asteroids, although the madreporic vesicle or dorsal sac is closely apposed to the axial gland.

With the extensive muscular development and locomotor function of the arms, each radial nerve exhibits a series of ganglionic enlargements. Immediately adjacent to these nerves aborally are the radial nerves of the so-called hyponeural system. This arrangement corresponds closely with the condition in asteroids.

Brittle stars are hermaphroditic or dioecious. Eggs undergo holoblastic cleavage typically and a *pluteus* similar to that of echinoids is developed. In metamorphosis the blastopore disappears, since brittle stars have no anus. Ectodermal thickenings in the region of the mouth are probably homologous to the vestibule of echinoids and holothuroids. As is characteristic of echinoderms, a portion of the coelom on the left of the bilateral larva develops around the anterior alimentary canal to form the water ring and pentaradiate primary podia outpockets, to indicate an external manifestation of the developing radial adult. In some forms, the gradual loss of the larval arms and rounding out of contours produces a larval stage somewhat resembling the doliolaria.

FOSSIL ECHINODERMATA

A considerable number of totally extinct classes have been set up by various investigators, in addition to modern classes with fossil relatives. In the two recent comprehensive treatments of Echinodermata, Hyman follows Cuénot in listing five established extinct classes. There is still considerable uncertainty as to the number of fossil classes. One recent text in invertebrate zoology lists ten, and a recent text in invertebrate paleontology has eight extinct classes. Nichols' book emphasizes the fossil history.

Of the five extinct classes treated by Cuénot and by Hyman, four belong in subphylum Pelmatozoa, which includes the crinoids and is characterized by being attached throughout life or during immature stages, and by the upward orientation of the oral surface with its open ciliated ambulacral grooves. These grooves, aided by podia, presumably functioned for the gathering of food and its transport to the mouth at the confluence of the grooves. Pelmatozoan fos-

Fig. **18-24** Ophiuroidea; section through disc and an arm of *Ophiothrix*. After Cuénot 1948, in *Traité de Zoologie*, Tome XI (P. Grassé, ed.),courtesy of Masson et Cie.

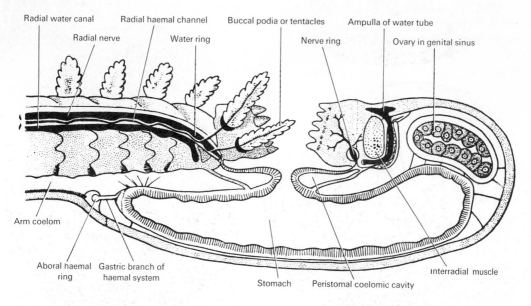

Radial water canal   Radial haemal channel   Buccal podia or tentacles   Ampulla of water tube

Radial nerve   Water ring   Nerve ring   Ovary in genital sinus

Arm coelom

Aboral haemal   Gastric branch of   ring   haemal system

Stomach   Peristomal coelomic cavity   Interradial muscle

Fig. 18-25 (a) Edrioasteroidea *Cystaster* (*Hemicystites*), (b) *Lepidodiscus* (*Agelacrinites*) and *Agelacrinites*, and (c) *Carneyella* (*Agelacrinus*) and *Carneyella*. After Bassler 1936, courtesy of the Smithsonian Institution.

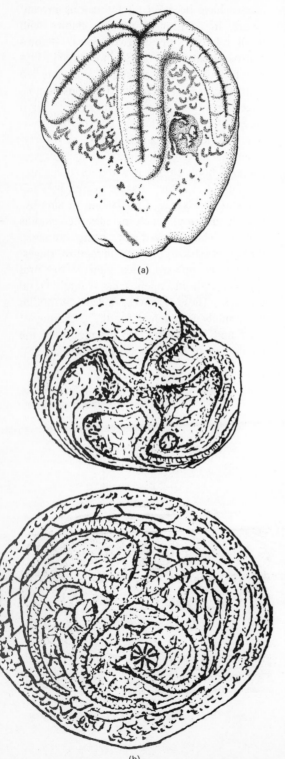

(a)

(b)

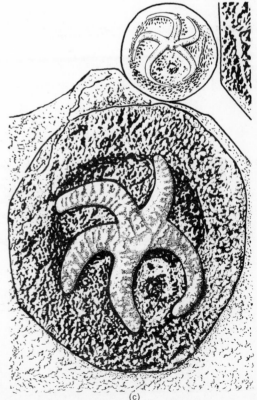

(c)

sils developed fused calcareous plates or ossicles forming a heavy endoskeleton.

The four classes of wholly extinct Pelmatozoa are the Heterostelea, Cystidea, Blastoidea, and Edrioasteroidea. Although these four classes seem to show a progression from a total lack of radial symmetry to an increasingly pentaradiate arrangement, this does not establish a phylogenetic sequence. The Heterostelea are less modified from a bilateral ancestor than are the other groups. Their geologic history runs from the Cambrian to the Lower Silurian. The Edrioasteroidea appeared somewhat earlier in the Paleozoic Era, but survived into the Mississippian Period (Fig. 18-25). Podia apparently penetrated through pores formed by the apposition of two half-pores in adjacent ambulacral plates. This feature parallels the structure in the Eleutherozoa, which are the unattached echinoderms in which the oral surface normally never faces upward. Whether the similarity of podial pores is considered to be the result of homology or convergence largely determines the relationship between Edrioasteroidea and the Eleutherozoa. No other Pelmatozoa share this pore structure.

The Cystidea and Blastoidea are two closely related groups. The former are usually attached and usually stalkless; the latter more commonly have a short stalk and are more distinctly pentaradiate. The geologic history of these two classes as well as of the Crinoidea begins in the middle Ordovician Period. The Cystidea became extinct in the mid-Devonian, while the Blastoidea survived into the lower Permian.

The only wholly extinct eleutherozoan class is the Ophiocistioidea. This small class appeared in the Ordovician and disappeared in the late Devonian period.

ECHINODERM CLASSIFICATION

Subphylum Pelmatozoa

These Echinodermata are transitorily or permanently attached to the substrate by the aboral surface, which may be provided with a stalk. The ciliated ambulacral grooves aided by podia collect and transport food to the mouth. Both mouth and anus open on the oral surface. Viscera lie within a cavity walled principally by calcareous plates. This structure is called a *theca*. It may be an irregular shape or vary symmetrically as a disc, spheroid, cone, or double-walled cup. Frequently arms arise radially from the theca.

Class Heterostelea This is a heterogeneous group of Pelmatozoa which lack radial symmetry. The theca is commonly flattened in the plane of the substrate and attached by a short stalk. The nonporous theca apparently was flexible, at least in part.

Class Cystidea These Pelmatozoa were sessile or attached by a short stalk. The thecal plates were porous and symmetrically or asymmetrically disposed. The radial symmetry appears to be in a state of flux, with variation occurring in the arrangement of thecal plates and in the number of unbranched brachioles or arms, and of ambulacral grooves.

Class Blastoidea These stalked Pelmatozoa exhibit a more consistent pentaradiate symmetry. The pentagonal theca has a definite arrangement and number of thecal plates, and typically five ambulacra radiate symmetrically from the mouth, as either straight or sinuous channels. On each side of each ambulacrum the endoskeleton develops a series of folds opening to the surface by parallel slits, or by their coalescence forming a single pore. These structures, presumably of respiratory function, are called *hydrospires*.

Class Crinoidea This is the only group of Pelmatozoa which have survived to the present, but many more fossil than living species are known. In over 87 per cent of living species the stalk does not persist. The cup-shaped theca is covered orally by the flexible tegmen. Arms, which are commonly branched and provided with pinnules, extend from the thecal rim. The ambulacra radiate from the mouth across the tegmen and continue on the oral side of arms or brachia and of some pinnules. Sea feather.

Class Edrioasteroidea These discoidal Pelmatozoa probably had a flexible theca with an irregular arrangement of plates. They did not develop a stalk or arms and were mostly sessile. The ambulacra bear pores (Fig. 18-14) between ambulacral plates for the passage of podia, a structural feature shared by Eleutherozoa.

Subphylum Eleutherozoa

These echinoderms lack stalks and are oriented with the oral surface against the substrate except for the Holothuroidea which lie on one side. The symmetrically radiating ambulacral grooves or zones contain paired rows of podia often provided with sucking discs. The body surface is variously covered with knobs and spines. The anus typically is at or near the aboral pole.

Class Holothuroidea These elongate Eleutherozoa have a cylindrical or slightly pentagonal body resting laterally upon one median and two latero-ventral ambulacral areas. Peristomial podia or tentacles rim the mouth at the oral end. The endoskeleton is reduced or absent and at most consists of scattered ossicles embedded in the leathery, often warty, body wall. The pentagonally disposed ambulacral areas may be obscured by spread of podia into interradial areas. This group is characterized by the presence of a single gonad, and by a water-vascular system that opens internally in most subgroups. Sea cucumbers.

Class Asteroidea These typically star-shaped Eleutherozoa possess five ambulacral grooves radiating from the mouth to the tips of the arms or rays on the oral surface. The rays are never sharply demarked from the central disc, and in some forms are so reduced that the body forms a pentagonal disc. Gonads and diverticula of the digestive tract occur in the hollow arms. The anus and madreporite lie on the aboral surface of the central disc. Sea stars or starfish.

Class Echinoidea These Eleutherozoa have a spinose body which ranges from a subglobular to a discoidal shape (Fig. 18-26), modified to a heart shape in some species. The principal endoskeleton is composed of closely fitted plates to form a rigid test or shell. The five ambulacral areas are disposed meridionally between the oral mouth and the aboral pole. Anus and madreporite are located aborally. Gonads commonly have a pentaradiate distribution. Sea urchins, heart urchins, sand-dollars.

Class Ophiuroidea In these pentamerous echinoderms, the elongate, slender arms or rays are attached as appendages to the sharply demarked disc. The arms are relatively solid with a large core, composed of a series of articulating vertebral ossicles or vertebra, covered by external plates or shields on oral, aboral, and lateral faces. Small podia emerge between lateral and oral shields to distinguish the oral surface, and spines commonly protrude from the lateral arm shields. The mouth and madreporite are oral and the anus is lacking. Brittle stars, serpent stars, and basket stars.

Class Ophiocistioidea This small group possessed a test of fused plates aborally arched and orally flattened. A pentagonal structure is apparent in some species in the disc contour and orally by the arrangement of jaws and of oral plates, and of gigantic podia occurring in series in each ambulacral area. Podia are cov-

Fig. **18-26** Variation in shape among Echinoidea, oral and profile views. (a) through (c) regular crinoids; (d) through (i) irregular crinoids: (a) oral view of either (b) *Echinus* or (c) *Strongylocentrotus*, (d) oral and (e) profile view of sand-dollar, (f) oral and (g) profile view of keyhole urchin, (h) oral and (i) profile view of heart urchin. After Shrock and Twenhofel 1953, courtesy of the McGraw-Hill Book Company.

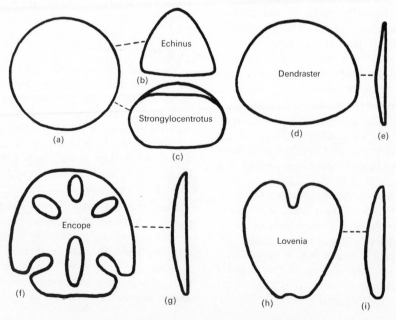

ered by series of overlapping scales. No representatives of this group possessed arms.

PHYLOGENETIC CONSIDERATIONS

The phylum Echinodermata includes a variety of animals distinguished from each other by their specializations on the one hand, and unified by ontogenetic and structural similarities on the other. Throughout the phylum, small-yolked eggs undergo indeterminate, holoblastic, radial cleavage and hatch to ciliated, free-swimming larvae (Fig. 18-27). Gastrulation occurs primarily by invagination, and the blastopore is posterior. The coelom outpockets from the archenteron, either as paired cavities or as a median growth which develops into paired pouches. The early larva is a bilaterally symmetrical free-swimming organism. Ontogenetically, echinoderms arose from immature stages with bilateral symmetry, and it is accepted that phylogenetically, ancestral organisms with bilateral symmetry were the forerunners of this phylum with its consistent pentaradiate symmetry.

A structural feature common to members of the phylum is an endoskeleton of calcareous ossicles lying adjacent to the epidermis. These ossicles vary from closely fitted plates superficially disposed, to minute isolated spicules dispersed in a thick body wall. Locomotion serves as an escape mechanism for many organisms. Animals that are attached must develop other defensive means. One of these, seen in many different groups of animals, is the development of armor. The echinoderm endoskeleton, covered only by an epidermis that is not seriously vulnerable, is such an armor. The extinct classes of Pelmatozoa are sessile or stalked animals and possess heavy endoskeletons. The development of stalks in many Pelmatozoa would favor food collection on the upward-oriented oral surfaces. Embryology of Recent sea feathers (crinoid group) shows the development of transitory stalks, but among the Eleutherozoa, only asteroid larvae undergo temporary attachment during metamorphosis. The derivation of Eleutherozoa from Pelmatozoa is accepted, but a monophyletic origin is not implied. Each class of Recent Eleutherozoa shows

Fig. 18-27 Echinoderm larvae. The black lines mark the course of ciliated bands; *a*, anus; *m*, mouth. (a) A form somewhat common to all echinoderms; (b), (c) development of auricularia (Holothuroidea); (d), (e) Asteroid bipennaria; (f) echinopluteus ;(g) Brachiolaria of *Asterias forbesi*. (a) Through (f) from Hertwig (after J. Muller) *A Manual of Zoology* (translated and edited by J. S. Kingsley) 1902, Holt, Rinehart & Winston, Inc. (g) After Mead 1901, *Bull. U. S. Fish. Comm.* No. 19.

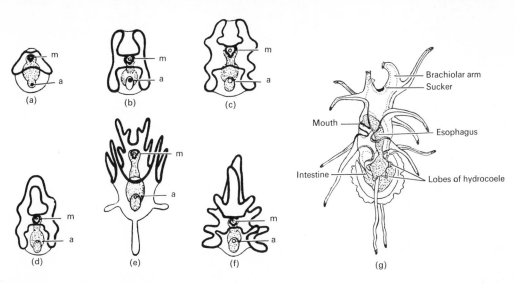

primitive characteristics not shared by any or most of the others. Starfish have open ambulacral grooves, which seem closer to the condition in Pelmatozoa. Holothuroidea did not develop pentamerous gonads, as if the metamorphosis to pentaradiate structure were incomplete in this group. In addition, sea cucumbers have a looped alimentary canal which also lacks a radial conformity. Echinoids possess a shell or test which is reminiscent of the theca of some extinct Pelmatozoa. In the Apoda (Class Holothuroidea) and in the Ophiuroidea, the canals to the buccal podia or tentacles arise directly from the water ring. Among living Eleutherozoa, the Holothuroidea and Asteroidea diverged early and may have arisen from different Pelmatozoan ancestors, although the conformation of their larval stages suggests relationship. Ophiuroidea and Echinoidea show affinities in the encasement of the radial nerve cords and water canals by ectoderm, and in the very similar larval stages, both of which are *plutei*. However, their subsequent development diverges.

The Eleutherozoa have an uncertain relationship to the Pelmatozoa. Marcus, following the opinions of Bather, Mortensen, and some paleontologists, believes that three different groups arose from the Edrioasteroidea (Fig. 18-25). These groups are Holothuroidea, Echinoidea, and the asteroid-ophiuroid combination. The Edrioasteroidea achieve this prominence by reason of the location of their ambulacral pores; a flexible theca; armless and stalkless structure; and their occasional unattached existence. Shrock and Twenhofel suggest that Holothuroidea probably, and Echinoidea possibly, were derived from Edrioasteroidea, with other Eleutherozoa, and possibly some Echinoidea, developing from some unknown Precambrian ancestors. Hyman does not accept the asteroid-ophiuroid relationship

Fig. 18-28 Diagrammatic reconstruction of hypothetical Dipleurula. Redrawn from various sources.

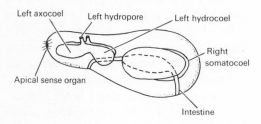

Fig. 18-29 Pentactula larvae. (a) Diagram of hypothetical ancestor from left side, (b) dorsal view, showing transition to radial stage, and (c) radial stage, lateral view, with part of atrium and two tentacles removed. After Bury 1895, *Quart. J. Micros. Sci.*, Vol. 38, courtesy of the Company of Biologists Limited.

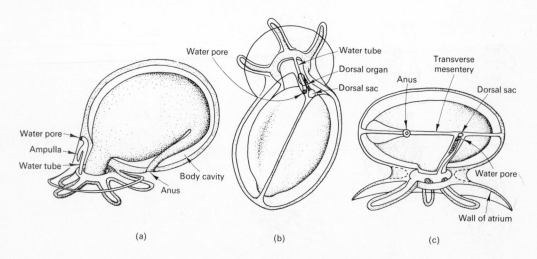

and considers that little real linkage can be established between the two subphyla.

The acceptance of a bilateral ancestor to pentaradiate echinoderms sets up a problem in metamorphosis that can be attacked principally through ontogeny. Bather developed the hypothesis of an ancestral larva called a *dipleurula* (Fig. 18-28). This larva can be pictured as an elongate, pear-shaped, ciliated organism with a mouth opening on the slightly flattened ventral side, an arched intestine running to the anus (blastopore) at the posterior end, and a series of three paired coelomic pouches. The first pair of pouches is somewhat preoral in position. These are the *axocoels* or *protocoels*. They communicate with the exterior dorsally, through paired hydroporic canals, and join broadly with the *hydrocoels (mesocoels)* which represent the second pair of pouches. More caudally, the large *somatocoels (metacoels)* are pinched off in the development or arise laterally from the archenteron. Hyman believes that the dipleurulan hypothesis fails to explain the relationship of buccal podia or tentacles to a water-vascular system of coelomic origin. Marcus suggests that a pair of tentacles developed from coelomic diverticula and that later a third diverticulum developed caudally, apparently from near the confluence of the first pair. This seems like a convenience to fit with a triradiate ambulacral pattern in a few fossils,

and with an intermediate stage of ambulacral development in some ontogenies, but some such intermediate stage may have existed between the dipleurula and the pentactula (Fig. 18-29). The hypothesis based on this larval type is supported by Hyman.

The pentactula is conceived as having five tentacles arising from a circumesophageal water ring derived from the left hydrocoel in the metamorphosis from bilateral to pentagonal symmetry. The *left* side of the embryo can thus be correlated with the oral side of the adult echinoderm. The five tentacles are considered to be the primordia of the radial canals, and subsequently the definitive podia developed laterally from them.

Despite the extensive geologic history of echinoderms (except for the Holothuroidea), the phylogenetic relationships within the group are not apparent. The uncertainty between the two subphyla has already been stated, although it is accepted that Eleutherozoa were derived from Pelmatozoa. Several groups were well established in the Cambrian. The development of these echinoderms must have been from radiation occurring in the Precambrian. Perhaps the Heterostelea with heavy endoskeleton and lack of radial symmetry are indicative of transitional forms, bridging the gap between the bilateral ancestor and the pentaradiate echinoderm.

REFERENCES

Bather, F. A., The Echinoderma. *In* (R. Lankester, ed.) A treatise on zoology, Part 4, 344 pp. London: A. & C. Black, 1900.

Bury, Henry, Studies in the embryology of the Echinoderms. Quart. J. Microsc. Sci., 29:409, 1889.
———, The metamorphosis of the Echinoderms. Quart. J. Microsc. Sci., 38:45, 1895.

Clark, A. H., A monograph of the existing crinoids. The Comatulids. Bull. U.S. Nat. Mus., Vol. I, Part 2, 795 pp., 1921.

Clark, A. M., Starfishes and their relations. London: British Museum (Natural History), 1962.

Cuénot, L., Anatomie, éthologie, et systématique des Echinodermes (pp. 1-365). *In* (P. Grassé, ed.) Traité de zoologie, Tome XI. Paris: Masson et Cie, 1948.

Feder, H. M., On the methods used by the starfish, *Pisaster ochraceus,* in opening three types of bivalved mollusks. Ecol., 36:764, 1955.

Hyman, L. H., The invertebrates: Echinodermata, Vol. IV (pp. 1-763). New York: McGraw, 1955.

Ludwig, H., Echinodermen. *In* (H. G. Bronn, ed.) Klassen und Ordnungen des Tierreichs, Band II, Abt. 3 (Books 1 and 5 by H. Ludwig; Books 2, 3, and 4 by H. Ludwig and O. Hamann), 1889-1907.

Marcus, E., On the evolution of the animal phyla. Quart. Rev. Biol., 33:24, 1958.

Mortensen, Th., Handbook of the echinoderms of the British Isles. London: Oxford U. P., 1927.

Mortensen, Th., Studies in the development of Crinoids. Carnegie Inst. Depart. Marine Biol. Wash., 16:1, 1920.

Nichols, D., Echinoderms. London: Hutchinson University Library, 1962.

Smith, J. E., On the nervous system of *Marthasterias glacialis*. Philos. Trans. Roy. Soc. London, (B) 227:111, 1937.

Thomson, Wyville, On the embryogeny of *Antedon rosaceus*. Philos. Trans. Roy. Soc. London, 155-259, 1865.

19

MINOR ENTEROCOELOUS COELOMATES

Since early in the present century, animals with strong bilaterality have been considered to fall into two major groups. Three features particularly mark the divergence between the two groups. These are the fate of the blastopore, the mode of origin of the coelom, and the onset of differentiation in the cytoplasm of blastomeres in embryology. A combination of these features is especially prominent in nemertines, annelids, molluscs, and polyclad flatworms. In these the blastopore is anterior and the definitive mouth forms in proximity to it, the coelom arises from the splitting of a pair of solid mesodermal bands, and the fate of blastomeres in early segmentation is predestined. Respectively these invertebrates are protostomatous, schizocoelic animals with determinative (or mosaic) cleavage.

In the echinoderms, the phyla considered in the present chapter, and the Protochordata the blastopore is posterior and the mouth is a new or secondary formation. The name *Deuterostomia* is derived from this feature. The coelom arises from evagination of the primitive gut wall which primarily or secondarily develops bilaterally. Such a formation is described as being enterocoelous. Thirdly, the early blastomeres are not earmarked for a given destiny—that is, they lack the differentiation that would limit their subsequent fate. Such blastomeres undergo indeterminative cleavage and are considered to be totipotent. In general, the Chordata are deuterostomous, enterocoelous animals with indeterminative cleavage also. Perhaps related to determinative cleavage, the Protostomia have diverged through a more narrow funnel and therefore exhibit greater uniformity than is characteristic of the Deuterostomia.

Each of the three small phyla to be considered briefly in this chapter possesses some unique features which militate against any consideration of close mutual relationship. These phyla are the Pogonophora, the Chaetognatha, and the Hemichordata.

This assemblage of animals is grouped by Hyman as enterocoelous coelmates. This coelom structure arises by the bilateral out-pocketing of mesoderm from the archenteron and appears to be subdivided into cavities called protosome, mesosome, and metasome. In the alternate pattern of coelom formation (schizocoelous), paired solid bands of meso-derm split or delaminate to form the coelom. The deuterostomes have a number of other features in common such as blastopore fate and presumed larval type (dipleurula), but the latter may have appeared by convergence and deuterostomes lack the close knit uni-formity seen in Protostomia. As Hyman notes, neither of these terms should be considered as taxonomic but only as a convenience. The Pogonophora show the three body divisions, correlated with coelomic development held characteristic for deuterostomates, and they show some affinity for Hemichordata. Adult chaetognaths, as Hyman points out, show most similarity to the pseudocoelomate Aschelminthes, but development of the coelom is enterocoelous, indicative of deu-terostomates. Larval structure of Hemichor-data supports affinity of this group for deu-terostomatous echinoderms. It is plain that the evidence for the phylogenetic position of this group is contradictory and puzzling.

PHYLUM POGONOPHORA

In his translator's preface to Ivanov's monograph, Pogonophora, D. B. Carlisle points out that doubtlessly tons of pogono-phorans were jettisoned as unrecognized animal life from the very expeditions that were hunting new marine species, and that this happened less than 60 years ago. Such an error suggests the very unusual character-istics of these animals, which were first reported in 1914 from material dredged from very deep marine waters in the East Indies. The initial description placed all of this material in a single species, *Siboglinum weberi,* but recent re-examination indicates that at least four genera and 16 species belonging to two different families were rep-resented. Only three species had been described by the midpoint of the present century, but Ivanov (1963) lists 70 species in 14 genera. Doubtlessly many more will be found as examination of the very deep ocean fauna is pressed and as better equip-ment is developed. One species has been found in depths ranging from about 400 to over 1,800 feet, but most species appear to be restricted to a much narrower range along much deeper areas of the continental slope and in deep ocean trenches (Fig. 1-2). Prob-ably a considerable degree of geographic isolation occasioned by shallower water leading into the trenches has accounted for the species variations. So far, most species have been found in the waters of the north-ern Pacific Ocean off the east coast of Asia and in the deep waters of the East Indies north of Australia, but many other areas have representatives such as New Zealand, the western coasts of North America and of Europe, as well as Arctic and Antarctic depths.

There are several unusual or curious features exhibited by Pogonophora. The name means beard-bearing and was derived from the lateral projections from the ten-tacles or brachia called *pinnules.* These had a filamentous or hairlike appearance on some of the early described species, although some later-discovered forms lack pinnules entirely. The dimensions of these worms are unusual; Ivanov points out that the length is at least 100 times the breadth and in one species, *Siboglinum caulleryi,* this ratio may reach 600 to one. Such dimensions suggest that these animals would be very susceptible to injury, but they live in an environment of great constancy and in addition they are all tube-dwellers, living in unbranched tubes which are always longer than the inhabitant. These tubes probably extend more or less vertically from the bottom sediment.

A feature of Pogonophora not previously seen consistently in any but parasitic metazoa is the absence of an intestine. This deficiency suggested to many investigators that Pogonophora are colonial worms with feeding function relegated to members of the colony, which by chance were not obtained in the collections. However, many complete specimens representing a variety of species have since been described. Also the absence of branched tubes indicates a solitary existence.

As in many sedentary animals, the anterior end bears tentacles or brachia which vary from one in one genus (*Siboglinum*) to more than 250 in *Galathealinum brachiosum*. In multitentaculate species, the tentacles form a one- to three-rowed horseshoe, with some species showing new tentacle formation at the open end of the horseshoe. In *Spirobrachia,* one end of the base, upon which the tentacles rest, continues growth as an internal spiral at the inner end of which new brachia are added. Pinnules, when present, occur in one or more rows on the inner face of the tentacle.

Pogonophora are elongate animals with the body unevenly divided into three sections: *protosome, mesosome,* and *metasome.* The anterior section or protosome is the shortest region of the body and bears a dorsal cephalic lobe and the tentacle or tentacles. In a number of species in the order Thecanephria the protosome is not demarked externally from the mesosome (Fig. 19-1). In the rest of this order and in all species in order Athecanephria a circumferential groove, which may not meet dorsally or ventrally, marks the separation of protosoma and mesosoma.

The mesosoma is cylindrical, or the upper and lower surfaces may be slightly flattened or even grooved. It is a relatively short region which lacks appendages but is characterized by a pair of darkly pigmented cuticular ridges called *bridle* or *frenulum* running caudally from the dorsal side in an oblique or half-spiral to meet or end separately on the ventral side (Fig. 19-1). The most probable function of the bridle is

as a temporary anchoring device enabling the animal to move up and down within its tube and especially in the more rigid lower portions of the tube. A slightly oblique annular groove, more prominent on the dorsal and ventral surfaces, separates the mesosome from the long trunk or metasome (Fig. 19-2).

Fig. 19-1 Ventral view of female, *Lamellisabella zachsi* (Pogonophora). 1, pinnules; 2, tentacles; 3, protomesosome; 4, bridle (frenulum); 5, constriction between protomesosome and trunk; 6, ventral groove; 7, metameric features on preannular section of trunk; 8, ventral folds; 9, adhesive platelets; 10, adhesive papillae; 11, trunk; 12, section of trunk without metameric features; 13, trunk; 14, belts or ridges; 15, constriction; 16, postannular part of trunk; 17, rows of adhesive papillae. After Ivanov 1954 (translated by A. Petrunkevitch), *Syst. Zool.,* **3**: 69.

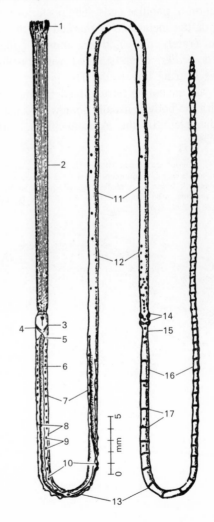

The metasome is regionally differentiated into an anterior and a posterior portion. The former has a wide ventral furrow or sulcus, bordered on either side by a ridge bearing adhesive papillae which may be capped with small cuticular studs or plaques. The papillae, probably in coordination with the bridle, serve as temporary anchors to facilitate movement within the tube or to maintain a position in it. The regular distribution of the papillae at the cephalad end of the trunk suggests a metameric condition, but further back the arrangement is very haphazard. Dorsally, the metasome integument is ciliated medially from just behind the mesosome to about the region where the metameric distribution of papillae ends. The posterior portion of the metasome is marked by two or three (rarely more) thick annular ridges called *girdles,* often studded with rasplike plates bearing tiny teeth. The girdles function as anchoring structures. Behind the girdles the body is usually somewhat smaller in diameter. In the Athecanephria, large glandular papillae or structures called shields occur dorsally, while in the Thecanephria regularly disposed transverse rows occur on the ventral side and the dorsal shields are lacking. The apparent metamerism seen in the trunk has suggested annelid relationship to some workers, but internal anatomy and embryology do not support such a contention.

The unbranched pogonophoran tube generally tapers very gradually from the anterior terminus to the smaller end of the tube embedded in the bottom sediment. The tube is always longer than the inhabitant, and the worm moves up and down inside the tube with partial emergence for feeding and respiration. The tubes have laminated walls composed principally of chitin and protein, and usually they are annular. In some species the entire tube is relatively rigid, whereas in others the anterior end is pliant and flaccid and will collapse when the inhabitant retires to the more rigid posterior section.

The tentacles typically form a crown, and pinnules (absent in a few species) extend from the tentacles toward the crown axis (Fig. 19-3). Afferent and efferent blood vessels are attached to the inner wall of the coelomic caeca which occur in the tentacles. Pinnules in *Lamellisabella zachsi* arise from a protruding base or ridge flanked on either side with a row of gland cells adjacent to the pinnules, followed by a row of ciliated cells. Cuticle occurs on the surface of other cells of the tentacles. A pinnule is reminiscent of a root-hair on plant roots since it is an epidermal cell with a protruding elongation. A minute intracellular capillary loops into the pinnule connecting the blood vessel in the tentacle. Respiration is undoubtedly a function of tentacles and of pinnules.

In at least some pogonophores the pinnules form a network or filter within the crown or intertentacular space into which microscopic food is carried by a flow activated by the cilia. Ivanov suggests that extracellular digestion occurs in this space, and that the pinnules absorb the dissolved

Fig. 19-2 Anterior end of male *Polybrachia barbata*. 2, tentacles; 3, protomesosome; 5, constriction between protomesosome and metasome; 13, trunk; 19, cephalic lobe; 24, ringed section of protomesosome. After Ivanov 1954 (translated by A. Petrunkevitch), *Syst. Zool.*, **3**: 69.

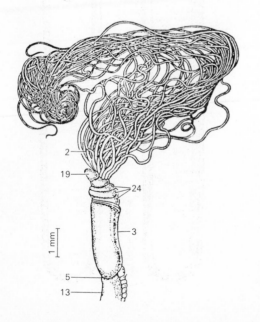

food. However, there is some evidence that in *Siboglinum ekmani,* which has a single tentacle provided with pinnules, the tentacle gropes over the surrounding mud to obtain food. In one species of this genus the single tentacle is coiled into a helix, at least when the animal is within the tube.

Excretion is accomplished by special portions of the protosomal coelomoducts. These excretory sections are restricted to the protosoma in the Athecanephria, but protrude into the mesosoma in Thecanephria. In the latter order, the elongated "renal sacs" are especially enveloped with blood vessels. The excretory fraction of the protosomal coelomoduct in the Athecanephria also are in contact with major blood vessels, from which they probably accumulate waste materials. In the mesosoma and metasoma, excretory products are accumulated by so-called coelomic nephrocytes.

The blood contains hemoglobin, and oxygenated blood returns from the tentacle area into a median dorsal vessel. In the mesosoma, this vessel broadens into a lacuna-like chamber but narrows again in the trunk. Lateral connectives serve to carry blood through the tissues to the ventral vessel, which carries it forward through a muscular enlargement termed the heart lying in the protosome. It is presumed that the heart functions to propel the blood into the tentacles. At about the level of the heart, the dorsal vessel supplies the cephalic lobe with a median and two lateral vessels which communicate by commissures and serve to supply the brain, which lies in the cutaneous epithelium in this area.

Fig. 19-3 Transverse section through tentacular crown of *Lamellisabella zachsi.* After Ivanov 1955 (translated by A. Petrunkevitch), *Syst. Zool.,* **4:** 174.

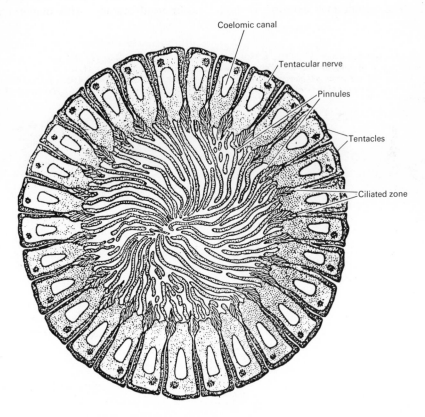

Pogonophora apparently are restricted to sexual reproduction. Gonads occur in the metasomal segment in these dioecious animals. In the male, paired sperm ducts arise from paired testes. The sperm undergo gametogenesis in groups called morulae. In specialized portions of the sperm ducts the sperm are encased in a covering called a spermatophore. It has been suggested that spermatophores are transferred to the female by use of tentacles.

A pair of elongate ovaries occupies the anterior part of the metasome in the female. The caudal end of the ovary may protrude into the coelomodual funnel, and the coelomoducts function as gonoducts. The elongate eggs are fertilized and undergo development within the tube occupied by the female, a condition which probably prevents the mother from feeding during this time.

Unequal holoblastic segmentation eventually produces an ovoid embryo in *Siboglinum caulleryi*. The ectodermal exterior is first demarked from the mass of interior cells, but no blastocoele or blastopore is formed. Most of the internal cells are heavily laden with yolk, and from the anterior end of this mass the mesoderm begins to differentiate and forms a single median *protocoele*. Lateral proliferation of the mesoderm gives rise to paired coelomic cavities which later are separated into mesocoelic and metacoelic portions (Fig. 19-4 (a), (b)). The similarity of coelomic development in Enteropneusta is seen in Figure 19-4 (c).

PHYLUM CHAETOGNATHA

This small phylum is composed of marine organisms with a body differentiated into head, trunk, and tail (Fig. 19-5). The common name for these animals is arrowworm, a name derived from the resemblance to a blunt, stocky arrow. Chaetognatha are cylindroid animals with bilateral symmetry

Fig. 19-4 Comparing coelom development in Pogonophora and Enteropneusta. The development of a median protocoele and paired lateral coeloms is seen in (a), while the isolation of the metacoele by constriction is shown in (b). These two diagrams are adapted from Ivanov 1963, for the pogonophoran, *Siboglinum caulleryi*. (c) Is a time-lapse composite diagram of the enteropneustan, *Saccoglossus pusillus*. The three part condition of the coelom actually appears considerably after blastopore closure is obliterated. Greatly modified from Davis 1908.

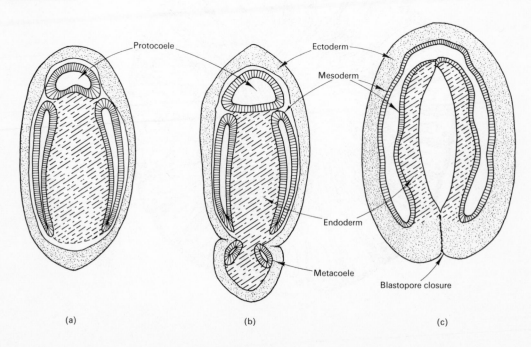

(a)　　　　　　　　(b)　　　　　　　　(c)

externally emphasized by one or two pairs of lateral fins, a commonly bilobed tailfin, and a head armed with paired groups of spines and teeth. Since these small animals are nearly transparent, the bilaterality is evident internally, particularly in the prominent genital organs. Some chaetognaths are nearly four inches long, but most are less than half that length.

Six genera of Chaetognatha are recognized. Most of these are planktonic or more correctly, nektonic, but one genus occurs on the ocean floor in relatively shallow water. Chaetognaths have a cosmopolitan distribution in marine waters, and they also show a considerable vertical range.

The head is rounded or slightly angular and usually is a little larger than the anterior trunk. A fold of the body wall called a hood encircles the head obliquely, and acts as a

retractile cover for the movable curved spines which are attached laterally in rows. The slitlike mouth opens on the ventral surface of the head from a concavity called the vestibule. The alimentary canal, enlarged as a muscular pharyngeal bulb, continues thereafter in a straight line to the anus, which opens ventrally near the posterior end of the trunk lumen.

The nervous system is well developed. There is a cerebral ganglion or brain connected to paired ganglia lateral to the pharynx, and these are joined by a ventral commissure. Another pair of commissures encircle the foregut obliquely to join the ventral ganglion in the trunk, from which paired lateral and posterior nerves arise and branch to form plexuses. Special organs include a pair of eyes lying dorsally on the head and a glandular ciliated oval ring situated dorsally on the anterior trunk. This ring may extend forward on the head where it lies between the eyes. It is presumed to be chemoreceptive. Various tactile bristles also are characteristic of these animals.

The pair of ovaries in the monoecious chaetognaths are elongated organs lying in the posterior trunk lumen, where they are attached to the lateral walls by a membrane (Fig. 19-6). A flattened double-walled oviduct extends along this side of each ovary

Fig. 19-5 Chaetognatha, *Sagitta*, diagrammatic drawing, ventral view. After Lea 1955, courtesy of the Journal of the Fisheries Research Board of Canada, **12:** 593.

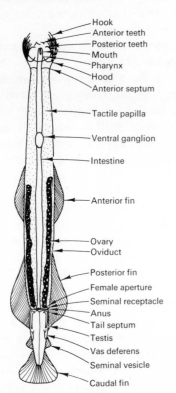

Fig. 19-6 Chaetognatha. Transverse section of the body of *Sagitta*. In a less contracted specimen, the ovary and oviduct form a rodlike structure attached to a wall by a mesentery. Modified after L. Hertwig, from R. Hertwig, *A Manual of Zoology* (translated and edited by J. S. Kingsley) 1902, Holt, Rinehart & Winston, Inc.

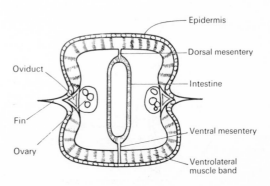

and expands to form a seminal receptacle. The testes occur in the coelomic cavity of the tail segment. Sperm ducts (vasa deferentia) lead to laterally bulging seminal vesicles where spermatophores are formed. Fertilization is internal, but whether by self-fertilization or cross-fertilization is not clear, since some chaetognaths are protandrous. Cleavage is holoblastic and eventually produces a coeloblastula. The blastopore appearing at embolic gastrulation is posterior, and the coelom develops by paired outfolding of the primitive gut (Fig. 19-7).

Fig. 19-7 Composite diagrams to show endomesodermal folds and primordial germ cells in *Sagitta*. Highly modified from Hertwig, *A Manual of Zoology* (translated and edited by J. S. Kingsley) 1902, Holt, Rinehart & Winston, Inc.

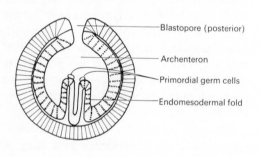

Blastopore (posterior)

Archenteron

Primordial germ cells

Endomesodermal fold

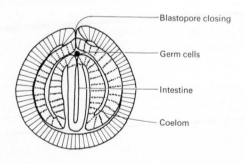

Blastopore closing

Germ cells

Intestine

Coelom

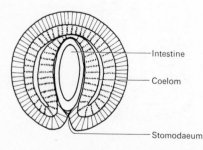

Intestine

Coelom

Stomodaeum

The unquestionable enterocoelous formation of the early coelom is well substantiated, but later the coelomic cavities as well as the gut lumen disappear, being obliterated by growth of the larva within the confines of the egg shell. Later cavities reappear in both head and trunk, but neither the lining of these cavities nor the mesenteries are characteristic of typical coelomic structures. The mesenteries appear to have an endodermic origin.

Nektonic species of chaetognaths are able to remain at a given depth for a considerable period without swimming. Since they eventually do sink, it is possible that some hydrostatic mechanism is functioning while suitable energy is available. Swimming is initiated if the chaetognath begins to sink.

Swimming results in a spasmodic or saltatory action occasioned by a very rapid, almost vibratory movement of the tail and trunk. The forward swimming movement carries the animal about two inches, but the momentum engendered results in a considerable coast, after which the chaetognath resumes a stationary position.

Planktonic or nektonic chaetognaths are predaceous and capture food by a talonlike action of the anterior spines, which clutch the prey as the chaetognath darts toward it. The benthonic genus, *Spadella*, which occurs in more shallow waters, is equipped with adhesive papillae, and is able to grab prey without losing its hold on the substrate. Food consists of various small animals forming part of the plankton. Crustacea, especially copepods, and minute fish are common in the diet, but cannibalism is frequent for some chaetognaths. Food is swallowed whole, apparently aided by a lubricating secretion from pharyngeal glands. Digestion occurs in the posterior, relatively nonglandular section of the intestine.

Chaetognaths serve as hosts to a number of parasites. Amoebae, some sporozoa, and representatives of flagellate and ciliate protozoa have been found. Among metazoa, nematodes, larval cestodes, and both larval and adult trematodes have been described from Chaetognatha.

PHYLUM HEMICHORDATA

A variety of marine animals occurs in this phylum described in the Traité de Zoologie under the name of Stomochordata. This group has been divided into classes, two of which are universally accepted. The Class Pterobranchia has three genera, some of which superficially resemble Bryozoa with a crown of arms bearing tentacles and a recurved digestive tract. The three genera are *Cephalodiscus, Rhabdopleura,* and *Atubaria. Cephalodiscus* lives in aggregates within a common more or less tubular housing secreted by the animals and called a *coenecium; Atubaria* is a related form which lacks a coenecium, and *Rhabdopleura* produces a septate coenecium which gives rise to erect branches housing individual zooids (Fig. 19-8). This last genus exists as a colonial form, with a living stolon joining the various zooids. The zooids in these three genera have no gill slits or only one.

The Pterobranchia are found in deep marine waters, more commonly south of the equator although they have been found off Japan, the northern coast of Europe, and west Greenland. A number of species have been found in Antarctic waters.

Pterobranchia appear to be very primitive hemichordates. The genus *Cephalodiscus* produces a ciliated larva with an apical organ similar to the enteropneustan *tornaria,* a form long recognized for its similarity to echinoderm larvae. Hyman supports the argument that the echinoderm water-vascular system originally functioned as a food-getting device. The tentaculated arms containing coelomic extensions of the mesosomal coelom in the pterobranchs may well be homologous with the radial canal system of echinoderms. Possibly a pterobranchlike ancestor gave rise to the Enteropneusta with loss of tentacles and increased emphasis on a system of gill slits. Some features of the nervous system, such as its dorsal position and its infrequent formation as a hollow structure, have been used as supportive evidence for vertebrate affinities. The pterobranch-enteropneust line seems to supply

Fig. 19-8 Class Pterobranchia. Sagittal section of a single zooid of *Rhabdopleura* partly extended from a coenocium joining other members of the colony. Redrawn from Shrock and Twenhofel 1953 (modified after Delage and Hérouard, 1897), courtesy of the McGraw-Hill Book Company.

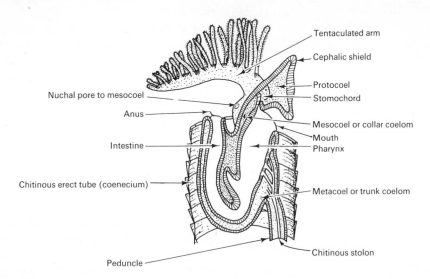

much more convincing evidence of vertebrate affinity than does the echinoderm, which thereby takes a position as a blind branch developing from the pterobranchs. The reader is referred to the Traité de Zoologie, Tome XI, or to The Invertebrates, Volume V, for an extensive discussion of these genera.

Class Enteropneusta are substantial, solitary hemichordates. They are most common in the intertidal zone but are often secreted in burrows or under available protective coverage. Most enteropneusts are between six and eighteen inches in length, but one species is only about one inch long and another may exceed six feet. They differ from representatives of Class Pterobranchia in the presence of numerous gill slits, a straight alimentary canal, and the absence of a crown of tentaculated arms.

The Enteropneusta, often under the name of Hemichordata, were formerly considered to be primitive members of Phylum Chordata. The notochord characteristic of this phylum was thought to be represented by a tube or rod of tissue which projected forward in the median line from the anterior, dorsal wall of the foregut. This same structure was called *stomochord* by other investigators, and this term has been carried over as an alternate name (Stomochordata) for this phylum. This outpocket of the endo-

Fig. 19-9 Hemichordata, diagrammatic drawing of *Dolichoglossus*. From Schechter 1959, courtesy of Prentice-Hall, Inc.

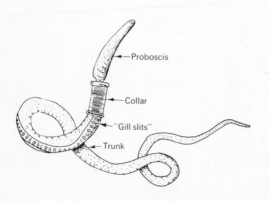

dermal epithelium is no longer considered to be a notochord, and in fact it appears to be comparable to a transitory structure seen in vertebrate embryology, called *Seessel's Pouch*. The presence of gill slits in Enteropneusta and Chordata is probably the closest point of similarity between the two phyla, and an independent origin has been suggested for this feature.

The body of an enteropneustan (Fig. 19-9) is divided into three regions as is generally characteristic of invertebrate deuterostomes. The anterior section is the proboscis, equivalent to the protosome of Pogonophora. It is a short conical or globular knoblike structure which narrows caudally to a neck often hidden by the mesosome.

The proboscis coelom is unpaired anteriorly, but more caudally it continues as paired compartments. As is common with coeloms of the collar and trunk, the cavity in the proboscis tends to be reduced by modification of coelomic walls into connective tissue and muscle, often with loss of a well-defined peritoneum. The proboscis coelom opens to the outside through a median, unilateral or paired pores connecting with the compartments. When only a single pore is present, whether median or lateral, it usually joins the left coelomic compartment, analogous to a situation occurring in developing echinoderms.

The mesosome or collar is also a short region. It is a cylindrical structure, the anterior end of which encompasses the posterior end of the proboscis. The surface of the collar is often wrinkled or it may be irregularly bossed.

The collar coelom in enteropneusts actually, albeit sometimes indistinctly, is a paired structure, and paired pores open to the exterior. The coelomic fluid in both proboscis and collar coeloms is very similar to sea water.

The trunk or metasome forms the major portion of the body. Commonly the trunk is demarked into two general zones: the anterior portion is somewhat flattened with the paired gill pores opening laterally, while the more cylindrical posterior portion, often more uniform in diameter, may taper caudally. In some genera the gonads form protuberances or pronounced flanges. The latter often occur caudally for some distance on the anterior trunk, and this finlike flange tends to curl dorsally so that in these genera the metasome is further differentiated.

The coelom of the metasome or trunk is paired and the two sides are in communication by an interrupted dorsal mesentery. Unlike fluid in the other coelomic cavities, that of the trunk contains many cellular elements and will coagulate.

The digestive tract is generally or regionally ciliated along most of its length. The mouth opens ventrally in the anterior recess of the collar below its junction with the proboscis. Unicellular glands and tall cilia are prominent in the short portion of the diges-

tive tract within the collar. Starting just behind the collar, gill pores open laterally into the digestive canal, here called the pharynx, with the more ventral part of the lumen specialized for digestive function. The tract continues behind the pharynx with varying histological differentiation to the terminal anus. The Enteropneusta are ciliary feeders. Microscopic food, entangled in mucus from the proboscis, is swept into the mouth by ciliary action.

The nervous system (Fig. 19-10) is not strongly developed in this class. In the proboscis a dorsal cord and usually a ventral cord are prominent. A ring commissure is present near the proboscis base. In some species, a series of longitudinal nerves extend toward the anterior end of the proboscis from this commissure. The dorsal cord of the proboscis is continuous into the collar, where it lies deeper and in some gen-

Fig. 19-10 Plan of the nervous system in *Saccoglossus cambrensis*. *a*, anterior nerve ring; *c*, nervous layer of collar epidermis; *d*, dorsal nerve cord (trunk); *dp*, middorsal nerve cord (proboscis); *fn*, nervous system fans out on proboscis base; *n*, dorsal nerve cord (collar); *r*, circumenteric nerve rings; *v*, ventral nerve cord (trunk). After Knight-Jones 1952, courtesy of the Royal Society of London.

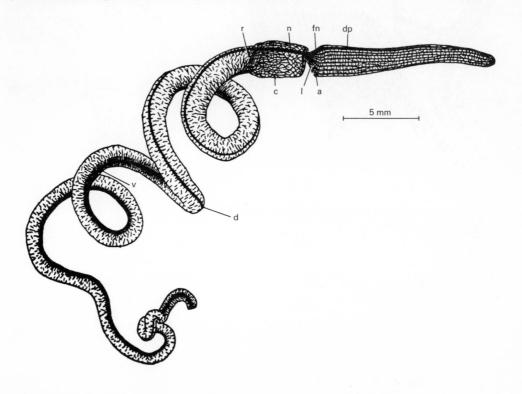

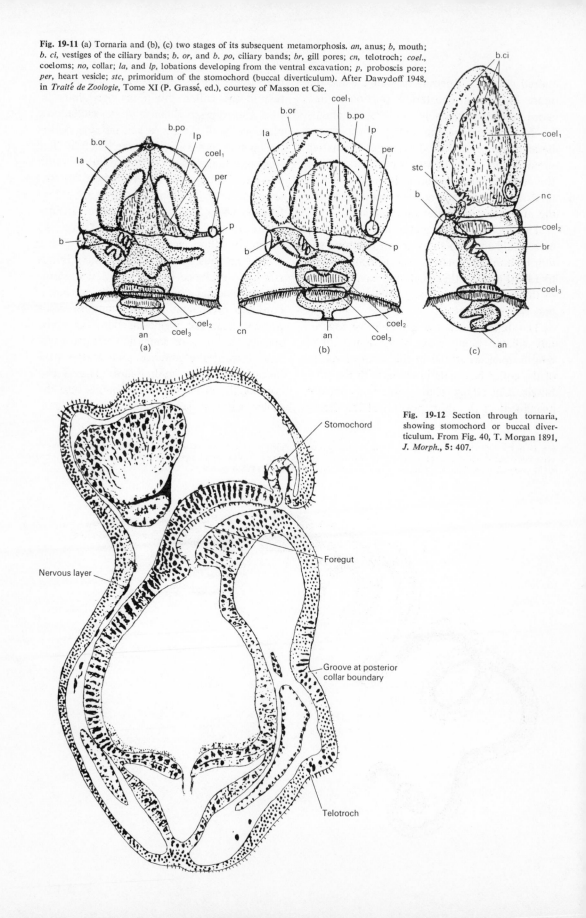

Fig. 19-11 (a) Tornaria and (b), (c) two stages of its subsequent metamorphosis. *an*, anus; *b*, mouth; *b. ci*, vestiges of the ciliary bands; *b. or*, and *b. po*, ciliary bands; *br*, gill pores; *cn*, telotroch; *coel.*, coeloms; *no*, collar; *la*, and *lp*, lobations developing from the ventral excavation; *p*, proboscis pore; *per*, heart vesicle; *stc*, primoridum of the stomochord (buccal diverticulum). After Dawydoff 1948, in *Traité de Zoologie*, Tome XI (P. Grassé, ed.), courtesy of Masson et Cie.

Fig. 19-12 Section through tornaria, showing stomochord or buccal diverticulum. From Fig. 40, T. Morgan 1891, *J. Morph.*, **5**: 407.

era possesses a lumen. The dorsal cord continues into the metasome, lying in the intraepidermal situation characteristic of its position in the proboscis. At the junction of mesosome and metasome, the dorsal cord connects with prominent branches that pass on either side of the alimentary canal to join and continue in the trunk as the ventral cord.

The circulatory system is well developed. A dorsal blood vessel situated immediately below the dorsal nerve cord carries blood forward into a complex of lacunar spaces, some of which are contractile lying in the proboscis base. All the blood from this area circulates through a set of loops projecting into the protocoele. This set of loops constitutes the *glomerulus* and is considered to have excretory function. Blood leaves the glomerulus to circulate through the proboscis or to join the ventral vessel in the posterior part of the collar. Blood flows caudally in the ventral vessel, which like the dorsal vessel is contractile. Various plexuses join these two blood vessels. In the region of the pharynx the blood is presumably aerated in passing to the dorsal vessel through the gill complex.

The Enteropneusta are dioecious and the gonads lie in the cephalad end of the metacoele. Fertilization occurs in sea water. Development in species having small-yolked eggs involves the formation of a ciliated larva called a *tornaria* (Fig. 19-11), which bears considerable resemblance to some echinoderm larvae. Metamorphosis of this larva into an adult enteropneust involves formation of a constriction which is the primordium of the proboscis-collar junction (Fig. 19-12).

REFERENCES

de Beauchamp, P., Classe des Chetognathes (pp. 1500-1520). *In* (P. Grassé, ed.) Traité de zoologie, Tome V, Fasc. II. Paris: Masson et Cie, 1960.

Bullock, T., The anatomical organization of the nervous system of Enteropneusta. Quart. J. Microsc. Sci., 86:55, 1945.

Burfield, S. C., *Sagitta*. Liverpool Mar. Biol. Comm. Memoirs, 28, 104 pp., 1927.

Davis, B. M., The early life history of *Dolichoglossus pusillus* Ritter. Univ. Calif. Publ. Zool., 4:187, 1908.

Dawydoff, C., Classe des Enteropneustes (pp. 367-453). *In* (P. Grassé, ed.) Traité de zoologie, Tome XI. Paris: Masson et Cie, 1948.

Hyman, L. H., The invertebrates: smaller coelomate groups, Vol. V. New York: McGraw, 1959.

Knight-Jones, E., The nervous system of *Saccoglossus cambrensis*. Philos. Trans. Roy. Soc. London, (B) 236:315, 1952.

Ivanov, A. V. (trans. A. Petrunkevitch), New Pogonophora from far eastern seas. Syst. Zool., 3:69, 1954.

———— (trans. A. Petrunkevitch), On external digestion in Pogonophora. Syst. Zool., 4:174, 1955.

———— (trans. A. Petrunkevitch), The nervous system of Pogonophora. Syst. Zool., 8:96, 1959.

————, Classe des Pogonophores (pp. 1521-1622). *In* (P. Grassé, ed.) Traité de zoologie, Tome V, Fasc. II. Paris: Masson et Cie, 1960.

————, Pogonophora (trans. D. B. Carlisle). London: Academic, 1963.

Lea, Helen E., The Chaetognaths of western Canadian coastal waters. J. Can. Fisheries Research Board, 12:593- 617, 1955.

20
PROTOCHORDATA

Man belongs to the phylum Chordata and has an abiding interest in the possible ancestral path pursued in the evolutionary development of that group as we know it today. At some stage in the ontogenetic development of chordates there are a notochord, a hollow dorsal nerve cord, paired pharyngeal gill pouches, and a postanal tail. One or more of these features are lost or modified in that group of chordates called vertebrates. One uniform change is the replacement of the notochord with cartilaginous or bony vertebrae. The chordates that possess vertebrae also possess a brain case called a skull or cranium. The presence of vertebrae and a skull separates the Vertebrata or Craniata from a smaller group of invertebrate chordates. Two divisions or subphyla compose the acraniate chordates. These are the Urochordata (Tunicata) and the Cephalochordata. One view also includes the Hemichordata with the protochordates, but they are considered here as a separate invertebrate phylum.

SUBPHYLUM UROCHORDATA

The urochordates are a successful group composed of more than a hundred extant genera, the more typical members of which occur in the littoral zone. This subphylum is divided into three classes—the Ascidacea, the Thaliacea, and the Larvacea (Appendicularia).

An alternate name for the urochordates is Tunicata, a name derived from an external integument or tunic absent in the neotenic Larvacea. This protective investment is composed of a ground substance called *tunicin,* with protein and polysaccaride components and water. The polysaccharides usually include varying amounts of cellulose, a substance no longer unique among chordates, since a structurally related cellulose occurs in mammalian connective tissue.

Class Ascidiacea

The ascidians are typically sessile or stalked urochordates widely distributed in the coastal waters of the continental shelf (Fig. 1-2) where they are usually attached to the sides or undersurfaces of relatively unfouled substrates such as rocks, shells, or wood pilings. Those ascidians occurring in the deeper ocean waters appear to be specialized.

Class Ascidiacea contains the more representative and typical tunicates and Berrill considers *Ciona* and *Diazona,* both of which belong to the Order Enterogona and suborder Phlebobranchiata, as the least specialized solitary and budding genera extant respectively. *Ciona* will serve as the example for discussion of the group (Fig. 20-1).

Ascidians, commonly called sea squirts from the ability to propel water from the siphons, are cylindroid, often vase-shaped animals typically attached as adults. In *Ciona,* there is no stalk or peduncle and the organ systems twist through the base of the trunk. In many pedunculate forms, loops of these organ systems extend into the stalk.

Urochordates are microphagous ciliary feeders. In the tunicates, water carrying the plankton that serves as food enters the buccal siphon. The propulsive force is due principally to the rather long cilia on the stigmata opening from the pharynx to the atrium. Note the arrows on the right side of the cross-sectional diagram of *Ciona* (Fig. 20-2). These cilia are of such length (not indicated in the diagram) that the double row spanning the opening would serve to close the stigma if these cilia were inactive, but their normal beat forces water from the pharynx to the surrounding atrium. Large particles are prevented from entering the

Fig. 20-1 Composite diagram of sectioned tunicate, *Ciona intestinalis,* modified after Hertwig, *A Manual of Zoology* (translated and edited by J. S. Kingsley) 1902, Holt, Rinehart & Winston, Inc.

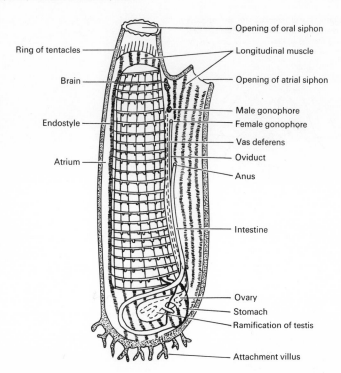

Ring of tentacles

Brain

Endostyle

Atrium

Opening of oral siphon

Longitudinal muscle

Opening of atrial siphon

Male gonophore

Female gonophore

Vas deferens

Oviduct

Anus

Intestine

Ovary

Stomach

Ramification of testis

Attachment villus

pharynx by the oral tentacles (Fig. 20-1). The microscopic food that enters the pharynx is filtered through a sheet of mucus secreted principally by the *endostyle* in ascidians. This sheet of mucus is moved laterally from the endostyle by the short cilia situated on the inner and upper aspects of this elongate organ. Cilia lining the sides of the pharynx serve to carry the filtering mucus sheet dorsally, and plankton is filtered from the water passing out the stigmata. In tunicates, like *Ciona,* fingerlike *languets* (Fig. 20-2) concentrate the mucus sheets into a cord, and this cord with its entrapped food is carried back to the esophagus. Probably most digestion occurs in the stomach lumen. The intestine leads from the stomach and opens into the atrial cavity.

The pharyngeal wall also serves as a respiratory organ. Both the longitudinal and transverse bars delimiting the stigmata as well as papilla projecting inward from these bars contain blood channels (Figs. 20-2 and 20-3). The heart of *Ciona* is a looped fold developing from the wall of an initially paired pericardial cavity communicating with the pharynx. In this genus, the heart is associated with an intestinal loop and opens at either end into sinuslike vessels. The heart is remarkable for the reversal of its beat. The pericardial cavity (epicardium of some tunicates) is of mesodermal origin and is sometimes considered to be a

Fig. 20-3 Section of pharyngeal wall of the tunicate, *Ciona intestinalis,* from the side adjacent to the pharyngeal cavity. Modified from Hertwig, *A Manual of Zoology* (translated and edited by J. S. Kingsley) 1902, Holt, Rinehart & Winston, Inc.

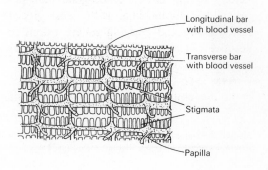

Fig. 20-2 Composite diagram of a cross-section of the tunicate *Ciona.* Horizontal pharyngeal bars are indicated on the left and vertical pharyngeal bars on the right. Blood vessels are present in both. Arrows indicate water movement.

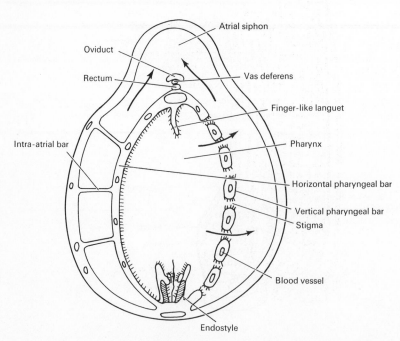

coelomic remnant. The blood contains a variety of cells, some of which are phagocytic and which may have excretory function. Some amoebocytes apparently collect and store nitrogenous wastes. Such cells are apt to occur in aggregates near gonads and intestine. A finely branched diverticulum of the intestine called the pyloric gland extending over the exterior of the intestine may have some excretory function. Finally, a structure closely associated with the brain opens in front of the gill region and shows some indication of excretory function.

Ciona and its closer relatives are hermaphroditic, oviparous, and produce small eggs which are fertilized externally and hatch in about 24 hours to a tadpole stage that initially is negatively geotropic or positively phototropic. *Ciona* tadpoles often produce a gas bubble which favors movement to sur-

Fig. 20-4 Composite diagram to show chordate characteristics of tadpole larva (a) and metamorphosis to adult ascidian (b) through (d). Adapted from various sources.

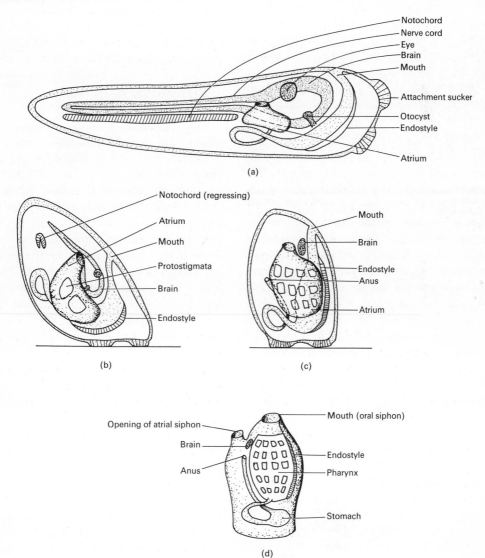

face waters. Depending upon the genus, the nonfeeding tadpole stage develops in the surface plankton in one-half to several hours, when its tropistic behavior is reversed and shaded substrates are sought. It must be borne in mind that most ascidian tadpoles are minute—*Ciona* for instance is less than a millimeter in length after attachment, and an attached position where heavy debris might accumulate would likely be fatal for such small larvae.

Tunicates reveal most chordate structures only during the larval tadpole stage. There is a notochord lying mostly in the tail, a feature responsible for the name of Urochordata. A hollow nerve tube lies dorsal to the notochord and is continuous with a somewhat larger trunk vesicle which usually is associated with sensory units called ocelli and otoliths. This trunk vesicle gives rise to the cerebral ganglion or brain of the adult.

On the anterior surface of the trunk are three papillae which secrete adhesive material when the free-swimming tadpole becomes attached. The secreted tunic is already present over the entire body of the tadpole. Present in the trunk area is the *atrium,* which invaginates as a paired or single vesicle adjacent to the pharynx. A pair of primary stigmata or gill slits open from the pharynx into the atrial cavity or cavities. Later the stigmata increase in number, initially giving rise to six protostigmata which subsequently subdivide to achieve the definitive number. These may achieve a bent-U or even a spiral pattern in some genera. The mouth, which may or may not be perforate, opens into an enlarged pharynx containing a ventral *endostyle*. The digestive tract continues as a sinuous tube which initially ends blindly but in later metamorphosis opens into the atrial cavity.

At the time of attachment the tail with its contained notochord and nerve cord is resorbed, and differential growth results in a rotation of about 180 degrees of the organs within the trunk region (Fig. 20-4). The mouth becomes the buccal siphon, and in

Ciona a single atrial opening with a somewhat elevated rim becomes the definitive atrial siphon (Fig. 20-1). The cerebral ganglion or brain of the adult tunicate lies between the two siphons, and a variable number of mixed nerves arise from it.

Asexual reproduction in the form of budding is highly developed in many urochordates. An extensive colony of separate individuals is connected by a common stolon from which they have budded. In some genera budding occurs elsewhere than from a stolon. Some ascidians have groups of small individuals radiating from a central point at which is located a common atrial opening. Two or more of these star-shaped groups may occur within a common tunic.

Class Thaliacea

The Thaliacea, comprising only a few genera, are divided into three subgroups. These animals have a free-swimming existence in the plankton. The atrial and oral openings are at opposite ends of the barrel-shaped body. *Doliolum* is a solitary thalacian widespread in the North Atlantic. Locomotion is effected by propulsion of water through the animal caused by the periodic contraction of eight muscular bands, but the feeding current is produced by the ciliated stigmata—a situation not unlike that in ascidians, although the mucus-filter functions as a net in the funnel-shaped pharynx (Fig. 20-5).

The sexual individual produces gonads and is oviparous. Cleavage is rapid and soon leads to an elongated tailed larval stage enclosed in a large perivitelline cavity and with an anterior transitory rostellum. The tail appears to be without function unless as a temporary storage of nutrients. There is little metamorphosis; the ovoid body of the adult remains after resorption of rostellar and tail portions. This adult lacks gonads, but develops a budding stolon, some of the buds eventually producing sexual individuals.

Fig. 20-5 *Doliolum*, Class Thaliacea. This is a solitary type. Adapted from Hertwig, *A Manual of Zoology* (translated and edited by J. S. Kingsley) 1902, Holt, Rinehart & Winston, Inc.

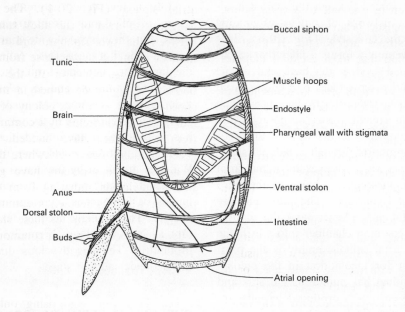

Buccal siphon

Tunic

Muscle hoops

Endostyle

Brain

Pharyngeal wall with stigmata

Ventral stolon

Anus

Dorsal stolon

Intestine

Buds

Atrial opening

Fig. 20-6 The urochordate, *Salpa*, asexual stage. (a) ventral view, (b) lateral view. The stolon will give rise by budding to a chain of salps in which some individuals will develop sexual organs. Modified from Hertwig, *A Manual of Zoology* (translated and edited by J. S. Kingsley) 1902, Holt, Rinehart & Winston, Inc.

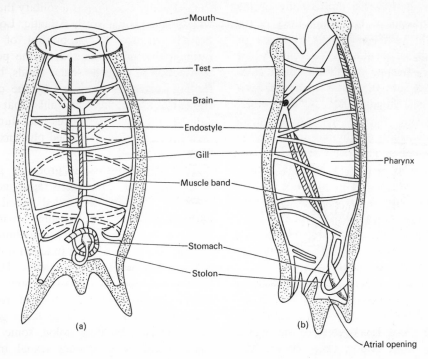

Mouth

Test

Brain

Endostyle

Gill

Pharynx

Muscle band

Stomach

Stolon

(a)

(b)

Atrial opening

In *Salpa,* the gills are reduced to a pair of elongate openings flanking the median gill bar. Water forced through the animal is filtered by a network of mucus originating mainly in the endostyle (Fig. 20-6). This network eventually forms a filter that catches suspended food at the back end of the pharynx. *Salpa* reproduces by budding from a stolon. Some organisms produce eggs which obtain nourishment from the mother and which develop into adults without undergoing metamorphosis through a tadpole stage.

Pyrosoma, which derives its name from its high luminescence, belongs to the third subgroup of Thaliaceans. The individuals are joined in tubular colonies, and the outflow through a common chamber into which the individual atrial siphons empty is the principal factor for locomotion in the colony. Each individual has numerous gill slits and the feeding current is produced by cilia lining the gill slits. Each member of the colony produces a large-yolked egg which develops into a larva that reproduces by budding after escaping from the parent organism.

Class Larvacea

Only a few genera compose this subgroup of planktonic, transparent urochordates, but they have a wide marine distribution. The Larvacea (also called Appendicularia) are neotenic forms most closely related to *Doliolum* and its relatives. The tadpole stage is somewhat masked by the sharp ventral curvature of the tail. The group has no cellulose in the tunic, which is a mucoid layer entirely enveloping the animal. Water is drawn in by the action of the tail, and food is entrapped in the surrounding mucus or in mucous secretions of the endostyle. The animals become sexually mature as larvae and are hermaphroditic and protandric. The egg develops directly into the neotenic tadpole stage.

SUBPHYLUM CEPHALOCHORDATA

The animal familiarly known as Amphioxus to the general zoology student is a

Fig. 20-7 Composite diagram of the cephalochordate, *Branchiostoma lanceolatum* (Amphioxus) to show some chordate features and some organ systems. Protonephridia are not indicated.

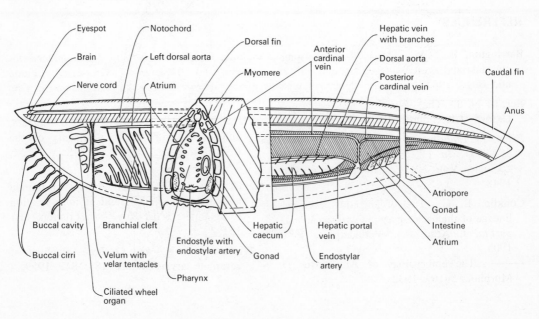

cephalochordate. However, the correct generic designation is *Branchiostoma*. One other living genus, *Asymmetron*, belongs to the Cephalochordata.

Since Amphioxus is commonly studied in vertebrate zoology as representing an animal near the ancestry of the vertebrates, no discussion of its anatomy and physiology will be attempted here, except for some features possibly indicative of its evolutionary position.

Amphioxus possesses the chordate characteristics of a notochord, paired gill slits, a hollow dorsal nerve cord, and a postanal tail (Fig. 20-7). In addition it has an iodine-binding endostyle. Iodine binding occurs to a lesser degree in ascidians as well as with the ammocoete larva of lampreys. Such biochemical evidence supports homology with the vertebrate thyroid gland, but it must be remembered that iodine-binding occurs in a number of invertebrates. Much weaker evidence suggests a possible homology between certain cells in the floor of the Amphioxus cerebral vesicle and part of the vertebrate pituitary. Some other elements of the nervous system suggest relationship between vertebrates and cephalochordates, and the lack of jaws in Amphioxus is paralleled among jawless vertebrates such as lampreys. Segmentation appears to have arisen more than once in the animal kingdom. Establishment of homology is a difficult procedure, as is the alternate proof for similarity by convergence, and it is well to remember Pasteur's admonition, "Be very careful when you are looking for a thing or you will be sure to find it."

The ascidian tadpole larva has a number of features similar to those in Amphioxus and in vertebrates. Also Amphioxus like most Urochordata has an atrium and is a microphagous, ciliary feeder. The embryology of ascidians and Amphioxus is very similar.

Amphioxus is a bottom-dwelling animal, widespread but restricted to marine substrata in the littoral zone below low-tide level where it lives a relatively sedentary existence burrowing in sand.

Finally one feature of Amphioxus is of peculiar interest. The adults possess protonephridial excretory organs, unique among the deuterostomates.

REFERENCES

Barrington, E. J. W., The biology of Hemichordata and Protochordata. London: Oliver and Boyd, 1965.

Berrill, N. J., The origin of the vertebrates. Oxford: Clarendon, 1955.

Brien, P., Embranchement des Tuniciers (pp. 553-894). *In* (P. Grassé, ed.) Traité de zoologie, Vol. XI. Paris: Masson et Cie, 1948.

Conklin, E. G., The organization and cell lineage of the ascidian egg, *Cynthia* (*Styela*) *partita*. J. Acad. Sci., Philadelphia, 13:1, 1905.

———, The embryology of Amphioxus. J. Morphol., 54:69, 1932.

Drach, P., Embranchement des Cephalocordes (pp. 931-1040). *In* (P. Grassé, ed.) Traité de zoologie, Vol. XI. Paris: Masson et Cie, 1948.

Garstang, W., The embryology of the Tunicata, and its bearing on the phylogeny of the Chordata. Quart. J. Microsc. Sci., 72:51, 1928.

Hall, D. A., and H. Saxl, Studies of human and tunicate cellulose and of their relation to reticulin. Proc. Roy. Soc. London, (B) 155:202, 1961.

Wickstead, J. H., and Q. Bone, Ecology of acraniate larvae. Nature, 184:1849, 1959.

21

PHYLOGENETIC
RESUME

Two of the bases upon which Darwin built his theory of the Origin of Species were, first, the tendency of living organisms to overproduce and, second, the chances for survival in the face of the competition thereby established. It is surely apparent that the livable environments of our planet are heavily populated. At the same time, we are constantly astonished at the number and variety of organisms that have become adapted to environments intolerable to the majority. It is generally accepted that the multitudinous variety of organisms both living and extinct are the descendants of a single or of a relatively few primordial organized aggregates of chemicals endowed with the characteristics by which we define life. Therefore the living and fossil organisms which have been described bear geneological relationships to each of the others as well as to the undoubtedly many extinct forms that left little or no fossil trace.

Classification of organisms is the science of taxonomy or systematics, and it involves placing organisms into a proper and ordered relationship. Classification obviously is essential for communication whether in science or in everyday life. Books in the library or groceries on the supermarket shelves have an ordered arrangement. The classification of tomato products in the supermarket might serve as an illustration for artificial classification. Fresh tomatoes, canned tomatoes, tomato juice, tomato paste, and tomato catsup under a natural or phylogenetic system would all be shelved together. In practice, however, we look for fresh tomatoes among vegetables (a nonscientific designation) and only by chance among fruits (which botanically they are). Tomato juice is found with the other juices, both vegetable and fruit, and tomato paste is often found near the spaghetti. This is a practical classification with which we are familiar and is akin to an artificial system in zoology whereby animals are grouped by obviously similar characteristics without special regard for homology and other features indicative of relative lineage. Artificial classification has a useful and demonstrably practical place in biology and is a familiar component of *keys,* the commonly used tool for rapid identification. A natural system of classification is based on the aggregate similarities of many characteristics, since the possibility of convergent development in a single feature well may mask an otherwise unrelated or only remotely related condition. Obviously, since homologous structures often exhibit close structural similarity, artificial systems may overlap on natural systems, but the ideal goal is to mirror true phylogenetic relationship. Anything less represents disorder—or at best a purely pragmatic solution. As Simpson points out (p. 50), "Phylogeny is the appropriate theoretical background for taxonomy."

An important feature in the development of a phylogenetic system is recognition that the word species symbolizes not an individual but a group: that the individual represents one variant in a population. This is one of the reasons that species is a most difficult term to define, as is apparent from the discussion in Chapter 1. The practical and essential function of the type concept is to designate a type specimen as a standard of reference for the application of a zoological name. A type specimen is a name-bearer, and it provides an objective representation or point of reference for the *name* of a species. It does not and cannot determine the limits of the species to which it gives a name. A description of a type specimen should include how it differs from other specimens. A type specimen can never be assumed to be typical, average, or median. The student may better appreciate this problem if he or she attempts to define one individual as typical of the class in invertebrate zoology, or one car on a city street as median. Understanding that a type specimen (although objective) is nevertheless a *variant* of the species group it represents, and

that inherited variations provide the material of evolution, we see that we must explore all possible areas that might provide evidence for phylogeny.

Evidences for evolutionary relationships come from many sides. Structural similarities both larval and adult suggest homologous structures, and embryology confirms or denies their common origin. Geological strata properly interpreted reveal relative ages of fossils and hence provide sequences of related fossils. Histochemistry is indicative of many relationships. Study of function, such as that of gills, or nephridia, or locomotor organs, provides evidences as does comparative parasitism.

Phylogeny is the evolutionary sequence of a group of organisms as evidenced in the modifications present in successive adult stages. Of course larval stages, especially free-living ones, are subject to environmental stresses so that many adaptations occur that are not mirrored in ancestors. It is certainly probable that the larvae of unrelated species living in a like environment may have produced similar structural adaptations so that convergence rather than homology accounts for resemblances (Fig. 21-1).

In a number of animals maturity of the reproductive system may occur while other structures still retain larval features. This phenomenon is best known by the term *neoteny.* There are a number of neotenous animal species subsequently metamorphosing to adults which also reproduce. It seems highly probable that sexually reproducing species in which various larval characters have persisted are actually neotenous with the definitive adult stage lost, since it would no longer be essential to reproduce the species. Thus neoteny can account for the development of new evolutionary lines often differentiating sharply from ancestral types.

It is generally believed that life on this planet originated some 2,000,000,000 years ago. One theory holds that the earth passed through a molten phase in its early development. Another theory suggests that both the

Fig. 21-1 Free-swimming larvae of various invertebrates. (a) *Polygordius*, an annelid worm, (b) an oyster, *Ostrea*, (c) *Eupomatus*, one of the serpulid worms, (d) *Pedicellina*, one of the Bryozoa, (e) *Dreissensia*, a bivalved mollusc, (f) Tornaria of *Balanoglossus*, (g) a brachio-pod, *Megathyris*, (h) a crinoid, *Antedon*, (i) a sea star, Bipinnaria, (j) a sea cucumber or holothurian, Auricularia, and (k) a sea urchin or echinoid, Pluteus. After Berry 1929, courtesy of the McGraw-Hill Book Company.

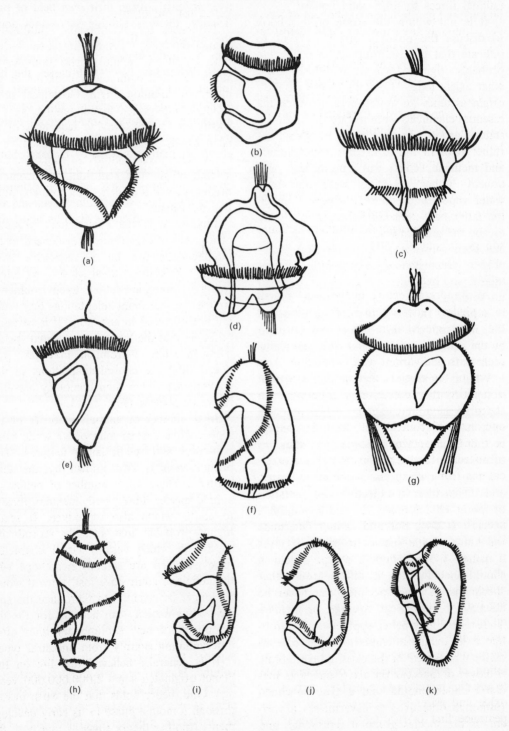

sun and the planets were formed at very low temperature from a suspension of cosmic dust eventually compressed by gravitational forces to form solid bodies.

It is not within the scope of this book to discuss the possible origins, except to indicate that the environment in which life probably originated was vastly different from what exists today. Oparin's theory of life's origin assumes an atmosphere in which the essential chemicals were mostly in a reduced state. Carbon was present as hydrocarbons rather than in the form of carbon dioxide and methane (CH_4) was a prominent component. Other materials were ammonia, water vapor, and some hydrogen, although the latter had sufficient lightness to largely escape the gravitational pull of the earth. It has been shown experimentally that under proper circumstances methane, water, ammonia, and hydrogen can form various amino acids if energy from an electric source is supplied. In the formation of primitive life, it is thought that energy was supplied by the sun or by natural electrical discharge such as from lightning.

What is significant about this theory is that it supports the conclusion that the first life appeared in an atmosphere devoid of free oxygen so that energy requirements had to be met by anaerobic fermentation. This life subsisted on the reservoir of organic compounds from which the primitive life itself arose. Thus these first organisms were *heterotrophic*. With the advent of life, the hydrocarbon food reservoir became depleted faster than it could be replenished. Survival may well have depended upon the chance ability of some of the primitive organisms to utilize additional carbon compounds including carbon dioxide, which was being built up in the atmosphere from anaerobic processes and by the reaction of chemicals in the primitive atmosphere. The gradual evolution of photosynthesizing organisms able to use the increasingly abundant carbon dioxide and water probably preceded the appearance first of facultative anaerobes and

finally of strict aerobes dependent upon available oxygen.

Although scientists tend to be conservative, at least outside their own field of proficiency, there is nothing sacrosanct about the division of living forms into the two time-honored kingdoms of plants and animals. Whittaker (1959) discusses the historical background and the arguments for dividing living organisms into three or more kingdoms. A familiar three-kingdom system includes animals, plants, and *Protista,* a group originally proposed by Haeckel. Some alternate definitions of the term Protista are given. The most widely inclusive definition covers unicellular or acellular organisms and some multicellular forms such as algae and fungi. The blue-green algae and bacteria are often separated as a subkingdom, called *Monera,* a group without nuclear envelops. Whittaker proposes a four-kingdom system in which three kingdoms are derived from the fourth (Protista) and separated on the primary basis of nutritional processes. His interesting views are schematically expressed in the figure from his paper (Fig. 21-2).

Hutner (1962) presents a phylogenetic tree that suggests evolutionary relationships between anaerobic and aerobic organisms (Fig. 21-3). His hypothesis may help to bridge the gap between a possible ancestral flagellate stock (*Mastigamoeba*) and primordial life.

There are two major views about the origin of metazoa from protozoan Protista. One camp holds that metazoa evolved from plasmodial ciliates and the other from colonial flagellates. The student should reread the discussion of the compartmentalization and colonial theories in Chapter 3.

In his paper in the volume entitled The Lower Metazoa, edited by Dougherty and others, Remane discusses the evidence and supports the colonial hypothesis. In the same volume, Hanson supports the cellularization theory, in which he follows Hadži in considering acoele turbellarians at the bottom of the metazoan phylogenetic totem pole. The gymnostomatous ciliates are considered representative of the most probable ancestors, and Hanson points out that bilateral symmetry, rather uniform ciliation, anterior-posterior polarization, and a ventral mouth are features occurring in this group of ciliates as well as in the Acoela. A number of ciliates are multinuclear or polyenergid protozoans. Evidence for the cellularization hypothesis would suggest the ultimate separation of these nuclei by cell membranes, and Hanson (1958) cites electron-microscope studies indicating that a cytoplasmic network in cells is continuous with the cell membrane. If this reticulum gave rise to new cell membranes isolating the nuclei, a multicellular organism would result. Supporters of the cellularization theory would consider a so-called plasmodial condition present in acoeles as indicative of origin from a multinucleate ancestor. However, it appears that the condition in acoeles interpreted as plasmodial is in reality a syncytial condition which followed a cellularized embryonic development.

Remane (see The Lower Metazoa) lists supportive evidence for the colonial theory as well as some of the special problems of the cellularization hypothesis. Colonial organization with appropriate differentiation in function and form can lead to a primitive metazoan. In a broad sense, the colonial flagellate *Volvox* can be defined as a metazoan with localization and specialization of

Fig. 21-2 A phylogenetic tree utilizing a four-kingdom hypothesis. After Whittaker 1959, courtesy of the *Quart. Rev. Biol.*

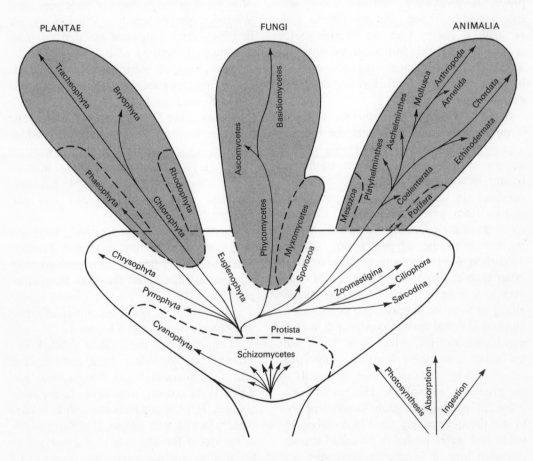

some of the cells of the colony for reproduction and with the development of early polarity. Other significant facts include the great similarity between protozoan flagella and metazoan gamete flagella. Fertilization follows copulation in many flagellates as it does in metazoa, whereas in ciliates the fusion of nuclear material is internal and is part of a process of conjugation. Two major problems for the supporters of the cellularization hypothesis to consider are (1) the absence of cellularized gametes in ciliates, and (2) the absence of macronuclei in the Acoela. In general, it would appear that the colonial hypothesis has the better foundation and the less serious impediments.

The Porifera do not fall in the direct line of ascent of Metazoa according to most authorities, but Tuzet (see paper in The Lower Metaoza) thinks that Hydrozoa (Cnidaria) can be derived from sponges and hence places them in or near the direct ancestral line. The collared cells (choanocytes) of sponges suggest an origin from protozoan choanoflagellates, but Tuzet reports collared cells in some echinoderms, which suggests possibilities for convergence. The inversion of the blastula seen in calcareous sponges is paralleled by similar action in some Volvocidae (colonial flagellates). Siliceous sponges do not show this inversion, but calcareous sponges are recognized as more primitive. Porifera may have arisen from the same stem that gave rise to Cnidaria and Cteno-

Fig. 21-3 A phylogenetic tree suggesting evolutionary relationships between anaerobic and aerobic organisms. After Hutner (In) *This is Life: Essays in modern biology,* edited by W. H. Johnson and W. C. Steere. Copyright 1962, Holt, Rinehart & Winston, Inc.

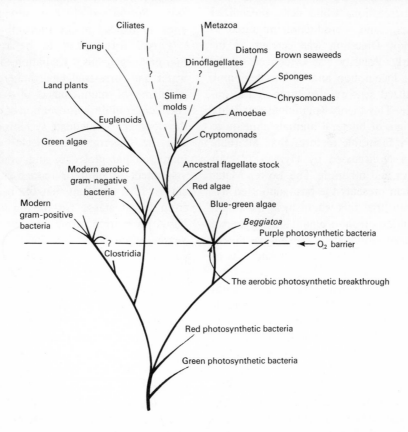

phora; or from a separate protozoan ancestor, not necessarily a choanoflagellate; or from a colonial line that gave rise to Volvocidae on the one hand and Porifera on the other. Marcus derives sponges from Zoomastigina.

In the evolution of metazoa, the position of the Cnidaria and Ctenophora is open to question. What is involved is the origin of bilateral symmetry. The colonial theory discussed above goes directly from a flagellated spherical protozoan colony to a radial type of metazoan, perhaps exemplified by some ancestral hydrozoan, by way of an acoelous organism termed *stereogastrula* or *planula*. In this change cell adaptation occurred, with some cells early becoming specialized for reproduction. At first all surface cells had a nutritive function, but division of labor left surface cells adapted for locomotion and sensory perception, while cells specialized for digestion and reproduction migrated to the interior. Digestion was carried on intracellularly. Polarity was evidenced by direction of locomotion and by the beginning of centralized sensory structures at the anterior pole. This theory (planuloid-acoeloid) of the origin of bilateral animals appears to have more favorable features than alternate theories also discussed by Hyman (1951) and by Ax and others in The Lower Metazoa. Hyman presents the best-supported hypothesis. In brief this would have the origin of the Cnidaria from a planulalike organism which metamorphosed to a primitive medusoid, the *actinula* larva. Subsequently actinulae gave rise by budding to medusae from an attached colonial stalk, which was the forerunner of the polyp. Hydrozoa are considered to be the most primitive cnidarians. Through a different radiation, the planula gave rise to the Bilateria by way of acoeloid flatworms.

The phylogenetic tree here presented (Fig. 21-4) follows the well-established pattern dividing bilaterally symmetrical animals into two main branches. These are the schizocoelous protostomates, originating from an acoeious flatworm through determinative cleavage and a trochophore larval type; and the enterocoelous deuterostomes, which, however, are less clearly defined. The protozoan classification is adapted from Corliss (1959), and the diphyletic arthropod grouping from Tiegs and Manton (1958). The Mesozoa are placed as a regressive offshoot of the Malacobothridia (Digenea) following Stunkard (1954). For variations, the phylogenetic trees of Hyman, Hadži, Hanson, and Marcus should be examined.

Position of the groups are necessarily conjectural. Lack of living descendants or of fossils leaves great blanks throughout. Many animals with no hard body parts left no certainly recognizable record. In addition, some groups such as Trilobita and Arachnomorpha were well established by the Cambrian Period, so their presumed common ancestor existed in the Precambrian.

Larval forms tend to be restricted to marine organisms. Radiation into freshwater and terrestrial environments involved problems of maintenance of osmotic and chemical equilibria, prevention of dessication, development of adequate systems for respiration, and insurance of species survival by increased parental care and precocious development to omit or reduce fragile larval stages. It is apparent that the best evidence from larval stages for phylogeny must be based on marine forms, but even here convergence must certainly be a frequent occurrence, particularly for pelagic organisms, so that interpretation is difficult. In addition, free-living larvae, whether or not they are able to feed, are not universal among marine organisms, and the question arises: in which direction has radiation proceeded?

Scarcely half a century ago, the atom was the indivisible unit of matter. Perhaps in phylogeny some revolutionary new methods and techniques will be developed to bring some additional clarity out of the dim geologic past, and the continual discovery

Fig. 21-4 A hypothetical phylogenetic tree of the animal kingdom.

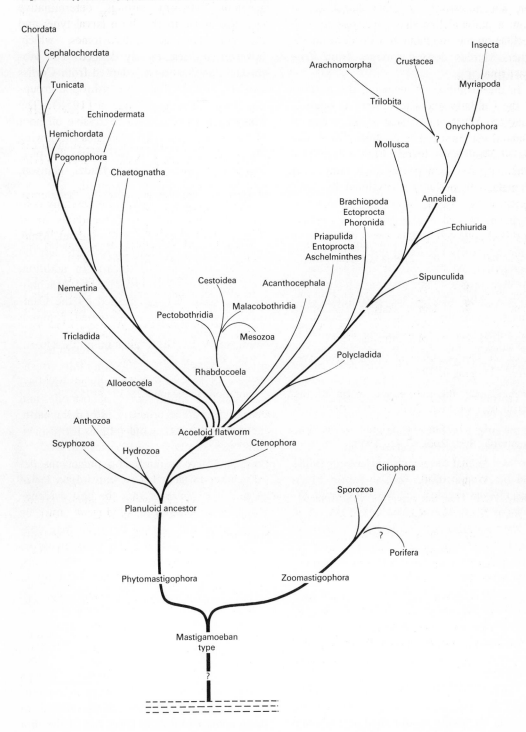

of new species of animals such as *Neopilina* as well as extensive study of present known ones will add significant information, increasing man's knowledge and decreasing the speculative elements in the ancestry of animals.

REFERENCES

de Beer, G., The evolution of the Metazoa (pp. 22-33). *In* (J. C. Huxley, A. C. Hardy, and E. B. Ford, eds.) Evolution as a process. London: G. Allen, 1954.

———, Embryos and ancestors (3rd ed.). London: Oxford U. P., 1958.

Carter, G. S., On Hadži's interpretations of animal phylogeny. Syst. Zool., 3:163, 1954.

Corliss, J. O., Comments on the phylogeny and systematics of the Protozoa. Syst. Zool., 8:169, 1959.

Dougherty, E. C., Z. N. Brown, E. D. Hanson, and W. D. Hartman (eds.), The lower Metazoa: comparative biology and phylogeny. Berkeley: U. of California, 1963.

Hadži, J., The evolution of the Metazoa. Oxford: Pergamon, 1963.

Hand, C., On the nature and origin of the coelenterates. Syst. Zool., 8:191, 1959.

Hanson, E. D., On the origin of the Eumetazoa. Syst. Zool., 7:16, 1958.

———, Animal diversity. Englewood Cliffs, N. J.: Prentice-Hall, 1961.

Hardy, A. C., On the origin of the Metazoa. Quart. J. Microsc. Sci., 94:441, 1953.

———, Escape from specialization (pp. 122-142). *In* (J. Huxley, A. C. Hardy, and E. B. Ford, eds.) Evolution as a process. London: G. Allen, 1954.

Hutner, S. H., Nutrition of protists (pp. 109-137). *In* (W. H. Johnson and W. C. Steere, eds.) This is life: essays in modern biology. New York: Holt, Rinehart & Winston, 1962.

Hyman, L. H., The invertebrates: Protozoa through Ctenophora, Vol. I. New York: McGraw, 1940.

———, The invertebrates: Platyhelminthes and Rhynchocoela, Vol. II. New York: McGraw, 1951.

Marcus, E., On the evolution of the animal phyla. Quart. Rev. Biol., 33:24, 1958.

Mayr., E., E. G. Linsley, and R. L. Usinger, Methods and principles of systematic zoology. New York: McGraw, 1953.

Miller, S. L., The origin of life (pp. 317-341). *In* (W. H. Johnson and W. C. Steere, eds.) This is life: essays in modern biology. New York: Holt, Rinehart & Winston, 1962.

Needham, A. E., The origination of life. Quart. Rev. Biol., 34:189, 1959.

Newell, N. D., Periodicity in invertebrate evolution, J. Paleon., 26:371, 1952.

Oparin, A. I., The origin of life on the earth (trans. A. Synge). Edinburgh: Oliver and Boyd, 1957.

Ross, H. H., A synthesis of evolution theory. Englewood Cliffs, N. J.: Prentice-Hall, 1962.

Simpson, G. G., Principles of animal taxonomy. New York: Columbia U. P., 1961.

Stunkard, H. W., The life history and systematic relations of the Mesozoa. Quart. Rev. Biol., 29:230, 1954.

———, Systematics, taxonomy, and nomenclature of the Trematoda. *Ibid.*, 38:221, 1963.

Whittaker, R. H., On the broad classification of organisms. Quart. Rev. Biol., 34:210, 1959.

INDEX